Ceratocystis and *Ophiostoma*

Taxonomy, Ecology, and Pathogenicity

Edited by Michael J. Wingfield, Keith A. Seifert, and Joan F. Webber

APS PRESS

The American Phytopathological Society
St. Paul, Minnesota

Cover illustration of *Ceratostomella pini* by E. Münch, 1907

This book has been reproduced directly from computer-generated copy submitted
in final form to APS Press by the editors of the volume. No editing or proofreading
has been done by the Press.

Reference in this publication to a trademark, proprietary product, or company
name is intended for explicit description only and does not imply approval or
recommendation to the exclusion of others that may be suitable.

Library of Congress Catalog Card Number: 93-79368
International Standard Book Number: 0-89054-156-6

Printed in the United States of America on acid-free paper

The American Phytopathological Society
3340 Pilot Knob Road
St. Paul, Minnesota 55121-2097, USA

TABLE OF CONTENTS

LIST OF CONTRIBUTORS

Blackwell, M.   Department of Botany, Louisiana State University, Baton Rouge, LA 70803, U.S.A.

Brasier, C.M.   Forest Research Station, Alice Holt Lodge, Farnham, Surrey GU10 4LH U.K.

Breuill, C.   Forintek Canada Corp., Eastern Laboratory, Ottawa, Ontario, K1G 3Z5, Canada.
                        Present address: Pulp and Paper Research Institute of Canada, 3800 Westbrook Mall, Vancouver, B.C. V6T 1W5, Canada

Duke, E.E.   Dermatology, 301-770 Broadview Avenue, Ottawa, Ontario, K2A 325, Canada

Cates, R.G.   Chemical Ecology Laboratory, Department of Botany and Range Science, Brigham Young University, Provo, UT 84602. U.S.A.

Erasmus, S.C.   Department of Microbiology and Biochemistry, University of the Orange Free State, Bloemfontein 9300, South Africa

Gibbs J.N.   Forest Research Station, Alice Holt Lodge, Farnham, Surrey GU10 4LH U.K.

Grylls, B.T.   Forintek Canada Corp., Eastern Laboratory, Ottawa, Ontario, K1G 3Z5, Canada

Hanssen, H-P.   IMB - Industrielle Mikrobiologie & Biotechnologie GmbH, Lurup 4, D-2070 Großhansdorf, Germany

Harrington, T.C.   Department of Plant Pathology, Iowa State University, Ames, Iowa 50011, U.S.A.

Hausner, G.   Department of Botany, University of Manitoba, Winnipeg, MB, R3T 2N2, Canada

Hoog, G.S.de   Centraalbureau voor Schimmelcultures, Baarn, The Netherlands

Kane, J.   Mycology, Laboratory Services Branch, Ontario Ministry of Health, Toronto, Ontario, M5W 1R5, Canada

Kendrick, W.B.   Department of Biology, University of Waterloo, Waterloo, Ontario, N2L 3G1, Canada

Kile, G.A.   Division of Forestry and Forest Products, CSIRO, Stowell Avenue, Battery Point, Tasmania 7004, Australia

Klassen, G.R.   Department of Microbiology, University of Manitoba, Winnipeg, MB, R3T 2N2, Canada

Klepzig, K.D.   Departments of Plant Pathology and Entomology, University of Wisconsin-Madison, Madison, Wisconsin 53706, U.S.A.

Kock, J.L.F.   Department of Microbiology and Biochemistry, University of the Orange Free State, Bloemfontein 9300, South Africa

Kojima, M.   Institute for Biochemical Regulation, Faculty of Agriculture, Nagoya University, Chikusa-ku, Nagoya 464-01, Japan

Krajden, S.   Microbiology Department, St Joseph's Health Centre, Toronto, Ontario, M6R 1B5, Canada

Lieutier, F.   INRA Station de Zoologie Forestière, Ardon, 45160, Olivet, France

Malloch, D.   Department of Botany, University of Toronto, Ontario, M5W 1A1, Canada

Nag Raj, T.R.   Department of Biology, University of Waterloo, Waterloo, Ontario, N2L 3G1, Canada

Okada, G.   Japan Collection of Microorganisms, RIKEN, Wako-shi, Saitama 351-01, Japan

Paine, T.D.   Department of Entomology, University of California, Riverside, CA 95251, U.S.A.

Proctor, R.H.   Departments of Plant Pathology and Entomology, University of Wisconsin-Madison, Madison, Wisconsin 53706, U.S.A.

Raffa, K.F.   Department of Entomology, University of Wisconsin-Madison, Madison, Wisconsin 53706, U.S.A.

Reid, J.   Department of Botany, University of Manitoba, Winnipeg, MB, R3T 2N2, Canada

Samuels, G.J.   Systematic Botany and Mycology Laboratory, United States Department of Agriculture, Agriculture Research Service, Beltsville, MD 20705, U.S.A.

Seifert, K.A.   Forintek Canada Corp., Eastern Laboratory, Ottawa, Ontario K1G 3Z5, Canada.
Present address: Centre for Land and Biological Resources Research, Agriculture Canada, Research Branch, Ottawa, Ontario, K1A 0C6, Canada

Smalley, E.B.   Department of Plant Pathology, University of Wisconsin-Madison, Madison, Wisconsin 53706, U.S.A.

Solheim, H.   Norwegian Forest Research Institute, Section of Forest Ecology, Division of Forest Pathology, N-1423 Ås-NLH, Norway

Spatafora, J.W.   Department of Botany, Louisiana State University, Baton Rouge, LA 70803, U.S.A.

Stephen, F.M.   Department of Entomology, University of Arkansas, Fayetteville, AR 72701, U.S.A.

Summerbell, R.C.   Mycology, Laboratory Services Branch, Ontario Ministry of Health, Toronto, Ontario, M5W 1R5, Canada

Taylor, J.W.	Department of Plant Science, University of California, Berkeley, CA 94720, U.S.A.
Upadhyay, H.P.	Departamento de Micologia, Unversidade Federal de Pernambuco, Recife, PE, 50740, Brasil
Van Wyk, P.S.	Department of Microbiology and Biochemistry, University of the Orange Free State, Bloemfontein 9300, South Africa
Van Wyk, P.W.J.	Department of Botany and Genetics, University of the Orange Free State, Bloemfontein 9300, South Africa
Van der Walt, J.P.	Department of Microbiology and Biochemistry, University of the Orange Free State, Bloemfontein 9300, South Africa
Webber, J.F.	Forest Research Station, Alice Holt Lodge, Farnham, Surrey GU10 4LH U.K.
Wingfield, M.J.	Department of Microbiology and Biochemistry, University of the Orange Free State, Bloemfontein 9300, South Africa

PREFACE

This book on *Ceratocystis* and *Ophiostoma* is based on an international symposium that was held in the spa village of Bad Windsheim, Germany during August 1990. The aim of the symposium was to bring together researchers from different disciplines to discuss the many aspects of the biology of the ophiostomatoid fungi in a single forum. The broader subjects under consideration included taxonomy, ecology and pathogenicity; the arrangement of chapters in this book follows this pattern.

The thirty chapters in this book are grouped into five sections. The first set of chapters considers morphological taxonomy of the ophiostomatoid fungi, including their anamorphs. In the second set of chapters, nonmorphological taxonomic approaches are considered, including genetic, biochemical, developmental and molecular characters. In part three, the pathological aspects are introduced, beginning with a consideration of saprobic growth and progressing through tree diseases to human diseases. The fourth part includes reviews of a variety of insect vector systems and host responses to both the insects and the fungi that they carry. A few chapters, including information on methods for handling ophiostomatoid fungi, a key for their identification, and a list of described species, represent material that was not presented at Bad Windsheim. They have been added to this book, in the hope that they will be of use to future researchers of this group of fungi.

We have attempted to provide coverage of subjects that have not been reviewed previously and those that are likely to stimulate future research. The treatments of some subjects in this book are of a preliminary nature, or review work that, upon completion, proved to have little application to future research. To a certain extent, the choice of chapters for inclusion was based on the scientists who were able to join us in Bad Windsheim. There are undoubtedly many subjects pertaining to the ophiostomatoid fungi that are not included. An example is the dieback of oak trees in central Europe that has been associated with various species of *Ophiostoma*. In this and other cases, we felt that insufficient information was currently available to support a book chapter. We hope that information on these topics will be forthcoming and that sometime in the future some brave souls will compile it for us.

We are grateful to the participants of the symposium at Bad Windsheim and to the authors of the chapters in this book for supporting this venture with such enthusiasm. Our respective employers have patiently supported this project, which has been secondary to our primary responsibilities to them. We very much appreciate the technical assistance of Mr. Francois Wolfaardt, Mrs Marnél Mouton, Mrs. Chrissie Moolman, Ms Christa Visser and Dr Brenda Wingfield without whose help this book could not have been completed. Mrs Jackie Wingfield was responsible for preparing the camera ready copy; this mammoth task occupied a tremendous amount of time and we sincerely appreciate this contribution. Dr. Joyce Loper, senior editor for APS Press, also expended considerable effort to ensure that this book was free of grammatical and typographical errors. Financial contributions from Forintek Canada, Corp. to KAS and from the Foundation for Research Development to MJW are greatly appreciated. Finally, editorial responsibilities have necessitated considerable sacrifice of time usually spent with family and friends. We owe these special people in our lives sincere thanks for their understanding and support.

INTRODUCTION

The ophiostomatoid fungi including genera such as *Ophiostoma, Ceratocystis sensu stricto* and *Ceratocystiopsis* (Table 1), are adapted to insect dispersal and include a number of important plant pathogens. It was approximately one hundred years ago that the genus *Ceratocystis* was described. The first studies were primarily taxonomic. It was not until the early decades of the twentieth century, with the expansion and mechanization of the forestry and forest products industries, that the economic importance of these fungi became evident. Then, the first pandemic of Dutch Elm disease, caused by *Ophiostoma (Ceratocystis) ulmi*, swept through the elm populations on both sides of the Atlantic and the extraordinary biological talents of these fungi began to be unravelled.

Although we began this book with the lofty objective of summarizing a century of work on the ophiostomatoid fungi, it is now clear that the picture is far from complete. It is not unusual for the taxonomy of economically important fungi to be controversial; for these fungi, this is illustrated by our use of the taxonomically neutral (and somewhat cumbersome) term "ophiostomatoid fungi". The pathological and ecological information also lacks a convincing synthesis. This is partly a reflection of the parochial nature of forestry. The silvicultural and trading practices of modern man have resulted in a mixing of hitherto separated host, pathogen and vector populations. This book is a first attempt to make sense of one part of the biological stew that man's economic activity has been brewing.

When we first conceived of the symposium on which this book is based, our intention was to bring together scientists from many different subdisciplines of biology with a common interest in ophiostomatoid fungi. The best known of these fungi is *Ophiostoma ulmi*, which together with its recently described sibling species, *O. novo-ulmi*, causes Dutch Elm Disease. The disease illustrates many characteristics of this group of fungi as a whole. The pathogen produces different spore types that are dispersed in the sap of infected trees, and most importantly, from tree to tree by scolytid bark beetles. While acknowledging its importance as a model for this group of fungi, we chose not to emphasize Dutch Elm Disease in any way in this book, focussing instead on other, less well-known organisms. The search for patterns demands a broad canvas. We make no apology for this and simply refer the reader exclusively interested in Dutch Elm Disease to the many excellent volumes and reviews that already exist.

The ophiostomatoid fungi produce morphologically similar sexual states, but are remarkably diverse in the types of asexual spores they produce. The multitude of spore forms and dispersal mechanisms make these fungi highly adaptable. There is evidence that they evolve rapidly to exploit new hosts when introduced to a new environment. But despite their importance, the taxonomy, ecology and pathogenicity of the ophiostomatoid fungi remain poorly understood. Researchers interested in these fungi are spread around the world and work in several disciplines, including mycology, entomology, plant pathology, biochemistry and human pathology. It is not surprising, therefore, that communication among scientists interested in the ophiostomatoid fungi has been sporadic and that the literature is scattered in a diverse selection of journals.

A Taxonomic Debate in Progress

As with most economically-important fungal groups, the seeds of taxonomic discontent for the ophiostomatoid fungi were sown long before the significance of the fungi was understood. Controversy now exists at the ordinal, family, generic, species and subspecies levels. The details of these controversies are considered at length in this book. Rather than present specifics of these disagreements here, we would like to provide a broader context for the debate.

The generic names *Ceratocystis, Ophiostoma* and *Ceratostomella* were in use near the turn of the century; *Europhium* and *Ceratocystiopsis* were added later to the mix. A number of obscure genera have also been referred to this group of fungi (Table 1). The morphology of the sexual state, or teleomorph, has always been of primary importance in fungal taxonomy, but in the 1950's and 1960's, several developments changed the way taxonomists classified fungi. In 1951, Luttrell published a mammoth study on centrum development in ascomycetes. These studies, and subsequent studies by other taxonomists, demonstrated that the ascomycetous fungi traditionally classified together in the plectomycetes had ascocarps that developed in different ways. One axiom of taxonomic thought is that ontogeny recapitulates phylogeny. Ascomycetes with cleistothecial or similar fruiting bodies were shown to have affinities with a variety of pyrenomycete and discomycete groups. Their simple morphology reflects convergent evolution.

In 1953, Hughes published a paper that revolutionized the way that taxonomists classified the asexual, or anamorphic fungi, traditionally treated in the form taxon Deuteromycetes. Employing the same taxonomic axiom as Luttrell, Hughes proposed a classification of anamorphic fungi based on the ontogeny of conidia. The now familiar emphasis on phialidic, annellidic and sympodially proliferating conidiogenous cells had a dramatic impact on the taxonomy of the ophiostomatoid fungi. When Upadhyay

TABLE 1. Genera of ascomycetes referred to as ophiostomatoid fungi, possessing reduced ascocarps, deliquescent asci and generally associated with arthropods.

Genus	Status
Ceratocystiopsis Upad. & Kendrick	generally accepted but see Chapter 3
Ceratocystis Ellis & Halstead	two competing concepts, see Chapters 1, 2
Ceratostomella Sacc.	type species not ophiostomatoid
Endoconidiophora Münch	synonym of *Ceratocystis s.str.*
Europhium Parker	generally considered synonym of *Ophiostoma* but possibly distinct
Kathistes Malloch & Blackwell	see Chapter 21
Klasterskya Petrak	see Chapter 21
Ophiostoma H. & P. Sydow	widely accepted but see Chapter 1
Pyxidiophora Bref. & Tav.	see Chapter 21
Rhynchonectria Höhnel	rejected name see Chapter 21
Sphaeronaemella Karsten	generally accepted but see Chapter 1
Spumatoria Massee & Salmon	no known specimens, see Chapter 21
Subbaromyces Hesseltine	see Chapter 21
Treleasia Speg.	only type specimens known, see Chapter 21
Viennotidia Negru & Verona	segregate of *Sphaeronaemella*

monographed the group in 1981, he associated sixteen anamorph genera with the three teleomorph genera that he recognized. These anamorph genera included segregates of traditional genera such as *Graphium* and *Leptographium*, differentiated primarily by modes of conidium ontogeny.

During the 1980's, Minter and his coworkers reevaluated the available information on conidium ontogeny and proposed a uniform descriptive system. As a consequence, certain apparently dramatically different modes of conidium ontogeny (percurrent and sympodial) were shown to sometimes differ only slightly. In contrast, apparently similar conidiogenous cells (the phialidic conidiogenous cells of *Chalara* species and *Penicillium* species, for example) were suggested to be fundamentally different. These ideas have been applied to the ophiostomatoid fungi, with the result that fewer anamorph genera are now recognized, and the presence of *Chalara* anamorphs has been accorded special significance.

Some taxonomists, attempting to delineate genera among morphologically similar, though perhaps phylogenetically distantly related groups of teleomorphs chose anamorphs as supplementary characters. In the case of *Ceratocystis* and *Ophiostoma*, the presence or absence of a *Chalara* anamorph was considered a primary character for separating teleomorph genera. This inflation of the taxonomic value of anamorphic characters remains a virtual heresy in some schools of taxonomic thought. Traditional fungal systematics emphasizes the teleomorph; all widely accepted suprageneric taxa in the fungal system continue to be based entirely on these sexual characters. The anamorphic fungi are still treated as an embarassing appendage to the orderly hierarchy based on teleomorphic characters. The construction of a complete taxonomic system based on the concept of the holomorph, or whole fungus, is a job that has just begun.

As some taxonomists squabbled about the relative value of particular morphological characters, others explored physiological, biochemical, ultrastructural and genetic traits. Correlations between certain morphological characters and nonmorphological characters were noted and debated. The problem with this data is that it is incomplete, in some cases extremely fragmentary. Taxonomy is about recognizing patterns but how much concrete data is needed before the patterns can be predicted with confidence?

In the second section, the taxonomic impact of nonmorphological information is considered. Much of this information is preliminary; the majority of the studies deal with only a handful of species.

This, then, provides the backdrop for the taxonomic debates that make up the first part of this book. What orders and families should this group of morphologically reduced fungi be assigned to? Can anamorph characters really be used to delineate 'teleomorph' genera? What is the significance of ascospore morphology? How reliable are the characters that have been used to distinguish anamorph genera? The answers to some of these questions are in this book. The answers to others may be forthcoming only when the promises of the approaches considered in the second part of the book have been fulfilled.

Especially to the nontaxonomist, the contents of this book will at first appear heavily skewed towards

TABLE 2. Some diseases caused by ophiostomatoid fungi.

Fungus	Host	Disease	Distribution
Ceratocystis coerulescens	Sugar maple	Sapstreak	northern USA
Ceratocystis fagacearum	Red oak	Oak wilt	USA, [1]Europe
Ceratocystis fimbriata	Coffee	Trunk rot	S. America
	Fig	Canker	Japan
	Mango	Wilt	Brazil
	Poplar	Canker	N. America, Europe
	Rubber	Mouldy rot	Brazil
	Sweet potato	Black rot	E. Asia
	Sycamore	Canker	Europe
Ceratocystis laricicola	Larch	Canker stain	Europe
Ceratocystis paradoxa	Citrus	Soft rot	India
	Coconut	Stem bleeding	Asia
	Pineapple	Pineapple disease	Tropical
	Sugar Cane	Pineapple disease	Tropical
Leptographium procerum	Pines	Root disease	N. America, [1]Europe, New Zealand
Leptographium wageneri	Conifers	Black stain	N. America
Leptographium serpens	Pines		Europe, South Africa
Ophiostoma minus	Pines	Canker stain	N. America
Ophiostoma montia	Pines	Canker stain	N. America
Ophiostoma polonica	Spruce	Canker stain	Europe
Ophiostoma ulmi/novo-ulmi	Elms	Dutch Elm Disease	[1]N.America, [1]Europe, [1]Asia, [1]New Zealand
Ophiostoma sp.	Oak	Oak decline	Central Europe
Sporothrix schenkii	Humans	Sporotrichosis	Cosmopolitan

[1] designates locations to which the disease appears to have been spread by man

taxonomy. As editors, we would have preferred to present a picture of a neat and tidy taxonomy of the ophiostomatoid fungi, but this is impossible. The disagreements between the authors are there for all to see. Contrasting opinions are presented only pages apart. But it should be obvious, even to those with only a casual interest in taxonomy, that our taxonomic obsessions have provided us with a wealth of information on the ecology, physiology, biochemistry and pathology of these fungi. Much of this information is presented in the first two parts of this book, some of it for the first time, and we hope that the ideas and controversies that surround the facts will make for stimulating rather than frustrating reading.

We believe that a careful reading of the first two parts of this book will give the reader the impression that the taxonomic debate is actually drawing to a close. For the first time, solutions to taxonomic problems that have irritated us for a century appear to be in sight. But if the ophiostomatoid fungi are as phylogenetically heterogeneous as we are now beginning to suspect, why do we then continue to treat them as some kind of entity in this book?

Diseases, Insects and the Global Economy

If the ophiostomatoid fungi are indeed polyphyletic,

then they are one of the most striking examples of convergent evolution in biology. The simple ascocarps with their deliquescent asci and slimy ascospores are found not only in the species of *Ceratocystis* and *Ophiostoma* that are the focus of this book, but also in species of a number of smaller genera that occupy unusual or highly specialized habitats, and which have been seen by only a handful of mycologists. In their broadest sense, the ophiostomatoid fungi exhibit a spectrum of life styles, from saprobic to mildly parasitic to extremely virulent, from casual arthropod association to intimate symbiosis with insects. There are many variations on the theme of simple morphology and insect vectors and these are explored in the second half of the book.

If the taxonomic controversies seem unwieldy, imagine the aggravation of forest pathologists trying to cope with the first ophiostomatoid epidemic of the twenty-first century. Even as this book goes to press, a new epidemic races through the oaks of central Europe. It appears to be caused by one or more ophiostomatoid fungi, but by which species transmitted by which vectors?

The idea that epidemics of plant diseases can be caused by poorly regulated international trade practices is certainly not new. Nor is this a problem confined to ophiostomatoid fungi. It seems to us, though, that with two pandemics of Dutch Elm Disease behind us, and an oak wilt epidemic brewing, that the ophiostomatoid fungi have been exploiting man's activities far more than we have exploited theirs. Where do these epidemics come from, how do they spread, and is there anything we can do to prevent them in the future?

It seems likely that future epidemics will originate with the many indigenous disease systems that presently exist (see Table 2). Or, it is possible that future problems may arise from presently obscure fungi referred to above. Our present concern with species of *Ophiostoma* and *Ceratocystis* should not stop us from learning lessons from their lesser known relatives.

Reviews of the pathology and vector relationships of several diseases comprise the last two parts of this book. Anyone who works in forestry knows that it is a regional industry. Because of different tree species, different climates and different forest management strategies, wisdom gained on forest pests in the Pacific Northwest of North America, for example, may not pertain to the intensively managed forests of western Europe. In this book, we have reviews of the fungi, insect vectors and host responses involved in some localized disease systems. Some parallels and patterns are evident but the synthesis is far from complete.

At first glance, there appears to be a considerable amount of duplication between some chapters. Indeed, many of these contributions start at the same point, the discovery that insects, particularly bark beetles, and the ophiostomatoid fungi are intimately associated in many disease systems. From there, however, the papers diverge. Individual papers consider *Leptographium* diseases of conifers in the Pacific northwest of North America, diseases of angiosperms in central North America, conifer diseases in Scandinavia and in France, including specifics of the insects and host responses involved. There is even an important fungal disease of humans caused by an ophiostomatoid fungus.

When we began this project in 1988, we naively believed that science knew a lot about the ophiostomatoid fungi, and that this book would be a testament to that knowledge. Now, we feel as if we are presenting a progress report, and only a preliminary one at that. In comparison with what is known about many agricultural disease systems, our knowledge of the ophiostomatoid fungi seems particularly fragmentary. It is our hope, however, that the gaps in our understanding that this book exposes will serve to stimulate science, not to stifle it.

4

PART I

MORPHOLOGY AND TAXONOMY

Chapter 1

CLASSIFICATION OF THE OPHIOSTOMATOID FUNGI

H. P. UPADHYAY

"Scientific work is in its essence fluid and progressive, and from time to time it outdistances the principles which formerly it had assumed as basic. It is thus necessary to scrutinize them repeatedly and, need to be, subject them to drastic revision".

Agnes Arber, The Mind and the Eye. 1954.

INTRODUCTION

The ophiostomatoid fungi[1] comprise an ubiquitous group of over 100 species distributed in the genera *Ceratocystis* and *Ceratocystiopsis* in a single family Ophiostomataceae in the order Microascales of the Plectomycetes. This economically important group of Ascomycetes contains species with highly divergent anamorphs and teleomorphs, characterized by differing patterns of conidium ontogeny and ascomatal centrum development, variable biochemical composition, association with insect vectors as symbionts[2] and a broad geographical distribution. The ophiostomatoid fungi are found world-wide on a wide variety of substrates, from the high arctic to the tropics, from mountain tops to sea level. The absence of reports in certain countries probably indicates a shortage of collectors rather than fungi.

Many species of *Ceratocystis* are of economic importance. Some cause diseases of crop plants, such as sweet potato, coffee, rubber, mango, pineapple, sugarcane, and *Narcissus*, whereas others cause sapstain of lumber and forest products. Dutch-elm disease caused by *C. ulmi* and oak-wilt caused by *C. fagacearum* have brought these fungi to the attention of the general public. The ophiostomatoid fungi are even of importance in medical mycology, where *Sporothrix schenkii* and *C. stenoceras* have been implicated in human disease (Summerbell *et al.*, this volume).

A highly developed mutualistic association exists between the ophiostomatoid fungi and bark beetles (11,12,25). Dowding (12) reported two kinds of

associations: saprophagous and pathogenic. The mucilagenous ascospores and conidia, in the form of "stalked spore-drops" (23), are principally dispersed by bark beetles on or in the body of the insect, although rain splash, water flow and other animal vectors may be important. Bark beetles introduce spores into new hosts when making their brood chambers at the interface of sapwood and bark (35). Some fungi, such as *C. fagacearum* and *C. ulmi*, are wound parasites, gaining entry at sites where xylem is exposed. These two species, as well as *C. ips*, are so intimately associated with specific insect vectors that the existence of symbiotic relationships between fungus and insect may be considered.

In this review, the ophiostomatoid fungi are seen as living organisms that have adopted complicated life cycles and ecological partnerships to overcome a succession of problems during their evolution. In order to understand the whole, we must first understand how the components of the holomorph function, and reduce them to their most basic physiological and chemical factors. It may appear premature to contemplate phylogenetic relationships but recent work has produced a body of information undoubtedly far broader and deeper than realized by most mycologists.

New information, published since the appearance of my taxonomic monograph in 1980, is stimulating a reevaluation of our taxonomic schemes and invites renewed speculation on phylogenetic relationships. Controversies exist at all taxonomic levels. As is reviewed below, some taxonomists classify the genera under consideration in a single family, the Ophiostomaceae. Others regard the same taxon as an order, the Ophiostomatales. I will also attempt to clarify certain points of the continuing taxonomic controversy surrounding the use of the generic names

---

[1] The figures cited within this chapter are in Upadhyay (54), to which the reader is referred for more details than can be given in the following pages. *Ceratocystis* is used here with "sensu lato" implied; sensu stricto will be indicated when it is intended.

[2]"Symbiosis": used here in the sense originally used by de Bary (6) and most recently by Hawksworth (17)

Ceratocystis and *Ophiostoma*. Disagreement on several aspects of this controversy stems not from the nature of alternative taxonomic treatments (2,3,18,48), but from inconsistencies between the different treatments. As a consequence of inconsistencies in generic disposition (16,19,22,26,54), taxonomists are accused, with some justification, of changing names over and over.

Regardless of their correct placement, the ophiostomatoid fungi are one of the most fascinating groups of extant Ascomycetes. This is true, not only because of their exquisite ascocarps but especially because their taxonomy, ecology and pathology provide unique opportunities for research on many current problems in fungal biology.

A DEFINITION OF THE OPHIOSTOMATOID FUNGI

It is difficult to give a tidy taxonomic definition of the ophiostomatoid fungi. Because different taxonomists emphasize different characters in their classifications, no single definition would be accepted by all. However, it is clear from Nannfeldt's description of the new family Ophiostomataceae in the order Plectascales (45) that he was seeking a natural evolutionary grouping of these fungi within the modern ascomycete system and his classic concept should be seen in this context. The following definition is a modification of Nannfeldt's concepts, taking into consideration a number of new characteristics brought to light by subsequent workers (see also Malloch and Blackwell, this volume). Ascocarps are globose to subglobose or flask-shaped, dark, hyaline or lightly colored in whole or in part, leathery or ornamented, ostiolate (perithecial) or entirely closed (cleistothecial). Ostiolate ascocarps usually have long necks that may or may not be terminated with fringes of ostiolar hyphae. The asci are borne irregularly throughout the centrum and are clavate to subspherical, spherical or fusiform, deliquesce early in the development of the ascospores and lack a crozier. Ascospores are hyaline, usually unicellular (sometimes bicellular with a median septum) and variable in shape. In many species, the ascospores have a multilayered wall that appears as a gelatinous sheath with light microscopy, but some species lack this distinctive ornamentation. The ascospores lack germ-pores, are produced in a mucilagenous matrix and exude through the long neck into a mucilagenous droplet at the apex.

CLASSIFICATION INTO ORDERS AND FAMILIES

As has been suggested above, the ophiostomatoid fungi have been given very different circumscriptions by different taxonomists. It is uncertain whether the ophiostomatoid fungi should be considered Plectomycetes (8,29,32,33,45) or intermediate between the Plectomycetes and Sphaeriales/ Pyrenomycetes (43,52). At the ordinal and family levels, current opinions vary as to whether the ophiostomatoid fungi constitute a single family, the Ophiostomataceae in the order Microascales (28,29,30,45,54), or a separate order, the Ophiostomatales (8). Redhead and Malloch (48) reduced the Ophiostomataceae to synonymy with the Endomycetaceae. Barr (5) accepted neither family and classified the genera in different orders, *Ceratocystis* in the family Lasiosphaeriaceae (Sordariales) and *Ophiostoma* in the family Ophiostomataceae (Microascales).

The Ophiostomataceae as defined by Nannfeldt included the genera *Ophiostoma* and *Microascus*. Later, Nannfeldt (45) regarded *Ophiostoma* and *Ceratocystis (Ceratostomella)* to be congeneric. Although the name *Ceratocystis* had priority over *Ophiostoma*, it did not affect the name of the family.

Centrum development and ascus development are important characters in ascomycete taxonomy. Luttrell (28) placed the genus *Microascus* into a new family, the Microascaceae, on the basis of centrum structure. The centrum tissue of the Ophiostomataceae was considered pseudo-parenchymatous and that of the Microascaceae as filamentous. In the angiocarpous ascocarp, dehiscence is effected by breakdown of the upper wall; sticky ascospores are released in mass. In *Ceratocystis* species, the ascus wall breaks down quickly and is difficult to see, but the fusiform asci of *Ceratocystiopsis* species are more persistent, so that intact asci are often seen (figs. 470, 488). The 'Ophiostoma type' of ascus development was described by Luttrell (28) thus: "the asci mature progressively from the apex to base of the perithecium ....". Since then, three patterns of ascus develment have been observed among species of *Ceratocystiopsis* and *Ceratocystis*: (i) acropetal as described by Luttrell, (ii) centripetal and (iii) basipetal (54). Despite the different developmental patterns, in all cases the asci fill the centrum irregularly at maturity. Although these observations remain essentially preliminary, it is to be hoped that future research will clarify the situation (see Van Wyk *et al.* this volume).

With the exception of Redhead and Malloch (48), most authors have accepted the family Ophiostomataceae, but there has been little agreement on ordinal classification. Apart from the genus *Ceratocystis*, there has been considerable dispute concerning the validity, inclusion or exclusion of specific genera in this family. Müller and von Arx (43), for example, included the genera *Ceratocystis* (as *Ophiostoma*), *Europhium*, *Chadefaudia* and *Sphaeronaemella* in the Ophiostomataceae, whereas Webster (56) recognized only *Ceratocystis* and *Sphaeronaemella*. Redhead and Malloch (48) accommodated *Ceratocystiopsis, Ceratocystis s. str., Europhium* and *Ophiostoma* in the family Endomycetaceae, which was classified by Malloch (32,33) in the order Dothidiales within his scheme of the Plectomycetes. With the merging of *Europhium* into *Ophiostoma*, Benny and Kimbrough (8) placed *Ceratocystiopsis, Ceratocystis s. str., Ophiostoma* and *Sphaeronaemella* in the Ophiostomatales. Upadhyay (54) considered *Europhium, Ophiostoma* and *Sphaeronaemella* synonyms of *Ceratocystis* and recognized another genus *Ceratocystiopsis*. Minter (36) included *Klasterskya* in the Ophiostomataceae, but this is problematic because the description and figure of the teleomorph given by Petrak (47) and Müller and von Arx (42) are quite different to typical members of the Ophiostomataceae. There are several ascomycete genera in which the ascospores are discharged through a long neck and accumulate on the ostiole tip (34). Cannon and Hawksworth (9) transferred the genus *Sphaeronaemella*, and its type species *S. helvellae*, into the family Melanosporaceae (Sphaeriales/Hypocreales, Pyrenomycetes). The remaining species of *Sphaeronaemella* were placed in the genus *Viennotidia* (9), which replaced the invalidly published generic name *Viennotidia*. Malloch (31) regarded *Viennotidia* a synonym of *Sphaeronaemella* (see reference 22 for more nomenclatural information).

GENERIC CONCEPTS

Today, there are two schools of classification for the ophiostomatoid fungi. One school follows Bakshi's taxonomic arrangement (4), with *Ceratocystis* and *Ophiostoma* congeneric, and has a large number of proponents (15,21,22,26,40,46,54,59). The second school supports the recognition of *Ophiostoma* as a distinct genus from *Ceratocystis* and has a growing number of proponents (16,18, 58).

To approach the problem of the systematic position of the ophiostomatoid genera, perhaps the most pragmatic solution is to begin with the single genus concept of Nannfeldt. *Ceratocystis*, which has nomenclatural priority over *Ophiostoma* if the two are considered synonymous, is clearly the "core" genus in the circumscriptions of most contemporary and past workers. The first detailed systematic treatment of these fungi was provided by Nannfeldt (45), followed by a comprehensive review by Bakshi (4). These concepts were accepted by most workers except von Arx (1,2,3), and de Hoog (18), who divided *Ceratocystis* into *Ceratocystis s. str.* and *Ophiostoma*. It is somewhat sobering to consider that after forty years we are still debating many of the same questions.

Ceratocystis versus *Ophiostoma*

It is conceivable that the fungi included in *Ceratocystis* are not monophyletic. For that reason, an infrageneric classification was created by Upadhyay (54) to accommodate ascospores of different morphology: Section *Ceratocystis*, Section *Endoconidiophora*, Section *Ips* and Section *Ophiostoma*. The inclusion of the separate sections in a single genus binds together fungi that have many specialized characters in common.

The proposed segregation of *Ceratocystis s. str.* and *Ophiostoma* does not produce homogeneous genera. Von Arx (2) stated that his concepts would "...restrict *Ceratocystis* to species with phialidic anamorphs of the genus *Chalara*. The species with *Sporothrix, Graphium* or similar states forming blastic sympodial conidia must be classified in a separate genus, *Ophiostoma*". Can anamorph characters override those of the teleomorph in generic delimitation, as was attempted by Münch (44) and Goidànich (14)? To me, von Arx's taxonomic treatment of *Ceratocystis* and *Ophiostoma* raises more questions than it answers. According to the concepts of conidiogenesis used in hyphomycete systematics (20,27), von Arx's circumscription is clearly confused. The anamorphs of the ophiostomatoid fungi are extensively considered in various chapters of this book, but a brief review is in order here.

The more than one hundred species presently included in the genera *Ceratocystiopsis* and *Ceratocystis* (*sensu* Upadhyay) exhibit a bewildering array of anamorphs that exhibit astounding pleomorphism.

Of all these known species, only *Ceratocystis hyalothecium*, *C. acericola* and *Cp. ochracea* are not known to produce anamorphs, and reproduce exclusively by their teleomorphic states. The known anamorphs of the other species include representatives of as many as 16 hyphomycete genera, having a wide range conidiophores, conidiomata and conidiogenous cells (54,55). They include both mononematous and synnematous, hyaline and pigmented, and slimy and dry-spored genera.

The mononematous conidiophores of some species are well-differentiated from the vegetative mycelium and the apex of the stipe is penicillately branched, forming a complex conidiogenous apparatus capped by a slimy head of conidia. The synnematous conidiophores are analogues of the penicillate-mononematous conidiophores. Other species produce anamorphs with simple, mononematous conidiophores that may or may not be differentiated from the vegetative hyphae.

The one constant feature is that conidium development is always blastic, although Ellis (13) suggested that arthroconidia occur in the *Thielaviopsis* anamorph of *C. paradoxa*. Conidium ontogeny is of two kinds: enteroblastic and holoblastic. The enteroblastic conidia are phialidic, while holoblastic conidia may be produced in three ways: (1) in acropetal chains, (2) sympodially and (3) from annellidic conidiogenous cells (see table 2 in 54). In addition, a number of species produce more than one type of conidiogenous cell on a single conidiophore, namely *C. abiocarpa*, *C. cainii*, *C. huntii*, *C. leptographioides*, *C. olivaceapinii* and *C. piceaperda*. In *C. piceaperda*, for example, some conidiogenous cells may be interpreted as annellidic (fig. 143), while others seem to be phialidic (fig. 139) or sympodial (fig. 142). Conidia secede schizolytically and are usually truncate at the base. This concurrent enteroblastic-holoblastic pattern of conidial development is reminiscent of that exemplified in *Pseudospiropes saskatchewanensis* and *Acrogenospora sphaerocephala* (39, p. 84). This cocktail of conidiogenesis in the *Leptographium* complex has been discussed extensively in a series of publications by Wingfield and coworkers. Wingfield (57) reduced *Verticicladiella* to synonymy with *Leptographium*, demonstrating that *V. truncata* exhibits both percurrent and apparently sympodial proliferation of conidiogenous cells. This variability within a single species is not surprising because several genera of Hyphomycetes have more than one type of conidiogenesis (10,13). In addition to the similarities

between percurrent and sympodial proliferation, many mycologists consider annellidic and phialidic conidiogenesis similar (41,54).

In addition to the differences in anamorphs between species, there is also the problem of pleoanamorphism within a species. One species may produce two kinds of conidiophores with conidium ontogenies that bear little resemblance to each other. In *C. cana*, *C. piceae* and *C. ulmi*, mononematous conidiophores as well as synnematous conidiophores are produced. The mononematous, hyaline conidiophores are assigned to the anamorph genus *Sporothrix* in all three species (figs. 327, 331, 424), and synnematous, dark conidiophores represent the anamorph genus *Pachnodium* in *C. cana* (fig. 325), and *Pesotum* in the remaining two species (fig. 422). *Ceratocystis autographa* and *C. nigra* produce anamorphs in which enteroblastic phialidic and holoblastic sympodial ontogenies coexist. Both these species have anamorphs belonging to the anamorph genus *Hyalorhinocladiella*, in which conidiogenous cells appear to proliferate sympodially (figs. 227, 278-280). In *C. autographa*, a synanamorph is produced that is representative of the anamorph genus *Chalara*, having conidia borne in chains within a hyaline, cylindrical or lageniform collarette from a phialide (fig. 225). In *C. nigra*, the synanamorph belongs to the anamorph genus *Acremonium*, forming enteroblastic phialidic conidia (fig. 281). *Ceratocystis pluriannulata* produces an anamorph that can be interpreted at first as typical of *Sporothrix* (figs. 387-389), but subsequently proliferates in a manner reminiscent of species of *Hyalodendron* (fig. 399).

To return to the concept that the presence of a *Chalara* anamorph is sufficient to distinguish *Ceratocystis* from *Ophiostoma*, we know that phialides occur not only in the *Chalara* anamorphs of *Ceratocystis sensu stricto*, but also in the *Acremonium*, *Phialocephala* and *Phialographium* anamorphs of some species placed in *Ophiostoma*. It is also true that some *Chalara* anamorphs do not have phialides with deep seated conidiogenous loci, for example, the *Chalara* anamorphs of *C. adiposa* (figs. 26-27) and *C. moniliforme* (figs. 110-111). The anamorphs of *C. paradoxa* and *C. radicicola*, belonging to the form genera *Thielaviopsis* and *Chalaropsis* respectively, produce dark, thick-walled conidia with a distinct longitudinal germ-slit. The ontogenies of these conidia are quite different from that seen in true *Chalara* species (figs. 197, 208-210). Furthermore, when enteroblastic phialidic (*Chalara* type) and holoblastic-sympodial (*Hyalorhinocladiella* type) conidial ontogenies occur concurrently in a single species, as is seen in *C. autographa*, or a species is found exclusively in its teleomorphic state, as with *C. hyalothecium*, von Arx's classification becomes unworkable.

Biochemical and molecular techniques have also been used to justify separating *Ophiostoma* and *Ceratocystis s. str.* (see 16, 51). The result of Jewell's (see table 1 in 24) original screening of 47 species of *Ceratocystiopsis* and *Ceratocystis* for chitin (as chitosan) and cellulose are inconsistent with the hypothesis that only *Ceratocystis sensu stricto* lack cellulose in their cell walls. Of the major fungal groups, only the Hyphochytridiomycetes and Oomycetes were previously regarded as having cellulosic cell walls; all other groups are reported to contain chitin in their cell walls (7). Not only do six species with *Chalara* anamorphs lack cellulose, but ten other species having different anamorphs also lack cellulose in their cell walls. Of these ten species, three with *Hyalorhinocladiella* anamorphs are now placed in *Ceratocystiopsis*, viz. *C. alba*, *C. minuta*, and *C. minuta-bicolor*. *Ceratocystis adiposa*, *C. coerulescens*, *C. megalobrunnea* and *C. serpens* lacked both chitosan and cellulose; the latter two have anamorphs in which the conidiogenous cell proliferates sympodially. It is clear that the species with *Chalara* anamorphs do not have uniform chitosan composition. In my opinion, the absence of information on the cell walls of those species that have not yet been studied renders taxonomic application premature, especially at levels higher than the species. Nevertheless, biochemical characters may be useful taxonomic tools in combination with morphological features at the species level.

Ceratocystis versus *Sphaeronaemella*

The final topic to be discussed is the disagreement over the synonymy of *Sphaeronaemella* with *Ceratocystis*. The taxonomy of the former genus remains controversial (53, 8, 9). Since the publication of my monograph, in which I proposed the inclusion of *Sphaeronaemella* species in *Ceratocystis*, new information on the species of the former genus has come to light. According to Samson and Gams (in 49), *Sphaeronaemella* can be distinguished from *Ceratocystis* and other related genera by its *Gabarnaudia* anamorph (22,34). As has been related above, *Ceratocystiopsis* and *Ceratocystis* species exhibit a bewildering array of anamorphs, encompassing up to 16 hyphomycete genera with a great diversity of

conidiogenesis. If we differentiate teleomorph genera based on anamorphs, there will a flood of genera within *Ceratocystiopsis* and *Ceratocystis*.

Hutchison and Reid (22) suggested that *Sphaeronaemella* could be differentiated from *Ceratocystis* by the differences in substrate. I disagree. *Sphaeronaemella fimicola*, *S. helvellae* and *S. humicola* have quite different substrates. Furthermore, Hutchison and Reid (22) did not accept the division of *Sphaeronaemella* proposed by Cannon and Hawksworth (9) on the basis of host.

CONCLUSIONS

The complexity of relationships among the ophiostomatoid fungi has perplexed taxonomists for one century and the resolution of problems will consume many more years. Great uncertainty remains over the proper position of the entire group on the phylogenetic map of the Plectomycetes. The competing taxonomies emphasizing ascospore morphology or variable conidiogenesis, confounded by puzzling biochemical information on cell walls, have created a great dilemma. Samuels and Rossman (50) state, "Ascomycetes having similar perithecium morphology also tend to have morphologically similar anamorphs". Unfortunately, this statement does not apply to species of *Ceratocystis* and *Ceratocystiopsis*. By deviating from the Hughesian concepts of conidiogenesis, many mycologists have inconsistently applied conidium ontogeny in segregating *Ophiostoma* from *Ceratocystis s. str.* (2,3,34). Conidial states are valuable tools in interspecific identification but their use in delimiting teleomorph genera is problematic. In my opinion, the fungi classified in the family Ophiostomataceae are a natural group in an evolutionary sense, bound together by the structure of their ascocarps and the morphology of their ascospores. However, future biochemical and molecular work may provide us with a better understanding of this group of fungi.

My opinion is that this group of fungi constitutes the family Ophiostomataceae in the order Microascales and the Plectomycetes. The insertion of the order Ophiostomatales by Benny and Kimbrough (8) emphasizes the differences between the Microascaceae and Ophiostomataceae. Certainly, some of the similarities between the two families are superficial rather than real, particularly centrum development. But these differences may not be so great as to warrant ordinal ranks for the two groups. In addition to ascocarp structure, these families have anamorphs in common, such as *Graphium* and *Sporothrix*, and the dark, thick-walled conidia with a longitudinal germ-slits produced in the *Chalaropsis* and *Thielaviopsis* anamorphs of *Ceratocystis* species and the *Wardomyces* and *Wardomycopsis* anamorphs of *Microascus* species (37,38). It seems evident that these families have a common ancestry. I submit that further juggling with the Luttrellian classification is to be discouraged until we know more about the taxa being classified.

ACKNOWLEDGEMENTS

I wish to thank the "Conselho Nacional de Desenvolvimento Cientifico e Tecnologico" for grant Proc. 400900/90, which allowed me to participate in the symposium on the Ophiostomatales and the Fourth International Mycological Congress.

LITERATURE CITED

1. Arx, J.A. von. 1952. Über die Ascomycetengattungen *Ceratostomella* Sacc., *Ophiostoma* Syd. und *Rostrella* Zimmermann. Antonie van Leeuwenhoek 18:201-213.
2. Arx, J.A. von. 1974. Centraalbureau voor Schimmelcultures, progress report 1973. Verh. Kon. Ned. Akad. Wet. Afd. Natuurkd., Reeks 2, 63:1-20.
3. Arx, J.A. von. 1974. The genera of fungi sporulating in pure culture, 2nd ed. J. Cramer, 315 pp.
4. Bakshi, B.K. 1951. Studies on four species of *Ceratocystis*, with a discussion of fungi causing sapstain in Britain. Mycol. Pap. 35:1-16.
5. Barr, M.E. 1990. Prodromus to nonlichenized, pyrenomycetous members of class Hymenoascomycetes. Mycotaxon 39:43-184.
6. Bary, A. de. 1879. Die Erscheinung der Symbiose. Strasburg. 121 pp.
7. Bartnicki-Garcia, S. 1968. Cell wall chemistry, morphogenesis and taxonomy of fungi. Annu. Rev. Microbiol. 22:87-108.
8. Benny, G.L. and Kimbrough, J.W. 1980. A synopsis of the orders and families of Plectomycetes with keys to genera. Mycotaxon 12:1-90.
9. Cannon, P.F. and Hawksworth, D.L. 1982. A re-evaluation of *Melanospora* Corda and similar Pyrenomyctes with a revision of the British species. Bot. J. Linn. Soc. 84:115-160.
10. Carmichael, J.W., Kendrick, W.B., Conners I.L. and Sigler L. 1980. Genera of Hyphomyctes. Univ. Alberta Press, Edmonton. 368 pp.
11. Dowding, P. 1969. The dispersal and survival of species of fungi causing bluestain in pine. Trans. Br. Mycol. Soc. 52:125-137.
12. Dowding, P. 1984. The evolution of insect-fungus relationships in the primary invasion of forest timber. Pages 133-153 in: Invertebrate-microbial interactions. J. M. Anderson, A.D.M. Rayner and D.W.H. Walton, eds.

13. Ellis, M.B. 1971. Dematiaceous Hyphomycetes. Commonwwealth Mycological Institute, Kew, U.K., 507 pp.
14. Goidànich, G. 1936. Il genere di Ascomyceti "Grosmannia" G. Goid. Boll. Staz. Patol. Veg. Roma, n.s. 16:26-60.
15. Griffin, H.D. 1968. The genus *Ceratocystis* in Ontario. Can. J. Bot. 46:689-718.
16. Harrington, T.C. 1987. New combinations in *Ophiostoma* of *Ceratocystis* species with *Leptographium* anamorphs. Mycotaxon 28:39-43.
17. Hawksworth, D.L. 1988. The variety of fungal-algal symbioses, their evolutionary significance, and the nature of Lichens. Bot. J. Linn. Soc. 96:3-20.
18. Hoog, G.S. de. 1974. *Blastobotrys, Sporothrix, Calcarisporium* and *Calcarisporiella* gen. nov. Stud. Mycol. 7:1-88.
19. Hoog, G.S. de and Scheffer, R.J. 1984. *Ceratocystis* versus *Ophiostoma*: a reappraisal. Mycologia 76:292-299.
20. Hughes, S.J. 1953. Conidiophores, conidia and classification. Can. J. Bot. 31:577-659.
21. Hunt, J. 1956. Taxonomy of the genus *Ceratocystis*. Lloydia 19:1-58.
22. Hutchison, L.J. and Reid, J. 1988. Taxonomy of some potential woodstaining fungi from New Zealand. I. Ophiostomataceae. N. Z. J. Bot. 26:63-81.
23. Ingold, C.T. 1953. Dispersal in Fungi. Claredon Press, Oxford. 197 pp.
24. Jewell, T.R. 1974. A qualitative study of cellulose distribution in *Ceratocystis* and *Europhium*. Mycologia 66:139-146.
25. Juzwick, J. and French, D.W. 1983. *Ceratocystis fagacearum* and *C. piceae* on the surface of free flying and fungus mat inhabiting nitidulids. Phytopathology 73:1164-1168.
26. Kawalski, T. and Butin, H. 1989. Taxonomy of known and new species of *Ceratocystis* from oak (*Quercus robur* L.). Phytopathol. Z. 124:236-248.
27. Kendrick, W.B. (Ed.). 1971. Taxonomy of Fungi Imperfecti. University of Toronto Press, Toronto. 309 pp.
28. Luttrell, E.S. 1951. Taxonomy of the Pyrenomycetes. Univ. Mo. Stud. 24:1-121.
29. Luttrell, E.S. 1955. Ascostromatic ascomycetes. Mycologia 47:511-532.
30. Malloch, D. 1970. New concepts in the Microascaceae. Mycologia 62:727-740.
31. Malloch, D. 1974. *Sphaeronaemella helvellae*. Fungi Canadenses. No. 53.
32. Malloch, D. 1979. Plectomycetes and their anamorphs. Pages 153-165 in: The Whole Fungus, Vol. 1. B. Kendrick, ed. National Museum of Natural Sciences, Ottawa. 793 pp.
33. Malloch, D. 1981. The Plectomycete centrum. Pages 73-91 in: Ascomycete systematics. The Luttrellian concept. D. R. Reynolds, ed. Springer-Verlag, New York. 242 pp.
34. Malloch, D. and Blackwell, M. 1990. *Kathistes*, a new genus of pleomorphic ascomycetes. Can. J. Bot. 68:1712-1721.
35. Melin, E. and Nannfeldt, J.A. 1934. Researches into the blueing of ground wood pulp. Svenska SkogsFor. Tidskr. 32:397-616.
36. Minter, D. 1983. Redisposition of *Klasterskya* in the Ophiostomataceae. Trans. Br. Mycol. Soc. 80:162-163.
37. Minter, D. 1985. A re-appraisal of the relationships between *Arthrinium* and other hyphomycetes. Proc. Indian Acad. Sci. (Plant Sci.). 94:281-308.

38. Minter, D. 1987. The significance of conidiogenesis in pleoanamorphy. Pages 241-262 in: Pleomorphic Fungi. J. Sugiyama, ed. Kodansha, Tokyo and Elsevier, Amsterdam. 325 pp.

39. Minter, D., Kirk, P.M. and Sutton, B.C. 1982. Holoblastic phialides. Trans. Br. Mycol. Soc. 79:75-93.

40. Moreau, C. 1952. Coexistence des formes *Thielaviopsis* et *Graphium* chez une souche de *Ceratocystis major* (van Beyma) comb. nov. Rev. Mycol.(Paris) Suppl. Colon. 17:17-25.

41. Morgan-Jones, G., Nag Raj, T.R. and Kendrick, W.B. 1972. Conidium ontogeny in Coelomyctes. IV. Percurrently proliferating phialides. Can. J. Bot. 50:2009-2014.

42. Müller, E. and von Arx, J.A. 1962. Die Gattungen der didymosporen Pyrenomyceten. Beitr. Kryptogamenflora Schweiz 11 (2):1-922.

43. Müller, E. and von Arx, J.A. 1973. Pyrenomycetes: Meliolales, Coronophorales, Sphaeriales. Pages 87-132 in: The fungi, Vol. 4A. G. C. Ainsworth, F. K. Sparrow and A. S. Sussman, eds. Academic Press, New York. 640 pp.

44. Münch, E. 1907. Die Blaufäule des Nadelholzes. Naturw. Z. Forst. Landw. 5:531-573.

45. Nannfeldt, J.A. 1932. Studien über de Morfologie und systematik der lichenisierten inoperculaten Discomyceten. Nova Acta Reg. Soc. Scient. Upsal., Ser. 4,8:1-368.

46. Olchowecki, A. and Reid, J. 1974. Taxonomy of the genus *Ceratocystis* in Manitoba. Can. J. Bot. 52:1675-1711.

47. Petrak, F. 1940. Mycologische notizen XIII. Ann. Mycol. 28:181-267.

48. Redhead, S.A. and Malloch, D.W. 1977. The Endomycetaceae: new concepts, new taxa. Can. J. Bot. 55:1701-1711.

49. Samson, R. A. 1974. *Paecilomyces* and some allied hyphomycetes. Stud. Mycol. 6:1-119.

50. Samuels, G.J. and Rossman, A.Y. 1979. Conidia and classification of the nectrioid fungi. Pages 167-182 in: The Whole Fungus. Vol. 1. W.B. Kendrick, ed. National Museum of Natural Sciences, Ottawa. 793 pp.

51. Suzuki, K., Kawasaki, M. and Ishizaki, I. 1988. Analysis of restriction profiles of mitocondrial DNA from *Sporothrix schenckii* and related fungi. Mycopathologia 103:147-151.

52. Udagawa, S. 1987. Geographical distribution of the pleomorphic Plectomycetes in Asia and their teleomorph-anamorph connections. Pages 9-28 in: Pleomorphic Fungi. J. Sugiyama, ed. Kodansha, Tokyo and Elsevier, Amsterdam. 325 pp.

53. Upadhyay, H.P. 1978. Proposal for the conservation of the generic name *Ceratocystis* Ell. & Halst. (1890) against *Sphaeronaemella* Karsten (1884). Taxon 27:553.

54. Upadhyay, H.P. 1981. A Monograph of *Ceratocystis* and *Ceratocystiopsis*. University of Georgia Press, Athens, GA. 176 pp.

55. Upadhyay, H.P. and Kendrick, W.B. 1974. A new *Graphium*-like genus (conidial state of *Ceratocystis*). Mycologia 66:181-183.

56. Webster, J. 1980. Introduction to Fungi, 2nd ed. Cambridge University Press, Cambridge. 669 pp.

57. Wingfield, M.J. 1985. Reclassification of *Verticicladiella* based on conidium development. Trans. Br. Mycol. Soc. 85:81-93.

58. Wingfield, M.J., van Wyk, P.S. and Marasas, W.F.O. 1988. *Ceratocystiopsis proteae* sp. nov., with a new anamorph genus. Mycologia 80:23-30.

59. Wright, E.F. and Cain, R.F. 1961. New species of *Ceratocystis*. Can. J. Bot. 39:1215-130.

Chapter 2

THE CASE FOR DISTINGUISHING *CERATOCYSTIS* AND *OPHIOSTOMA*

G.J. SAMUELS

Ceratocystis was first published in November 1890 (15). *Ophiostoma*, published in 1919 (46), is virtually identical to *Ceratocystis* in morphology and ecology. In the one hundred years that have passed since the publication of *Ceratocystis*, there is no agreement as to whether the species included in *Ceratocystis* and *Ophiostoma* comprise one, two, or more genera and there is no agreement as to how these fungi relate to other Ascomycetes.

The taxonomic histories of these genera have been reviewed many times (3,21,47, Upadhyay, this volume) and I will not repeat the chronology here. *Ceratocystis* and *Ophiostoma* led independent generic lives until 1950 when Bakshi (2,3) recognized the identical concepts of the genera and recombined *Ophiostoma* species in *Ceratocystis*. *Ceratocystis* was originally described for *C. fimbriata*, a species with a *Chalara* anamorph. The fungus was not recognized to be an ascomycete until Elliott's (8) cytological study confirmed its ascigerous nature. Elliott (8) transferred the species to *Ceratostomella* apparently unaware that Höhnel (18) had earlier removed species with evanescent asci from *Ceratostomella* to *Linostoma*. That *Linostoma* is a later homonym for a genus of flowering plants, *Linostoma* (Thymeleaceae), was recognized by Sydow and Sydow (46), who proposed the new name *Ophiostoma*. Luttrell (25) recognized a single type of ascomatal development in the complex that he termed the *Ophiostoma*-type, which is characterized by the irregular production of asci throughout the locule from chains of ascogenous cells, never from a basal hymenium.

Anamorphs have directed taxonomy of the blue-stain fungi from an early time but the taxonomic power of the anamorphs has never been clear. Basically, there are two morphologically distinct and easily recognized types of anamorphs occurring in the *Ceratocystis/Ophiostoma* complex: the *Chalara/Thielaviopsis* type (Fig. 1 A,B), with enteroblastic conidia and dark brown chlamydospores and the *Graphium/Sporothrix* type (Fig. 1 C-F), with holoblastically produced conidia. Münch (28) and Goidànich (13) evidently followed the philosophy of "one teleomorph genus, one anamorph genus," when they described, respectively, the genera *Endoconidiophora*, for species with *Chalara* anamorphs and *Grosmannia*, for species with *Leptographium* anamorphs in the *Graphium /Sporothrix* complex. Most workers did not accept this philosophy and, for approximately twenty-five years from 1950, when Bakshi (2,3) recognized the synonymy of *Ceratocystis* and *Ophiostoma*, *Ceratocystis* was accepted as the appropriate genus for these fungi. With the exception of Griffin (14), who considered anamorphs variable and unreliable as aids in identification, succeeding taxonomists (1,21,47) have included the species with *Chalara* anamorphs in subdivisions of *Ceratocystis*.

The taxonomic value of morphology, biology, and anamorph were well established by 1934. The arguments that took place between 1906 and 1972 as to whether to recognize one or more genera for these fungi did not offer new supporting information.

Much new taxonomically useful information became available in the late nineteen-sixties and nineteen-seventies. Perithecial characters, which had received little attention, were reevaluated. *Europhium* (32) was described for non-ostiolate species of *Ceratocystis* but this segregate has not been widely accepted. On the other hand, *Ceratocystiopsis* (48), which was described for species with falcate ascospores, is generally accepted (but see Wingfield, this volume). Luttrell's (25) conclusion that only one ontogenetic type of ascoma is represented by species of this complex has been challenged by Banville (as reported in 44), Parguey-Leduc (31), and van Wyk *et al.* (this volume). Asci of species with *Chalara* anamorphs may arise from ascogenous cells that line the interior of the locule and proliferate into the centrum. Asci of species with holoblastically produced conidia may arise from a column of ascogenous cells that is centrally attached at the base of the centrum. Few ontogenetic studies have been undertaken, however, and the consistency of these observations is yet to be tested.

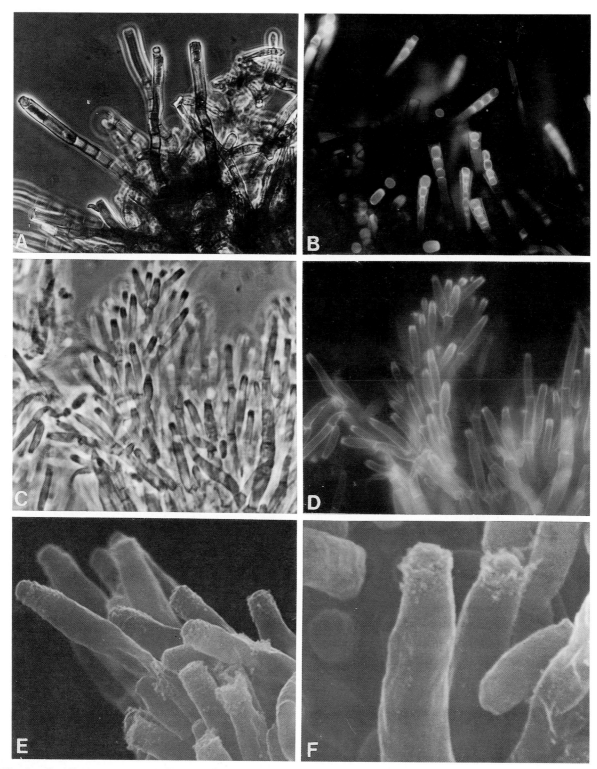

Fig. 1. Conidiogenous cells of *Ceratocystis* and *Ophiostoma* species. A, B, *Chalara* anamorph of *Endoconidiophora virescens* Davids. [= *Ceratocystis coerulescens* (Münch) Bakshi] showing conidia forming within a tubular phialide (BPI, from type collection; A, phase contrast microscopy; B, fluorescence microscopy with Calcafluor); C-F, *Phialocephala* anamorph of *Ceratocystis vesca* Davids. (= *Ophiostoma olivaceum* Mathiesen) from type collection showing periclinal thickening at the conidiogenous locus (BPI; C, phase contrast microscopy; D, fluorescence microscopy with Calcafluor), E, F, scanning electron microscopy showing frilled annellations indicating successively produced conidiogenous loci. Scale bars: A-D = 10 μm; E, F = 1 μm.

In 1964, Rosinski and Campana (36) published the first report of the presence of cellulose in hyphal walls of *Ceratocystis ulmi*. Smith *et al.* (45) could not find cellulose in hyphal walls of *C. fimbriata*, a species with a *Chalara* anamorph, and suggested that the distribution of cellulose among *Ceratocystis* species is correlated with anamorph type. Jewell (22) looked more widely in the broadly conceived *Ceratocystis*. He studied six of the nine known species with *Chalara* anamorphs and did not detect cellulose in the hyphae of any of them. Of the species with holoblastic conidiogenesis, thirty-one species had cellulosic cell walls while cellulose was absent from the hyphal walls of ten species.

Spencer and Gorin (45) found a correlation between polysaccharides in the cell wall and conidial type. The species that have *Chalara* anamorphs also tended to be characterized by the formation of glucomannans or galactoglucomannans rather than the rhamnose- and mannose-containing polysaccharides of species with *Graphium/Sporothrix* anamorphs. The pattern of polysaccharide distribution corresponded to the distribution of cellulose later reported by Jewell (22), who summarized the distribution of cellulose among the ophiostomatoid fungi. Harrington (16) correlated sensitivity to cycloheximide with cell wall chemistry and anamorph. Once again, the species with *Chalara* anamorphs were sensitive to the antibiotic, while most of the species with holoblastic anamorphs were tolerant.

De Hoog (19) and de Hoog and Scheffer (20) noted the constant correlation between hyphal wall chemistry, sensitivity to cycloheximide, and *Chalara* anamorphs and reintroduced *Ophiostoma* as distinct from *Ceratocystis*. Upadhyay (47), on the other hand only accorded these correlations sectional significance. *Ceratocystis* sect. *Endoconidiophora* included only species with *Chalara* anamorphs whereas sect. *Ceratocystis* included three *Chalara* teleomorphs and several *Graphium/Sporothrix* teleomorphs. *Ceratocystiopsis* likewise included both types of anamorphs, *C. falcata* having a *Chalara* anamorph.

Doubt has been cast upon the taxonomic consistency of conidiogenesis, wall chemistry, and sensitivity to cycloheximide. Upadhyay (47) did not distinguish teleomorph genera on the basis of mode of conidiogenesis because some species have both holoblastic and enteroblastic conidiogenesis (*C. autographa* and *C. nigra*). In other species, anamorphs are "rarely produced" and still others

are not known to have anamorphs (*C. hyalothecium* apparently does not produce an anamorph in culture; various species cited by Upadhyay in this category have not been cultured). De Hoog and Scheffer (20) also observed the holoblastic and enteroblastic formation of conidia in cultures of *C. araucariae* and concluded that conidiogenesis alone will not reveal the phylogenetic relationships of these fungi. In the case of *Ceratocystis* and *Ophiostoma*, more than conidiogenesis must be compared.

Few characteristics of the *Chalara/Theilaviopsis* combination are similar to those of the *Graphium* complex. Even in those few cases within the *Graphium* complex where enteroblastic conidiogenesis is reported for species where holoblastic conidiogenesis is normal, the enteroblastic synanamorph does not resemble *Chalara* or any anamorph genus close to *Chalara*. There are no transitional forms between the *Chalara* and *Graphium* types of anamorphs. The types differ in conidiogenous cell morphology, conidial ontogeny and morphology, and in arrangement of conidia on the conidiogenous cell.

Although the presence of cellulose in cell walls of *O. ulmi* and other *Ophiostoma* species is considered unusual, it is not unique and the taxonomic significance of its occurrence has been questioned. Farr (9), as early as 1954, demonstrated cellulose and chitin in walls of two species of *Aspergillus*. More recently, Benhamou (5) and Benhamou *et al.* (6) demonstrated cellulose in conidial walls of species of *Fusarium*, *Penicillium*, *Trichoderma* and *Verticillium* as well as *O. ulmi*, but cellulose could only be detected in hyphae of germinating conidia of *O. ulmi*. Although only *Ophiostoma* species with *Graphium* anamorphs are tolerant of cycloheximide, Seifert (personal communication) has found variable sensitivity to the antibiotic in other genera of Hyphomycetes.

The taxonomic significance of a given character may be different in different taxa. Evidently one or more of these biochemical characters are equivocal in taxonomic significance in the teleomorphs of the *Graphium* complex. However, the combined attributes of *Chalara* anamorph, glucomannans or galactoglucomannans in the cell walls, absence of cellulose from the cell walls, and sensitivity to cycloheximide do seem to delimit a taxon. The level of that taxon remains the question.

One way of answering that question is to consider how the *Ophiostoma/Ceratocystis* complex relates to other ascomycetes. Perithecial characters are unfortunately too simplified to give clues to relationships. The characters that are essential for unequivocal taxonomic placement of Ascomycetes, a distinctive ascal discharge mechanism and a hamathecium of sterile filaments within the ascoma, are lacking. For Benny and Kimbrough (7), the ascoma of species of the Ophiostomatales is a functional cleistothecium. Genera and families of pyrenomycetous ascomycetes that have well developed ascal discharge mechanisms and hamathecia and that are considered to be homogeneous are also homogeneous in their anamorphs. Obvious examples are the families Gnomoniaceae, Hypocreaceae, Xylariaceae, and the genera *Cochliobolus, Embellisia, Lasiosphaeria, Pleospora, Setosphaeria* and many more. Sometimes the relationship is one teleomorph genus for one anamorph genus and sometimes the relationship is one genus or family to a set of morphologically and developmentally similar anamorphs.

The distribution of *Chalara* anamorphs in ascomycetes, reviewed by Nag Raj and Kendrick in this volume, is limited. Although *Chalara* anamorphs are found among the inoperculate Discomycetes (17), the relatives of *Ceratocystis* and *Ophiostoma* are more likely to be Pyrenomycetes. Among the Pyrenomycetes, *Chalara* is the anamorph of one species of *Lulworthia* Sutherland (Halosphaeriales, Halosphaeriaceae (30)) and has a synanamorph with the morphologically similar *Sporoschisma*, in the life-cycle of a species of *Melanochaeta* (Sordariales, Lasiosphaeriaceae (27). *Sporoschisma* has also been linked to a second species of *Melanochaeta* (26) and a species of *Porosphaerellopsis* (Lasiosphaeriaceae, (39). *Chalara elegans* with its synanamorph, *Thielaviopsis basicola* (29), can be compared to the *Chalara/ Sporoschisma* synanamorph pair of *Melanochaeta aotearoae* (27). If the dark, cylindrical, phragmosporous conidia of *Sporoschisma* failed to disarticulate either within the tube of the conidiogenous cell or in the extruded chain, it could easily be identified as a *Thielaviopsis* chlamydospore. Another similarity between *Chalara* and the Lasiosphaeriaceae is seen in the chlamydospores of species such as *Chalara paradoxa*, which are terminal, often solitary, and sometimes with a vertical slit. These chlamydospores are similar to the chlamydospores of *Mammaria echinobotryoides* (Fig. 2), which is synanamorphic with a *Phialophora* species and part of the life-cycle of *Cercophora solaris* (Lasiosphaeriaceae, unpublished). On the basis of these similarities of *Chalara* and *Sporoschisma* species to

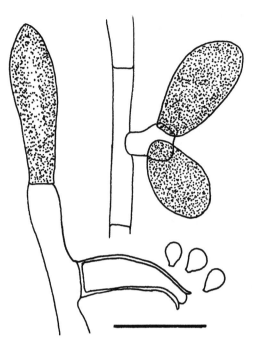

Fig. 2. *Mammaria* anamorph of *Cercophora solaris* (PDD 46472). Scale bar = 10 μm.

anamorphs of genera of the Lasiosphaeriaceae, I follow Barr (4) in distinguishing *Ophiostoma* from *Ceratocystis* and in placing *Ceratocystis* in the Sordariales, Lasiosphaeriaceae.

Just as the *Chalara* anamorph is limited in its distribution among the Pyrenomycetes, so is holoblastic conidiogenesis. There is a general correlation between holoblastic conidiogenesis and ascal amyloidy in the Amphisphaeriaceae *sensu lato* (40,41,42), the Diatrypaceae (10,11), Hyponectriaceae (37) Xylariaceae (33,35), and all families of the Xylariales *sensu* Barr (4). This type of conidial development is also found in some members of the Clavicipitales (e.g. Balansioideae) but these are not considered related to *Ophiostoma* because they are obligate parasites of grasses.

There is strong morphological similarity in conidiogenous cells between the hyphomycetous *Dematophora, Nodulisporium* and *Rhinocladiella* anamorphs of various genera of the Xylariaceae and those of the *Sporothrix* anamorphs of *Ophiostoma*. The anamorph of *Rosellinia limoniispora* is a species of *Sporothrix* (33). There is also morphological and ultrastructural similarity between the conidiogenous cells of the pycnidial anamorphs of the Diatrypaceae (10,11). Conidiogenous cells of *Eutypa lata* (11) and various species of *Diatrype* and *Diatrypella* proliferate sympodially and percurrently, the latter giving an annellate aspect to the conidiogenous cell.

Conidiogenous cells in the *Leptographium* anamorphs of *Ophiostoma* species also proliferate both percurrently and sympodially (49,50 Wingfield, this volume). Conidiogenesis and percurrent proliferation of the conidiogenous loci of *Diatrype stigma* (10, Fig. 27) and *L. terebrantis* (50, Fig. 21) appear to occur through the same process of holoblastic formation and dehiscence of a single conidium followed by enteroblastic extension of the locus through the old scar and holoblastic formation of a second conidium; the process continues with the formation of many conidia, the site of each conidium marked by a frill or annellation.

The most conspicuous members of the Xylariales (e.g. *Diatrype, Eutypa, Hypoxylon* and *Xylaria*) are lignicolous, encountered on dead trees where they may cause white rots (12,35). This apparently saprobic life-style might seem to preclude relationship to *Ophiostoma* or *Ceratocystis* because of their biotrophic biology. However, some members of the Xylariales are weak parasites of trees (12,35), or endophytes resident within leaves and bark of symptomless, healthy plants (33,34,43), that may sporulate when the plant is weakened or dies. Thus a wide range of habits - commensal, biotrophic, saprobic - is exhibited within the order and physiology does not rule out a relationship of *Ophiostoma* and *Ceratocystis* to the Xylariales.

The Xylariales is characterized in part by the formation of carbonaceous stromata (4) but the amount of stromal formation is variable according to the genus, lacking in some e.g. *Ascotricha erinacea* (23). At least two species of *Ophiostoma, O. roraimense* and *O. grande* (38), have thick, carbonized perithecial walls in common with some Xylariaceae such as species of *Camillea* Fr. (24). Ascospores in *Camillea* are also colorless, as in *Ophiostoma*. Ascospores in the Diatrypaceae tend to be allantoid and colorless or pale brown, thus reminiscent of ascospores in some species of *Ophiostoma*.

Ophiostoma and its close relative *Ceratocystiopsis* are probably derived from the Xylariales and can be classified in that order but they cannot be assigned to any of the families that Barr (4) included. Therefore, I retain them in their own family, the Ophiostomataceae, in the Xylariales.

CONCLUSIONS

Ceratocystis, Ophiostoma, and *Ceratocystiopsis* are distinct genera derived from pyrenomycetous ancestors. Because their ascomata are cleistothecial, the teleomorphs do not shed light on relationships. On the other hand, the anamorphs are conservative and indicate different lines of derivation. *Ceratocystis* is most likely derived from the Lasiosphaeriaceae and is referred to that family. *Ophiostoma* and *Ceratocystiopsis* are probably derived from members of the Xylariales that have amyloid ascal rings, possibly the Xylariaceae or Diatrypaceae. Because I cannot now see close familial relationships, I retain the Ophiostomataceae as a distinct family of the Xylariales.

Comparison of species of *Ceratocystis* and *Ophiostoma* to species of well defined genera such as *Xylaria, Diatrype,* and *Lasiosphaeria* using molecular techniques may give clues as to the broader relationships of the ophiostomatoid fungi.

ACKNOWLEDGEMENTS

I am grateful to James C. Plaskowitz for performing the scanning electron microscopy, and for preparing the photomicrographs.

LITERATURE CITED

1. Arx, J.A. von 1952. Über die Ascomycetengattungen *Ceratostomella* Sacc., *Ophiostoma* Syd. und *Rostrella* Zimmermann. Antonie van Leeuwenhoek 18:201-213.

2. Bakshi, B.K. 1950. Fungi associated with ambrosia beetles in Great Britain. Trans. Br. Mycol. Soc. 33:111-120.

3. Bakshi, B.K. 1951. Studies on four species of *Ceratocystis*, with a discussion on fungi causing sapstain in Britain. Mycol. Pap. 35:1-16.

4. Barr, M.E. 1990. Prodromus to nonlichenized, pyrenomycetous members of Class Hymenoascomycetes. Mycotaxon 39:43-184.

5. Benhamou, N. 1988. Ultrastructural localization of carbohydrates in the cell walls of two pathogenic fungi: a comparative study. Mycologia 80:324-337.

6. Benhamou, N., Chamberland, H., Noel, S. and Ouellette, G.B. 1990. Ultrastructural localization of ß-1,4-glucan-containing molecules in cell walls of some fungi: a comparative study between spore and mycelium. Can. J. Microbiol. 36:149-158.

7. Benny, G.L. and Kimbrough, J. W. 1980. A synopsis of the orders and families of plectomycetes with keys to genera. Mycotaxon 12:1-91.

8. Elliott, J.A. 1925. A cytological study of *Ceratostomella fimbriata* (E. & H.) Elliott. Phytopathology 16:417-422.

9. Farr, W.K. 1954. Structure and composition of the wall of *Aspergillus niger* and *A. carbonarius*. Trans. N. Y. Acad. Sci., Ser. II, 16:209-214.

10. Glawe, D.A. and Rogers, J.D. 1982a. Observations on the

anamorphs of six species of *Diatrype* and *Diatrypella*. Can. J. Bot. 60:245-251.

11. Glawe, D.A. and Rogers, J.D. 1982b. Observations on the anamorphs of six species of *Eutypa* and *Eutypella*. Mycotaxon 14:334-346.

12. Glawe, D.A. and Rogers, J.D. 1984. Diatrypaceae in the Pacific Northwest. Mycotaxon 22:401-460.

13. Goidànich, G. 1936. Il genere di Ascomiceti "Grosmannia" G. Goid. Boll. Staz. Patol. Veg. Roma, n.s. 16:26-60.

14. Griffin, H.D. 1968. The genus *Ceratocystis* in Ontario. Can. J. Bot. 46:689-718.

15. Halsted, B.D. 1890. Some fungous diseases of the sweet potato. N. J. Agr. Exp. Sta. 76:1-32.

16. Harrington, T.C. 1981. Cycloheximide sensitivity as a taxonomic character in *Ceratocystis*. Mycologia 73:1123-1129.

17. Hennebert, G.L. and Bellèmere, A. 1979. Les formes conidiennes des discomycetes. Essai taxonomique. Rev. Mycol. (Paris) 43:259-315.

18. Höhnel, F. von. 1918. Mykologische Fragmente. CXCV. Über die Gattung *Parodiopsis* Maublanc. Ann. Mycol. 16:40-41.

19. Hoog, G.S. de. 1974. The genera *Blastobotrys*, *Sporothrix*, *Calcarisporium* and *Calcarisporiella* gen. nov. Stud. Mycol. 7:1-84.

20. Hoog, G.S. de and Scheffer, R. J. 1984. *Ceratocystis* versus *Ophiostoma*: a reappraisal. Mycologia 76: 292-299.

21. Hunt, J. 1956. Taxonomy of the genus *Ceratocystis*. Lloydia 19:1-58.

22. Jewell, T.R. 1974. A qualitative study of cellulose distribution in *Ceratocystis* and *Europhium*. Mycologia 66:139-146.

23. Kahn, R.S. and Cain, R.F. 1977. The occurrence of amyloid plugs in asci of *Ascotricha erinacea*. Mycotaxon 5:409-414.

24. Laessøe, T., Rogers, J.D. and Whalley, A.J.S. 1989. *Camillea*, *Jongiella* and light-spored species of *Hypoxylon*. Mycol. Res. 93:121-155.

25. Luttrell, E.S. 1951. Taxonomy of the pyrenomycetes. Univ. Mo. Stud. 24:1-120.

26. Müller, E., Harr, J. and Sulmont, P. 1969. Deux ascomycètes dont le stade conidien présent des conidies phaeophragmiées endogènes. Rev. Mycol. (Paris) 33:369-378.

27. Müller, E. and Samuels, G.J. 1982. Anamorphs of pyrenomycetous Ascomycetes III. The *Sporoschisma* and *Chalara* anamorphs of *Melanochaeta aotearoae*. Sydowia 35:155-161.

28. Münch, E. 1907. Die Blaufäule des Nadelholzes. Naturw. Z. Forst. Landw. 5:531-573.

29. Nag Raj, T.R. and Kendrick, B. 1975. A monograph of *Chalara* and allied genera. Wilfrid Laurier University Press, Waterloo, Ontario. 200 pp.

30. Parguey-Leduc, A. 1967. Recherches sur l'ontogénie et l'anatomie comparée des ascocarpes des pyrénomycètes ascoloculares. Ann. Sci. Nat., Bot. & Biol. Vég. 12, Sér., 8:1-110.

31. Parguey-Leduc, A. 1977. Les asques des pyrénomycetes. Rev. Mycol. (Paris) 41:281-338.

32. Parker, A.K. 1957. *Europhium*, a new genus of the ascomycetes with a *Leptographium* imperfect state. Can J. Bot. 35:173.

33. Petrini, L. and Petrini, O. 1985. Xylariaceous fungi as endophytes. Sydowia 38:216-234.

34. Petrini, O. 1985. Wirtsspezifität endophytischer Pilze bei einheimischen Ericaceae. Bot. Helv. 95:213-238.

35. Rogers, J.D. 1979. The Xylariaceae: systematic, biological and evolutionary aspects. Mycologia 71:1-42.

36. Rosinski, M.A. and Campana, R.J. 1964. Chemical analysis of the cell wall of *Ceratocystis ulmi*. Mycologia 56:738-744.

37. Samuels, G.J. and Hallett, I.C. 1983. *Microdochium stoveri* and *Monographella stoveri*, new combinations for *Fusarium stoveri* and *Micronectriella stoveri*. Trans. Br. Mycol. Soc. 81: 473-483.

38. Samuels, G.J. and Müller, E. 1978a. Life-history studies of Brazilian ascomycetes 5. Two new species of *Ophiostoma* and their *Sporothrix* anamorphs. Sydowia 31:169-179.

39. Samuels, G.J. and Müller, E. 1978b. Life-history studies of Brazilian ascomycetes 1. Two new genera of the Sphaeriaceae having, respectively, *Sporoschisma*-like and *Codinaea* anamorphs. Sydowia 31:126-136.

40. Samuels, G.J., Müller, E. and Petrini, O. 1987. Studies in the Amphisphaeriaceae (*sensu lato*) 3. New species of *Monographella* and *Pestalosphaeria*, and two new genera. Mycotaxon 28:473-499.

41. Samuels, G.J., Rogers, J.D. and Nagasawa, E. 1987. Studies in the Amphisphaeriaceae (*sensu lato*) 1. *Collodiscula japonica* and its anamorph, *Acanthodochium collodisculae*. Mycotaxon 28: 453-459.

42. Samuels, G.J. and Rossman, A.Y. 1987. Studies in the Amphisphaeriaceae (*sensu lato*) 2. *Leiosphaerella cocoes* and two new species of *Oxydothis* on palms. Mycotaxon 28:461-471.

43. Sieber, T.N. 1989. Endophytic fungi in twigs of healthy and diseased Norway spruce and white fir. Mycol. Res. 92:322-326.

44. Smith, M.J., Patik, C.M. and Rosinski, M.A. 1967. A comparison of cellulose production in the genus *Ceratocystis*. Mycologia 59:965-969

45. Spencer, J.F.T. and Gorin, P.A.J. 1971. Systematics of the genera *Ceratocystis* and *Graphium*. Proton magnetic resonance spectra of the mannose-containing polysaccharides as an aid in classification. Mycologia 63:387-402

46. Sydow, H. and Sydow, P. 1919. Mykologische Mitteilungen. Sydowia 1: 33-47.

47. Upadhyay, H.P. 1981. A monograph of *Ceratocystis* and *Ceratocystiopsis*. University of Georgia Press, Athens, GA. 176 pp.

48. Upadhyay, H.P and Kendrick, W.B. 1975. Prodromus for a revision of *Ceratocystis* (Microascales, Ascomycetes) and its conidial states. Mycologia 67:798-805.

49. Wingfield, M.J. 1985. Reclassification of *Verticicladiella* based on conidial development. Trans. Br. Mycol. Soc. 8:81-93.

50. Wingfield, M.J., Van Wyk, P.S. and Wingfield, B.D. 1987. Reclassification of *Phialocephala* based on conidial development. Trans. Br. Mycol. Soc. 89:509-520.

Chapter 3

PROBLEMS IN DELINEATING THE GENUS *CERATOCYSTIOPSIS*

M.J. WINGFIELD

INTRODUCTION

The genus *Ceratocystiopsis* was established by Upadhyay and Kendrick (27) to accommodate species of *Ceratocystis sensu lato* that have elongate to falcate ascospores enclosed in sheaths with attenuated ends. Species in the genus also usually have ascomata with short conical necks terminating in convergent ostiolar hyphae. At present, fifteen species are accommodated in *Ceratocystiopis* (Table 1).

Originally, the establishment of *Ceratocystiopsis* appeared to segregate a reasonably well defined group of species from *Ceratocystis s.l.* Recently, however, it has led to a number of taxonomic problems. I suggest that there are at least three arguments against retaining the genus. Firstly, a number of distinct groups within *Ophiostoma* can be defined on the basis of ascospore morphology. Segregation of *Ceratocystiopsis* alone, without equal treatment of other groups, seems illogical. Secondly, considerable support exists for the separation of

Ceratocystis s.l. into two genera that can be based on two distinct patterns of conidium development. The current delineation of *Ceratocystiopsis* that includes anamorphs with both patterns of conidial development is therefore inconsistent with the separation of *Ceratocystis* and *Ophiostoma*. Finally, recent studies on ascospore morphology (P.W.J. van Wyk and M.J. Wingfield, unpublished) suggest that remains of the centrum can attach to the ends of elongate ascospores in *Ceratocystiopsis proteae*. This can give a false impression that these spores have elongate sheaths similar to those found in *Ceratocystiopsis*. This anomaly can lead to incorrect placement of species in *Ceratocystiopsis* and thus considerable confusion.

The aim of this chapter is to discuss these problems associated with the genus *Ceratocystiopsis* and attempt to place the genus in perspective, arguing for its reduction to synonymy with *Ophiostoma*.

TABLE 1. Species included in *Ceratocystiopsis* and their associated anamorphs

Teleomorph	Anamorph	Reference
Ceratocystiopsis alba	*Hyalorhinocladiella*	(26)
Ceratocystiopsis concentrica	*Sporothrix*	(26)
Ceratocystiopsis conicicollis	*Hyalorhinocladiella*	(26)
Ceratocystiopsis crenulata	*Hyalorhinocladiella*	(26)
Ceratocystiopsis falcata	*Chalara*	(26)
Ceratocystiopsis fasciata	*Hyalorhinocladiella*	(26)
Ceratocystiopsis longispora	*Sporothrix*	(26)
Ceratocystiopsis minima	*Hyalorhinocladiella*	(26)
Ceratocystiopsis minuta	*Hyalorhinocladiella*	(26)
Ceratocystiopsis ochracea	Unknown	(25)
Ceratocystiopsis pallidobrunnea	*Sporothrix*	(26)
Ceratocystiopsis protea	*Knoxdaciesia protea*	(29)
Ceratocystiopsis ranaculosus	*Sporothrix*	(2)
Ceratocystiopsis retusi	*Allescheriella* (sic)	(26)
Ceratocystiopsis spinulosa	*Sporothrix*	(26)

SUBDIVISION OF *OPHIOSTOMA* BASED ON ASCOSPORE MORPHOLOGY

In the past, various authors have implemented subdivisions of *Ceratocystis s.l.* based on the morphology of ascospores. For example, in a study of *Ceratocystis s.l.*, Griffin (7) established groups of species based on ascospores with and without sheaths. Those with sheaths were further subdivided based on the morphology of the sheaths. Olchowecki and Reid (20) followed this trend and divided *Ceratocystis s.l.* into four groups based on ascospore morphology. These were (i) the **Minuta Group** with elongate, usually curved ascospores having hyaline sheaths; (ii) the **Ips Group** with cylindrical to dumbell-shaped ascospores having uniform to pillow-shaped sheaths; (iii) the **Fimbriata Group** with curved, lunate or orange-section-shaped ascospores and with either uniform gelatinous sheaths or sheaths, extended to appear half-moon, hat- or cucullate-shaped in side view; and (iv) the **Pilifera Group** with curved, ovoid or cylindrical ascospores lacking sheaths.

Upadhyay and Kendrick (27) chose to segregate those species of *Ceratocystis s.l.* with elongate to falcate and sheathed ascospores in the new genus *Ceratocystiopsis*. Later, Upadhyay (26) further subdivided *Ceratocystis* (other than *Ceratocystiopsis*) into four Sections based on ascospore morphology. **Section Ophiostoma** (Type *O. piliferum*) accommodated the species lacking sheaths; **Section Ips** (Type *C. ips*) accommodated species with pillow-shaped sheaths; **Section Ceratocystis** (Type *C. fimbriata*) was established for those species having hat, half moon or cucullate-shaped sheaths; **Section Endoconidiophora** (Type *C. coerulescens*) accommodated species with elongate or inequilateral sheaths. It seems surprising, however, that having previously established *Ceratocystiopsis*, Upadhyay (26) chose to establish these sections and not give them generic status. Certainly, there seems little logic in assigning generic rank to one group and not applying uniform standards throughout.

DEFINITION OF ASCOSPORE SHEATHS

The recent description of *Cp. proteae* from South Africa (29) provides an interesting study, highlighting the problems associated with the genus *Ceratocystiopsis*. This species is frequently found fruiting in the dried infructescences of *Protea* species and shares characteristics of *Ophiostoma*, *Ceratocystis* and *Ceratocystiopsis*. For example, the ascospores of *Cp. proteae* are elongate with distinct sheaths and

pointed ends as would be expected in *Ceratocystiopsis* but the perithecia have relatively long necks and the anamorph (*Knoxdaviesia proteae*) is reminiscent of *Leptographium*. Both the latter characteristics suggest *Ophiostoma* as a possible genus in which to accommodate this fungus (29). However, this conflicts with the sensitivity of *Cp. proteae* to low concentrations of cycloheximide, a trait regarded as typical of the genus *Ceratocystis sensu stricto* (12). The presence of elongate ascospores with falcate sheaths, therefore, eventually led us to choose *Ceratocystiopsis* as the genus for this unusual fungus.

Recently, on collections of *Protea* infructescences, a number of fungi were regularly observed, including *Cp. proteae* and a similar species with some distinct differences. Like *Cp. proteae,* the 'new' fungus has a *Knoxdaviesia* anamorph, although it is readily distinguishable from *K. proteae* on the basis of its morphology. However, this previously-undescribed species has reniform ascospores that lack any indication of a sheath. Clearly, the similarity in anamorph as well as the unusual ecological niche occupied by these fungi, dictates that they should share the same genus. I suggest *Ophiostoma* would be the most acceptable for them.

The discrepancy in ascospore morphology of *Cp. proteae* and the related undescribed species has led us to examine ascospores of the former fungus more closely. In preliminary ultrastructural studies (P.W.J. van Wyk and M.J. Wingfield, unpublished), we have been unable to detect the presence of the sheath on developing ascospores within ascomata of *Cp. proteae*. From these observations, we have concluded that the 'sheath' of this fungus observed under the light microscope is comprised of the remains of the ascocarp centrum. We believe that, as the elongate ascospores are extruded from the necks of the ascocarps, they retain vestiges of the centrum, giving them the appearance of falcate sheaths with pointed ends. It would be interesting to conduct ultrastructural studies on other species of *Ceratocystiopsis* to determine the extent of the phenomenon within the genus. The existence of this anomaly has already led to the incorrect generic placement of *Cp. proteae* and the retention of *Ceratocystiopsis* could exacerbate such problems.

ANAMORPHS IN CERATOCYSTIS *S.L.*

The taxonomic significance of anamorphs in *Ceratocystis s.l.* has long been recognized. For example, Münch (19) established *Endoconidiophora* as distinct from *Ceratostomella* based on the presence of a *Chalara* anamorph in the former genus. Indeed, this custom was adopted by various authors (1,3,4). Similarly, in his monographic work, Hunt (13) subdivided *Ceratocystis s.l.* into three sections based on the morphology of the anamorph. Thus, species with *Chalara* anamorphs were distinguished from those having *Leptographium/Graphium* states and those with less obvious or "mycelial" conidiophores, such as those placed in the genera *Sporothrix* and *Hyalorhinocladiella*.

In recent years, outstanding evidence has been provided for the unique nature of species of *Ceratocystis s.l.* with *Chalara* anamorphs (see Samuels, this volume). These fungi lack cellulose in their cell walls (15,23,25) while cellulose is found in the walls of most species with anamorphs other than *Chalara*. Similarly, Weijman and de Hoog (28) provided a strong argument for the separation of *Ceratocystis* and *Ophiostoma* based on the presence of rhamnose in species with holoblastic conidium development, rhamnose is not present in species with endoconidia.

Upadhyay (26) also refers to the importance of the anamorph in the taxonomy of *Ceratocystis s.l.* For instance, he stated that Hedgcock (10) "was ahead of his time" in his recognition of the anamorph of *Ceratostomella schrenkiana* (= *O. piliferum*). Similarly, he stated that Rumbold (24) "apparently understood the importance of conidial states in species separation". It is therefore surprising that in his taxonomic treatise, Upadhyay (26) all but ignored the two distinct patterns of conidial ontogeny exhibited by species of *Ceratocystis s.l.* This might possibly be ascribed to the fact that early interpretations of conidial development (14) treated species with enteroblastic and phialidic conidial development as a uniform group. Thus, after Hunt (13), most treatments of *Ceratocystis s.l.* emphasized ascospore and not anamorph morphology. Upadhyay (26) obviously followed this trend despite the fact that he was aware of the studies of de Hoog (11) and Weijman and de Hoog (28).

However, subdivision of *Ceratocystis* from *Ophiostoma* as suggested by Weijman and de Hoog (28) gained further support with the discovery that species of *Ceratocystis s.l.* with *Chalara* anamorphs are sensitive to low concentrations of cycloheximide. In contrast, those in the group assigned to *Ophiostoma* by Weijman and de Hoog (28) tolerate high concentrations (up to 2.5 g/ℓ) of this antibiotic (8). The argument for the separation of *Ophiostoma* and *Ceratocystis s.str.* is well summarized by de Hoog and Scheffer (12, see also Samuels, this volume), who also provide new combinations in *Ophiostoma* for many species of *Ceratocystis*.

In contrast, a distinct anomaly exists in the anamorphs of *Ceratocystiopsis*. All but one species in this genus have conidia that are formed by replacement wall building (18) and can be disposed in *Sporothrix*, *Hyalorhinocladiella* or *Knoxdaviesia*. Thus, in terms of conidial development, the exception in this group is *C. falcata*, which has a *Chalara* anamorph. Although this species has falcate ascospores, they are also unusual in being two-celled, suggesting that the species is misclassified (see also Nag Raj and Kendrick, this volume). If this species was transferred to *Ceratocystis s.str.*, it would be the only species in that group with falcate and two-celled ascospores. Nevertheless, species of *Ceratocystis s.str.* have a range of ascosporal forms and I believe that, at present, *C. falcata* would best be accommodated in that genus.

Ceratocystiopsis crassivaginata is also unusual amongst species of *Ceratocystiopsis* in having a *Leptographium* anamorph. For this reason, Harrington (9) transferred this species to *Ophiostoma*. This logical step has, however, resulted in a single species of *Ophiostoma* with unusually long ascospores and elongate sheaths.

In terms of conidial states, I believe that a continuum exists amongst anamorphs of *Ophiostoma*. Species with *Hyalorhinocladiella* and *Sporothrix* anamorphs are closely related to those with *Graphium* and *Leptographium* states. Hence, the transfer of *C. crassivaginata* to *Ophiostoma* sets the stage for incorporation of other *Ceratocystiopsis* species (excluding *C. falcata*) in *Ophiostoma*.

ASCOCARP MORPHOLOGY AND ECOLOGICAL ADAPTATION

Species of *Ceratocystis s.l.* are closely associated with, and known to be carried by, insects (6,16,17,26). It is believed that the elongated ascocarp necks that bear masses of slimy ascospores at their apices are an important aid to insect dispersal (5). However, fungi within this group exhibit considerable variation in neck length. These range from being absent in species previously accommodated in *Europhium* (20,22,26,27) to extremely long, such as in *O. piliferum* where they can be up to 3000 μm in length. Despite this fact, even species without necks or with only short necks are associated with insects. It is therefore necessary to question how, if at all, neck lengths play a part in vector associations.

Most species of *Ceratocystiopsis* have relatively short tapering necks with convergent ostiolar hyphae.

Nonetheless, many species have been associated with insect vectors (26). This would suggest that long necks are not necessary for spores of these fungi to come into contact with their vectors. However, in a recent study (Wingfield, unpublished data), I have observed that a number of species of *Ceratocystiopsis* that have long tapered ascospores also tend to exude their spore masses in thread-like tendrils. Short necks could possibly be compensated for, in some species, by long tendrils of sticky ascospores, thus ensuring that contact is made with insect vectors. Similarly, there appears to be a reasonable correlation between ascomatal neck and ascospore length in *Ophiostoma* and *Ceratocystiopsis* (Wingfield, unpublished data). Here, species with short ascomatal necks tend to have long ascospores and *vice versa*. A continuum of neck and spore lengths occurs across the range of *Ophiostoma* and *Ceratocystiopsis* species.

If short ascomatal necks in ophiostomatoid fungi are compensated for by long ascopores and long spore tendrils, this would suggest that necks (or neck substitutes) are important in the dispersal biology of these fungi. This would further explain a continuum of neck and spore lengths in *Ophiostoma* and *Ceratocystiopsis*. Consequently, these would be poor criteria on which to base the separation of *Ceratocystiopsis* from *Ophiostoma*.

CONCLUSIONS

1. Species of *Ceratocystiopsis* are segregated from *Ophiostoma* purely on the basis of their falcate, sheathed ascospores. Numerous other distinct ascospore forms occur in species of *Ophiostoma*. Recognition of only one group at the generic level seems illogical.

2. *Ophiostoma* is a large, heterogeneous genus that could perhaps benefit from further subdivision. Ascospore morphology would be one characteristic on which to base such a subdivision. However, I believe that ascospore morphology is presently insufficiently understood to be used to delineate these genera.

3. Recent studies have suggested that the falcate sheaths in some *Ceratocystiopsis* species might represent vestiges of the ascomatal centrum and not distinct sheaths. This could cause considerable confusion in the delineation of *Ceratocystiopsis* from *Ophiostoma*.

4. The anamorphs of all but one species of *Ceratocystiopsis* are extremely similar to those of *Ophiostoma*. Species of the two genera are also similarly adapted to dispersal by bark beetles. These

facts suggest that *Ophiostoma* and *Ceratocystiopsis* form a homogeneous group and that *Ceratocystiopsis* should be considered a synonym of *Ophiostoma*.

ACKNOWLEDGEMENTS

I am most grateful to Drs B.D. Wingfield and Z.A. Pretorius for critical reviews of the manuscript. Financial support from the Foundation for Research Development is gratefully acknowledged.

LITERATURE CITED

1. Bretz, T.W. 1952. The ascigerious stage of the oak wilt fungus. Phytopathology 42:435-437.

2. Bridges, J.R. and Perry, T.J. 1987. *Ceratocystiopsis ranaculosus* sp. nov. associated with the Southern pine beetle. Mycologia 79:630-633.

3. Davidson, R.W. 1935. Fungi causing stain in logs and lumber in the southern states, including five new species. J. Agric. Res. 50:789-807.

4. Davidson, R.W. 1944. Two American hardwood species of *Endoconidiophora* described as new. Mycologia 36:300-306.

5. Dowding, P. 1973. The evolution of insect-fungus relationships in the primary invasion of forest timber. Pages 133-153 in: Invertebrate-microbial Interactions. J.M. Anderson, A.D.M. Rayner, and D.W.H. Walton, eds. Cambridge University Press, New York. 350 pp

6. Francke-Grosmann, H. 1963. Some new aspects of forest entomology. Annu. Rev. Entomol. 8:415-438.

7. Griffin, H.D. 1968. The genus *Ceratocystis* in Ontario. Can. J. Bot. 46: 689-718.

8. Harrington, T.C. 1981. Cycloheximide sensitivity as a taxonomic character in *Ceratocystis*. Mycologia 73:1123-1129.

9. Harrington, T.C. 1987. New combinations in *Ophiostoma* of *Ceratocystis* species with *Leptographium* anamorphs. Mycotaxon 28: 39-43.

10. Hedgcock, G.G. 1906. Studies upon some chromogenic fungi which discolor wood. Ann. Mo. Bot. Gard. 17:59-114.

11. Hoog, G.S. de 1974. The genera *Blastobotrys*, *Sporothrix*, *Calcarisporium* and *Calcarisporiella* gen. nov. Stud. Mycol. 7:1-88.

12. Hoog G.S. de and Scheffer, R.J. 1984. *Ceratocystis versus Ophiostoma*: a reappraisal. Mycologia 76:292-299.

13. Hunt, J. 1956. Taxonomy of the genus *Ceratocystis*. Lloydia 19:1-58.

14. Hughes, S.J. 1953. Conidiophores, conidia and classification. Can. J. Bot. 31:577-659.

15. Jewell, T.R. 1974. A qualitative study of cellulose distribution in *Ceratocystis* and *Europhium*. Mycologia 66:139-146.

16. Leach, J.G., Orr, L.W. and Christiansen, C.M. 1934. The interrelationships of bark beetles and blue-staining fungi in felled Norway pine timber. J. Agric. Res.

49:315-341.

17. Mathiesen-Käärik, A. 1960. Studies on the ecology, taxonomy and physiology 'of Swedish insect-associated blue stain fungi, especially the genus *Ceratocystis*. Oikos 11:1-25.

18. Minter, D.W., Kirk, P.M. and Sutton, B.C. 1982. Holoblastic phialides. Trans. Br. Mycol. Soc. 79:75-93.

19. Münch, E. 1907. Die blaufäule des nadelholzes. Naturw. Z. Forst. Landw. 5:531 - 573.

20. Olchowecki, A. and Reid, J. 1974. Taxonomy of the genus *Ceratocystis* in Manitoba. Can. J. Bot. 52: 1675-1711.

21. Parker, A.K. 1957. The nature of the association of *Europhium trinacriforme* with pole blight lesions. Can. J. Bot. 35:845-846.

22. Robinson-Jeffrey, R.C. and Davidson, R.W. 1968. Three new *Europhium* species with *Verticicladiella* imperfect states on blue-stained pine. Can. J. Bot. 46:1523-1527.

23. Rosinski, M.A. and Campana, R.J. 1964. Chemical analysis of the cell wall of *Ceratocystis ulmi*. Mycologia 56:738-744.

24. Rumbold, C. T. 1931. Two blue-staining fungi associated with bark-beetle infestation of pines. J. Agric. Res. 43:847-873.

25. Smith, M.J., Patik, C.M. and Rosinski, M.A. 1967. A comparison of cellulose production in the genus *Ceratocystis*. Mycologia 59:965-969.

26. Upadhyay, H.P. 1981. A monograph of *Ceratocystis* and *Ceratocystiopsis*. University of Georgia Press, Athens, GA. 176 pp.

27. Upadhyay, H.P. and Kendrick, W.B. 1975. Prodromus for a revision of *Ceratocystis* (Microascales, Ascomycetes) and its conidial states. Mycologia 67:798-805.

28. Weijman, A.C.M. and Hoog, G.S. de 1975. On the subdivision of the genus *Ceratocystis*. Antonie van Leeuwenhoek 41:353-360.

29. Wingfield, M.J., Van Wyk, P.S. and Marasas, W.F.O. 1988. *Ceratocystiopsis proteae* sp. nov. with a new anamorph genus. Mycologia 80:23-30.

Chapter 4

GRAPHIUM ANAMORPHS OF *OPHIOSTOMA* SPECIES AND SIMILAR ANAMORPHS OF OTHER ASCOMYCETES[1]

K.A. SEIFERT and G. OKADA

INTRODUCTION

The anamorph genus *Graphium*, described by Corda (3), is one of the classical genera of hyphomycetes and has been the subject of several interpretations in the 150 years since its description. Identification of species of *Graphium* is difficult because the genus has never been comprehensively revised and critical comparisons of closely related species have not been made. The only usable treatments are those of Ellis (5), in which three species, *G. penicillioides*, *G. putredinis* and *G. calicioides* are briefly described and illustrated, and de Hoog (7), who described and illustrated the synnematous anamorphs of *Ophiostoma ulmi* and *O. piceae*.

In this paper, we review generic concepts applied to *Graphium* and to synnematous anamorphs of *Ophiostoma* species. We offer a critical analysis of contemporary generic concepts for these fungi and enumerate the problems that must be solved before satisfactory generic concepts for *Graphium*-like fungi can be achieved. Finally, we comment on species concepts in this group of fungi, emphasizing the need for critical comparisons of related anamorphs.

HISTORICAL BACKGROUND

The anamorph genus *Graphium* was established for two species (3), one with synnemata, *G. penicillioides*, and one lacking synnemata, *G. tenuissimum*. Corda's original concept included fungi with dark stalks, penicillate conidiophores, slimy heads and small aseptate conidia. Saccardo (16) included *Graphium* in his group Phaeostilbae, Amerosporae, encompassing many synnematous species with dark stipes and aseptate conidia. Saccardo's concept of *Graphium* allowed the inclusion

of species with dry conidia and more than one hundred species were described in *Graphium* following this broad concept.

In 1935, Goidànich (6) published a critical analysis of the species attributed to *Graphium* up to that time and restricted the genus to synnematous species with dark stipes, slimy heads and aseptate conidia, a circumscription similar to Corda's original concept. Fifteen species were included and several segregate genera were proposed or recognized. *Nematographium* was proposed for synnematous species with dark stipes and aseptate "acrogenous" conidia. The status of this genus is presently uncertain because the species included have not been re-examined. *Graphiopsis* was recognized for synnematous species, with dark stalks and aseptate conidia borne on denticles. The seven species attributed to this genus are now included in, or are synonyms of species in *Phaeoisaria* or *Nodulisporium*. Finally, *Pleurographium* was described for synnematous species with dark stipes and splayed apices with hyphae bearing aseptate conidia along their length. Three species were included, all of which now have been referred to *Dematophora*.

Significantly, Goidànich (6) noted the occurrence of *Ophiostoma* teleomorphs and/or *Sporothrix* synanamorphs in some species of *Graphium sensu stricto*. Furthermore, he reiterated that species of *Graphium* should have slimy conidia and, although he did not emphasize conidium ontogeny, his concept of the genus was very similar to that proposed in this paper.

In 1953, Hughes (8) published his classic evaluation of conidiophores, conidia and classification on the taxonomy of Hyphomycetes. His proposal that conidium ontogeny be used as a primary taxonomic criterion led to reevaluation of generic concepts in anamorphic fungi. Crane and Schoknecht (4) studied conidium ontogeny of *Graphium penicillioides*, the lectotype species selected

---

[1] In this chapter, teleomorph names in *Ophiostoma* are used when they are available. When the appropriate new combinations have not been made, we use the epithet in *Ceratocystis*.

by Hughes (9), and some *Graphium* anamorphs of *Ophiostoma* species using light and scanning electron microscopy. They confirmed that the conidiogenous cells of *G. penicillioides* proliferated percurrently to produce annellations. In contrast, the synnematous anamorphs of *O. ulmi* and *O. piceae* produced conidiogenous cells that appeared to proliferate sympodially. Because of this difference in conidium ontogeny, they described the anamorph genus *Pesotum* for *Graphium*-like anamorphs with sympodially-proliferating conidiogenous cells, with *Pesotum ulmi* as the type species.

Upadhyay and Kendrick (21) continued this trend when they described *Phialographium* for *Graphium*-like anamorphs with phialidic conidiogenous cells. *Phialographium sagmatosporae*, the anamorph of *Ceratocystis sagmatospora*, was designated as the type species. In 1975, they further continued the segregation of the *Graphium*-like *Ophiostoma* anamorphs on the basis of conidium ontogeny and pigmentation of synnemata, by describing the following segregate genera (22):

Graphilbum (type species: *G. sparsum*, anamorph of *Ophiostoma sparsum*) for *Graphium*-like anamorphs with creamy white synnemata and annellidic conidiogenous cells; the hyaline counterpart to *Graphium sensu stricto*;

Hyalopesotum (type species: *H. introcitrina*, anamorph of *Ceratocystis introcitrina*), the hyaline counterpart to *Pesotum*;

Pachnodium (type species: *P. canum*, anamorph of *Ceratocystis cana*) for *Graphium*-like species producing single or catenate holoblastic conidia.

Upadhyay (20), in his monograph of *Ceratocystis* and *Ceratocystiopsis*, maintained the use of these segregate genera and described four *Ceratocystis* species with *Phialographium* anamorphs, four with *Pesotum* anamorphs, three with *Hyalopesotum* anamorphs, two with *Graphilbum* anamorphs, two with *Graphium s. str.* anamorphs, and one with a *Pachnodium* anamorph (Table 1). In addition, he described a new genus, *Graphiocladiella* for the synnematous anamorph of *Ophiostoma clavigerum*, which produces zero to seven septate conidia on annellated or apparently sympodially proliferating conidiogenous cells.

Although Upadhyay (20) described and illustrated the holomorphs, no critical comparison of the anamorphs was attempted. It is still necessary today, in most cases, to have material of the teleomorph before the anamorph can be identified.

THE IDENTITY OF *GRAPHIUM PENICILLIOIDES*

The type species of *Graphium*, *G. penicillioides*, has been redescribed and illustrated by several modern authors (4,5,13,18) but there are several discrepancies among the descriptions. In the sense of Sutton (18) and Crane and Schoknecht (4), *G. penicillioides* (Fig. 1 A, B, D) produces dark brown to black synnemata 75-630 μm long, 5-13 μm wide. The conidiogenous cells are 10-28(-37.5) x 2 μm, with inconspicuous annellations at the end of the cell. The conidia are produced in slime, oblong-ellipsoidal to somewhat clavate, often curved, with a truncate base and marginal frill, measuring 2-5.5 x 1-2 μm. Ellis (5) and Matsushima (13) listed the conidiogenous cells as 50-70 x 1-2 μm, and Ellis reported conidia up to 7 μm long. Our own examination of the type specimen, PRM 155518 (Fig. 1 A), revealed that most of the conidiogenous cells were 16-26 μm long, with only one seen as long as 40 μm. Wingfield (personal communication) has collected a similar species in South Africa several times, but the conidia have a more pronounced basal frill than is seen on European, Japanese or North American collections of *G. penicillioides*. It seems obvious that *G. penicillioides*, as currently treated, is a species aggregate, and that further studies are necessary to delimit species within the complex.

Corda (3) originally described *G. penicillioides* from a single specimen on *Populus nigra* cv. 'italica' collected in Prague. The type specimen is now in very poor condition and according to Holubová-Jechová (personal communication), the trees of this cultivar no longer grow in the areas of Prague where Corda might have collected. Until authentic *G. penicillioides* can be recollected from its original host, as close as possible to the original collection site, it will be very difficult to critically compare this fungus with the fungi identified under this name by other authors.

We have studied conidium ontogeny in one isolate of *G. penicillioides*, CBS 506.86, using scanning electron microscopy. Two types of conidiogenous cells are produced in the synnemata; one with dense annellations at the fertile apex (Fig. 2 A) and the other with nodular annellations at the fertile apex (Fig. 2 B). Both types of annellation can sometimes be seen on a single conidiogenous cell (Fig. 2 C). These two types of annellations are not readily distinguished and there may be continuity between the two types.

The teleomorph of *G. penicillioides* is unknown but it seems likely that this anamorph species aggregate is related to species of *Ophiostoma*. One

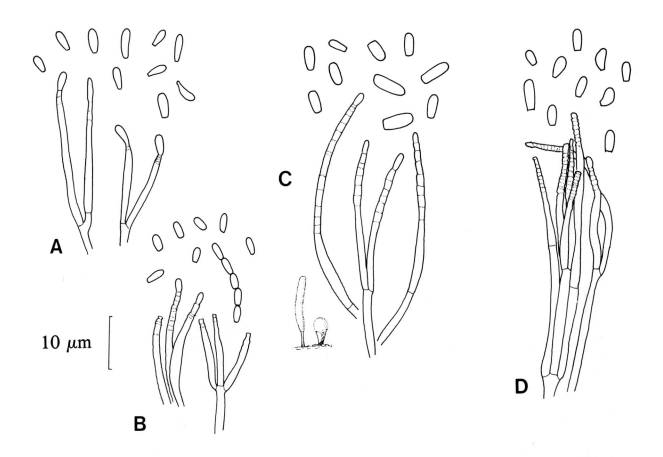

Fig. 1. Conidiophores and conidia of the *Graphium penicillioides* aggregate. A. Holotype of *G. penicillioides* (PRM). B. Specimen from *Betula* collected in Soviet Far East (LE). C. Holotype of *Ceratocystis columnaris*, with habit sketch of synnemata showing columns of conidia [WIN(M) 71-27]. D. Culture from England ex *Ulmus* on oatmeal agar (FTK 608B). All figures except habit sketch in C, 1000 x.

strain fitting the *G. penicillioides* aggregate, originating from *Ulmus* in England (Fig. 1 D), grew in the presence of 1000 ppm cycloheximide, indicating an affinity with *Ophiostoma*. *Graphium penicillioides* is microscopically similar to the anamorph of *Ceratocystis columnaris* (Fig. 1 C). This species produces synnemata with annellated conidiogenous cells 19-40 x 1.5-2 μm, and cylindrical conidia with a truncate base, measuring 4-7 x 1-2.5 μm. These microscopic characteristics are similar to those reported for *G. penicillioides* but the synnemata of this anamorph are brown at the base, fading to subhyaline below the capitulum and the spore mass is white-yellow, often produced in columns similar to

cirrhi.

VARIABILITY IN SYNNEMATOUS *OPHIOSTOMA* ANAMORPHS

Upadhyay (20) distributed the synnematous anamorphs of *Ophiostoma* species into seven anamorph genera distinguished by conidium ontogeny, pigmentation of synnemata and septation of conidia. Based on conidium ontogeny, these genera fall into four groups; the annellidic group (*Graphium, Graphilbum*), the sympodial group (*Pesotum, Hyalopesotum, Graphiocladiella*), the phialidic group (*Phialographium*) and the holoblastic group (*Pachnodium*).

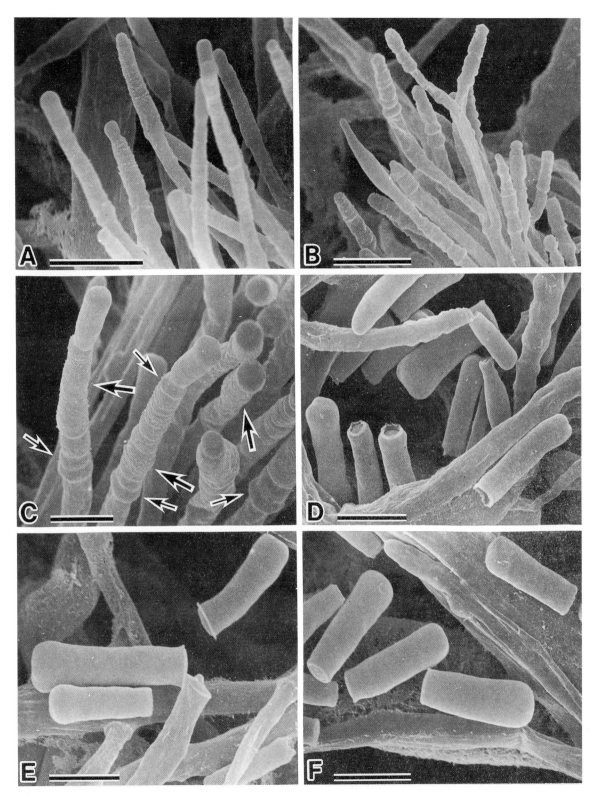

Fig. 2. Scanning electron micrographs of *Graphium penicillioides*, CBS 506.86. A. Dense annellations on conidiogenous cells; bar = 5 μm. B. Nodular annellations; bar = 5 μm. C. Dense (large arrows) and nodular (small arrows) annellations on a single conidiogenous cell; bar = 2 μm. D, E. Conidia with a pronounced basal frill; bars = 3 μm. F. Conidia lacking a basal frill; bar = 3 μm.

Can these genera be distinguished reliably by their conidium ontogeny? The conidiogenous cells of some synnematous *Ophiostoma* anamorphs are small and difficult to interpret. Clearly, detailed studies by scanning and transmission electron microscopy are required for unequivocal interpretation. In our light microscope studies of type and authentic specimens of the *Graphium* complex, we found a continuity between modes of conidium ontogeny, and apparent misinterpretations of ontogeny in some species (see also Wingfield, next chapter). When attempting to interpret conidium ontogeny in these organisms using only the light microscope, it is important to make observations employing both phase contrast and differential interference contrast (DIC) illumination. The periclinal thickenings of phialides are more noticeable with phase contrast and can scarcely be seen with DIC. Annellations on the surfaces of conidiogenous cells can usually be detected with DIC but are practically invisible with phase contrast.

Species with annellated conidiogenous cells occur in most of the segregate genera. The annellidic conidiogenous cells of *Graphilbum sparsum* (Fig. 3 A) cannot be distinguished from those of *Graphium penicillioides* on the basis of conidium ontogeny. *Graphiocladiella clavigerum* has annellated conidiogenous cells similar to those of *G. penicillioides*, as well as sympodially proliferating conidiogenous cells (19). Conidiogenous cells in the anamorphs of *Ceratocystis columnaris* (Fig. 1 C) and *C. ossiformis* (considered synonyms by Upadhyay, 20) appear annellidic, not phialidic or percurrent-phialidic as described by Upadhyay (20). In *Pachnodium canum* (Fig. 3 F), reported to produce holoblastic conidiogenous cells, we have seen annellations on the cylindrical portions of the conidiogenous cells. The peculiar swellings on the conidiophores and conidiogenous cells may represent aborted conidia, from which a new conidiogenous locus has regenerated. We believe that the genus *Pachnodium* should be considered a synonym of *Graphium*.

The apparently sympodial conidiogenous cells of *Pesotum piceae* (Fig. 4 C) and *Hyalopesotum introcitrinum* (Fig. 3 C) are almost identical and intermediates exist with the annellated conidiogenous cells of *Graphium* spp. A similar situation exists in the *Leptographium* complex, as has been demonstrated by Wingfield (23). Annellidic and sympodially proliferating conidiogenous cells are often difficult to distinguish with light microscopy. The apex of the conidiogenous cell in both cases tends to be uneven in outline. In the apparently sympodially proliferating conidiogenous cells, the attached conidia are often asymmetrically placed on the apex of the cell, or a small lateral protrusion may be visible if the conidium has already been released. We concur with Wingfield's explanation (this volume) that the appearance of sympodial proliferation can be caused by incomplete conidium dehiscence in otherwise normal percurrently proliferating conidiogenous cells.

The phialidic conidiogenous cells of different *Phialographium* species are very similar, leading us to believe that these are closely related species. Usually, periclinal thickening is visible in the conidiogenous apertures of these cells using phase contrast. Flared collarettes may also be visible, particularly with DIC. The type species, *P. sagmatosporae*, produces compactly percurrent phialides that look like annellides. Wingfield *et al.* (24) observed that the phialidic conidiogenous cells in the anamorph of *Ophiostoma cucullatum* could proliferate within the collarette to produce periclinal thickening, percurrently to produce annellations, or sympodially. Combinations of these sometimes occur in one conidiogenous cell. *Ceratocystis cainii* (Fig. 3 D) produces both phialides and apparently sympodially proliferating conidiogenous cells on the same conidiophore, as was noted by Upadhyay (20). Although the phialides of *Phialographium* species might appear significantly different from the annellides and apparently sympodially proliferating conidiogenous cells of other *Graphium*-like species, detailed analysis reveals the presence of a continuum among these three patterns. Two of the three modes sometimes exist in a single species. This confirms the statement by Wingfield *et al.* (24) that genera of the *Graphium* complex cannot be distinguished by conidium ontogeny alone. The question remains whether the segregate genera can be distinguished by other characters.

The other characters used to distinguish the segregate genera are pigmentation of the synnemata and septation of conidia. Pigmentation of synnemata is a variable character in *Ophiostoma* species, often within a single colony. Synnemata may be white when first produced, but become pigmented at the base with age. In *O. piceae*, this coloration may be the result of pigments developing in the basal hyphae, or of pigmented marginal hyphae growing up from the base and surrounding the hyaline hyphae (15). For this reason, it is difficult to maintain differences between anamorph genera in this complex, based on synnema pigmentation.

Likewise, conidial septation is a variable character. Although *Graphiocladiella* was distinguished from *Graphium* because it produces septate conidia, abundant aseptate conidia occur. Many genera of hyphomycetes contain species with septate and aseptate

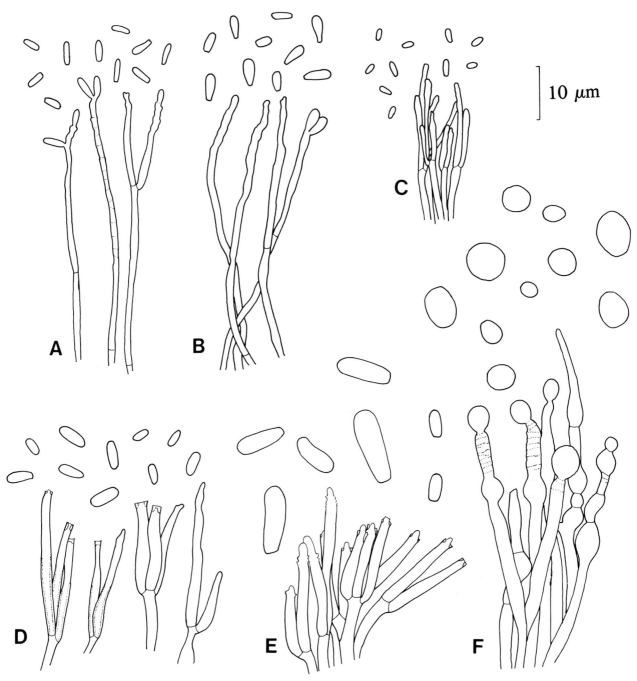

Fig. 3. Conidiophores and conidia of synnematous anamorphs of various *Ophiostoma* species. A. Annellidic and apparently sympodial development in the *'Graphilbum'* anamorph of *O. sparsum* (CBS 405.77). B. Apparently sympodial development in the *'Hyalopesotum'* anamorph of *C. arborea* [Holotype, WIN(M) 69-23]. C. Apparently sympodial development in the *'Hyalopesotum'* anamorph of *C. introcitrina* [WIN(M) 69-47]. D. Phialidic and apparently sympodial development in the anamorph of *C. cainii* [WIN(M) 69-18]. E. Phialides and percurrently proliferating phialides in the *'Phialographium'* anamorph of *C. sagmatospora* (Holotype, TRTC 36247). F. Annellidic development in the *'Pachnodium'* anamorph of *Ceratocystis cana* (DAOM 22448). All figures 1000 x.

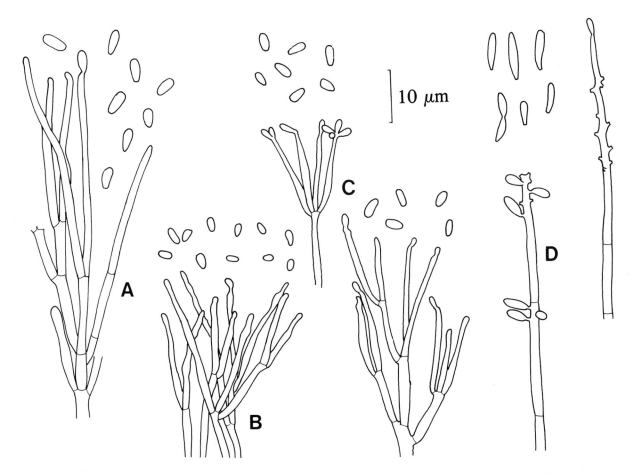

Fig. 4. Conidiophores and conidia of synnematous anamorphs of various *Ophiostoma* species. A. Sympodial development in the *'Pesotum'* anamorph of *Ophiostoma ulmi* (holotype of *Graphium ulmi*, CBS-H). B. Sympodial development in the *'Pesotum'* anamorph of *Ceratocystis torticiliata* [Holotype, WIN(ᴍ) 70-15]. C. Sympodial development in the *'Pesotum'* anamorph of *O. piceae*. D. *Sporothrix* synanamorph of *O. piceae* (C, D VPI-8 in herb. Seifert). All figures 1000 x.

conidia, including *Arthrobotrys*, *Didymostilbe* and *Stilbella*. Clearly, septation of conidia is not a suitable character for distinguishing anamorph genera in the *Graphium* complex.

On the basis of similarities (rather than differences) in conidium ontogeny, we believe that a natural concept of *Graphium* would include species with dark or lightly pigmented synnemata; annellidic, phialidic or apparently sympodially proliferating conidiogenous cells; aseptate or septate conidia, and slimy conidial masses. This is a broad generic concept, but nevertheless would include all synnematous

Ophiostoma anamorphs in an apparently natural anamorph genus. The segregate genera might eventually be considered for use as sections or groups within *Graphium* in future revisions.

An additional argument for abandoning use of these segregate genera involves the relationships of the teleomorphs. The species with known synnematous anamorphs described by Upadhyay (20), Solheim (17) and Hutchison and Reid (10) are shown in Table 1. If the infrageneric classification of *Ceratocystis* proposed by Upadhyay (20) is correct, then species with *Pesotum* anamorphs, for example,

TABLE 1. Species of *Ophiostoma* and *Ceratocystis* with synnematous anamorphs, the generic assignment of those anamorphs and the sectional assignment of the teleomorphs following Upadhyay (20).

Teleomorph	Anamorph	Section
C. cainii	*Graphium*	*Ceratocystis*
C. clavigera	*Graphiocladiella*[1]	*Ceratocystis*
O. cucullatum	*Phialographium*	*Ceratocystis*[2]
O. davidsonii	*Phialographium*	*Ceratocystis*
O. olivaceum	*Phialographium*	*Ceratocystis*
C. olivacea-pinii	*Graphium*	*Ceratocystis*
C. sagmatospora	*Phialographium*[1]	*Ceratocystis*
C. torticiliata	*Pesotum*	*Ceratocystis*
O. aionae	*Pesotum*	*Ips*[2]
C. arborea	*Hyalopesotum*	*Ips*
O. brunneo-cilliatum	*Pesotum*	*Ips*
C. columnaris	*Phialographium*	*Ips*
O. ips	*Graphilbum*	*Ips*
O. sparsum	*Graphilbum*[1]	*Ips*
C. araucariae	*Hyalopesotum*	*Ophiostoma*
O. cana	*Pachnodium*[1]	*Ophiostoma*
C. introcitrina	*Hyalopesotum*[1]	*Ophiostoma*
C. novae-zelandiae	*Pesotum*	*Ophiostoma*[3]
O. piceae	*Pesotum*[1]	*Ophiostoma*
O. ulmi	*Pesotum*	*Ophiostoma*

[1] Indicates the type of the anamorph genus.
[2] These two species were described by Solheim (17). We have assigned them to sections according to the system of Upadhyay (20).
[3] This species was described by Hutchison & Reid (10). We have assigned it to this section following the system of Upadhyay (20).

are found in three of the four sections. The only anamorphic genera restricted to a single section are *Graphilbum* with two species, and the monotypic *Pachnodium* and *Graphiocladiella*. It is apparent that the disposition of synnematous anamorphs of *Ophiostoma* species does not correspond with the infrageneric classification of the teleomorphs as presently understood. Therefore, there are no practical or biological reasons to accept any of the segregate genera.

Unfortunately, the emended concept of *Graphium*, or even *Graphium sensu stricto*, is complicated by two factors. The first involves the validity of separating mononematous *Leptographium* and synnematous *Graphium* anamorphs of *Ophiostoma* species into distinct anamorph genera. This is practical but may not reflect species relationships within *Ophiostoma*. We lack the information for a thorough analysis and will not consider the question further in this paper (see Wingfield, next chapter). The second complication is the presence of annellidic *Graphium*-like anamorphs with teleomorphs in other orders of Ascomycetes.

This anomaly is discussed below.

ANNELLIDIC *GRAPHIUM*-LIKE ANAMORPHS OF OTHER ASCOMYCETES

Even when *Graphium* is restricted to species with annellated conidiogenous cells, it may be polyphyletic. The species of Ascomycetes in the orders Microascales and Sphaeriales with *Graphium*-like anamorphs are listed in Table 2. In a phylogenetic classification of anamorphic fungi, these anamorphs should be classified separately from anamorphs of the Ophiostomataceae.

The *Graphium putredinis* aggregate and its teleomorphs in the Microascales

The anamorphs of the several species of *Petriella*, *Pseudallescheria* (=*Petriellidium*), *Kernia* and *Microascus* generally correspond to the fungus described as *Graphium putredinis* by Ellis (5) and as *Graphium cuneiferum* by Matsushima (13). These anamorphs (Figs. 5A-D,6) produce grey to black

TABLE 2. Species of the Microascales and Sphaeriales reported to have anamorphs assignable to *Graphium sensu stricto*.

Holomorph	Reference
Microascales	
Kernia hippocrepida	11
Microascus singularis	11
Petriella boulangeri	2
Petriella guttulata	1, 2
Petriella lindforsii	2
Petriella setifera	1, 2
Petriella sordida	1, 2
Pseudallescheria boydii	1, 14
Pseudallescheria ellipsoidea	1
Pseudallescheria fimeti	1
Pseudallescheria fusoidia	1
Sphaeriales	
Chaetosphaeria sp.	this chapter

synnemata 250-2000 μm tall, often consisting of only a few hyphae. The conidiophore branching is usually monoverticillate, sometimes 2-level verticillate, with whorls of 3-6 conidiogenous cells. The conidiogenous cells are (7-)15-30 x 2-3 μm, with a constricted terminal zone of conspicuous, nodular annellations 1-2 μm wide and up to 8 μm long. The conidia are aggregated in a slimy grey to black mass, and individually are oblong-ellipsoidal to slightly clavate, usually with a truncate base, 4-6.5 (-11) x 2-3.5 μm, and eventually become greyish and slightly thick walled.

Two synanamorphs occur in cultures of *G. putredinis*-like anamorphs of the Microascales, one assigned to *Sporothrix*, the other to *Scedosporium*. The *Sporothrix* anamorph (Fig. 5 C) is hyaline, and produced in the aerial mycelium of the colony. The conidiophores are erect and have several randomly arranged lateral conidiogenous cells, or short branches with terminal whorls of conidiogenous cells. The conidiogenous cells are of two shapes. Terminal and occasional lateral conidiogenous cells are cylindrical to subulate, 11-27 x 1.5-2 μm. Most lateral conidiogenous cells, and some terminal ones, are ellipsoidal, clavate or subulate and 5-15 x 2-3 μm. Cylindrical denticles about 1 μm wide and up to 2 μm long are obvious on both types of conidiogenous cells, either forming an apical crown or scattered over the upper part of the cell. The conidia are solitary, ovoid to ellipsoidal with a truncate or slightly denticulate base, and measure 4.5-8.5 x 3-5 μm. Eventually the conidia become greyish, develop a wall about 0.5 μm thick, and may swell up to 7.5 μm wide.

The *Scedosporium* anamorph (Fig. 6 C, D) is produced on the surface of the colony and slowly turns it black. The conidia are produced on micronematous to semimacronematous conidiophores. The annellations on the conidiogenous cells are not clear under the light microscope but can be seen using scanning electron microscopy. The conidia are initially hyaline, but turn dark brown and are usually ellipsoidal, sometimes globose, 6-12.5 x 4.5-8 μm, sometimes with a thickened wall.

The teleomorphs of most of the species listed in Table 2 produce cleistothecial ascomata. In culture, ascomata occur on the surface of the agar, often hidden by the aerial mycelium. Unfortunately, the production of ascomata in culture is inconsistent, suggesting the species may be heterothallic. Most of these teleomorphs have been described and illustrated by von Arx *et al.* (1).

There are differences between the anamorphs of the Microascales and similar anamorphs related to the Ophiostomataceae. Although the synnemata and conidiogenous cells are similar, the pigmentation tends to be gray or olivaceous, rather than distinctly brown as is seen in the synnemata of most *Ophiostoma* species. The synnematal conidia of *Graphium putredinis* tend to become pigmented with age, a feature not seen in the synnematous anamorphs of *Ophiostoma* species. The *Sporothrix* synanamorph also differs somewhat from the *Sporothrix* anamorphs of *Ophiostoma* species (Fig. 4 D) that also produce synnematous anamorphs. In the anamorphs of the Microascales, the conidia are not catenate and tend to become pigmented. *Scedosporium* anamorphs do not occur in the Ophiostomataceae.

According to McGinnis *et al.* (14), the differences between the teleomorphs of several *Pseudallescheria* species are slight and several species may be placed in synonymy when additional material is studied. No critical comparison of the anamorphs of these species has been attempted. However, the species vary with respect to the number of different synanamorphs. Morphological differences between comparable synanamorphs should allow some anamorph species within this aggregate to be identified in the absence of the teleomorph.

When these comparisons are finally made, there are a number of species epithets that will have to be

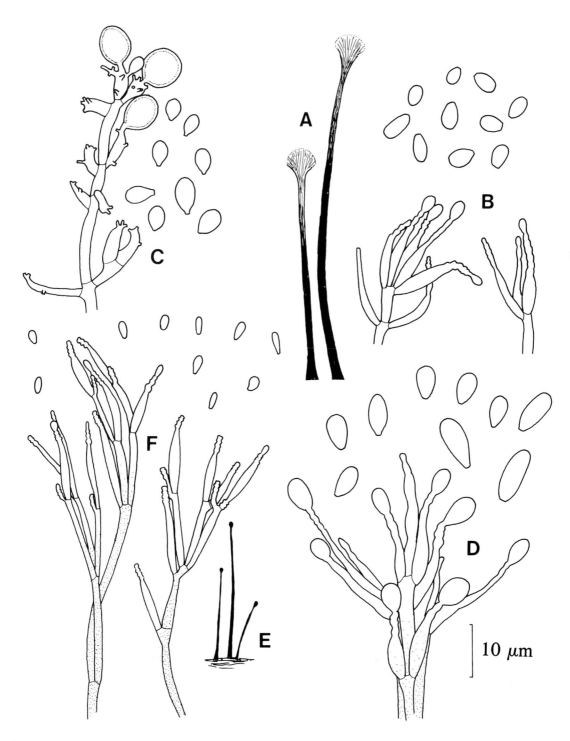

Fig. 5. Synnemata, conidiophores and conidia of the *Graphium putredinis* aggregate and *G. calicioides*. A-C. *Graphium tectonae* holotype (IMI). A. Synnemata. B. Conidiophores and conidia. C. *Sporothrix* synanamorph. D. Anamorph of *Petriella setifera*, DAOM 39487. E, F. Synnemata, conidiophores and conidia of *Graphium calicioides* (CBS-H 3835). A. 100x, E. 40 x, all other figures 1000 x.

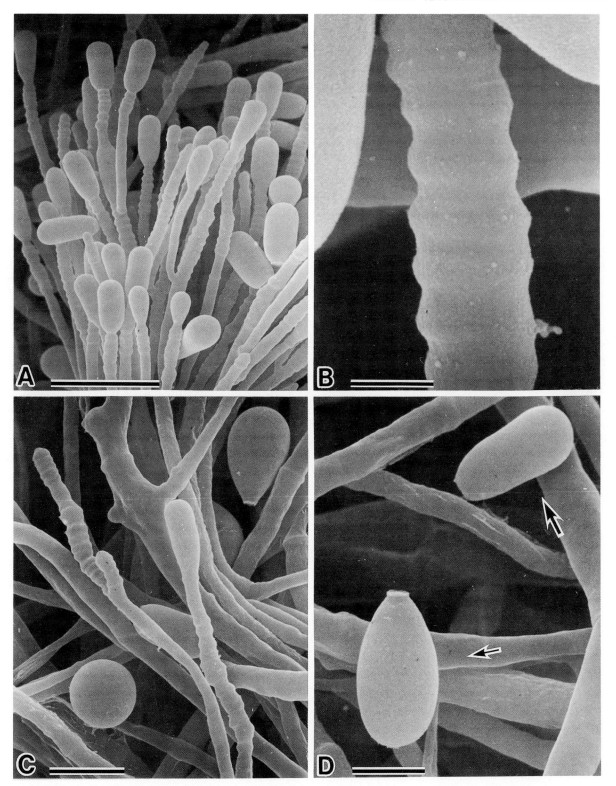

Fig. 6. *Graphium putredinis* aggregate, scanning electron microscopy of conidiogenous cells, JCM 7866. A. Nodular annellations on the conidiogenous cells of the *Graphium* synanamorph; bar = 10 μm. B. Higher magnification of the nodular annellations of the *Graphium* synanamorph; bar = 1 μm. C. Nodular annellations in the conidiogenous cells of the *Scedosporium* synanamorph; bar = 5 μm. D. Conidia of the *Graphium* (large arrow) and *Scedosporium* (small arrow) synanamorphs; bar = 3 μm.

considered for application to the segregated taxa. These include *Graphium bulbicola*, *G. cuneiferum*, *G. eumorphum*, *G. fructicola*, *G. stilboideum* and *G. tectonae* (Fig. 5 A-C). Unfortunately, the name used in this paper for the species aggregate may have to be abandoned. The type specimen of *G. putredinis* (PRM) contains two species of synnematous hyphomycetes and the same basionym is currently being used in two different genera, *Graphium* and *Doratomyces*.

Should these synnematous anamorphs of the Microascales be included in *Graphium*? In relative terms, *Ophiostoma* species are closely related to the Microascales (Upadhyay, this volume) and it is not surprising to find similar anamorphs. Given the controversy about the ordinal classification of *Ophiostoma* (Upadhyay, this volume), it is possible that some mycologists may prefer to keep the members of the *G. putredinis* aggregate in the same genus as synnematous *Ophiostoma* anamorphs. In our opinion, however, members of the *G. putredinis* aggregate should be removed to a different anamorph genus if a practical means of differentiating them is discovered.

Graphium calicioides and its *Chaetosphaeria* teleomorph

The third species of *Graphium* illustrated and described by Ellis (5) is *G. calicioides* (Figs. 5 E, F, 7). Mason and Ellis (12) have traced the history of names applied to this species. It occurs on decayed wood in temperate climates around the world. The synnemata (Fig. 5 E) are black and up to 5 mm tall, 50-250 μm wide at the base, tapering to 25-55 μm wide subapically. The conidiophores (Figs. 5 F, 7 A) usually have a basal verticillate branch of 3 or 4 chains of 2 or 3 acropleurogenously developing conidiogenous cells (Fig. 7 B, C). The conidiogenous cells are annellidic, 8-25(-30) x 1-2 μm when terminal, and 10-17 x 1-2 μm with lateral conidiogenous extensions 2-8.5 μm long when intercalary. The annellations (Fig. 7 B, C) are usually conspicuous, forming a zone up to 11 μm long and about 1 μm wide. The conidial mass is hyaline or grey when fresh, black when dry. The conidia are 2.5-4.5 x 1-2 μm and ovate, ellipsoidal, or clavate with the base pointed or truncate. In culture, synnemata are scarcely produced, but instead, mononematous or fasciculate conidiophores, similar to those in the synnemata, are produced in slimy masses on the surface of the agar. No *Sporothrix* or *Scedosporium* synanamorphs are found in this species.

Specimens of *G. calicioides* collected in Japan sometimes have perithecial ascomata assignable to the genus *Chaetosphaeria* closely associated with the synnemata (Fig. 8). Single ascospore isolations have demonstrated conclusively that this fungus is the teleomorph of *G. calicioides*.

Subsequent reexamination of specimens collected in Scotland, the Netherlands and New Zealand has demonstrated the widespread occurrence of this teleomorph. The perithecia (Fig. 8 A, B) are 200-300 μm wide, 160-240 μm high, dark brown to black, almost globose with a circular ostiole, lacking a beak, with wart-like cells on the surface (Fig. 8C). The asci (Fig. 8 D-F) are unitunicate, thick-walled apically, cylindrical but broadest in the middle, with a short stalk, and contain 8 biseriate to tetraseriate ascospores. The ascospores (Fig. 8 G) are 17-22 x 4-6 μm, pale brown, fusoid, straight or slightly curved, 5-6 septate, slightly constricted at the septa, with the central cell larger than the others.

Graphium calicioides differs from the *Graphium* anamorphs of *Ophiostoma* species by its acropleurogenously developing conidiogenous cells. Transmission electron microscopy reveals that the conidiogenous cells of this species are unusual because the inner wall is very thick (Fig. 7 D). The significant morphological differences combined with the presence of a *Chaetosphaeria* teleomorph in this species suggests that it should eventually be transferred from *Graphium* to a different anamorph genus.

CONCLUSIONS

1. The anamorph genus *Graphium* should be emended to include species with dark or lightly pigmented synnemata, annellidic, phialidic, or apparently sympodially proliferating conidiogenous cells, and aseptate or septate conidia produced in slimy masses.

2. The anamorph genera *Graphilbum*, *Pesotum*, *Hyalopesotum*, *Phialographium*, *Pachnodium* and *Graphiocladiella* should be considered synonyms of *Graphium*.

3. *Graphium* should be restricted to anamorphs of the Ophiostomataceae. At present, anamorphs of species in the Ascomycete orders Microascales and Sphaeriales are also included in *Graphium*.

4. *Graphium*-like anamorphs are found in the Microascales, in the genera *Petriella*, *Pseudallescheria*, *Kernia* and *Microascus*. These anamorphs are similar to *G. putredinis*.

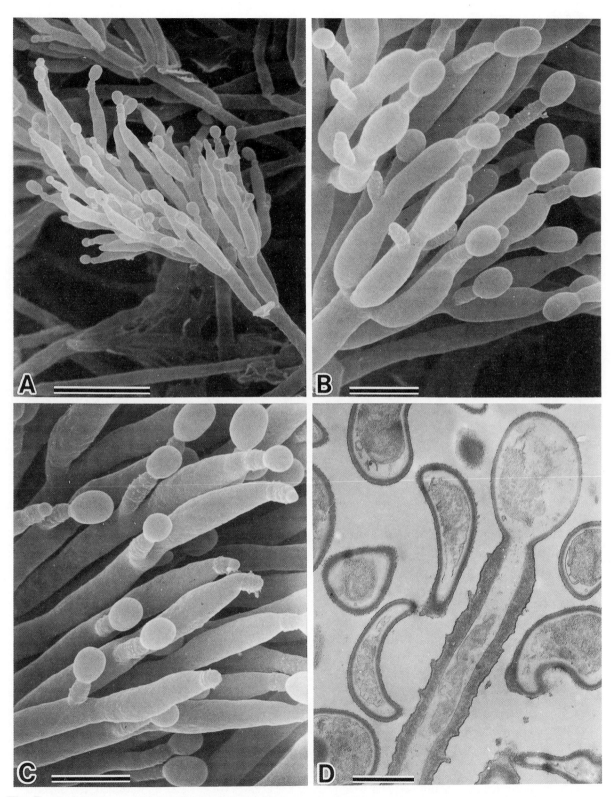

Fig. 7. Conidiogenous cells of *Graphium calicioides*, scanning and transmission electron microscopy, JCM 6030. A. Branching at apex of conidiophore; bar = 10 μm. B, C. Acropleurogenously developing annellidic conidiogenous cells; bars = 3 μm. D. An annellidic conidiogenous cell with a thick, electron-dense, inner wall layer; bar = 1 μm.

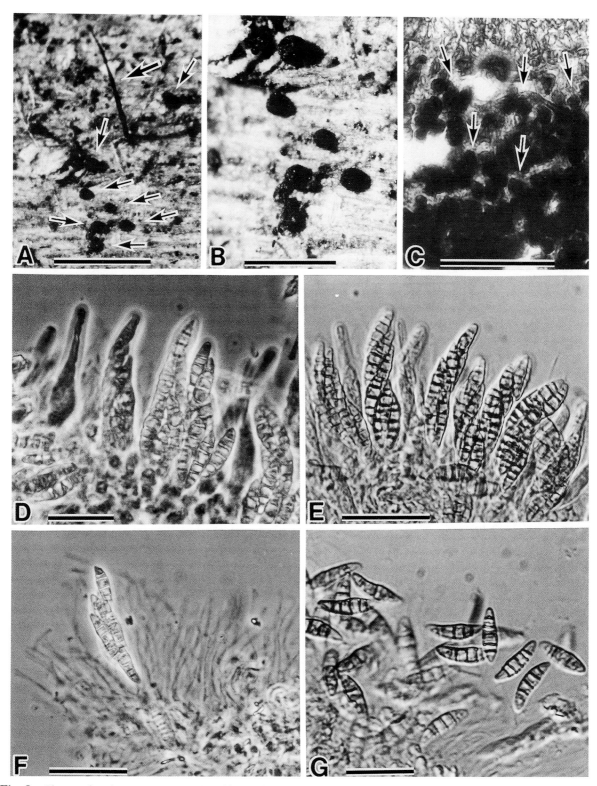

Fig. 8. *Chaetosphaeria* teleomorph of *Graphium calicioides*, herb. Okada nos. 856 and 1065. A. Single synnema of the anamorph (large arrow) with perithecia of the teleomorph (small arrows); bar = 1 mm. B. Magnified view of perithecia; bar = 0.5 mm. C. Wart-like cells on the surface of the perithecium wall, phase contrast; bar = 50 μm. D. Thick-walled, immature asci, phase contrast; bar = 20 μm. E. Mature asci containing eight ascospores, DIC; bar = 30 μm. F. Paraphyses and an ascus, phase contrast; bar = 30 μm. G. Ascospores, DIC; bar = 20 μm.

5. *Graphium calicioides* has a teleomorph tentatively identified as a species of *Chaetosphaeria* (Sphaeriales). The acropleurogenous development of the conidiophores and electron-dense, thick walls of the conidiogenous cells suggest that this species should be removed from *Graphium*.

6. *Graphium penicillioides* and *G. putredinis* should be considered anamorph species aggregates until critical studies are undertaken.

ACKNOWLEDGEMENTS

We are grateful to Dr. R.A. Shoemaker for examining the teleomorph of *Graphium calicioides* and to Drs. S.J. Hughes and J. Bissett for their critical comments on the manuscript. The curators of the following institutes kindly provided material for our examination: CBS, DAOM, IMI, K, LE, PR, S, UPS, WIN(M). We also thank Drs. R.J. Bandoni, J. Gibbs, V. Mel'nik, C.T. Rogerson and M.J. Wingfield for sending specimens that were used in this study.

LITERATURE CITED

1. Arx, J.A. von, Figueras, M.J. and Guarro, J. 1988. Sordariaceous Ascomycetes without ascospore ejaculation. Beih. Nova Hedwigia 94:1-104.

2. Barron, G.L., Cain, R.F. and Gilman, J.C. 1961. A revision of the genus *Petriella*. Can. J. Bot. 39:837-845.

3. Corda, A.C.J. 1837. Icones fungorum hucusque cognitorum. 1. Prague. 32 pp.

4. Crane, J.L. and Schoknecht, J.D. 1973. Conidiogenesis in *Ceratocystis ulmi, Ceratocystis piceae* and *Graphium penicillioides*. Am. J. Bot. 60:346-354.

5. Ellis, M.B. 1971. Dematiaceous Hyphomycetes. Commonwealth Mycological Institute, Kew. 608 pp.

6. Goidànich, G. 1935. Schema di una classificazione delle Stilbacee che erano riunite fin'ora nel genere *Graphium* Corda. Ann. Bot. (Torino) 21:40-50.

7. Hoog, G.S. de. 1974. The genera *Blastobotrys, Sporothrix,* *Calcarisporium* and *Calcarisporiella* gen. nov. Stud. Mycol. 7:1-84.

8. Hughes, S.J. 1953. Conidiophores, conidia, and classification. Can. J. Bot. 31:577-659.

9. Hughes, S.J. 1958. Revisiones hyphomycetum aliquot cum appendice de nominibus rejiciendis. Can. J. Bot. 36:727-836.

10. Hutchison, L.J. and Reid, J. 1988. Taxonomy of some potential wood-staining fungi from New Zealand. 1. Ophiostomataceae. N. Z. J. Bot. 26:63-81.

11. Malloch, D. and Cain, R.F. 1971. The genus *Kernia*. Can. J. Bot. 49:855-867.

12. Mason, E.W. and Ellis, M.B. 1953. British species of *Periconia*. Mycol. Pap. 56:1-127.

13. Matsushima, T. 1975. Icones Microfungorum a Matsushima lectorum. Kobe, Japan. 209 pp.

14. McGinnis, M.R., Padhye, A.A. and Ajello, L. 1982. *Pseudallescheria* Negroni et Fisher, 1943 and its later synonym *Petriellidium* Malloch, 1970. Mycotaxon 14:94-102.

15. Okada, G. and Tubaki, K. 1986. Conidiomatal structures of the stilbellaceous and allied fungi. Sydowia 39:148-159.

16. Saccardo, P.A. 1886. Sylloge fungorum omnium hucusque cognitorum, vol. IV. Padova. 807 pp.

17. Solheim, H. 1986. Species of Ophiostomataceae isolated from *Picea abies* infested by the bark beetle *Ips typographus*. Nord. J. Bot. 6:199-207.

18. Sutton, B.C. 1972. Hyphomycetes from Manitoba and Saskatchewan. Mycol. Pap. 132:1-143.

19. Tsuneda, A. and Hiratsuka, Y. 1984. Sympodial and annellidic conidiation in *Ceratocystis clavigera*. Can. J. Bot. 62:2618-2624.

20. Upadhyay, H.P. 1981. A monograph of *Ceratocystis* and *Ceratocystiopsis*. University of Georgia Press, Athens, GA. 176 pp.

21. Upadhyay, H.P. and Kendrick, W.B. 1974. A new *Graphium*-like genus (conidial state of *Ceratocystis*). Mycologia 66:181-183.

22. Upadhyay, H.P. and Kendrick, W.B. 1975. Prodromus for a revision of *Ceratocystis* (Microascales, Ascomycetes) and its conidial states. Mycologia 67:798-805.

23. Wingfield, M.J. 1985. Reclassification of *Verticicladiella* based on conidial development. Trans. Br. Mycol. Soc. 85:81-93.

24. Wingfield, M.J., van Wyk, P.S. and van Wyk, P.W.J. 1989. Conidial development in the anamorph of *Ophiostoma cucullatum*. Mycol. Res. 93:91-95.

Chapter 5

LEPTOGRAPHIUM SPECIES AS ANAMORPHS OF *OPHIOSTOMA*: PROGRESS IN ESTABLISHING ACCEPTABLE GENERIC AND SPECIES CONCEPTS

M.J. WINGFIELD

The anamorph genus *Leptographium* is broadly defined as having dark, mononematous conidiophores that give rise to a series of branching metulae. These terminate in hyaline conidiogenous cells that produce single-celled, hyaline conidia by enteroblastic ontogeny and holoblastic proliferation. Conidia accumulate in a slimy mass at the apex of the conidiophores and so are ideally situated for insect dispersal.

Species of *Leptographium* are best known as associates of bark beetles (Coleoptera: Scolytidae) and related insects that infest trees (14,37). Many of these fungi cause blue stain of lumber and are weakly pathogenic. There are also a number of species that are well recognized pathogens of conifers (15,40). The best known of these is probably *L. wageneri*, which causes black stain root disease of conifers in the Western United States and Canada (15,16,17).

Although considerable progress has been made in recent years, numerous problems continue to plague the taxonomy of *Leptographium*. While a considerable number of the described species are well known anamorphs of *Ophiostoma* (Table 1), others are of unknown affiliation (Table 2) and perhaps even unrelated to Ophiostomataceae. There are also several *Ophiostoma* species with purported *Leptographium* anamorphs that have not been clearly defined or described (Table 3).

Poor, inaccessible or even absent type material has hindered the resolution of taxonomic problems in the genus in a number of cases. Segregation of *Leptographium* from two closely related anamorph genera *Phialocephala* and *Graphium* has also been problematic. For example, *Phialocephala* is distinguished from *Leptographium* by phialidic conidial development as opposed to the percurrent/sympodial development in the latter genus. This definition requires clarification. Likewise, *Graphium* and *Leptographium* are distinguished by the presence of synnematous and mononematous conidiophores respectively. Here, to complicate matters, there are species of *Ophiostoma* that are

reported to have anamorphs with both mononematous as well as synnematous conidiophores. The reduction of synnematous conidiophores to a mononematous form, through progressive subculturing or extended preservation in culture collections, adds to the confusion and must also be considered.

The aim of this chapter is not to provide a comprehensive review of the taxonomy of *Leptographium*. A recent review has been provided by Harrington (14), which also includes information on host range and insect associates of the species. My aim in this chapter will be to highlight problems associated with the taxonomy of *Leptographium*, particularly at the generic level. I hope that this will stimulate research to answer the most pressing questions pertaining to the establishment of acceptable generic and species concepts. Moreover, it should also lead us to a point where a meaningful and useful monograph can be produced in the not too distant future.

EARLY HISTORY OF *LEPTOGRAPHIUM*

Shaw and Hubert (33) made a detailed study of the nomenclature of *Leptographium*, *Scopularia* and *Hantzschia*. More recently, Harrington (14) reviewed the analysis of Shaw and Hubert on the early history of *Leptographium*. Salient points are repeated here for completeness.

Leptographium dates back to the description of *Scopularia venusta*. Shaw and Hubert (33) showed that *Scopularia* Preuss was a later homonym of *Scopularia* Lindley and they were unable to locate the type material of *S. venusta*. These authors also recognized the similarity of *Hantzschia* Auerswald and *Leptographium* but noted that the homonym *Hantzschia* Grunow is also used for a genus of diatoms. This led to the conservation of the name *Hantzschia* Grunow. The genus *Leptographium* based on *L. lundbergii* then became available for *H. phycomyces* and species of *Scopularia*. Shaw and

TABLE 1. *Leptographium* species with known *Ophiostoma* states

Anamorph	Teleomorph	Reference
Leptographium aureum	*Ophiostoma aureum*	39
Leptographium crassivaginatum	*Ophiostoma crassivaginatum*	39
Leptographium dryocoetidis	*Ophiostoma dryocoetidis*	26,39
Leptographium grandifoliae	*Ophiostoma grandifoliae*	39
Leptographium huntii	*Ophiostoma huntii*	39
Leptographium penicillatum	*Ophiostoma penicillatum*	11,22
Leptographium robustum	*Ophiostoma robustum*	39
Leptographium serpens	*Ophiostoma serpens*	22,34,43
Leptographium wageneri var. *ponderosum*	*Ophiostoma wageneri*	17,18

Hubert (33), however, made no new combinations in *Leptographium* for *H. phycomyces* or species of *Scopularia*, most of which they considered to be of dubious status.

CONIDIUM DEVELOPMENT AFTER HUGHES

The introduction of patterns of conidium development as a taxonomic criterion by Hughes (19) led to a subdivision of *Leptographium*-like fungi and the subsequent establishment of the *Leptographium* complex. Hughes (19) illustrated percurrent proliferation in the form of the annellated conidiogenous cells in *L. lundbergii*. He considered these distinct from the apparently sympodially proliferating conidiogenous cells of *Sporocybe abietina*, for which *Verticicladiella* was established.

The awareness of conidium development in Hyphomycetes led Kendrick (21) to note the distinct collarettes at the apex of conidiogenous cells of many *Leptographium*-like fungi. For these fungi he established *Phialocephala*, based on *Phialocephala dimorphospora*. *Leptographium phycomyces* (12) was transferred to this genus. Thus, for almost three decades, the *Leptographium* complex (21,22,23,24,25) included the genera *Leptographium*, *Phialocephala* and *Verticicladiella* and these were separated primarily by modes of conidium development.

CONIDIUM DEVELOPMENT BASED ON ULTRASTRUCTURAL STUDIES

Leptographium and *Verticicladiella*

In a description of a new species belonging to the *Leptographium* complex, Wingfield and Marasas (44) noted the presence of distinct annellations on conidiogenous cells that apparently proliferated sympodially (Fig. 1). This led to confusion over the correct generic disposition for the fungus. Using light microscopy, sympodial development was overwhelmingly obvious whereas annellations were indistinct. The fungus was therefore described as *Verticicladiella truncata*.

The apparent contradictions experienced in describing *V. truncata* led to a more detailed study of conidium development in *Leptographium* and *Verticicladiella* (39). This revealed that both percurrent and sympodial proliferation could be seen in single species and even on single conidiophores of *Leptographium* and *Verticicladiella* (Fig. 2-3). Conidium development was thus an entirely unreliable criterion for separating the genera. *Verticicladiella* was consequently reduced to synonymy with *Leptographium*. Having clarified the generic concept, I now believe that *L. truncatum* is a synonym of *L. lundbergii* (41).

TABLE 2. *Leptographium* species for which a teleomorph has not been described

Species	References
Leptographium abietinum	22,39
Leptographium antibioticum	22,39
Leptographium brachiatum	22,39
Leptographium engelmannii	5
Leptographium hymenaeae	32
Leptographium lundbergii	27
Leptographium microsporum	4
Leptographium procerum	22,39
Leptographium pyrinum	7
Leptographium reconditum	20
Leptographium terebrantis	1
Leptographium truncatum	39,44
Leptographium wageneri var. *wageneri*	17
Leptographium wageneri var. *pseudotsugae*	17
Leptographium wingfieldii	31

TABLE 3: *Ophiostoma* species with undescribed anamorphs purported to belong in *Leptographium*

Teleomorph	Anamorph	Reference
Ophiostoma abiocarpum	*Leptographium*	14,37
Ophiostoma adjuncti[1]	*Leptographium*	14,37
	Graphium / Hyalorhinocladiella	
Ophiostoma araucarium	*Leptographium, Hyalopesotum*	2,37
Ophiostoma brevicollis	*Leptographium*	37
Ophiostoma cainii	*Leptographium, Graphium*	14,37
Ophiostoma clavigerum	*Graphicladiella clavigerum*	36,37
	Graphium/Leptographium	
Ophiostoma europhioides[2]	*Leptographium*	37
Ophiostoma francke-grosmanniae	*Phialocephala, Leptographium*	14,37, Wingfield this volume
Ophiostoma galeiformis	*Leptographium/Graphium*	(Wingfield, unpublished)
Ophiostoma ips	*Scopularia rumboldii*	10,37
	Hyalorhinocladiella, Graphium	
Ophiostoma leptographioides	*Leptographium*	37
Ophiostoma polonicum	*Leptographium*	35
Ophiostoma rostrocylindricum	*Leptographium*	37
Ophiostoma trinacriforme	*Leptographium*	37
Ophiostoma valdiviana	*Leptographium*	3

[1.] Considered a synonym of *O. ips* by Harrington (14).

[2.] Considered a synonym of *O. piceaperdum* by Upadhyay (37) but this is disputed by Harrington (14).

Despite the redefinition of *Leptographium* in terms of conidial development, it is ackowledged that some species do appear to have conidial development that is more prominantly sympodial than percurrent. For example, *Leptographium procerum* has conidia with somewhat indistinct points of attachment (Fig. 4) and, at least when viewed with the light microscope, the conidiogenous cells show little evidence of percurrent proliferation. In contrast, some species such as *L. pyrinum* have conidia with distinctly truncate bases and the annellations are obvious using a light microscope. Van Wyk *et al.* (38) showed that annellations are always present and suggested that these differences were due to variability in the extent of the proliferation phase. We have also questioned whether sympodial proliferation ever occurs in these fungi. Rather, we suggest that synchronization of conidium development creates an illusion of sympodial development on percurrently proliferating conidiogenous cells (Fig. 5). This phenomenon has been further discussed in *Graphium* (42) and in other fungi (9).

Phialocephala and *Leptographium*

Having examined conidium development in *Leptographium* and *Verticicladiella,* the taxonomic value of this criterion was examined in the remaining genus of the *Leptographium* complex, *Phialocephala* (46). Species of this genus could be divided into two distinct groups. One group had bacilliform conidia produced in chains with the conidia produced through a process defined by Minter *et al.* (28,29) as ring wall building. These species were transferred to the genus *Sporendocladia* Kendrick (46). Although species in the latter genus can be relatively easily identified by characteristic conidia, they may not be phylogenetically related.

The remaining *Phialocephala* species appear to produce conidia through apical wall building (30,46). Despite this unifying characteristic, there is a great deal of morphological diversity in the conidiogenous cells of species in the genus. For example, the type species *P. dimorphospora* and a number of other species such as *P. fortinii* have deep set conidiogenous loci with tubular collarettes. I believe that these species are closely related to *Phialophora*, which has similar conidium development. Other species probably represent a heterogeneous group that are of *Phialophora* anamorphs of a number of unrelated ascomycete genera (46).

Phialocephala and its synnematous analog *Phialographium* are genera that have been assigned to anamorphs of certain *Ophiostoma* species. For example, the mononematous anamorph of *Ophiostoma francke-grosmanniae* is purported to be a species of *Phialocephala* (6,37). When examined with a light microscope, conidiogenous cells do indeed appear to be distinctly phialidic (Fig. 6). A scanning electron microscope study of this species (Wingfield, unpublished) has shown distinct collarettes in some conidiogenous cells but percurrent proliferation of the conidiogenous cells is apparently also present (Fig. 7). Here, it is possible that secession of the first conidium can result in broadly flared outer wall layers of the conidiogenous cell. Subsequent conidial production with minimal proliferation would result in only the larger remains of the first conidium being obvious using light microscopy.

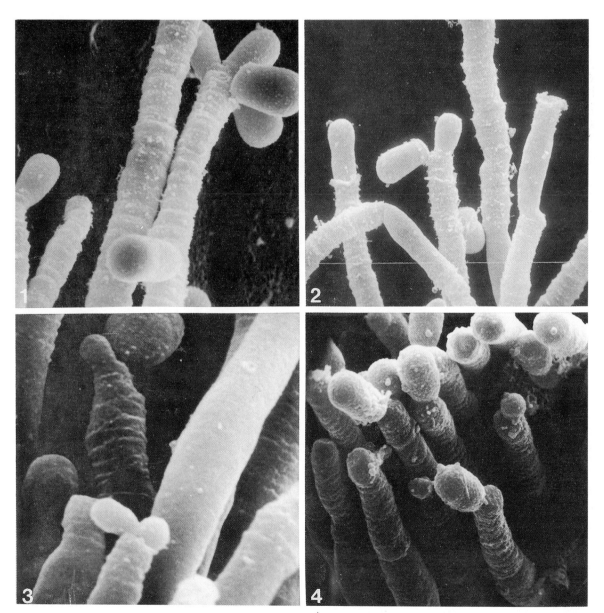

Figs. 1-4. Scanning electron micrographs of conidiogenous cells in species of *Leptographium* showing annellated conidiogenous cells as well as the appearance of sympodial development. Fig. 1. *L. truncatum.* Fig. 2. *L. lundbergii.* Fig. 3. *L. huntii.* Fig. 4. *L. procerum* Bars = 1 μm.

CONIDIOPHORE ASSOCIATION

The anamorph genus Graphium is closely allied to *Leptographium* (Seifert and Okada, this volume). The two genera have many characteristics in common, the most obvious of which are teleomorphs in *Ophiostoma*, similar patterns of conidial development (42,45) and corresponding ecological occurrence. The only conclusive difference between the two genera is in the synnematous conidiophores of *Graphium* and the mononematous conidiophores of *Leptographium*.

As might be expected, there are *Ophiostoma* species reported to have both synnematous (*Graphium*) and mononematous (*Leptographium*) states (14,37). These include *O. araucarium, O. cainii, O. clavigerum, O. galeiformis* and *O. ips*. In these cases, my inclination would be to give precedence to the synnematous state and the name attached to it because this state is the most obvious and prevalent.

It is likely that a continuum exists in the occurrence of synnematous and mononematous states. There are for instance species of *Leptographium* such as *L. lundbergii* in which conidiophores are produced in groups along the hyphae (Fig. 8). More closely aligned to a synnematous form would be *L. procerum*, in which conidiophores commonly occur in groups attached to a single base. These examples are clearly of mononematous species that are easily accommodated in *Leptographium*. In contrast, however, assigning a generic name to certain species, such as to the anamorph of *O. galeiformis*, is considerably more difficult. In this fungus, conidiophores are formed in groups attached at a common base. In many cases, they are free from each other, as is the case in *L. procerum*. They do, however, commonly aggregate along the lengths of the stipes (Fig. 9) and would then be considered synnematous. At this stage, I feel inclined to include the anamorph of *O. galeiformis* in *Leptographium* because even the apparently synnematous conidiophores separate when mounted in various media including water and lactophenol. Nonetheless, this is a matter that clearly deserves further attention.

It is possible for conidiophores to degenerate significantly through progressive subculturing. This problem has been well documented for *Leptographium serpens* (8,14,43). Similarly, Tsuneda and Hiratsuka (36) have illustrated a degeneration of the synnematous state of *O. clavigerum* to a mononematous form. Such difficulties are likely to

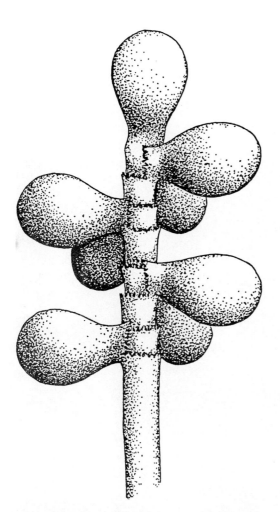

Fig. 5. Schematic representation of a conidiogenous cell in a species of *Leptographium* showing how incomplete dehiscence of conidia after percurrent proliferation can result in an illusion of sympodial development.

Preliminary observations suggest that the anamorph of *O. francke-grosmanniae* could well be accommodated in *Leptographium*. This would be consistent with our conclusions for the so-called *Phialographium* anamorph of *Ophiostoma cucullatum* (42,35). However, final judgement should be reserved until an ultrastructural study of conidium development in the anamorph of *O. francke-grosmanniae* is completed. If our suspicion in this case is true, the *Phialocephala sensu stricto* will no longer be considered associated with the ophiostomatoid fungi.

Figs. 6-9. Conidium development in the anamorph of *O. francke - grosmanniae* and conidiophore association in *L. lundbergii* and the anamorph of *C. galeiformis*. Fig. 6. Fluorescence micrograph of conidiogenous cells in *O. francke - grosmanniae* as apparently phialidic. Bar = 1 μm. Fig. 7. Scanning electron micrograph of conidiogenous cells in *O. francke - grosmanniae* showing percurrent proliferation. Bar = 1 μm. Fig. 8. Conidiophores of *L. lundbergii* in groups. Bar = 10 μm. Fig. 9. Conidiophores, single as well as aggregated in a group apparently surrounded by a pellicle in *C. galeiformis*. Bar = 10 μm.

plague the taxonomy of *Leptographium* and *Graphium* in the future so, ideally, material should be examined on the natural host before isolation in culture. Careful selection of media for cultivation and preservation also would assist in maintaining the original morphology.

DELIMITATION OF *LEPTOGRAPHIUM* IN TERMS OF TELEOMORPHS

Because many *Leptographium* species have *Ophiostoma* teleomorphs (Tables 1, 3), the genus could be restricted only to anamorphs of *Ophiostoma*. Conversely, we might justifiably predict an *Ophiostoma* state for *Leptographium* species where teleomorphs have yet to be identified (Table 2). Here, we face the dilemma and complications of dealing with anamorph genera. Two particular issues that deserve consideration are those of entirely anamorphic fungi (anamorphic holomorphs) and convergent evolution to exploit similar niches.

Anamorphic species

Leptographium species known to have *Ophiostoma* teleomorphs occur in the galleries of scolytid bark beetles that infest trees. Their slimy conidial masses and stalked fruiting structures facilitate dispersal by the vectors. Although quantitative data are unavailable, the *Leptographium* conidiophores appear to occur much more commonly than do the ascomata. For instance, in species such as *L. serpens*, the ascomata have been collected only once and appear to be extremely rare. Many of these fungi appear, therefore, to be almost entirely dependent on the conidial states for their survival. Indeed, it is possible that the teleomorphs of many *Leptographium* species have been lost through the course of time. Thus, species such as *L. procerum*, *L. lundbergii* and *L. terebrantis* that commonly occur in galleries of bark beetles might well have had *Ophiostoma* states at one time although the teleomorphs no longer exist. In terms of phylogeny, they are 'good' *Leptographium* species and, due to the lack of a teleomorph, should be considered holomorphs in their own right.

Convergent evolution

Acceptance of the concept of an entirely anamorphic species provides justification for considering certain *Leptographium* species to be related. However, the morphological characteristics of *Leptographium* species are probably strongly related to adaptation to insect dispersal. It is possible, if not probable, that distantly related or perhaps even unrelated fungi have evolved similar morphology in order to facilitate insect dispersal.

In the absence of a teleomorph, it is virtually impossible to define *Leptographium* in terms of phylogeny, although various characteristics might provide us with a hint of their natural grouping. For example, *Leptographium* anamorphs of *Ophiostoma* tolerate high concentrations of cycloheximide in growth media (13). Tolerance of cycloheximide is probably not adequate justification to include a species in the genus, although it is one of a suite of useful characteristics. A species that does not tolerate high concentrations of cycloheximide is probably not related to *Ophiostoma*. If this is true, species such as *L. antibioticum* and *L. brachiatum*, which are intolerant of cycloheximide (13), might not be related to anamorphs of *Ophiostoma*.

It seems likely that the genus *Leptographium* includes not only anamorphs of *Ophiostoma* but also a number of unrelated fungi of similar morphology. Here, as in the case of *Chalara* (Nag Raj and Kendrick, this volume) and *Graphium* (Seifert and Okada, this volume), we face the dilemma of assigning similar generic names to unrelated anamorphs. Through the use of sophisticated chemotaxonomic and molecular technology, however, scientists may gain a better understanding of the relationships between these fungi.

SPECIES CONCEPTS

Species identification in *Leptographium* is difficult and requires considerable experience. Comparison of unknown species with authenticated cultures is usually essential in making accurate identifications. Such comparison is complicated, however, by the lack of material available in culture collections and herbaria. Type material is unavailable for a number of species, including *L. lundbergii*, the type species of the genus (41). Where dried herbarium material is available, it is often in poor condition and inadequate for comparative study. Similarly, where only one or a few collections of a species have been maintained, evaluation of variation within species is virtually impossible.

Very little attention has been given to defining and evaluating characters for the identification of *Leptographium* species. Characters that appear to have some taxonomic value include: conidial size and shape; the number and arrangement of primary and subsequent metulae; the size, branching pattern and degree of association of the stipe; the presence or absence of rhizoids; hyphal growth patterns; and colony form and color on various growth media. Many of these characteristics are misleading when used alone. For example, the hyphae of *L. serpens* have a distinct serpentine growth pattern. Although perhaps not as distinct, this characteristic is also found in a number of other *Leptographium* species such as *L. wageneri* and *L. huntii*. It is therefore essential that suites of characters are categorized in order to clearly define species.

Considerable effort is required to improve our understanding of species concepts in *Leptographium*. Additional collections must be made to define the limits of known species more clearly. Furthermore, very little collecting of this group of fungi has been done in areas other than Europe and North America and many undescribed species are likely to exist.

CONCLUSIONS

1. In recent years, significant advances have been made in understanding the generic delimitation of *Leptographium*. Most problems that arose from separation of this group on the basis of conidial development have been resolved. This resolution has led to enhanced knowledge of conidium development as a whole.

2. Depending on the generic concepts employed, there are approximately 24 species of *Ophiostoma* that have *Leptographium* anamorphs, although epithets have not been provided for the majority of these. They form a natural and well-defined group and a sound foundation on which to base generic concepts for *Leptographium*. In additon to these, there are approximately 14 species of *Leptographium* for which teleomorphs are unknown. Although some may be related to anamorphs of *Ophiostoma*, they are more probably a heterogeneous group. Application of chemotaxonomic and molecular techniques will help to resolve questions pertaining to relationships between these species.

3. Many species of *Leptographium* are represented by single or a limited number of collections. In addition, there are species for which cultures are no longer available. There is a decided need to improve our collections of this group of fungi. Based on collections of undescribed species, it is possible that many species of *Leptographium* remain to be discovered.

4. At present, identification of *Leptographium* requires considerable experience; it is not uncommon for species to be incorrectly identified in the the literature. This is due partially to the lack of a monograph to these fungi, but also to the similarity between some species and the lack of an acceptable species concept. Moreover, comparison of unknown cultures to authentic cultures of known species is absolutely essential.

ACKNOWLEDGEMENTS

Financial support from the Foundation for Research Development, South Africa is gratefully acknowledged.

LITERATURE CITED

1. Barras, S.J. and Perry, T. Gland cells and fungi associated with prothoracic mycangium of *Dendroctonus adjunctus*(Coleoptera:Scolytidae). Ann. Entomol. Soc. Am. 64:123-126.

2. Butin, H. 1968. A new species of *Ceratocystis* causing blue-stain in *Araucaria araucana*. Can. J. Bot. 46:61-63.

3. Butin, H. and Aquilar, A.M. 1984. Blue-stain fungi on *Nothofagus* from Chile - including two new species of *Ceratocystis* Ellis and Halst. Phytopathol. Z. 109:80-89.

4. Davidson, R.W. 1935. Fungi causing stain in logs and lumber in the southern states, including five new species. J. Agric. Res. 50:789-807.

5. Davidson, R.W. 1978. Wood-staining fungi associated with bark beetles in Engelmann spruce in Colorado. Mycologia 47:58-67.

6. Davidson, R.W. 1971. New species of *Ceratocystis*. Mycologia 63:5-15.

7. Davidson, R.W. 1978. Staining fungi associated with *Dendroctonus adjunctus* in pines. Mycologia 70:35-40.

8. Gambogi, P. and Lorenzini, G. 1977. Conidiophore morphology in *Verticicladiella serpens*. Trans. Br. Mycol. Soc. 69:217-223.

9. Glawe, D. 1989. Variable proliferation of conidiogenous cells in Diatrypaceae and other fungi. Sydowia 41:122-135.

10. Goidánich, G. 1936. Il genere di Ascomiceti *Grosmannia*. G. Goid. Boll. Staz. Patol. Veg. Roma. n.s. 16:26-60.

11. Grosmann, H. 1931. Beiträge zur kenntnis der lebensgemeinschaft zwischen borkenkafern und pilzen. Z. Parasitenkd. 3:56-102.

12. Grosmann, H. 1932. Über die systematischen Beziehungen der Gattung *Leptographium* Lagerberg et Melin zur Gattung *Ceratostomella* Sacc. Nebst einigen Bemerkungen über *Scopularia venusta* Preuss und *Hantzschia phycomyces* Awd. Hedwigia 72:183-194.

13. Harrington, T.C. 1981. Cycloheximide sensitivity as a taxonomic character in *Ceratocystis*. Mycologia 73:1123-1129.

14. Harrington, T.C. 1988. *Leptographium* species, their distributions, hosts and insect vectors. Pages 1 - 39 in: *Leptographium* root diseases on conifers. T.C. Harrington and F.W. Cobb, Jr. eds. American Phytopathological Society Press, St. Paul, MN. 149 pp.

15. Harrington, T.C. and Cobb, F.W. Jr. 1983. Pathogenicity of *Leptographium* and *Verticicladiella* species isolated from roots of western North American conifers. Phytopathology 73:596-599.

16. Harrington, T.C. and Cobb, F.W. Jr. 1984. Host specialization of three morphological variants of *Verticicladiella wageneri*. Phytopathology 74: 286-290.

17. Harrington, T.C. and Cobb, F.W. Jr. 1986. Varieties of *Verticicladiella wageneri*. Mycologia 78:562-567.

18. Harrington, T.C. and Cobb, F.W. Jr. 1987. *Leptographium wageneri* var *pseudotsugae* var nov. cause of black stain root disease on Douglas fir. Mycotaxon 30:501-507.

19. Hughes, S.J. 1953. Conidiophores, conidia and classification. Can. J. Bot. 31:577-659.

20. Jooste, W.J. 1978. *Leptographium reconditum* sp. nov. and observations on conidiogenesis in *Verticicladiella*. Trans. Br. Mycol. Soc. 70:152-155.

21. Kendrick, W.B. 1961. The *Leptographium* complex. *Phialocephala* gen. nov. Can. J. Bot. 39:1079-1085.

22. Kendrick, W.B. 1962. The *Leptographium* complex. *Verticicladiella* Hughes. Can. J. Bot. 40:771-797.

23. Kendrick, W.B. 1963a. The *Leptographium* complex. *Penicillium repens* C.& E. Can. J. Bot. 41:573-577.

24. Kendrick, W.B. 1963b. The *Leptographium* complex. Two new species of *Phialocephala*. Can. J. Bot. 41: 1015-1023.

25. Kendrick, W.B. 1964. The *Leptographium* complex. *Hantzschia* Auerswald. Can. J. Bot. 42: 1291-1295.

26. Kendrick, W.B. and Molnar, A.C. 1965. A new *Ceratocystis* and its *Verticicladiella* imperfect state associated with the bark beetle *Dryocoetes confusus* on *Abies lasiocarpa*. Can. J. Bot. 43:39-43.

27. Lagerberg, T., Lundberg, G. and Melin, E. 1927. Biological and practical researches into blueing in pine and spruce. Skögsvardsfören. Tidskr. 25:145-272.

28. Minter, D.W., Kirk, P.M. and Sutton, B.C. 1982. Holoblastic phialides. Trans. Br. Mycol. Soc. 79: 75-93.

29. Minter, D.W., Kirk, P.M. and Sutton, B.C. 1983. Thallic phialides. Trans. Br. Mycol. Soc. 80:39-66.

30. Minter, D.W., Sutton, B.C. and Brady, B.L. 1983. What are phialides anyway? Trans. Br. Mycol. Soc. 81:109-120.

31. Morelet, M. 1988. Observations sur trois Deutéromycètes inféodés aux pins. Annales de la S.S.N.A.T.V. 40:41-45.

32. Ram, C. and Ram, A. 1972. Timber attacking fungi from the state of Mara-Nahao, Brazil. Some new or interesting wood staining fungi. IX. Broteria 41:89-112.

33. Shaw, G.C. and Hubert, E.E. 1952. A review of the *Leptographium-Scopularia-Hantzschia* nomenclature. Mycologia 44:693-704.

34. Siemasko, W. 1939. Fungi associated with bark beetles in Poland. Planta Polonica 7:1-54.

35. Solheim, H. 1986. Species of Ophistomataceae isolated from *Picea abies* infested by the bark beetle *Ips typographus*. Nord. J. Bot. 6:199-207.

36. Tsuneda, A. and Hiratsuka, Y. 1984. Sympodial and annellidic conidiation in *Ceratocystis clavigera*. Can. J. Bot. 62:2618-2624.

37. Upadhyay, H.P. 1981. A monograph of *Ceratocystis* and *Ceratocystiopsis*. University of Georgia Press, Athens, GA. 176 pp.

38. Van Wyk, P.S., Wingfield, M.J. and Marasas, W.F.O. 1988. Differences in synchronization of stages of conidial development in *Leptographium* species. Trans. Br. Mycol. Soc. 90:451-456.

39. Wingfield, M.J. 1985. Reclassification of *Verticicladiella* based on conidial development. Trans. Br. Mycol. Soc. 85:81-93.

40. Wingfield, M.J., Capretti, P. and Mackenzie, M. 1988. *Leptographium* species as root pathogens of conifers. An international perspective. Pages 113 - 128 in: *Leptographium* root diseases on conifers. T.C. Harrington and F.W. Cobb, Jr. eds. American Phytopathological Society Press, St. Paul, MN. 149 pp.

41. Wingfield, M.J. and Gibbs, J.N. 1991. *Leptographium* and *Graphium* species associated with pine-infecting bark beetles in England. Mycol. Res. 95:1257-1260.

42. Wingfield, M.J., Kendrick, B. and Van Wyk, P.S. 1991. Analysis of conidium ontogeny in anamorphs of *Ophiostoma*: *Pesotum* and *Phialographium* are synonyms of *Graphium*. Mycol. Res. 95:1328-1333.

43. Wingfield, M.J. and Marasas, W.F.O. 1981. *Verticicladiella alacris*, a synonym of *V. serpens*. Trans. Br. Mycol. Soc. 76:508-510.

44. Wingfield, M.J. and Marasas, W.F.O. 1983. Some *Verticicladiella* species, including *V. truncata* sp. nov., associated with root diseases of pine in New Zealand and South Africa. Trans. Br. Mycol. Soc. 80:231-236.

45. Wingfield, M.J., Van Wyk, P.S. and Van Wyk, P.W.J. 1989. Conidial development in the anamorph of *Ophiostoma cucullatum*. Mycol. Res. 93:91-95.

46. Wingfield, M.J., Van Wyk, P.S. and Wingfield, B.D. 1987. Reclassification of *Phialocephala* based on conidial development. Trans. Br. Mycol. Soc. 89: 509-520.

Chapter 6

SPOROTHRIX-LIKE ANAMORPHS OF *OPHIOSTOMA* SPECIES AND OTHER FUNGI

G.S. DE HOOG

INTRODUCTION

The genus *Sporothrix* was established in 1909 by Hektoen and Perkins (9) for the agent of human sporotrichosis. The causative agent, *S. schenckii,* has a characteristic clinical pathology and therefore the genus *Sporothrix* long remained monotypic.

Sporothrix schenckii exhibits a simple morphology, consisting of one-celled conidia produced in more or less sympodial order on densely aggregated denticles. The conidiogenous cells are hyaline and generally poorly differentiated. In the 1970s, a number of superficially similar species were added to the genus (11), irrespective of any possible phylogenetic relationships. As the identification of Hyphomycetes still depends primarily on microscopic morphology, the creation of more natural but morphologically similar genera would create confusion. *Sporothrix* was therefore explicitly maintained as an artificial form genus. In a number of species, taxonomic relationships are known through available teleomorphs; they belong either to the hyphal yeasts (Endomycetes), to the true Ascomycetes (*Ophiostoma* and similar genera) or to the Phragmobasidiomycetes (Dacrymycetales) (Figs. 1-3). Weijman and de Hoog (41) acknowledged the existence of these unrelated taxonomic groups by proposing a number of sections within *Sporothrix,* the genus being maintained as an entity for practical reasons only.

The relationships of *Sporothrix* species are reviewed below. The main criteria for attribution to any major taxonomic group are, in the absence of teleomorphs, secondary characters such as coenzyme Q systems (Co-Q), cell wall carbohydrate composition, and ultrastructure of cell wall and septal pores (Fig. 4).

OPHIOSTOMA ANAMORPHS

The majority of species described in *Sporothrix,* including the generic type species, *S. schenckii,* have electron transparent cell walls and simple, central septal pores about 50 nm wide, mostly with one or several adjacent Woronin bodies (30,31). They can be regarded as of euascomycetous affinity. All species studied thus far have dihydrogenated coenzyme Q-10 systems (32).

Several *Sporothrix* species, including the generic type, have rhamnose in their cell walls (Table 1). They share this character with species of *Ophiostoma,* in which the outermost wall layers contain variously interconnected rhamnopyranose units (34). The character seems to be a generic hallmark (40,41). The invariable presence of rhamnose, a relatively uncommon sugar in the fungal kingdom, warrants the supposition that the rhamnose-containing *Sporothrix* species are *Ophiostoma* anamorphs.

The number of named rhamnose-containing *Sporothrix* species is low, while, on the other hand, quite a few *Ophiostoma* with unnamed *Sporothrix* states are known (Table 1). Many *Ophiostoma* species produce their ascomata with relative ease in culture, at least when freshly isolated. Among the exceptions are the heterothallic species, such as the common *O. piceae* (Brasier, this volume). Fresh isolates of this species mostly produce *Graphium* and *Sporothrix* anamorphs in abundance, but no perithecia. Nearly monomorphic variants can be isolated by transferring one conidial type only (27). The somewhat degenerate *Sporothrix* cultures still form some *Graphium* synnemata, the conidia of which can restore the abundantly sporulating, nearly monomorphic synnematous culture. The optimal form of propagation apparently is by spore slime, either from ascomata or from the synnematous morph. The *Sporothrix* anamorph may assist with rapid colonization of the substrate.

Among the strictly anamorphic, rhamnose-containing *Sporothrix* species, *S. inflata* is a common soil inhabitant, with a world-wide distribution. Degenerated cultures lose the *Sporothrix* state, with lateral, brown conidia remaining (=*Humicola*

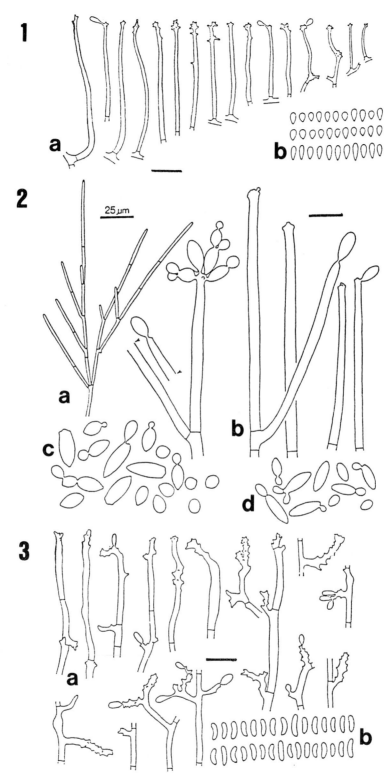

Figs. 1-3. Ascomycetous, Endomycetous and Basidiomycetous species of *Sporothrix.* Fig. 1. Ascomycetous species *Sporothrix schenckii,* various cultures. a. Conidiogenous cells. b. Conidia. (Reproduced with permission from 11). Fig. 2. Endomycetous species *Sporothrix fungorum,* CBS 508.72. a. Branching system. b. Conidiophores. c. Primary conidia. d. Secondary conidia. Bar represents 10 μm, unless stated otherwise. (Reproduced with permission from 14). Fig. 3. Basidiomycetous species *Sporothrix luteoalba,* CBS 209.48. a. Conidiogenous cells. b. Conidia. (Reproduced with permission from 11).

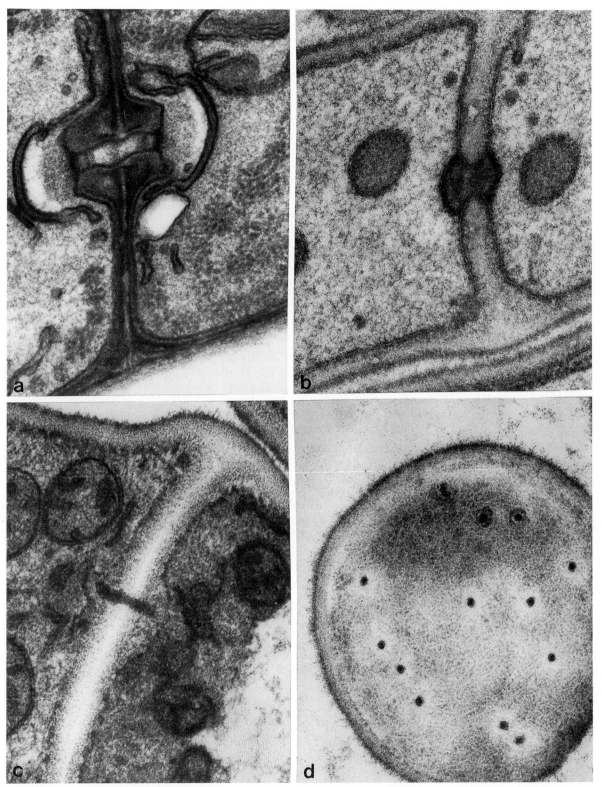

Fig. 4. TEM pictures of pore structures of various *Sporothrix* species. a. Basidiomycetous species *Sporothrix luteoalba*, CBS 209.49, x 80000. b. Ascomycetous species *Sporothrix schenckii*, CBS 292.55, x 125000. c-d. Endomycetous species. c. Section of central micropore in *Stephanoascus farinosus*, CBS 140.71, x 85000. d. Face view of randomly distributed micropores in *Stephanoascus ciferrii*, CBS 6699, x 60000. (Reproduced with permission from 30).

TABLE 1. Ophiostomatoid *Sporothrix* species, classified in section *Sporothrix*.

Species	Teleomorph	Pore	Wall	Co-Q (reduced)
S. curviconia	-	s	rh	$10H_2$
S. inflata	-	s	rh	$10H_2$
S. nivea	-			
S. pallida	? *O. stenoceras*		rh	
S. schenckii	-	s	rh	$10H_2$
unnamed	*O. epigloeum*		rh	
unnamed	*O. nigrocarpum*		rh	
unnamed	*O. piliferum*		rh	
unnamed	*O. longirostellatum*			
unnamed	*O. multiannulatum*			
unnamed	*O. narcissi*			
unnamed	*O. piceae*		rh	$10H_2$
S. subannulata	*O. subannulatum*			
unnamed	*O. tetropii*			
unnamed	*O. ulmi*		rh	

s = simple central pore with Woronin bodies (30); rh = rhamnose (40); $10H_2$ = reduced Co-Q-10 (32).

dimorphospora) as the only form of propagation.

Sporothrix schenckii is found on various substrates, particularly on dead wood. When propagules are introduced traumatically into humans, a subcutaneous sporotrichosis may develop. This chronic disorder is characterized by ulceration of regional lymph nodes. Although the proposed connection between *S. schenkii* and *O. stenoceras* has been refuted (Summerbell, this volume), the possibility remains that *O. stenoceras* is close to *Sporothrix pallida*, an uncommon, floccose counterpart of *S. schenckii* (23). *Sporothrix nivea* (17) is probably identical to that species.

Ophiostoma is known for its diversity of anamorphs (37), supposedly demonstrating the heterogenicity of the genus. Judging from ascospore morphology, the *Ophiostoma* species with *Sporothrix* anamorphs, however, constitute a rather homogeneous group, because they all have ellipsoidal to reniform ascospores (Table 2). Below, I will try to show that at least part of the supposed heterogeneity is caused by incorrect classification of anamorphs.

1. *Hyalodendron*: *Ophiostoma* anamorphs with conidia in short chains have often been referred to as *Hyalodendron* (36). However, this name is unavailable for *Ophiostoma* anamorphs because the type species is a Basidiomycete (12). Actually, catenulate conidia are quite common in *Sporothrix*. Chains are present in low abundance in cultures of many otherwise non-catenate species. The recognition of a separate genus for this group therefore seems unnecessary.

2. *Hyalorhinocladiella*: The distinction between *Sporothrix* and *Hyalorhinocladiella* (37) is problematic. *Sporothrix* conidiogenous cells usually bear sharp denticles on which lacrymoid to fusiform, basally acuminate conidia with narrow scars are formed. *Hyalorhinocladiella* has sessile conidia with truncate bases, the conidial shape being cylindrical, clavate or Y-shaped. With this circumscription, the anamorphs of 'Ceratocystis' deltoideospora, *Ceratocystiopsis concentrica*, *C. longispora* and *C. spinulosa*, all treated under *Sporothrix*, by Upadhyay (36), as well as that of *C. ranaculosus* (2), would fit *Hyalorhinocladiella*.

Considering the taxonomic position of the *Ophiostoma* and *Ceratocystiopsis* species with *Sporothrix* and *Hyalorhinocladiella* anamorphs, the following observation can be made. The *Hyalorhinocladiella* anamorphs are mostly found in the section *Ips*, characterized by presence of rectangular, sheathed ascospores, and in the genus *Ceratocystiopsis*, characterized by falcate ascospores with sheaths or sheath-like cell wall layers (Table 4). The anamorph of *Pyxidiophora spinulo-rostrata*, attributed to *Sporothrix* by Webster and Hawksworth (39), may also fit this group. Nearly all *Ophiostoma* species with *Sporothrix* anamorphs, on the contrary, fit in section *Ophiostoma* (Table 3),

TABLE 2. *Ophiostoma* ('*Ceratocystis*') species with *Sporothrix* anamorphs.

Species	Synanamorph	Ascospores	Source	Reference
epigloeum	-	reniform	fungus	11
grande	-	bean shaped	fungus	28
microsporum	-	bean shaped	*Quercus*	21
narcissi	-	ellipsoidal	*Narcissus*	11
nigrocarpum	-	crescent	*Abies*	11
nothofagi	-	crescent	*Nothofagus*	3
perfectum	*Pesotum*	ellipsoidal	*Picea*	11
piceae	*Pesotum*	reniform	*Picea, Quercus*	27
piliferum	-	reniform	*Pinus*	3
polyporicola	-	reniform	fungus	4
roraimense	*Sterigmatobotrys*	bean shaped	fungus	28
stenoceras	-	bean shaped	*Quercus*	16
subannulatum	-	reniform	*Abies*	19
tenella	-	bean shaped	*Picea, Pinus*	21
tetropii	*Leptographium*	reniform	*Picea*	22
ulmi	*Pesotum*	crescent	*Ulmus*	11
valdiviana	*Leptographium*	reniform	*Nothofagus*	3

characterized by ascospores without sheath-like layers on the cell walls. The two exceptions, falling in section *Ceratocystis* (*sensu* Upadhyay), have ellipsoidal to crescent-shaped ascospores with rather uniform sheath-like wall layers.

The only argument against the homogeneity of *Sporothrix*-forming *Ophiostoma* species is their ecology; two ecological subgroups can be distinguished. One subgroup is composed of blue stain fungi, whereas the other is composed of associates of higher fungi. *Ophiostoma epigloeum* is found on *Tremella* (8), *O. polyporicola* on *Polyporus* (4), and *O. grande* and *O. roraimense* on *Diatrype* (28). Mycoparasites with affinities to *Ophiostoma* are found in · *Pyxidiophora* and *Sphaeronaemella*, (see Malloch and Blackwell, this volume). The latter genera have endoconidial anamorphs, and are considered distant relatives of the species with *Sporothrix* anamorphs.

ASCOMYCETOUS SPECIES

In addition to anamorphs associated with *Ophiostoma* species, ascomycetous *Sporothrix* species fall into two additional subgroups. One subgroup is composed of species lacking rhamnose in their cell wall hydrolyzates (40; Table 5) whereas the second is related to hyphal yeasts.

TABLE 3. Classification of *Ophiostoma* species with published *Sporothrix*-like anamorphs.

Species	Section	Species	Section
angusticollis	*Ophiostoma*	*piliferum*	*Ophiostoma*
epigloeum	*Ophiostoma*	*pluriannulatum*	*Ophiostoma*
grande	*Ophiostoma*	*polyporicola*	*Ophiostoma*
leucocarpum	*Ophiostoma*	*populicola*	*Ceratocystis*
megalobrunneum	*Ophiostoma*	*populinum*	*Ophiostoma*
microsporum	*Ceratocystis*	*roraimense*	*Ophiostoma*
multiannulatum	*Ophiostoma*	*rostrocoronatum*	*Ophiostoma*
narcissi	*Ophiostoma*	*stenoceras*	*Ophiostoma*
nigrocarpum	*Ophiostoma*	*subannulatum*	*Ophiostoma*
nothofagi	*Ophiostoma*	*tenellum*	*Ophiostoma*
perfectum	*Ophiostoma*	*tetropii*	*Ophiostoma*
piceae	*Ophiostoma*	*valdiviana*	*Ophiostoma*

TABLE 4. Classification of *Ophiostoma* and *Ceratocystiopsis* species with *Hyalorhinocladiella* anamorphs.

Species	Section		Species	Genus
aequivaginata	*Ceratocystis*		*concentrica*	*Ceratocystiopsis*
allantospora	*Ophiostoma*		*conicicollis*	*Ceratocystiopsis*
bacillispora	*Ophiostoma*		*crenulata*	*Ceratocystiopsis*
bicolor	*Ips*		*fasciata*	*Ceratocystiopsis*
brunneo-citrina	*Ips*		*minima*	*Ceratocystiopsis*
ips	*Ips*		*minuta*	*Ceratocystiopsis*
nigra	*Ips*		*minuta-bicolor*	*Ceratocystiopsis*
seticollis	*Ips*		*pallidobrunnea*	*Ceratocystiopsis*
tremulo-aurea	*Ophiostoma*		*spinulosa*	*Ceratocystiopsis*

Kurata (18) found that the presence or absence of rhamnose in *Sporothrix* coincides with gross differences in glycoprotein composition. Teleomorphs are unknown in this subgroup; thus taxonomic relationships can only be speculated upon. Wang (38) reported a *Sporothrix* synanamorph in two collections of *Zygosporium masonii* Hughes. Sivanesan and Sutton (29) mentioned an association of *Sporothrix ghanensis* and a *Zygosporium* species but did not imply that these were connected. Some *Sporothrix* species of the group under consideration, such as *S. ghanensis* and *S. isarioides,* are insect pathogens, probably closely related to genera such as *Engyodontium, Aphanocladium* and *Verticillium.* sect. *Prostrata.* Other species of the subgroup, e.g. *Sporothrix phellini* (1), are mycoparasites. *Sporothrix ranii* and *S. ramosissima* are reminiscent of *Arthrobotrys* species with one-celled conidia. All these taxa occur preferentially on chitinous substrata. A clavicipitalean relationship seems likely.

TABLE 5. Clavicipitalean *Sporothrix* species, classified in section *Sporothrix.*

Species	Pore	Co-Q
S. alba (?)		
S. ghanensis	s	$10H_2$
S. insectorum	s	$10H_2$
S. isarioides (?)		
S. ramosissima		
S. ranii	s	$10H_2$
S. phellini (?)		
S. sclerotialis	s	$10H_2$
S. setiphila (?)		
S. vizei (?)		

s = simple central pore with Woronin bodies (30).
$10H_2$ = reduced Co-Q-10 (32)

YEAST-LIKE SPECIES

Another line of relationship among *Sporothrix* species is with the hyphal yeasts (Endomycetes). *Sporothrix catenata* (13) crossed with one of the tester strains of *Stephanoascus ciferrii*, and can thus be regarded as the *Sporothrix* synanamorph of the yeast-like or pseudomycelial *Candida ciferrii. Stephanoascus farinosus* (14) also has dimorphism of yeast-like and hyphal synanamorphs. Hyphal septa of *S. ciferrii* are perforated by scattered micropores, whereas *S. farinosus* has only one, central micropore (30). A single central micropore is shared by all species of *Blastobotrys* and by a number of *Sporothrix* species (Table 6: 30,31). Coenzyme Q systems are invariably Q-9 (32). These fungi apparently are closely related and all may be assigned to the Endomycetes (13).

Sporothrix ankangensis (5) is probably also an Endomycete. The two *Stephanoascus* species described by Traquair *et al.* (33) are, however, of basidiomycetous affinity, probably representing cultural states of smut fungi; their conidial states, *Sporothrix rugulosa* and *S. flocculosa* may be classified in *Tilletiopsis* or a similar genus.

BASIDIOMYCETOUS SPECIES

Basidiomycetous *Sporothrix*-like anamorphs were classified by Weijman and de Hoog (41) in the small section *Luteoalba.* One species, *Sporothrix luteoalba,* has xylose in the cell wall hydrolyzate, which may be regarded as a marker for tremellaceous fungi. This affinity was confirmed by its multilamellar cell wall structure when studied by TEM and septal dolipores with well-developed, unperforated parenthesomes (30). *Sporothrix luteoalba* was originally described as the anamorph of *Femsjonia luteoalba,* now known as *Ditiola*

TABLE 6. Endomycetous *Sporothrix* species, classified in section *Farinosa*

Species	Teleomorph	Pore	Co-Q (oxidized)
S. catenata	*Stephanoascus ciferrii*	m(r)	9
unnamed	*Stephanoascus farinosus*	m(c)	9
S. foliorum	-	m(c)	9
S. fungorum	-	m(c)	9
S. guttuliformis	-	m(r)	9

m(r) = randomly distributed micropores (30,31); m(c) = single, central micropore (30,31).
9 = oxidized Co-Q-9 (32,42).

TABLE 7. Basidiomycetous *Sporothrix* species, assigned to section *Luteoalba* or the anamorph genus *Cerinosterus*.

Species	Teleomorph	Pore	Wall	Co-Q(oxidized)
S. cyanescens		d		10
unnamed (15)	*Dacrymyces stillatus* (6)	d(p)		
S. luteoalba	*Ditiola pezizaeformis*	d(p)	xyl	10
unnamed (25)	*Ditiola haasii*	d(p)		
unnamed (7)	*Cerinomyces ceraceus*	d(p)		
unnamed (7)	*Cerinomyces aculeatus*	d(p)		
unnamed (7)	*Cerinomyces canadensis*	d(p)		
unnamed (15)	*Calocera cornea*	d(p)		
unnamed (15)	*Calocera viscosa*	d(p)		

d(p) = dolipore with parenthesome (20,25,26,30,35); d = dolipore (30); xyl = xylose (41)
10 = oxidized Co-Q-10 (32,42).

pezizaeformis (Dacrymycetales). Moore (24) introduced the anamorph genus *Cerinosterus*, with *S. luteoalba* as the type species, to accommodate basidiomycetous anamorphs with *Sporothrix* morphology.

Several members of Dacrymycetales, all characterized as such by the presence of septal dolipores with unperforated parenthesomes, produce similar *Sporothrix*-like anamorphs from monokaryotic hyphae (Table 7). Thus far, *Sporothrix*-like anamorphs have been reported for species of *Cerinomyces* (7, 20) *Ditiola* (25), *Dacrymyces* and *Calocera* (15).

Smith and Batenburg-van der Vegte (30) demonstrated that *Sporothrix cyanescens* (= *Cerinosterus cyanescens*) also has a basidiomycetous affinity, although the dolipores in this fungus were surrounded by fragments of endoplasmic reticulum only. The cell walls did not contain xylose (41); its coenzyme Q system is Q-10 (32). The taxonomic position of this species needs to be determined with more certainty.

Judging from its microscopic morphology, *S. cylindrospora* (10) may also be a basidiomycetous *Sporothrix,* but the species has not been cultured, a prerequisite for biochemical and ultrastructural studies.

CONCLUSIONS

The anamorph genus *Sporothrix* has thus far been considered as an entity based on morphological criteria as is common in Hyphomycete taxonomy. However, quite unrelated fungi propagate by the simple conidia on denticles that characterize the genus. Basidiomycetous species, having Co-Q-10 systems, xylose in cell wall hydrolyzates, multilamellar cell walls and various types of dolipores, are classified in *Cerinosterus*. Endomycetous species, with Co-Q-9 and septal micropores, should be classified in *Blastobotrys*.

Sporothrix should be restricted to anamorphs of Euascomycetes. They all have Co-Q-10(H_2) and simple septal pores with Woronin bodies. Ophiostomatoid *Sporothrix* species can be recognized by rhamnose in their cell wall hydrolyzates.

Denticulate anamorphs occur only in a limited number of rather closely related *Ophiostoma* species. These *Sporothrix* anamorphs may have a different ecological role from the more generally occurring *Leptographium* and *Graphium* anamorphs, which are dispersed by insects.

LITERATURE CITED

1. Arnold, G.R.W. 1987. Beitrag zur Kenntnis der Pilzflora Kubas. III. Feddes Rep. 98:351-355.
2. Bridges, J.R. and Perry, T.J. 1987. *Ceratocystiopsis ranaculosus* sp. nov. associated with the southern pine beetle. Mycologia 79:630-633.
3. Butin, H. and Aquilar, A.M. 1984. Blue-stain fungi on *Nothofagus* from Chile - Including two new species of *Ceratocystis* Ellis & Halst. Phytopathol. Z. 109:80-89.
4. Constantinescu, O. and Ryman, S. 1989. A new *Ophiostoma* on polypores. Mycotaxon 34:637-642.
5. Fan, M.-Z., Guo, C. and Zhang, T.-Y. 1990. A new species of *Sporothrix* from China. Acta Mycol. Sin. 9:137-140.
6. Flegler, S.L. , Hooper, G.R. and Fields, W.G. 1976. Ultrastructural and cytochemical changes in the basidiomycete dolipore septum associated with fruiting. Can. J. Bot. 54:2243-2253.
7. Ginns, J. 1982. *Cerinomyces ceraceus* sp. nov. and the similar *C. grandinioides* and *C. lagerheimii.* Can. J. Bot. 60:519-524.
8. Guerrero, R.T. 1971. On the real nature of the "setae" in *Tremella fuciformis.* Mycologia 63:920-924.
9. Hektoen, L. and Perkins, C.F. 1909. Refractory subcutaneous abscesses caused by *Sporothrix schenckii*, a new pathogenic fungus. J. Exp. Med. 5:77-89.
10. Holubová-Jechová, V. 1980. Lignicolous and some other saprophytic Hyphomycetes from the USSR. I. Biologia (Tartu) 29:131-147.
11. Hoog, G.S. de. 1974. The genera *Blastobotrys, Sporothrix, Calcarisporium* and *Calcarisporiella* gen. nov. Stud. Mycol. 7:1-84.
12. Hoog, G.S. de. 1979. Taxonomic review of *Moniliella, Trichosporonoides* and *Hyalodendron.* Stud. Mycol.19:1-36.
13. Hoog, G.S. de and Constantinescu, O. 1981. A new species of *Sporothrix* from calf skin. Antonie van Leeuwenhoek 47:367-370.
14. Hoog, G.S. de, Rantio-Lehtimäki, A. H. and Smith, M. Th. 1985. *Blastobotrys, Sporothrix* and *Trichosporiella*: generic delimitation, new species, and a *Stephanoascus* teleomorph. Antonie van Leeuwenhoek 51:79-109.
15. Ingold, C.T. 1983. Basidiospore germination and conidium development in Dacrymcetales. Trans. Br. Mycol. Soc. 81:563-571.
16. Kowalski, T. and Butin, H. 1989. Taxonomie bekannter und neuer *Ceratocystis*-Arten an Eiche (*Quercus robur* L.). Phytopathol. Z. 124:236-248.
17. Kreisel, H. and Schauer, F. 1985. *Sporothrix nivea* sp. n. - ein Methanol und Kohlenwasserstoffe verwertender Pilz. J. Basic Microbiol. 25:653-661.
18. Kurata, Y. 1981. Chemical composition and immunological properties of glycoproteins of *Sporothrix* species. Mycopathologia 76:46-53.
19. Livingston, W.H. and Davidson, R. W. 1987. *Ophiostoma subannulatum*, a new fungal species pathogenic to grand fir roots. Mycologia 79:144-147.
20. Maekawa, N. 1987. A new species of the genus *Cerinomyces.* Can. J. Bot. 65:583-588.
21. Maekawa, N., Tsuneda, A. and Arita, I. 1987. *Ceratocystis* species occurring on the *Lentinus edodes* bedlogs. Rep. Tottori Mycol. Inst. 25:6-14.
22. Mathiesen, A. 1951. Einige neue *Ophiostoma*-Arten in Schweden. Svensk Bot. Tidskr. 45:203-232.
23. Matsushima, T. 1975. Icones microfungorum a Matsushima lectorum. Kobe, Japan. 209 pp.
24. Moore, R.T. 1987. Micromorphology of yeasts and yeast-like fungi and its taxonomic implications. Stud. Mycol 30:203-226.
25. Oberwinkler, F. 1989. *Ditiola haasii* sp. nov., eine neue Art der Dacrymcetales. Z. Mykol. 55:197-206.
26. Patton, M. and Marchant, R. 1978. A mathematical analysis of dolipore/parenthesome structure in Basidiomycetes. J. Gen. Microbiol. 109:335-349.
27. Przybyl, K. and Hoog, G.S. de. 1989. On the variability of *Ophiostoma piceae.* Antonie van Leeuwenhoek 55:177-188.
28. Samuels, G.J. and Müller, E. 1979. Life-history study of Brazilean Ascomycetes 5. Two new species of *Ophiostoma* and their *Sporothrix* anamorphs. Sydowia 31:169-179.
29. Sivanesan, A. and Sutton, B.C. 1985. Microfungi on *Xanthorrhoea.* Trans. Br. Mycol. Soc. 85:239-255.
30. Smith, M.Th. and Batenburg-van der Vegte, W.H. 1985. Ultrastructure of septa in *Blastobotrys* and *Sporothrix.* Antonie van Leeuwenhoek 51:121-128.
31. Smith, M.Th. and Batenburg-van der Vegte, W.H. 1986. Additional information on the ultrastructure in the genus *Sporothrix.* J. Gen. Appl. Microbiol. 32:549-552..
32. Suzuki, M. and Nakase, T. 1986. Heterogeneity of ubiquinone systems in the genus *Sporothrix.* J. Gen. Appl. Microbiol. 32:165-168.
33. Traquair, J.A., Shaw, L.A. and Jarvis, W.R. 1988. New species of *Stephanoascus* with *Sporothrix* anamorphs. Can. J. Bot. 66:926-933.
34. Travassos, L.R. and Lloyd, K.O. 1980. *Sporothrix schenckii* and related species of *Ceratocystis.* Microbiol. Rev. 44:683-721.
35. Tu, C.C. and Kimbrough, J.W. 1978. Systematics and phylogeny of fungi in the *Rhizoctonia* complex. Bot. Gaz. 139:454-466.
36. Upadhyay, H.P. 1981. A monograph of *Ceratocystis* and *Ceratocystiopsis.* University of Georgia Press, Athens, GA. 176 pp.
37. Upadhyay, H.P. and Kendrick, W.B. 1975. Prodromus for a revision of *Ceratocystis* (Microascales, Ascomycetes) and its conidial states. Mycologia 67:798-805.
38. Wang, C.J.K. 1979. Pleomorphic Fungi Imperfecti. Pages 81-91 in: The Whole Fungus, Vol. 1. B. Kendrick, ed. National Museum of Natural Science, Ottawa. 793 pp.
39. Webster, J. and Hawksworth, D.L. 1986. *Pyxidiophora spinulo-rostrata*, a new species with denticulate conidiophores from submerged twigs in South-West England. Trans. Br. Mycol. Soc. 87:77-79.
40. Weijman, A.C.M. and Hoog, G.S. de. 1975. On the subdivision of the genus *Ceratocystis.* Antonie van Leeuwenhoek 41:353-360.
41. Weijman, A.C.M. and Hoog, G.S. de. 1985. Carbohydrate patterns and taxonomy of *Sporothrix* and *Blastobotrys.* Antonie van Leeuwenhoek 51:111-120.
42. Yamada, Y. and Smith, M.Th. 1985. The coenzyme Q system in strains of species in the genera *Stephanoascus* and *Sporopachydermia.* Trans. Mycol. Soc. Jap. 26:247-251.

Chapter 7

THE ANAMORPH AS GENERIC DETERMINANT IN THE HOLOMORPH: THE *CHALARA* CONNECTION IN THE ASCOMYCETES, WITH SPECIAL REFERENCE TO THE OPHIOSTOMATOID FUNGI

T.R. NAG RAJ and W.B. KENDRICK

INTRODUCTION

Mycologists are vitally concerned with the relationships between the anamorphs and teleomorphs of fungal holomorphs. In most groups of Ascomycetes and Basidiomycetes, the classification of the holomorphs is based almost entirely on features of the teleomorph, with the anamorphs either unknown or peripheral to the taxonomic framework. There are, however, some interesting exceptions. Whetzel (38), finding the teleomorphs of the Sclerotiniaceae rather uniform, and the anamorphs interestingly diverse, based several genera within the family on the nature of the anamorph. Members of the holomorph genus *Botryotinia* have *Botrytis* anamorphs; those of *Monilinia* have *Monilia* anamorphs; those of *Streptotinia* have *Streptobotrys* anamorphs; and the apothecial ascomata of *Sclerotinia* arise from *Sclerotium* sclerotial anamorphs.

Two mycologists who studied the Ophiostomataceae followed a similar strategy. Münch (30) proposed the segregate genus *Endoconidiophora* for species of *Ceratocystis sensu lato* that have 'endoconidial', i.e. *Chalara*, anamorphs. Goidànich (10) segregated species with *Leptographium* anamorphs into *Grosmannia*. More recently, the use of the generic names *Endoconidiophora* and *Grossmania* has been abandoned, as the number of different anamorph-genera associated with the Ophiostomataceae rose to sixteen (37). An anamorph-based classification would obviously have led to chaos. Developmental and ultrastructural studies have resulted in some amalgamation of those anamorph-genera but we still recognize about eight anamorph-genera among ophiostomatalean anamorphs.

De Hoog (16) and de Hoog and Scheffer (17) enunciated new criteria for the genus *Ceratocystis sensu stricto* (see Samuels, this volume). These authors restricted *Ceratocystis* to species with *Chalara* anamorphs, that have no cellulose or

rhamnose in their cell walls, and are intolerant of cycloheximide. These fungi occur on a wide range of herbaceous and woody plants in tropical and temperate zones and are vectored principally by flies and sap-feeding insects, but to some extent by bark beetles as well. We accept this new concept, in which the anamorph, although diagnostic, does not bear the entire burden of taxonomic significance. Nevertheless, since the demise of *Grosmannia* and *Endoconidiophora*, we feel that the relationship between *Chalara* and the other anamorphs needs to be clarified.

In this paper, we will analyze the concept of *Chalara* from morphological and ontogenetic points of view, review the occurrence of *Chalara* anamorphs elsewhere in the Ascomycete spectrum and reconsider our support for the current delimitation of the holomorph genus *Ceratocystis*.

MORPHOLOGICAL VARIATION WITHIN *CHALARA*

We published a monograph of the anamorph-genus *Chalara*, in which we recognized 70 species (31). Many more species have since been added to the genus. In our monograph, we adopted a broad generic concept, which embraced the pleomorphic genera *Chalaropsis* and *Thielaviopsis*, both of which exhibited a *Chalara* morph as well as another associated synanamorph. All species had simple, solitary or aggregated, septate, hyaline or pigmented conidiophores terminating in a phialide (Fig. 1). The phialides could be ampulliform, lageniform, obclavate, urceolate or subcylindrical, but were always composed of a clearly differentiated venter and a long, more or less cylindrical collarette. The conidia were cylindrical, obclavate or ellipsoid, mostly hyaline and less frequently subhyaline or pale brown, unicellular or septate, with truncate or rounded ends and were formed in basipetal chains, arising from a fixed, deep-seated conidiogenous locus (Fig. 2I). Some species also produce intercalary or solitary and terminal, pigmented chlamydospores of blastic-phialidic, holoblastic or thallic-arthric origin (Fig. 2II-IV). These synanamorphs were regarded as of secondary importance, though in some cases they can be ascribed to recognizable anamorph-genera such as *Humicola* or *Trichocladium*.

The type species of *Chalara* is *C. fusidioides*,

a saprobe recorded from *Fragaria vesca, Pinus* sp., *Podocarpus hallii, Vitis* sp. and even on old perithecia of a species of *Mycosphaerella*. It is characterized by lageniform, subhyaline to pale brown, smooth-walled phialides with a globose or occasionally ellipsoidal venter with a long cylindrical collarette and cylindrical, unicellular, hyaline, smooth-walled conidia extruded in easily dispersed chains (Fig. 3A). Unfortunately, no teleomorph is known for this species.

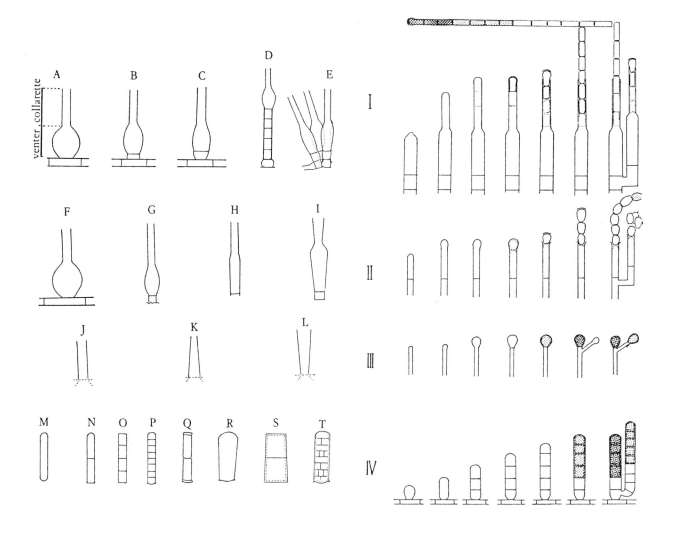

Fig. 1. Diagrammatic representation of the morphology of *Chalara* species. a - e. Phialophore types; f - i. Phialide types; j - l. Types of collarette; m - t. Types of conidia. Reproduced with permission from Nag Raj and Kendrick (31).

Fig. 2. Diagrammatic interpretation of conidiogenesis in *Chalara* species. I - Ring wall-building ontogeny; II & III - Replacement wall-building ontogeny; IV - Apical wall-building with ontogeny of all conidia integrated in the conidiogenous cells. Reproduced with permission from Nag Raj and Kendrick (31).

CONIDIUM DEVELOPMENT IN *CHALARA*

Developmental studies of a few species of *Chalara* have been published. Cole and Kendrick (7) recognized the following stages in conidium development in an early phase of growth in a culture of *Chalara paradoxa*: (A) simultaneous growth of outer wall of the conidiogenous cell and conversion of the protoplast; (B) basipetal differentiation of one to several conidia in the collarette; (C) cessation of apical growth and downward movement of the center of activity to a point at which an equilibrium was established between cytoplasmic conversion and cytoplasmic growth when the 'conidiogenous locus' assumes its final position; (D) enclosure of several physiologically independent conidia by the long collarette; (E) rupture of the outer wall at the apex of the conidiogenous cell to release conidia; (F) absence of any constriction or other morphological feature differentiating the deep-seated, fixed conidiogenous locus; and (G) absence of elongation of the conidiogenous cell after rupture of its apex.

Extending these studies to older cultures of *C. paradoxa*, Nag Raj and Kendrick (31) noted variations in these stages, in that the phialides and collarettes tend to be shorter; location of the conidiogenous locus is not as deep-seated; only a single conidium initial is enclosed in the collarette; and percurrent or sympodial proliferation of the conidiogenous cell occurs after its apex ruptures. In even older cultures, the conidiogenous cell may actually cease to be a phialide. A conidial initial is delimited at the swollen apex of the conidiogenous cell, then apical growth ceases; the apical wall of the conidiogenous cell becomes part of the conidium wall; and the conidium is delimited by a basal septum. Conidium development thus becomes holoblastic. Repeated development of new growing points beneath and to one side of successive terminal conidia results in sympodial proliferation of the conidiogenous cell, each proliferation culminating in the formation of a solitary, terminal, holoblastic conidium at a higher level. The fungus thus exhibits considerable plasticity in conidium development, initially producing conidia in phialides, then shifting in older cultures to holoblastic conidiogenesis. These stages of development are depicted diagrammatically in Fig. 2I-III. Similar developmental sequences were reported by Nag Raj and Kendrick (31) for *Ceratocystis radicicola*; by Hawes and Beckett (13) for *Ceratocystis adiposa*; and by Hawes and Beckett

(15), and Ingold (19) for *Thielaviopsis basicola* [more correctly *Chalara elegans*]. Hawes and Beckett (14) also provided more useful data at the ultrastructural level for *Ceratocystis adiposa*. Minter (27) provided a very plausible explanation of this unusual plasticity. He suggested that a life cycle that had evolved two separate anamorphs, perhaps originally for two different purposes, was now becoming shortened or condensed. This hypothesis had the advantage that it permitted the apparently aberrant conidiogenesis in such anamorphs to be explained in similar terms to those used for the great majority of conidial fungi.

Minter *et al.* (28,29) re-appraised available data on conidium development in hyphomycetous anamorphs and developed some new and rather basic concepts. We will apply their ideas to the case of *Chalara*. They recognized three types of wall building: **apical**, in which the organelles concentrated at the hyphal tip produce new wall by distal growth, resulting in the formation of a cylindrical hypha with the youngest wall material at the tip; **diffuse**, in which more widely distributed secretory organelles produce lateral growth by modification of the pre-existing wall, resulting in a swelling of the cylindrical hypha; and **ring**, in which the organelles are concentrated in a circle around the cell wall at some point below the tip, and produce new wall by proximal growth, forming a cylindrical hypha in which the youngest wall material is always at the base. Minter *et al.* (28,29) restrictively defined the term **conidium ontogeny** as the ways in which conidial cell walls are produced. Four other important steps were also recognized: **conidium delimitation** (the mode of formation of delimiting septa); **conidium secession** (the ways in which conidia become detached); **proliferation** (modification of the conidiogenous cells to produce more than one conidium or a new conidiogenous cell); and **regeneration** (the manner of replacement of a defunct conidiogenous cell). It was noted that these steps sometimes merge.

Two developmental patterns are now recognized in Hyphomycetes with phialidic conidiogenous cells and can be described as follows. In one group, exemplified by species of *Chalara*, the phialide is produced by the active, original, wall-building apex. When this apex stops growing, an extensive new, separate inner wall is quickly formed, lining the upper half of the phialide. The new inner wall, still totally enclosed by the original outer wall, contributes to the cell walls of the first conidia. Soon, retrogressive conidium delimitation occurs. A wall-building ring formed at the lowest part of the inner wall then adds continuously to it in an upward direction; this can be interpreted as the conidium ontogeny. The original outer wall of the conidiogenous cell ruptures close to the apex, leaving a small cap of wall material on the uppermost conidium. The influx of more cytoplasm and activity of the wall-building ring cause the chain of conidia to be pushed out of the cylindrical collarette formed by the original outer wall. The chain of conidia is held together by a continuous cylinder of wall material. After conidia leave the collarette, some conidial maturation may be observed in a few species. There is no periclinal thickening in the phialides and the conidiogenous cell appears to undergo no modification between production of successive conidia. The conidiogenous cells, therefore, can carry out repeated conidium ontogeny without any intervening proliferation. Presence of ring wall-building activity in a fungus can be recognized under the light microscope by the basipetal formation of true-chain conidia from a determinate conidiogenous cell.

By contrast, in the second group of phialidic Hyphomycetes, as exemplified by *Phialographium* and the phialidic anamorphs of the Hypocreaceae - *Fusarium, Cylindrocarpon, Cylindrocladium, Acremonium, Myrothecium, Tubercularia*, etc. - the conidiogenous cells, referred to as false- or no-chain phialides, produce conidia in gloeoid masses or in chains that are not held together by wall material. Conidiogenesis in this group can be explained by the following sequence of events. After the conidiogenous cells attain full size, a first conidium is formed by apical wall building and delimited by a septum. At this point the wall-building apex is lost, since it is no longer in the conidiogenous cell, and it is replaced by a new apex at the top of the conidiogenous cell. A second conidium is produced when the first secedes. This sequence of the loss and replacement of a wall-building apex is repeated each time a conidium is formed and secedes from the phialide. If secession occurs slightly below the open end of the collarette, new wall layers will be left just inside the collarette with the production of each new conidium, giving rise to the well known phenomenon of periclinal thickening.

According to Minter *et al.* (28), fungi with sympodial, annellidic and false-chain or no-chain phialidic proliferation form a group in which conidium development generally follows this pattern of replacement of successive wall-building apices. The common factor in this group of developmentally related fungi is that conidiogenous cells of all the members, if they are to produce more than one conidium, must proliferate between production of successive conidia. These authors also noted that no intergradation has been demonstrated between false-chain or no-chain phialides on the one hand, and true-chain phialides on the other; this is apparently an 'either-or' situation. There does, however, appear to be a continuum, with known intergrading examples, from false-chain or no-chain phialides, through annellidic (percurrently proliferating) conidiogenous cells, to sympodially proliferating conidiogenous cells.

Thus, it has been established that the phialides of *Chalara* are completely different from any of the other anamorphic manifestations found among the species of *Ophiostoma* or *Ceratocystiopsis*. On the one hand, we have a small group of species (*Ceratocystis s.str.*) that have true-chain phialides; on the other, we have a much larger group with members that never produce true-chain phialides, though they can exhibit several other kinds of conidiogenesis.

Of the 11 species of *Ceratocystis* listed by de Hoog (17), *C. major* and *C. variospora* were considered by Hunt (18) to be synonyms of *C. adiposa* and *C. fimbriata*, respectively. Nag Raj and Kendrick (31) endorsed Hunt's conclusions and also treated *C. musarum* as a synonym of *C. paradoxa*. This leaves us with eight species of *Ceratocystis* proper, all of which are characterized by the production of true-chain phialides (Fig. 3B-I), in some cases accompanied by a less common synanamorph (Fig. 3B, D, F, G) with enteroblastic, holoblastic or thallic development, depending on the growth-phase of the fungus and other factors.

In the developmental terminology of Minter *et al.* (28,29), conidiogenesis in these fungi can be described as follows. In the early phase of conidiation, conidium ontogeny involves ring wall-building, delimitation, schizolytic secession, lack of proliferation, and regeneration of the conidiogenous cell, if any, by percurrent growth. In a much later phase of conidiation characterized by the development of the synanamorph, conidium ontogeny proceeds by diffuse wall-building, delimitation, maturation, dehiscence or persistence, and sympodial proliferation.

In this group, as in some other fungi with true-chain phialides, factors such as increasing age or the accumulation of staling products in the medium switch the organism from ring wall-building to apical wall-building. Most of the available developmental data were derived from time-lapse studies of fungi growing on agar cultures. It is well known that cultures on artificial media are frequently unreliable for assessing some criteria of taxonomic value. Nag Raj and Kendrick (31) considered the non-phialidic synanamorphs of *Ceratocystis adiposa*, *C. fimbriata*, *C. paradoxa*, and *C. radicicola* to be less significant taxonomically than the *Chalara* anamorphs. We believe that a similar evaluation must be applied to the purportedly sympodial *Hyalorhinocladiella* synanamorph observed in *Ceratocystis autographa* by Upadhyay (36). In this respect, Nag Raj and Kendrick (31) were unable to confirm the method of conidiogenesis, although they observed the hyaline, thick-walled conidia of the synanamorph in the slides they studied. Gams and Holubová-Jechová (9) did not report the synanamorph in an isolate of *C. autographa* (CBS 670.75).

TELEOMORPH CONNECTIONS

Consideration of the *Chalara*-like anamorphs of Ascomycete genera other than *Ceratocystis* recalls an earlier comment made by the junior author: "It is now clear that there will be no natural classification [of conidial anamorphs] based on conidium ontogeny" (20). Anamorphs producing *Chalara*-like phialides with ring wall-building activity occur in dissonant holomorph genera of Ascomycetes, as will be detailed below.

Leotiales

The inoperculate Discomycete *Chlorociboria aeruginascens* grows on rotting wood and stains it green. It has a coelomycetous anamorph, *Dothiorina tulasnei* (8), which produces typical *Chalara*-like phialides (Fig. 3L).

Mention must also be made of two other Discomycetes. Though a genetic relationship could not be proved, Nag Raj and Kendrick (31) noted intimate and consistent association between the teleomorph of *Calycellina carolinensis* and the anamorphic fungus *Chaetochalara aspera*, and between the teleomorph of *Phaeoscypha cladii* and the anamorphic fungus *Chaetochalara cladii*. Kirk and Spooner (23) accepted Kendrick's (21) conclusion that there was little justification in retaining *Chaetochalara*, and published appropriate combinations in *Chalara* for the two anamorphs just mentioned.

Eurotiales

Cryptendoxyla hypophloia, which produces ring wall-building *Chalara*-like phialides (Fig. 3J) in cultures and is adapted for dispersal by arthropods, is characterized by non-ostiolate, often darkly pigmented ascomata, with cephalothecioid peridia, irregularly disposed asci, and hyaline or brown ascospores that lack germ pores.

Hypocreales ? Laboulbeniales ?

Species of *Pyxidiophora* must also be considered here. Members of the genus are coprophilous or saprobic on other substrates, or rarely mycoparasitic or entomogenous(see Blackwell *et al.*, this volume). According to Lundqvist (25), the characteristic features of the genus are: perithecia long-necked, hyaline to ochraceous, rarely partly brown, free or partly sunk in a soft, light-coloured stroma or subiculum; peridium membranaceous; asci, where observed, subclavate to ellipsoidal, 2-3-4(-8?) spored, rarely with a non-functional and non-amyloid apical ring; ascospores parallel to one another in the ascus, aggregating in a slimy mass at maturity at the ostiole, attenuated at the base, 0-4-septate at a late phase, usually with a gelatinized, swelling, smooth or verruculose wall, often with an apical, subapical or lateral brown body or with smaller pigmented spots or girdles. Anamorphs that could be described as *Chalara*-like have been reported for four species: *P. asterophora*, *P. arvernensis*, *P. grovei* and *P. trisporus* (25). In the case of *P. asterophora*, the connection between the teleomorph and the anamorph is assumed from the accounts of the fungus by Tulasne and Tulasne (35) and Brefeld and von Tavel (6), based on cultures of *Hypomyces asterophorus* and *Pyxidiophora nyctalidis* respectively. The illustrations published by these authors show the mycelium producing the perithecia intimately associated with *Chalara*-like phialides. However, lack of axenic culture techniques during the nineteenth century raised some questions. Were these authors dealing with pure cultures or was mycoparasitism involved? Brefeld's original material cannot be located and Lundqvist's account (25) of the anamorph does not appear to be based on study of lectotype material

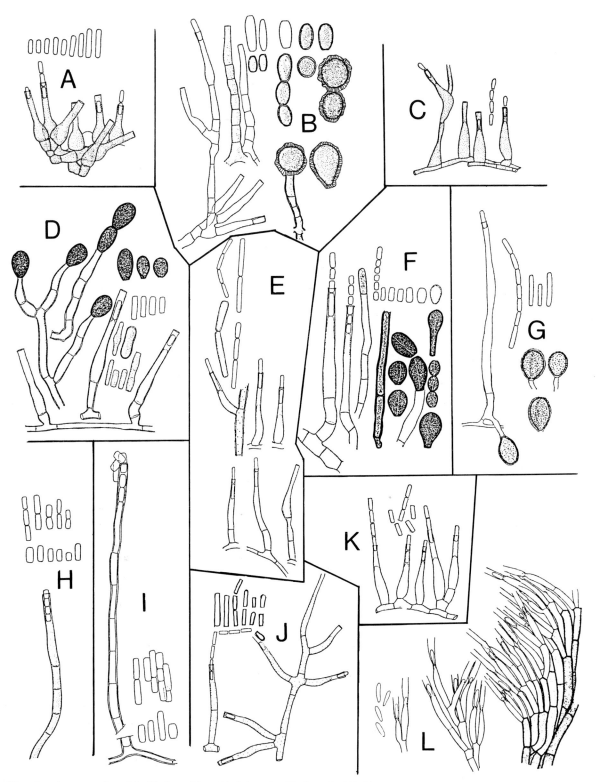

Fig. 3. Anamorphs with *Chalara*-like phialides. A. *Chalara fusidioides*; B. anamorph of *Ceratocystis adiposa*; C. anamorph of *C. autographa* ; D. anamorph of *C. fimbriata*; E. anamorph of *C. moniliformis*; F. *Chalara paradoxa* - anamorph of *Ceratocystis paradoxa*; G. anamorph of *C. radicicola*; H. *Chalara quercina* - anamorph of *Ceratocystis fagacearum*; I. *Chalara ungeri* - anamorph of *Ceratocystis coerulescens*; J. anamorph of *Cryptendoxyla hypophloia*; K. anamorph of *Ceratocystiopsis falcata* [≡ *Ceratocystis falcata*]; L. *Dothiorina tulasnei* anamorph of *Chlorociboria aeruginascens*. Reproduced with permission from Nag Raj and Kendrick (31).

of *P. asterophora* in PC. Therefore, we do not have reliable accounts of the anamorph of *P. asterophora*. In *P. arvernensis* and *P. grovei*, the supposedly *Chalara*-like anamorphs are indistinguishable from each other. In *P. trisporus*, a *Chalara*-like morph and another anamorph characterised by ventricose-rostrate conidiophores producing chains of subcylindrical to narrowly obovoid conidia (apical replacement wall-building activity?) were reported (25). However, in these three species of *Pyxidiophora*, the connections between the teleomorphs and the putative anamorphs still need to be established on a firmer basis.

The entomogenous species *Pyxidiophora kimbroughii* departs somewhat from the norm in the features of its anamorph. The ascospore develops directly into a non-mycelial *Thaxteriola* anamorph (5), its conidiogenesis being reminiscent of the "microendospore" formation reported in ascospores of *Ceratocystis ulmi* (32). The entire end cell of the ascospore acts as a phialide, with the attenuated tip breaking before conidium release. The range of anamorphs known in *Pyxidiophora* was extended by the addition of a yeast phase and anamorph phases with sympodial as well as percurrent proliferation of conidiogenous cells (3). *Pyxidiophora* ascospores can produce complex muriform thalli. This finding strongly supports the view that *Pyxidiophora* is closely related to the Laboulbeniales (4). Members of the Hypocreales do not produce yeast phases or anamorphs with annellidic percurrent proliferations. Blackwell and Malloch (3) were skeptical that *Pyxidiophora* belongs in the Ophiostomataceae.

Ophiostomataceae

Ceratocystiopsis, typified by *C. minuta*, is characterized by hyaline, mid- to dark-brown or black ascomata with a globose to subglobose base and a short neck that is usually tapered toward the apex; hyaline, 8-spored, evanescent asci; and falcate, hyaline ascospores surrounded by a gelatinous sheath. Most of the species have anamorphs that produce conidia by apical replacement wall-building activity. *Ceratocystiopsis falcata*, which has 1-septate, falcate ascospores, is atypical because it also has a *Chalara*-like anamorph (Fig. 3K), which was reported from single ascospore cultures by Rayner and Hudson (34). A more critical and comparative assessment of this species is needed. Considering the

conclusions already drawn in the present paper, we however, view the current generic disposition of this species with deep suspicion. *Chalara* anamorphs are not found in any other species of *Ceratocystiopsis*. We agree with de Hoog and Scheffer (17) that the general morphological features of *C. falcata* are suspiciously like those of *Pyxidiophora* rather than those of *Ceratocystiopsis*, but it may be accommodated equally well in *Ceratocystis*.

Parguey-Leduc (33) reported a *Chalara* anamorph for an Ascomycete tentatively placed in *Lulworthia*. The fungus that she isolated from *Bulgaria inquinans*, although having a superficial resemblance to *Lulworthia*, is unlikely to be a member of that genus because: (i) it is a laboratory isolate and clearly not a marine fungus; (ii) its ascospores are much shorter and narrower than those of species described in *Lulworthia sensu stricto* (24); (iii) its ascospores lack the mucus-filled terminal chambers characteristic of *Lulworthia*; and (iv) no anamorphs have been reported for other *Lulworthia* species. We strongly suspect that the affinities of this fungus lie with *Ceratocystiopsis*. Its ascospores are comparable in size and shape to those of *C. falcata*, which differ significantly only in the presence of septation. The asci of Parguey-Leduc's fungus are thin-walled and evanescent, like those of *Ceratocystiopsis*. The ascomata resemble those of *Ceratocystiopsis*. Finally, the anamorph of Parguey-Leduc's fungus closely resembles that of *C. falcata*.

Dothideales

Quasiconcha reticulata, a unique ascomycete from coniferous substrates (1), extends the spectrum of *Chalara*-like anamorph connections to the bitunicate ascomycetes. The teleomorph is characterized by clam-shaped hysterothecial ascomata with ridged walls, and brown, 2-celled, reticulate ascospores. Blackwell and Gilbertson (2) reported that single-ascospore isolates produced *Chalara*-like phialides with chains of unicellular conidia when grown on sterile pine twigs.

CONCLUSIONS

From the foregoing review, it is clear that although *Chalara*-like anamorphs occur in relatively few Ascomycetes, these belong to diverse taxonomic groups. Kendrick (22) wrote: "The expectation that there will be one anamorph per teleomorph is soon dispelled. It is equally clear that this concept breaks down when considered from either side. Anamorph-species of the anamorph-genus *Chrysosporium* are, pro tem, associated with representatives of no fewer than 17 ascomycetous genera and 1 basidiomycetous genus. Species of *Acremonium* are associated with 30 ascomycetous teleomorphs." Anamorphs with *Chalara*-like phialides can be added as another example of this phenomenon, being found associated with at least seven Ascomycete genera from at least five different orders. We note that the *Chalara*-like anamorph of 'Lulworthia' bulgariae appears to provide the best clue to the true affinities of the fungus.

This raises some interesting issues in terms of the evolution of ring wall-building phialides. Madelin (26) suggested that the phialide represents a unique line of evolution, "... and other kinds of conidiogenesis have evolved from it by varying kinds of breakdown in the precise regulatory mechanism required by a phialide ... the phialide may go back a long way - perhaps even to the time before ascomycetes and basidiomycetes evolved apart." Minter *et al.* (29), however, thought that those phialides with a succession of replacement wall-building apices and those phialides with wall-building rings evolved independently of each other. These authors also hypothesized that one of these patterns could be more recent than the other, because constant replacement of wall-building apices that have been lost seems primitive in comparison to the wall-building ring that does not require replacement. We are now prepared to go further than previous authors and suggest that even phialides as characteristic as those of *Chalara* have probably evolved several times in different groups of Ascomycetes and that they owe their similarities to convergent evolution rather than shared descent from a common ancestor. It is conceivable that a re-examination of these various anamorphs using ultrastructural or molecular techniques may reveal heterogeneity. At the light microscope level, on the other hand, the anamorphs are seen to produce unicellular, thin-walled conidia from simple *Chalara*-type phialides. We can see no way at present to segregate them from *Chalara sensu* Nag Raj and Kendrick (31). However, it does seem likely that the *Chalara* anamorphs of *Ceratocystis* species are of monophyletic origin.

In this review, although we cannot solve the problems inherent in the taxonomy of the Ophiostomataceae, we can support the conclusions of de Hoog (16), de Hoog and Scheffer (17) and Harrington (11,12). By downgrading the significance of the *Hyalorhinocladiella* synanamorph of *Ceratocystis autographa* as we did with the synanamorphs in *Chalaropsis* and *Thielaviopsis* (30), we can bring *C. autographa* into a coherent group with the other seven species of *Ceratocystis sensu stricto*. Similarly, we suggest removal of *Ceratocystiopsis falcata* with its *Chalara* anamorph from *Ceratocystiopsis*, pending a critical reappraisal of the species. In dealing with the group this way, some of the rough spots in its current taxonomic treatment are eliminated. In case this approach is found to be acceptable, the following key highlights our conclusions:

A. Conidiogenous cells *Chalara*-like phialides with wall-building rings   B
A. Conidiogenous cells with successive replacement wall-building apices; anamorphs false- or no-chain phialidic, annellidic or sympodial; teleomorphs with long or short necks, evanescent asci, and ascospores with or without mucilaginous sheaths *Ophiostoma/Ceratocystiopsis* (Ophiostomataceae)

B. Teleomorph a member of the Bitunicatae; ascomata clam-shaped hysterothecia with ridged walls; asci bitunicate, thin-walled at maturity; ascospores 2-celled, brown, reticulate
        Quasiconcha (Dothideales)
B. Teleomorph a member of the Unitunicatae   C

C. Teleomorph with apothecial ascomata   D
C. Teleomorph with perithecial or cleistothecial ascomata   E

D. Anamorph with stromatic, pycnidioid conidiomata and branched conidiophores; apothecial ascomata not setose; substrate stained green   *Chlorociboria* (Leotiales)
D. Anamorphs hyphomycetous; conidiophores mononematous, sterile setae present; substrate not stained   *Calycellina, Phaeoscypha* (Leotiales)

E. Teleomorphs with cleistothecial ascomata, peridia cephalothecioid, asci randomly disposed, ascospores hyaline or brown
        Cryptendoxyla (Eurotiales)
E. Teleomorphs with long-necked perithecial ascomata with a stroma or subiculum, peridium membranous, asci with or without a non-amyloid, non-functional apical ring; ascospores 2-3-4(-8?), attenuated at the base, 0-4-septate, with swollen,

gelatinized, smooth or rough wall, often with
pigmented spots or girdles
　　　Pyxidiophora(Hypocreales? Laboulbeniales?)
[Note: *Ceratocystiopsis falcata* may belong here]
E. Teleomorphs with long-necked perithecial
ascomata, asci evanescent, ascospores unicellular,
of at least 4 distinct shapes
　　　　　　　Ceratocystis (Ophiostomatales)
[Note: *Ceratocystiopsis falcata* may belong here]

LITERATURE CITED

1. Barr M.E. and Blackwell, M. 1980. A new genus of the Lophiaceae. Mycologia 72:1224-1227.

2. Blackwell, M. and Gilbertson, R.L. 1985. *Quasiconcha reticulata* and its anamorph from conifer roots. Mycologia 77:50-54.

3. Blackwell, M. and Malloch, D. 1989a. *Pyxidiophora*: life histories and arthropod associations of two species. Can. J. Bot. 47:779-789.

4. Blackwell, M. and Malloch, D. 1989b. *Pyxidiophora* (Pyxidiophoraceae): a link between the Laboulbeniales and hyphal ascomycetes. Mem. N. Y. Bot. Gard. 49:23-32.

5. Blackwell, M., Perry, T.J., Bridges, J.R. and Moser, J.C. 1986. A new species of *Pyxidiophora* and its *Thaxteriola* anamorph. Mycologia 78:605-612.

6. Brefeld, O. and von Tavel, F. 1891. Die Hemiasci und die Ascomyceten. Pages 1-7 in: Brefeld, O. Untersuchungen aus dem Gesammtgebiete der Mykologie 9. Leipzig, Germany. 156 pp.

7. Cole, G.T. and Kendrick, W.B. 1969. Conidium ontogeny in hyphomycetes. The phialides of *Phialophora, Penicillium* and *Ceratocystis*. Can. J. Bot. 47:779-789.

8. Dixon, J.R. 1975. *Chlorosplenium* and its segregates. II. The genera *Chlorociboria* and *Chlorencoelia*. Mycotaxon 1:193-237.

9. Gams, W. and Holubová-Jechová, V. 1976. *Chloridium* and some other dematiaceous hyphomycetes growing on decaying wood. Stud. Mycol. 13:1-99.

10. Goidànich, G. 1936. Il genere di Ascomiceti: "Grosmannia" G. Goid. Boll. Staz. Patol. Veg. Roma, n.s. 16:26-60.

11. Harrington, T.C. 1981. Cycloheximide sensitivity as a taxonomic character in *Ceratocystis*. Mycologia 72:1123-1129.

12. Harrington, T.C. 1987. New combinations in *Ophiostoma* of *Ceratocystis* spp. with *Leptographium* anamorphs. Mycotaxon 28:39-43.

13. Hawes, C.R. and Beckett, A. 1977a. Conidium ontogeny in the *Chalara* state of *Ceratocystis adiposa*. I. Light microscopy. Trans. Br. Mycol. Soc. 68:259-265.

14. Hawes, C.R. and Beckett, A. 1977b. Conidium ontogeny in the *Chalara* state of *Ceratocystis adiposa*. II. Electron microscopy. Trans. Br. Mycol. Soc. 68:267-276.

15. Hawes, C.R. and Beckett, A. 1977c. Conidium ontogeny in the *Thielaviopsis basicola*. Trans. Br. Mycol. Soc. 68:304-307.

16. Hoog, G.S. de. 1974. The genera *Blastobotrys, Sporothrix, Calcarisporium*, and *Calcarisporiella* gen. nov. Stud. Mycol. 7:1-84.

17. Hoog, G.S. de and Scheffer, R.J. 1984. *Ceratocystis* versus *Ophiostoma*: a reappraisal. Mycologia 76, 292-299.

18. Hunt, J. 1956. Taxonomy of the genus *Ceratocystis*. Lloydia 19:1-58.

19. Ingold, C.T. 1981. The first-formed phialoconidium of *Thielaviopsis basicola*. Trans. Br. Mycol. Soc. 76:517-519.

20. Kendrick, B. 1979. Foreword. Pages ix-x in: Patterns of development in conidial fungi. G.T. Cole and R.A. Samson, eds. Pitman, London. 190 pp.

21. Kendrick, B. 1980. The generic concept in Hyphomycetes - a reappraisal. Mycotaxon 11:339-364.

22. Kendrick, B. 1981. The systematics of Hyphomycetes. Pages 21-42 in: Biology of conidial fungi. Volume 1. G.T. Cole and W.B. Kendrick, eds. Academic Press, New York. 486 pp.

23. Kirk, P.W. and Spooner, B.M. 1984. An account of the fungi of Arran, Gigha and Kintyre. Kew Bull. 38:503-597.

24. Kohlmeyer, J. and Kohlmeyer, E. 1979. Marine Mycology. New York, Academic Press. 690 pp.

25. Lundqvist, N. 1980. On the genus *Pyxidiophora sensu lato* (Pyrenomycetes). Bot. Notiser 133:21-144.

26. Madelin, M.F. 1979. An appraisal of the taxonomic significance of some different modes of producing blastic conidia. Pages 63-80 in: The Whole Fungus, Vol. 1. B. Kendrick, ed. National Museum of Natural Sciences, Ottawa. 793 pp.

27. Minter, D.W. 1987. The significance of conidiogenesis in pleoanamorphy. Pages 241-262 in: Pleomorphic Fungi. J. Sugiyama, ed. Elsevier, Tokyo, Kodansha and Amsterdam. 325 pp.

28. Minter, D.W., Kirk, P.M. and Sutton, B.C. 1982. Holoblastic phialides. Trans. Br. Mycol. Soc. 79:75-93.

29. Minter, D.W., Kirk, P.M. and Sutton, B.C. 1983. Thallic phialides. Trans. Br. Mycol. Soc. 80:39-66.

30. Münch, E. 1907. Die Blaufäule des Nadelholzes. Naturw. Z. Forst. Landw. 5:531-573.

31. Nag Raj, T.R. and Kendrick, B. 1975. A monograph of *Chalara* and allied genera. Wilfrid Laurier University Press, Waterloo. 200 pp.

32. Ouellette, G.B. and Gagnon, C. 1960. Formation of microendospores in *Ceratocystis ulmi* (Buisman) C. Moreau. Can. J. Bot. 38:235-241.

33. Parguey-Leduc, A. 1967. Recherches sur l'ontogénie et l'anatomie comparée des ascocarpes des pyrénomycètes ascoloculaires. Ann. Sci. Nat., Bot. & Biol. Vég., 12 Sér., 8:1-110.

34. Rayner, A.D.M. and Hudson, H.J. 1977. *Ceratocystis falcata* and its conidial state. Trans. Br. Mycol. Soc. 68:315-316.

35. Tulasne, L.R. and Tulasne, C. 1860. De quelques Sphéries fongicoles à propos d'un mémoire de M. Antoine de Bary sur les *Nyctalis*. Ann. Sci. Nat. Bot. & Biol. Vég., 4 Sér., 13:17-19.

36. Upadhyay, H.P. 1981. A monograph of *Ceratocystis* and *Ceratocystiopsis*. University of Georgia Press. Athens, GA. 176 pp.

37. Upadhyay, H.P. and Kendrick, W.B. 1975. Prodromus for a revision of *Ceratocystis* (Microascales, Ascomycetes) and its conidial states. Mycologia 67:798-805.

38.   Whetzel, H.H. 1945. A synopsis of the genera and species of the Sclerotiniaceae, a family of stromatic inoperculate discomycetes. Mycologia 37:648-714.

Chapter 8

RELATIONSHIPS BETWEEN THE YEASTS WITH HAT-SHAPED ASCOSPORES AND THE OPHIOSTOMATOID FUNGI

W.B. KENDRICK, J.P. VAN DER WALT and M.J. WINGFIELD

HISTORICAL REVIEW

The possibility of relationships between certain groups of yeasts and filamentous fungi has been proposed and refuted several times. In order to place the question in proper perspective, we must give a historical review.

Nannfeldt (14) divided the Euascomycetes into three major groups: the Plectascales, Ascohymeniales and Ascoloculares. He characterized the Plectascales (which embraced the Ophiostomataceae, 'Aspergillaceae,' Gymnoascaceae and Chaetomiaceae) as having free ascogonia and antheridia that become surrounded by somatic hyphae that form either a loose weft within which asci are irregularly disposed, or a firm peridium (with or without an ostiole) that encloses scattered asci. He believed that if the centrum produced globose, scattered, deliquescent (i.e. non-shooting) asci, the fungus did not belong in the 'Pyrenomycetes' - even if the ascoma was ostiolate[3]. He made no mention of yeasts in this context, so we must assume that he did not contemplate any relationships of yeasts with the Ophiostomatoid fungi.

Cain (6), however, doubted that the 'Plectascales/Plectomycetes' was a natural grouping, and suggested that the shooting mechanism of the ascus had probably been lost many times in different groups. Malloch (13) agreed that the 'Plectomycetes,' the cleistothecial, or non-ascospore-shooting Ascomycetes, are heterogeneous and suggested that various lines had been derived independently from the bitunicate ascomycetes (Pleosporales) (members of Nannfeldt's Ascoloculares), and the unitunicate ascomycetes (Diaporthales, Hypocreales and Pezizales) (members of Nannfeldt's Ascohymeniales). Malloch thought that the Onygenaceae (in which he included the Gymnoascaceae) had evolved from the Pezizales, and the Endomycetaceae from the Diaporthales.

A rather revolutionary proposal, stating that several yeast-like genera that form asci on specialized individual hyphae called ascophores (e.g. *Ambrosiozyma*, *Cephaloascus*, *Botryoascus* and *Hormoascus*) could be related to the Ophiostomataceae, was first made by von Arx (1).

Following this line of reasoning, Redhead and Malloch (16) redefined the Endomycetaceae to include not only the unicellular 'yeasts,' but some fungi with ascophores (specialized hyphae bearing asci individually or in chains) and even some with ascomata. They restricted the family to genera in which at least some of the species had galeate or hat-shaped ascospores, or possessed other features indicating relationship to *Ceratocystis*, which they regarded as a 'central' genus. They included the following genera: *Ambrosiozyma*, *Amorphotheca*, *Ascoidea*, *Botryoascus*, *Cephaloascus*, *Ceratocystiopsis*, *Ceratocystis*, *Endomyces*, *Europhium*, *Hansenula*, *Hormoascus*, *Pachysolen*, *Ophiostoma*, *Phialoascus* and *Stephanoascus*. Redhead and Malloch (16) suggested that the hat-shaped ascospore represented a 'highly evolved cell type' requiring for its formation 'a carefully regulated series of gene expressions and considerable energy input.' They considered it unlikely that spores of this shape had evolved more than once. (We note, however, that they did not include in the Endomycetaceae the yeast genera *Saccharomycodes*, *Hanseniospora* and *Dekkera*, all of which have galeate or hat-shaped meiospores).

All genera discussed by Redhead and Malloch (16) also had other characteristics in common, including insect vectors, growth on plant exudates, blastic (never thallic-arthric) anamorphs and subglobose to short-clavate asci without croziers. Redhead and Malloch (16) synonymized the Amorphothecaceae, Ascoideaceae, Hansenulaceae, and Ophiostomataceae with the revised concept of

---

[3]We agree with this conclusion: it is inappropriate to term the ascomata of any of these fungi 'perithecia.' They require a new name that reflects the important differences in function and in evolutionary direction between them and the perithecial fungi that shoot their spores. The ecological differences are just as significant as those that exist between the epigeous and hypogeous basidiomycetes.

the Endomycetaceae.

Benny and Kimbrough (3) rejected the hypotheses of Redhead and Malloch (16) because these were based largely on morphology as seen through the light microscope and had not made use of all available developmental, ultrastructural and chemical evidence. Benny and Kimbrough began with a Nannfeldtian stance, placing emphasis on centrum development. They recognized six orders in the 'Plectomycetes', separated by different centrums and noted that in *Ceratocystis* the asci are initiated by a basal hymenium (15), although asci later become free, irregularly arranged, and deliquescent.

They defined the Ophiostomatales as having 'ascocarps ostiolate or non-ostiolate, globose, pyriform or irregular, sometimes with an elongate beak, dark, carbonaceous, or rarely light coloured and fleshy; asci solitary or catenulate, globose or broadly ellipsoid, irregularly disposed, eight spored, deliquescent; ascospores striate, laterally ridged or with a gelatinous sheath, without germination pores, non-dextrinoid; anamorphs variable, consisting of phialoconidia, blastoconidia, annelloconidia, or sympoduloconidia; mostly cellulosic'. They recognized within the Ophiostomatales only one family, Ophiostomataceae, with four genera: *Sphaeronaemella*, *Ceratocystiopsis*, *Ceratocystis* and *Ophiostoma*.

Septal Ultrastructure

Addressing the supposed 'yeast connection,' Benny and Kimbrough (3) pointed out that at the ultrastructural level, no fewer than four kinds of septal structure are known for filamentous yeasts. Septal features are regarded widely as very conservative characteristics that may be used to establish the affiliations of particular fungi with major, independent lines of evolution at the level of the Phylum or Division.

The following kinds of perforate septa have been observed by transmission electron microscopy in the filamentous ascomycetous yeasts: (a) Septa with numerous plasmadesmal canals (18) or micropores (plasmadesmata) as observed in *Botryoascus synnaedendrus* (5,10), *Endomyces fibuliger* (10,17), *Saccharomycopsis capsularis* (7,10) and *Dipodascus* spp. (11). Similar septa are found among the Mucorales and Chytridiomycetes; (b) Septa with a single, usually centrally located plasmadesmal canal, or so-called closure line, as observed in *Pichia beckiae*, *Hyphopichia burtonii* and *Yarrowia lipolytica*, (10); (c) Centrally thickened septa with a plugged

central pore, the apertures of which are occluded by an electron dense mass (but which lack the parenthosomes of the basidiomycetous doliopore), characteristic of the genera *Ambrosiozyma* and *Hormoascus* (2,9,10,19). Whether or not the electron-dense occluding masses represent homologues of Woronin bodies has not been assessed; (d) Simple porate septa lacking Woronin bodies, as observed in *Dipodascopsis uninucleata* (11) and *Cephaloascus albidus* (2,12).

Benny and Kimbrough (3) excluded all genera lacking type (d) septa from the Ophiostomataceae. They also excluded *Cephaloascus* on the grounds that its wall chemistry (another presumably highly conserved character) differs from that of the Ophiostomataceae *sensu stricto*. However, the possibility that *Cephaloascus* might be variable in terms of its septal ultrastructure cannot be excluded. Besson (4), in fact, reported the porate septa of *Cephaloascus fragrans* to be associated with Woronin bodies.

In a later re-evaluation of the Ascomycotina on the basis of septal ultrastructure, von Arx and van der Walt (2) came to similar conclusions, essentially defining the class Ascomycetes as having septa with Woronin bodies. However, von Arx and van der Walt (2) assigned *Cephaloascus*, *Ambrosiozyma* and *Hormoascus* to the family Cephaloascaceae in the order Ophiostomatales.

Thus it appears that Benny and Kimbrough (3) essentially negated the thesis of Redhead and Malloch (16) and returned to a more conservative concept of the Ophiostomataceae, while von Arx and van der Walt (2) had a broader concept of this group.

It is apparent that taxonomists used all the available information without being able to reach a consensus. Some linked yeast-like taxa with hat-shaped ascospores to the Ophiostomatales; others just as clearly excluded them. It was time for an infusion of new taxonomic information.

Ascospore Development

Recent ultrastructural studies (20,21; Van Wyk, Wingfield and Van Wyk, this volume) have demonstrated that ophiostomatoid fungi producing the so-called 'hat-shaped' or galeate ascospores are not nearly as uniform as has been generally assumed. Specifically, although these authors have so far investigated relatively few species, they have found important differences in three areas. First, there are at least three significantly different patterns of centrum development. Second, the developing ascospores are oriented towards each other in at least two different ways within the ascus. Third, there are at least two morphologically different kinds of 'hat-shaped' ascospores.

CONCLUSIONS

The more we examine genera usually placed in the Ophiostomataceae *sensu stricto*, especially *Ceratocystis* and *Ophiostoma*, the more we come to believe that they are not closely related, and that their similarities are probably the result of convergent evolution that occurred as they adopted similar habitats and methods of dispersal. We suspect that the ophiostomatoid form (dispersed by arthropods) has evolved more than once from the ascohymenial condition with sporeshooting asci and wind dispersed ascospores. This evolution has led to a loss of the spore-shooting mechanism and the development of several features facilitating insect vector dispersal, especially direct inoculation into suitable substrates, as occurs when the vectors are bark beetles and, to a lesser extent, flies.

The evolutionary process of morphological simplification and reduction involved in the abandonment of spore-shooting has presumably continued, in some cases, to its logical conclusion, the complete loss of the ascoma. In certain habitats, a complete ascoma is no longer necessary (such as when the organism grows in plant or animal exudates and can be dispersed by rain or by opportunistic vectors). There is little chance that the ascoma, once lost, will reappear; once an organism has given up the ability to make an extensive, branched mycelium, it has also concomitantly lost the ability to accumulate, then concentrate in one spot, the kind of energy needed to construct an ascoma. Finally, once a major feature has been lost, it is mathematically extremely improbable that it will re-evolve in the same organism with a form and function close to that of its original incarnation.

We believe that members of the several evolutionary series leading from filamentous Ascomycetes to unicellular yeasts (and possibly in the reverse direction, as certain yeasts re-evolve some form of hyphal structure) will be found to be distributed widely across the Ascomycete spectrum: in the 'Ascohymeniales,' the 'Plectomycetes,' and the filamentous and unicellular yeasts. However, it is still often impossible to be specific concerning the relationships between Ascomycetes that produce ascomata and yeasts that do not.

We note that at no point did von Arx give a rigorous definition of 'yeasts' because he believed, as we do, that they are evolutionarily heterogeneous - yeasts undoubtedly include representatives of many different fungal lineages. Kendrick (8) noted that yeasts or yeast-like fungi are found, or yeast-like morphology can be induced, in members of no fewer than 14 orders representing all three major groups of true fungi. It is frustrating, yet perhaps also intriguing, to conclude by suggesting that there may indeed be a true phylogenetic relationship between the Ophiostomatales and certain yeasts, (e.g. *Ambrosiozyma* and *Hormoascus*) but that we cannot as yet indicate the taxa involved with certainty.

LITERATURE CITED

1. Arx, J.A. von. 1974 pp. 3-4 in Centraalbureau voor Schimmelcultures Progress Report 1973. Verh. Kon. Ned. Acad. Wet. Afd. Natuurkd., Reeks 2, 63:1-20.

2. Arx, J.A. von. and van der Walt, J.P. 1986. Are yeast cells of the Endomycetales homologues of conidia of Eurotiales? Persoonia 13:161-167.

3. Benny, G.L. and Kimbrough, J.W. 1980. A synopsis of the orders and families of Plectomycetes with keys to genera. Mycotaxon 12:1-91.

4. Besson, M. 1967. La fructification d' *Ascocybe grovesii* Wells (= *Cephaloascus fragrans* Hanawa). Bull. Mens. Soc. Linn. Lyon 36:230-233.

5. Besson, M. and Pignal, M.C. 1972. Ultrastructure des septum mycéliens de deux levures: *Pichia cicatricosa* et *Pichia synnaedendra*. Bull. Mens. Soc. Linn. Lyon 41:111-114

6. Cain, R.F. 1956. Studies of coprophilous ascomycetes. II. *Phaeotrichum*, a new cleistocarpous genus in a new family, and its relationships. Can. J. Bot. 34:675-687.

7. Kwawakami, N. and Nehira, T. 1958. Electron microscopy of fungi. VI Sporulation and germination of *Endomycopsis capsularis*. Trans. Mycol. Soc. Japan 1(9):3-5

8. Kendrick, B. 1987. Yeasts and yeast-like fungi - new concepts and new techniques. Stud. Mycol. 30:479-486.

9. Kreger-van Rij, N.J.W. and Veenhuis, M. 1969. Septal pores in *Endomycopsis platypodis* and *Endomycopsis monospora*. J. Gen. Microbiol. 57:91-96.

10. Kreger-van Rij, N.J.W. and Veenhuis, M. 1973. Electron microscopy of septa in ascomycetous yeasts. Antonie van Leeuwenhoek 30:481-490.

11. Kreger-van Rij, N.J.W. and Veenhuis, M. 1974. Spores and septa in the genus *Dipodascus*. Can. J. Bot. 52:1335-1338.

12. Kurtzman, C.P. 1977. *Cephaloascus albidus*, a new heterothallic yeast-like fungus. Mycologia 69:547-555.

13. Malloch, D. 1979. Plectomycetes and their anamorphs. pp. 153-162 in: The Whole Fungus, Vol. 1. W.B. Kendrick, ed. National Museum of Natural Sciences, Ottawa. 793 pp.

14. Nannfeldt, J.A. 1932. Studien über die

Morphologie und Systematik der lichenisierten inoperculaten Discomyceten. Nova Acta Reg. Soc. Sci. Upsal., Ser. 4, 8:1-368.

15. Parguey-Leduc, A. 1977. Les asques des pyrenomycetes. Rev. Mycol. (Paris) 41:281-338.

16. Redhead, S.A and Malloch, D.W. 1977. The Endomycetaceae: new concepts, new taxa. Can. J. Bot. 55:1701-1711.

17. Takada, H. and Yagi, T. 1964. Elektronoptische untersuchungen und *Endomycopsis fibuliger* auf festen nährboden. Protoplasma 59:494-505.

18. Tsuneda, A. and Murakami, S. 1989. Sporogenesis and septum schizolysis in *Dipodascus aggregatus*. Can. J. Bot. 67:2150-2153.

19. Van der Walt, J.P. and Arx, J.A. von. 1985. The septal ultrastructure of *Hormoascus ambrosiae* and the emendation of the genus *Hormoascus*. Syst. Appl. Microbiol. 6:90-92.

20. Van Wyk, P.W.J., Wingfield, M.J. and Van Wyk, P.S. 1991a. Ascospore development in *Ceratocystis moniliformis*. Mycol. Res. 95:96-103.

21. Van Wyk, P.W.J. and Wingfield, M.J. 1991b. Ultrastructure of ascosporogenesis in *Ophiostoma davidsonii*. Mycol. Res. 95:725-730

PART II

NEW TAXONOMIC CRITERIA

Chapter 9

THE GENETIC SYSTEM AS A FUNGAL TAXONOMIC TOOL: GENE FLOW, MOLECULAR VARIATION AND SIBLING SPECIES IN THE 'OPHIOSTOMA PICEAE - OPHIOSTOMA ULMI' COMPLEX AND ITS TAXONOMIC AND ECOLOGICAL SIGNIFICANCE

C.M. BRASIER

INTRODUCTION

It is axiomatic that 'species' are genetic entities. However, as with most organisms, the early species concept in the fungi was, for historical and practical reasons, morphological rather than genetical. The genetical basis of species is now established in the modern 'biological species' concept, which emphasizes the role of interbreeding populations separated from similar populations by reproductive isolation [e.g. Dobzhansky (30); or Grant (35)]. In view of the relatively few useful morphological features in some fungal groups, the rapid advances in evolutionary theory and the comparatively early evidence of reproductively isolated subunits within morphological species of Basidiomycetes, it is surprising that the morphological species has remained virtually the only accepted fungal species concept.

It is partly because the fungi have a comparatively simple structure that their 'species' may not always show taxonomically useful morphological differences. Whether or not these have accumulated may depend upon the time since the speciation event and the nature of the habitat or niche. Recently evolved species or closely related species occupying similar niches may exhibit few morphological differences, yet be reproductively isolated (14). Such 'sibling species' are being increasingly discovered in the fungi (14, 27). Until recently, they received little formal taxonomic recognition, even though it may be these units that the ecologist, pathologist or technologist needs to distinguish for communication purposes.

While the biological or sibling species have already defined themselves, we as practising mycologists seem to face a problem in identifying them for ourselves. In reality, we have long had at our disposal a range of suitable biometrical, population and genetical techniques to identify biological species, which are now being enhanced by modern molecular methods. This paper examines the genetic system as a means of identifying population units below the morphological species level in two classic taxa within the Ophiostomataceae, *Ophiostoma piceae* and *Ophiostoma ulmi*. The wider taxonomic and ecological significance of the units identified is discussed.

THE GENETICAL AND MOLECULAR TOOLS

Making a genetical assessment of a traditional morphological species amounts to assessing its normal range of variation for continuous and discontinuous characters including cultural, physiological and molecular characters (ideally using freshly collected population samples). Evident clusters of characters or population units are then identified and the potential for gene flow between units is assessed.

In nature, gene flow between fungal populations may be restricted by geographical distance and by habitat isolation; by behavioural and genetic isolating mechanisms operating via sexual mating, somatic hyphal fusion and chromosomal systems; and by poor hybrid vigour (13,26). In the laboratory, the sexual and somatic hyphal fusion systems can sometimes be directly manipulated to analyze the outcrossing potential between fungal individuals from the same or different populations. Hybrid vigour can be examined by comparing the phenotypes of progenies of controlled crosses with that of their parents. The extent of gene flow between population samples may also be estimated from the extent of their shared patterns of diversity or polymorphism in proteins, enzymes, DNA and RNA and from their comparative chromosome number and structure.

Vegetative incompatibility

Among the known gene-flow regulating mechanisms in *Ophiostoma* is the so-called vegetative or somatic incompatibility system. This 'vc' system has been well characterized in *O. ulmi* [Fig. 1a, b; (10,44)]. A similar system occurs in *O. piceae* but is less well characterized (Fig. 1d; C.M.Brasier and

T.M.Stephens, unpublished). The vc system restricts viable hyphal fusion between adjacent mycelia of different genotypes or genets[1], and thereby restricts lateral nuclear and cytoplasmic exchange and the ability of a fungus to form heterokaryons and heteroplasmons (10). Such systems are likely to occur in the majority of outcrossing Ascomycetes, including most heterothallic *Ceratocystis* and *Ophiostoma* species.

In *O. ulmi*, and by analogy in *O. piceae*, the vc system is thought to be central to the social organization of a local population. It is a multigenic bi- or multiallelic system capable of generating large numbers of unique vegetative compatibility types. Most isolates collected from nature are of a different vc type; at the local population level, the fungus typically exists as a genetic mosaic comprised of many different vc types (Fig. 2). Within this mosaic, the vc system is believed to function (i) in maintaining the territorial integrity of individual genotypes or genets; (ii) by restricting of the spread of mycoviruses or other deleterious cytoplasmic agents between genets; (iii) by promoting sexual outcrossing between unrelated genets (10,11,15).

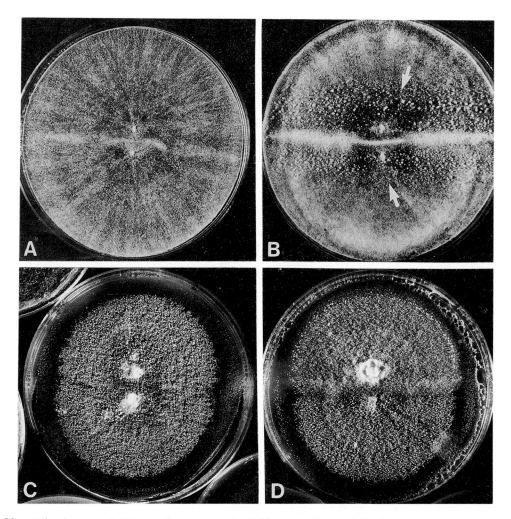

Fig. 1. Vegetative incompatibility reaction patterns in *Ophiostoma ulmi* and *O. piceae*. A, a compatible and B, an incompatible or 'wide' reaction in *O. ulmi* (NAN aggressive subgroup) on elm sapwood agar. Note the lack of a clear reaction in the compatible pairing and the diffuse mycelial barrage and associated synnemeta (arrowed) that characterize an incompatible reaction (see ref.10 for further details). C, a compatible and D, an incompatible reaction in *O. piceae* (OPC form) on oatmeal agar (C.M. Brasier and T.M. Stephens, previously unpublished).

[1]Genet: a genetically discrete unit or assemblage. See reference 23.

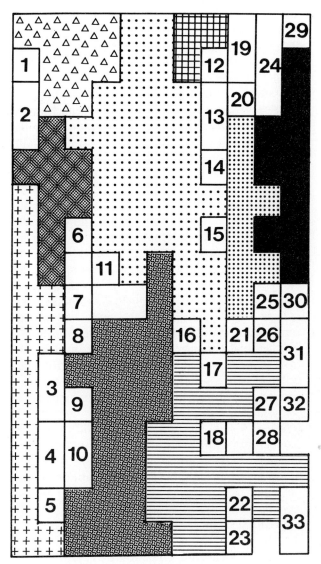

Fig. 2. Mosaic arrangement of *Ophiostoma ulmi* genotypes in inner elm bark. Each shaded or numbered area represents a distinct vc type; 39 different vc types were present. Unshaded areas represent an absence of *O. ulmi*. The smallest shaded area corresponds to 1cm². (Reproduced with permission from 56.)

Despite its ecological importance and its value in the assessment of diversity in population samples (16,44,56), vegetative incompatibility has been most useful for discerning genetic differences between individuals in *O. ulmi* and *O. piceae* rather than for the discrimination of major population subgroups. While the vc system does not, therefore, need to be considered further in the present paper, in largely non-outcrossing fungi, or in asexual fungi, the vegetative incompatibility system has become a

primary mechanism of reproductive isolation between evolutionary divergent populations. Examples include the analogous heterokaryon compatibility groups in the homothallic *Aspergillus nidulans* (29) and the complementation groups that occur in certain *Fusarium* and *Verticillium* species (e.g. 31,48,49). Also, mechanisms analogous to vegetative compatibility systems often maintain reproductive isolation between biological species in the somatogamous basidiomycetes, as for example in the rejection responses that promote isolation between paired homokaryons of different biological species in *Armillaria* (40).

The manipulation of the sexual mating system, the assessment of progeny vigour, and the study of protein and DNA polymorphisms have all contributed to the identification of sub-populations within the morphospecies *O. ulmi* and *O. piceae*. The use of these approaches will now be considered, beginning with *O. piceae*. Details of the molecular methods will not be presented because these are widely available in the literature.

SUBGROUPS WITHIN *OPHIOSTOMA PICEAE*

As currently understood, *O. piceae* is a ubiquitous sapstain fungus and a weak bark pathogen on a wide range of coniferous and hardwood trees. It is often closely associated with bark beetles that breed in trees weakened by stress or disease. It also often colonizes bark and wood surfaces following mechanical injury.

The species was described by Münch (45) as *Ceratostomella piceae*, based on material collected from spruce and fir. Georgevitch (33) later described a morphologically similar fungus, *Ceratostomella quercus*, from oak, while Loos (42) described another similar fungus, *Ophiostoma fagi*, from beech. These species are widely considered synonyms of *O. piceae* (e.g. 38,41,47,57). Another similar fungus described from oak is *O. roboris* (32). *O. roboris* has been implicated by Romanian and Soviet authors in the widespread decline of oak that has occurred in the Soviet Union and eastern Europe since the turn of the century (32, 46). However, the distinction between this species and *O. piceae* is also in doubt (34,21,41,47).

In my laboratory, gene flow between *O. piceae* isolates from different woody hosts is being assessed via the sexual mating system. *O. piceae* is classically heterothallic. Indeed heterothallism in *O. ulmi* and *O. piceae* was demonstrated as long ago as 1932 and 1933 respectively by the perceptive young Dutch

	1	2	5	7	3	4	6	8
1	0	−	−	−	+	+	+	+
2	−	0	−	−	+	+	+	+
5	−	−	0	−	+	+	+	+
7	−	−	−	0	+	+	+	+
3	+	+	+	+	0	−	−	−
4	+	+	+	+	−	0	−	−
6	+	+	+	+	−	−	0	−
8	+	+	+	+	−	−	−	0

Fig. 3. The separation of eight isolates of *Ophiostoma piceae* into two mating types. +, perithecia formed in a pairing; −, or o, no perithecia formed. From Buisman (25).

mycologist, Christina Buisman. Buisman (25) showed that *O. piceae* had two mating types which she termed + and − (Fig. 3).

In the present paper these will be called the A and B-types, consistent with the better characterized system now used in *O. ulmi* (see below). Perithecia are formed in *O. piceae* when isolates of the A and B-types are paired, and not in A-type x A-type or B-type x B-type pairings. (**Note**, partially to fully developed but sterile perithecia may sometimes be formed in felty-white mycelial patches developing in single cultures of *O. piceae*, i.e. in cultures of a single mating type; and fertile perithecia will form in cultures that are mixtures of the A and B mating types).

In 1975, a study was conducted by the author on perithecia of *O. piceae* developing on oak logs imported into Britain from Yugoslavia. Single ascospore colonies from individual perithecia segregated in a 1:1 ratio of A to B-mating types.

This showed, just as in *O. ulmi* (10), that mating type in *O. piceae* is controlled by two alleles at a single locus. In further tests, these Yugoslavian isolates were also shown to be fully interfertile, and hence conspecific with, either A or B-type isolates of *O. piceae* from oak in Britain, producing normal perithecia, plentiful ascospores and normal ascospore progeny (Brasier, cited in 34).

This study has recently been extended by gathering *O. piceae* isolates from hardwoods (oak, elm and beech) and conifers (spruce and pine) from

Britain, other European countries, and central Asia, and a single isolate of *O. roboris* from oak in Azerbaijan, USSR. All these isolates (apart from any degenerate white 'cottony to felty' isolates) fell within the broad, rather variable range of colony types shown in Fig. 4. Indeed, individual hardwood or conifer isolates often exhibit a similar colony phenotype. When paired together, the hardwood isolates were either of the A or B- mating types and were interfertile in all A x B-type combinations. The *O. roboris* isolate from Azerbaijan corresponded to a B-type, being interfertile with all the hardwood A-types. This isolate is therefore conspecific with the *O. piceae* hardwood group (21,22).

Similarly, when paired together, the conifer isolates also fell into A and B-types and were fertile in all A x B-type combinations. However, an important phenomenon was revealed when the hardwood and conifer isolates were paired together. No perithecia were obtained in any hardwood x conifer A x B-type or B x A-type combination. This indicated that there were at least two strongly reproductively isolated populations of 'O. piceae' in Europe, one coming from hardwood and the other from conifer hosts. Their level of reproductive isolation suggests that they are functioning as distinct species in nature, and may be sibling species of *Ophiostoma* (22). For the present, they will be referred to as the OPH (hardwood) and OPC (conifer) breeding groups. Recent studies indicate that the OPC group occasionally occurs on hardwoods, but the OPH group has not been found on conifers.

Molecular evidence

The evidence for OPH and OPC groups within *O. piceae* is supported by a preliminary electrophoretic study of their buffer soluble proteins (Fig. 5). The similarity coefficient for a sample of eight OPH isolates was 88%, and for a sample of six OPC isolates 92%. In contrast, the similarity coefficient for the OPH versus OPC isolate comparison was lower at 69%, and differences in banding patterns could be seen between them (Fig. 5). The 'O. roboris' isolate again grouped with the hardwood or OPH group isolates (55). These results therefore provide further evidence for the genetic divergence of the OPH and OPC populations. This study is being widened as additional isolates of *O. piceae* are obtained from Europe and other continents. It is also being extended to DNA polymorphism and to physiological studies.

Fig. 4. Variation in colony types of *Ophiostoma piceae* isolates. Isolates grown on Oxoid malt extract agar (7) for 8 days at 20 °C and 10 days in diffuse daylight.

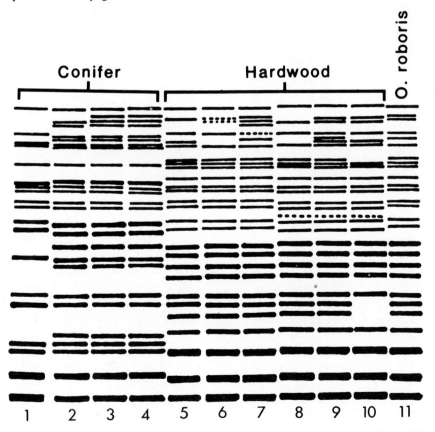

Fig. 5. Patterns of buffer-soluble proteins among isolates of *Ophiostoma piceae* from conifers (OPC form, lanes 1-4) and hardwood (OPH form, lanes 5-11). In lane 11 is an isolate of *O. roboris*. Note the various band differences, and particularly the differences between conifer and hardwood isolates (55).

SUBGROUPS WITHIN *OPHIOSTOMA ULMI*

A parallel situation to that in *O. piceae* occurs within the morphospecies *O. ulmi*. The fungus is well-known as a devastating pathogen of elm, invading the xylem where it induces a vascular wilt. Like *O. piceae*, it is also an efficient saprotroph, spending much of its existence in diseased elm bark in association with the galleries of the vector elm bark beetles (54,56). *O. ulmi* has been responsible for the two pandemics of Dutch elm disease that have swept across the northern hemisphere in this century (17). The anamorph of the fungus was first described as *Graphium ulmi* by Marie Schwarz (51) during the onset of the first pandemic of the disease in Europe in the 1920s. The teleomorph was later discovered by Buisman (24) and described as *Ceratostomella ulmi*.

Mycological studies conducted during the second pandemic, which has spread across Europe, central Asia and North America in recent decades, have revealed two distinct subgroups within *O. ulmi*.

Each subgroup has its own biological properties and range of variation. The two major subgroups are (i) the more weakly pathogenic non-aggressive subgroup, now believed responsible for the first pandemic of Dutch elm disease in the 1920s-40s; and (ii) the highly pathogenic aggressive subgroup, responsible for the current pandemic. The aggressive subgroup itself comprises two races termed the European or EAN, and North American or NAN races (6,11,12). The aggressive and non-aggressive subgroups exhibit considerable differences for many important behavioural and cultural characters such as colony morphology (Fig. 6), growth-rate, optimum temperature for growth, pathogenicity and toxin production. The EAN and NAN aggressive subgroups possess more similarities than differences. However the EAN exhibits a characteristic colony dimorphism (in which it switches between two distinct mycelial modes) and has longer perithecial neck lengths than the NAN. The two also have different geographical distributions (6,11,12,17,18).

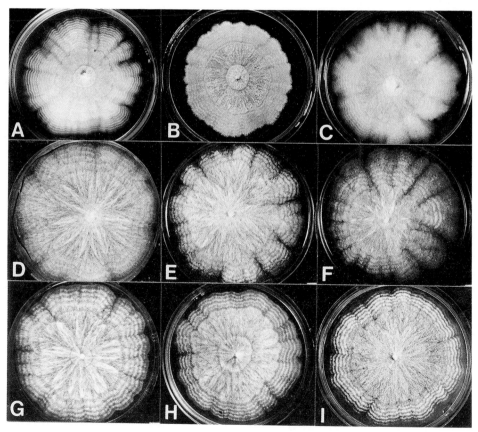

Fig. 6. Colony differences in *Ophiostoma ulmi*. A-C, non-aggressive subgroup isolates. D-F, EAN (European) aggressive isolates; G-I, NAN (North American) aggressive isolates. Cultures grown on Oxoid malt extract agar (7) for 7 days at 20°C and 10 days in diffuse daylight (7).

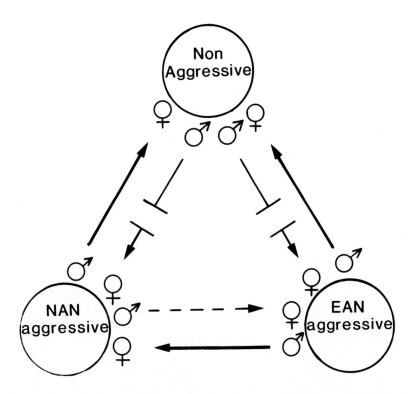

Fig. 7. The system of pre-zygotic fertility barriers which restrict hybridization between the *Ophiostoma ulmi* subgroups. ⊣⊢ strong (virtually total) barrier; – →partial barrier; ⟶ no barrier. NAN = North American isolates, EAN = European isolates. Brasier (11). For further details see refs. 4, 6 and 10.

Pre-zygotic mating barriers in *O. ulmi*

O. ulmi is a heterothallic species with A and B- mating types and, as in *O. piceae*, perithecia are normally formed only in A x B-type pairings (11, 29,50). Also as in *O. piceae*, a series of sexual fertility barriers exists between the subgroups that operate via the sexual mating system. However, these barriers are more subtle and more complex than those found between the OPH and OPC populations of *O. piceae*, in that they have a quantitative component (Fig. 7). Thus, when A-type x B-type pairings are carried out in culture using the patch fertilization method (7) (i) the non-aggressive subgroup as ♀ fully accepts both the EAN and the NAN aggressive as a mating partner; (ii) both the EAN and NAN as ♀ strongly reject the non-aggressive as a mating partner; (iii) the EAN as ♀ partially rejects the NAN as a mating partner, whereas the NAN fully accepts the EAN. The operation of these barriers is seen both in the

comparative numbers of perithecia produced and in their size and development, as illustrated in Table 1.

These barriers, like those in *O. piceae*, are prezygotic isolating mechanisms, restricting gene flow between the *O. ulmi* subgroups prior to ascospore production. Moreover, while the non-aggressive - aggressive barrier is clearly a strong barrier in the culture tests, it may be a near total barrier to gene flow in nature. This is indicated by experiments in which mites were used to carry spores from non-aggressive isolates to aggressive isolates growing on sterilized elm twigs (Fig. 8). In such experiments, no perithecia were formed when colonies of the aggressive isolates growing on the twigs were fed on by mites carrying mating type compatible spores of the non-aggressive subgroup. In contrast, perithecia were plentiful when the feeding mites carried mating type compatible spores of the aggressive subgroup (5).

TABLE 1. Perithecial production between an EAN aggressive isolate of *O. ulmi* and other isolates and subgroups of the *O. ulmi* - *O. piceae* complex.

RECIPIENT (♀) EAN A-type isolate R64	Control x self (R64)	DONER B-TYPES (♂)				
		Ophiostoma ulmi			*O. piceae* oak isolate H1042	Himalayan elm isolate H666
		EAN aggressive isolate CKT-11	NAN aggressive isolate W2	Non-aggressive isolate H200		
Total Perithecia per 6 cm²	0	2616	618	28	240	118
Relative frequency	N/A	1.0	0.26	0.01	0.09	0.05
Perithecial development	N/A	♂	♂♂♂	♂♂♂	♂♂♂	♂♂♂

Fertilizations of recipient isolate R64 were carried out on elm sapwood agar (7) by the 'patch' conidial fertilization method (4,6,7,). The totals are the means of 3 replicates, and are for normal sized perithecia only. Note isolate R64 is of the A compatability type while all the donor isolates are B-types (other than the 'self x self' control). Perithecial development: ♂, normal perithecia with ascospores; ♂♂♂, normal to partially developed perithecia, with ascospores; ♂♂♂, normal to partially developed perithecia, without ascospores.

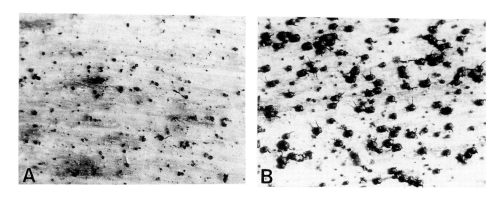

Fig. 8. Test of the non-aggressive → aggressive fertility barrier in *Ophiostoma ulmi* using mites as fertilizing agents. A. Twig surface of aggressive isolates (twig) x non-aggressive isolates (bark) combination showing unfertilized protoperithecia after mite feeding. B. Twig surface in aggressive (twig) x aggressive (bark) combination showing perithecia resulting from successful fertilization by mites (5).

Post-zygotic barriers in *O. ulmi*

Other experiments have shown that the F_1 progeny from perithecia produced in aggressive x non-aggressive crosses in the laboratory are extraordinarily variable in their colony patterns (Fig. 9). Moreover, these progeny tend to lack vigour in potential fitness characters such as pathogenicity, and many are female sterile (4,20, 39). If they are ever produced in nature, such hybrids appear unable to survive. Thus the low fitness and poor competitive survival of aggressive x non-aggressive progeny acts as a post-zygotic isolating mechanism, further restricting gene flow between the aggressive and non-aggressive subgroups and so maintaining their independence. The unusual phenotypic variability and poor fitness of the progeny therefore reflects and reinforces the evolutionary divergence of the two groups.

In contrast, progeny from crosses between the

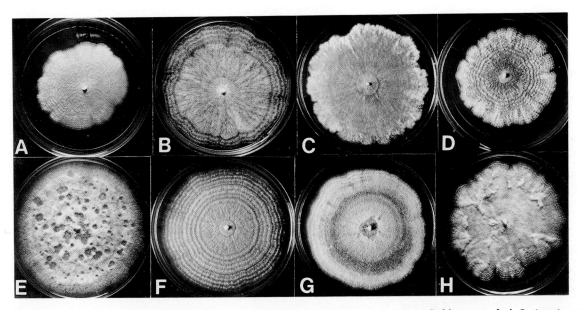

Fig. 9. Colony variation among F$_1$ progeny from an aggressive x non-aggressive cross in *Ophiostoma ulmi*. Isolate A, non-aggressive parent H173 from North America. Isolate B, NAN aggressive parent H175 from North America. Isolates C-H, F$_1$ progenies showing the remarkable range of colony variation (see also refs. 4, 20, 39).

EAN and NAN aggressives show no such unusual features. Indeed where the geographical distributions of the EAN and NAN have overlapped in nature, EAN/NAN hybrids are also appearing freely, and spreading and surviving (11,12). This reflects both the weak nature of the NAN → EAN pre-zygotic barrier and the absence of a strong post-zygotic barrier, the hybrids being generally fit and vigorous.

Molecular evidence

These patterns of gene flow between the *O. ulmi* subgroups are supported by molecular evidence. Phenograms generated from mitochondrial DNA restriction patterns of aggressive and non-aggressive isolates (Fig. 10) are very similar to those previously derived on the basis of cultural and behavioural characteristics (8,11). They reveal a wide genetic divergence between the non-aggressive and aggressive subgroups and support the view of a common origin for the EAN and NAN aggressive groups (1,3). The mitochondrial molecular weights of the three subgroups are also distinctive at 74-88kb for the non-aggressive, 65-69kb for the EAN aggressive and 50-59kb for the NAN aggressive, respectively (1,2).

Similarly, when nuclear DNA of a range of non-aggressive, and EAN and NAN aggressive isolates is enzymically restricted and then probed with random genomic DNA clones (Fig. 11), about 75% of the clones revealed distinguishing polymorphisms between the aggressive and non-aggressive subgroups, consistent with their presumed evolutionary divergence. There is again no evidence for free hybridization between the two groups, despite the fact that most isolates come from areas where they have recently been in close physical contact. In contrast, only about 10% of the clones reveal distinguishing polymorphisms between the EAN and NAN, reflecting their greater genetic relatedness (1,3).

CAN THERE BE GENE FLOW BETWEEN *O. ULMI* AND *O. PICEAE*?

Ophiostoma ulmi and *O. piceae* share many similarities in the morphology of their teleomorph and anamorph structures. They have broadly similar saprotrophic lifestyles, although *O. ulmi* is also a strong vascular wilt pathogen. These two morphospecies [and some other morphologically

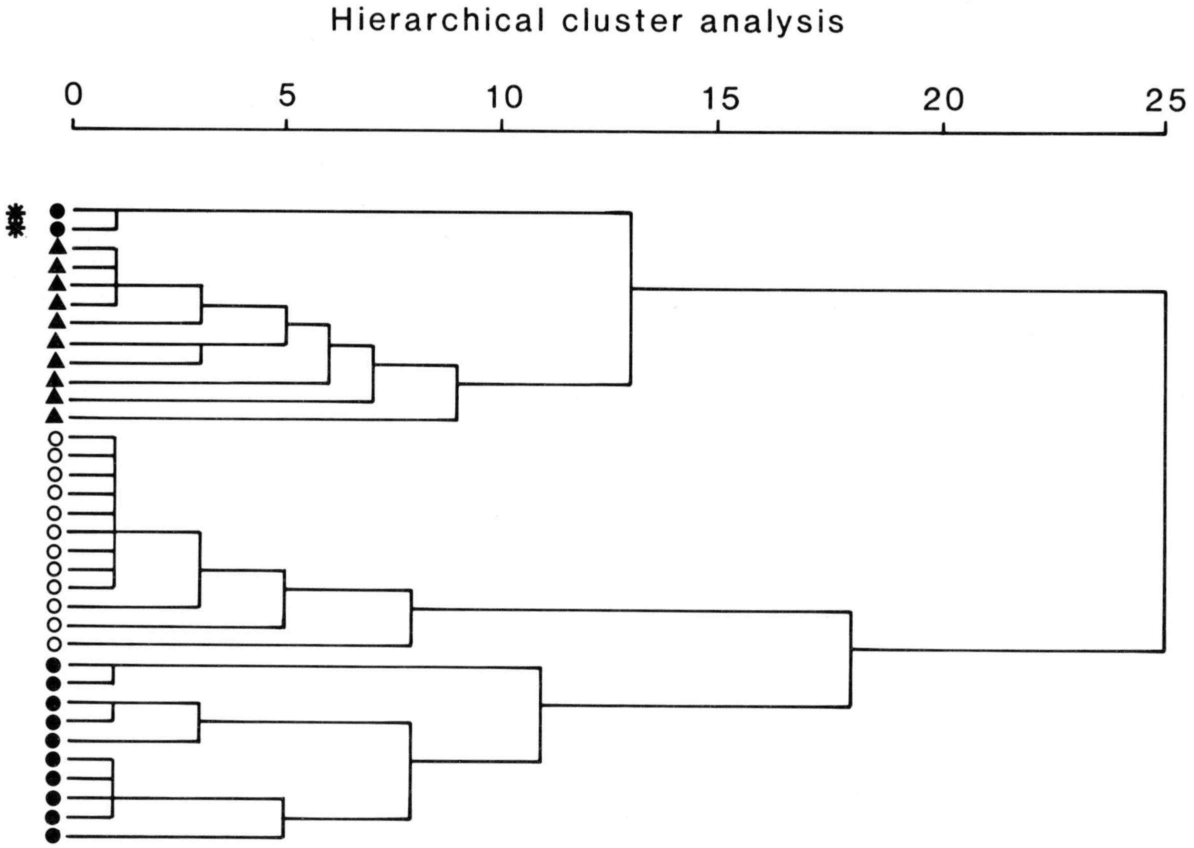

Hierarchical cluster analysis

Fig.10. Phenogram generated by hierarchical cluster analysis of a *Pvu*II restriction digest of the mtDNA of a range of non-aggressive, EAN aggressive and NAN aggressive isolates of *Ophiostoma ulmi*. Isolates marked * are two NAN isolates showing probable introgression of non-aggressive mtDNA. These two isolates otherwise have typical NAN nuclear DNA profiles. From Bates, Buck and Brasier (2) and see also Bates (1). ● = NAN aggressive, ○ = EAN aggressive, ▲ = non-aggressive.

similar *Ophiostoma* spp. such as *O. stenoceras* and *O. proliferum* (41)] might therefore be closely related, whether through an ancient progenitor or through more recent evolutionary divergence. Indeed, the possibility that the 'new' aggressive subgroup of *O. ulmi* has arisen only recently as a result of hybridization of non-aggressive *O. ulmi* with an *O. piceae*-like fungus has been proposed (17). The potential for gene flow between components of the wider 'O. piceae-O. ulmi complex' is therefore of considerable interest and is under investigation in our laboratory.

Because each of the subgroups within *O. ulmi*

and *O. piceae* possess both A and B- mating types, experimental inter-matings between them are possible. Inter-subgroup pairings have been carried out in various combinations as summarized in Fig. 12. A sample result is shown in Table 1. An important feature of these experiments is that perithecia are formed in low frequency by recipient isolates of all three *O. ulmi* subgroups in response to attempted fertilization with conidia of isolates of *O. piceae* (OPH or OPC group) of appropriate compatibility type. However, no ascospores are found in these perithecia; i.e. the pre-zygotic reproductive barrier from *O. piceae* → *O. ulmi* appears to be total. In the equivalent *O. ulmi* → *O. piceae* fertilizations, no perithecia are produced i.e. this reproductive barrier is also total, but more probably resembles that in pairings between the OPH and OPC forms of *O. piceae*. It is also interesting to note that a single isolate of ’*O. ulmi*’ originating from the Himalayas, isolate H666 (9), induces perithecial production by an EAN recipient

(Table 1) in a manner similar to that induced by the OPH isolate: perithecia are formed in low frequency but no ascospores are produced. H666 may represent a fourth subgroup of ’*O. ulmi*’ (9) but since it is the only isolate of the fungus obtained so far from this region, and has been in culture for some time, the relevance of this behaviour is difficult to evaluate.

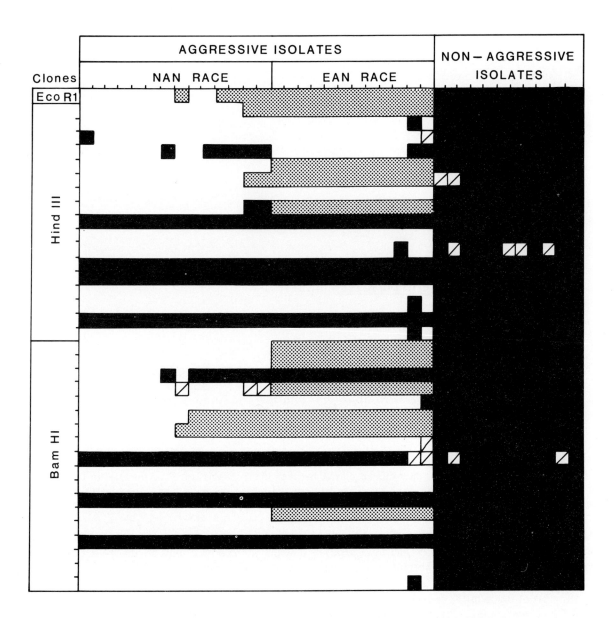

Fig.11. Nuclear DNA polymorphisms exhibited by a broad geographical range of non-aggressive, NAN and EAN aggressive isolates of *Ophiostoma ulmi* when their nDNA was digested with *Eco*RI, *Hind*III or *Bam*HI and probed with various cDNA clones (left). Black squares, polymorphisms characteristic of the non-aggressive subgroup. White squares, polymorphisms characteristic of both NAN and EAN aggressive subgroups. Stippled squares, polymorphisms characteristic of EAN aggressive subgroup. Squares with diagonals, unique polymorphisms. Based on data of Bates (1) and M.R. Bates, K.W. Buck and C.M. Brasier, in preparation.

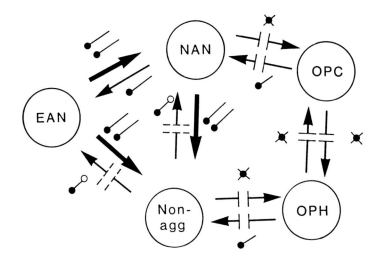

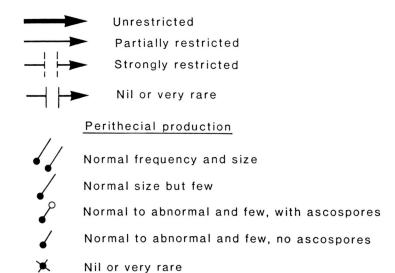

Gene flow / ascospore production

→ Unrestricted (thick arrow)

→ Partially restricted

—| |→ Strongly restricted

—|→ Nil or very rare

Perithecial production

Normal frequency and size

Normal size but few

Normal to abnormal and few, with ascospores

Normal to abnormal and few, no ascospores

✕ Nil or very rare

Fig.12. Summary of the pre-zygotic fertility barriers operating in the *Ophiostoma piceae - Ophostoma ulmi* complex. Some interactions are not shown in the illustration e.g. those between the EAN aggressive and the OPC or OPH groups. These 'missing ' interactions are similar to those shown between the non-aggressive subgroup and the OPH group or between the NAN aggressive and the OPC group.

The biological significance of the sterile perithecia formed by *O. ulmi* in response to *O. piceae* depends upon the mechanism involved in their induction. This is not yet known. These perithecia may represent a true mating event involving *O. ulmi* receptor hyphae (♀) and *O. piceae* conidia (♂), leading perhaps to plasmogamy but then to an eventual failure at karyogamy, meiosis or ascospore development. Alternatively, they may represent a 'false' mating, in which a chemical stimulus diffusing from the *O. piceae* conidia induces the protoperithecia of *O. ulmi*

to develop into mature but sterile perithecia; i.e. a sexual morphogen may be involved (28,52). These aspects are under investigation.

TAXONOMIC STATUS OF THE 'O. PICEAE' AND 'O. ULMI' SUBGROUPS

A traditional genetical approach has allowed the identification of three discrete groups within the old morphospecies *O. ulmi* and two groups within *O. piceae*. Molecular studies have supported the occurrence of these groups.

The two major *O. ulmi* groups, the aggressive and non-aggressive, are culturally, morphologically, physiologically and molecularly rather different, often exhibiting sharp discontinuities in the characters studied. That they are also strongly genetically isolated via pre- and post-zygotic mechanisms is evident from laboratory mating studies and from the study of their natural populations. It is now clear that these two groups are genetically very divergent and function in nature as separate, sibling species. In view of the practical importance of discriminating the historical and biological roles of these two taxa in the two recent pandemics of Dutch elm disease (17), they have now been formally designated. The old non-aggressive subgroup is retained as *O. ulmi sensu* Schwarz (51) and Buisman (24), and the aggressive described as the new species, *O. novo-ulmi* (18). In contrast, the EAN and NAN subgroups within *O. novo-ulmi* share many cultural and molecular characteristics and can hybridize freely in nature. However, they also exhibit some important morphological and cultural differences, and may yet be designated as subspecies (18).

The two *O. piceae* subgroups, the OPH and OPC groups, are morphologically rather similar, probably more similar than the EAN and NAN in *O. novo-ulmi*, yet they show strong reproductive isolation. They may also show useful protein polymorphisms (55), and almost certainly function in nature as discrete, sibling species (22). Assuming that the name *O. piceae* Münch is retained for the OPC form, then *O. querci* Georgevitch may need to be reinstated for the OPH form, with the beech isolates (*O. fagi*) and probably also *O. roboris* as synonyms. However, in accordance with modern nomenclatural practice, and to avoid further confusion, a much wider international collection of isolates must be examined both genetically and morphologically before any further formal proposal on the status of the OPC and OPH groups is made.

THE TAXONOMIC AND ECOLOGICAL SIGNIFICANCE OF SIBLING SPECIES

Sibling species, meaning here subgroups within classical morphospecies which show few or no morphological differences but exhibit strong reproductive isolation, are now being increasingly discovered in all groups of fungi (14,23,27). Almost by definition, they are more likely to be identified by population, genetical and molecular methods than by traditional morphological taxonomy. Because of the limited application of genetical and population methods in the Ophiostomataceae to date, similar examples may well be found within other *Ophiostoma* and *Ceratocystis* morphospecies, and in particular in those with wide geographical distributions and wide habitat or host relationships.

Another possible example in the Ophiostomataceae is that of the anamorph species *Leptographium wageneri*, the cause of black stain root disease of conifers in western North America. *L. wageneri* occurs as three host-specialized forms, one on Douglas fir, one on pinyon pine and one on hard pine. Although the three forms show only minor cultural differences, they exhibit characteristic isozyme patterns (36,37,58). There is some evidence for gene flow (via hyphal fusions) within each population, but probably no viable hyphal fusions occur between populations (58; Harrington, this volume). The three populations therefore appear to be genetically isolated sibling species.

The above examples highlight the fact that though morphologically similar, sibling species are likely to be behaviorally different. As already emphasized, where they are found it is these population units and not the original morphospecies, that the researcher must refer to for accuracy of communication. This will present the would be taxonomist with a greater challenge in terms of applying diagnostic and identification skills. However, any difficulties seem likely to be overcome in the future by improvements in rapid diagnostic techniques such as the use of DNA probes and of monoclonal antibodies, as taxonomy develops into a more machine-based science.

Role of host and vector in the speciation process

Sibling species, rather than the classical morphospecies, may prove to be the operational units of evolution in many fungal groups. In this case, the species concept may shift downwards to below the morphospecies level (19). This brings with it the further challenge of attempting to construct phylogenies of these genetic units, of elucidating the speciation processes that have led to their emergence, and of defining the niches they now occupy. The *O. ulmi-O. piceae* complex illustrates how fascinating a task this may be. The degree of pre-zygotic isolation between the various population units within this complex, ranges from low (*O. novo-ulmi → O. ulmi*) to partial (NAN → EAN) to near total (*O. piceae* OPH → *O. piceae* OPC) (Fig 12). These levels must reflect the original mode of divergence of the subgroups, whether sympatric or allopatric, recent or ancient, rapid or gradual; and the degree of continued physical contact between the respective populations following divergence. The partial isolation between EAN and NAN may reflect very recent divergence of the NAN from the EAN through geographic isolation of a new elm population in North America (17). This reproductive barrier might have developed passively, through adaptation to the new and more susceptible American elm population and genetic drift. In contrast, the strong isolation between the *O. piceae* OPC and OPH groups might reflect sympatric divergence on different host types (mainly conifer versus mainly hardwood) and their continued sympatric co-existence. Thus, if evolved gene complexes conferred higher levels of fitness in the conifer and hardwood niches for OPC and OPH respectively, energy would be wasted unnecessarily if OPC x OPH hybrids were produced that were of poor fitness in either niche. Hence, mutations that blocked hybridization between the OPC and OPH groups might confer a strong selective advantage to both and so be retained.

Another selective factor that is likely to drive speciation events in *Ophiostoma* and *Ceratocystis* is the vector. A high level of vector specificity towards a given host or substrate is likely to reinforce reproductive isolation between a common fungal associate of the vector and other related fungal populations associated with other vectors and hosts. Likewise, the greater a vector's efficiency in recycling an associated fungus population from an exhausted substrate to a new substrate of the **same** niche, the greater its influence on the continued adaptation and independent evolution of the poulation in that niche. Such processes will enhance the co-evolution of vector and fungus and will in particular encourage evolution of behavioral traits that lead to the mutual advantage of both. They have been discussed with regard to Dutch elm disease by Webber and Brasier (54) and Brasier (11) in terms of the role of 'pathogenic feedback' in the evolution of parasitism in *O. ulmi*; and in terms of the 'scoring' of the wood by adults and larvae of the elm bark beetle vectors when breeding in elm bark. The latter behaviour is likely to aid the release of pathogenic phase *O. ulmi* from the xylem into the bark and to enhance the fruiting potential of *O. ulmi* (54).

If the OPC and OPH forms of *O. piceae* represent a sympatric as opposed to an allopatric speciation event, then their divergence may have been driven and sustained by two factors in particular. First, dependence for dispersal on relatively host specialized conifer or hardwood bark beetles (e.g. *Scolytus intricatus* on oak, and *Ips* spp. on pine). Second, adaptation to and co-evolution with the different chemical regimes imposed by the host's anti-fungal defence mechanisms, e.g. an ability to tolerate conifer resins in the OPC or conifer form. The latter possibility is under investigation.

The apparently free gene flow between oak, elm and beech derived isolates of the OPH form of *O. piceae* from Europe, or between spruce and pine derived isolates of the OPC form, indicates that reproductive isolation has not extended to host genera. It is nevertheless possible that locally specialized oak, elm or beech biotypes occur within the OPH group and that pine and spruce biotypes occur within the OPC group. A common gene pool may be maintained within each group by the host 'cross-over potential' of more generalized vectors such as mites and sap feeding insects.

VECTOR 'CROSS-OVERS' AND GENETIC INTERACTIONS BETWEEN MORPHOSPECIES

The crossing-over of vectors between hosts or substrates will also bring about interactions between sibling species and between related fungal morphospecies. Thus, there is some evidence that the OPC form of 'O. piceae' can occur on hardwoods. This may reflect unusual vector crossover events. Also, while *O. ulmi* and *O. novo-ulmi* are highly specialized towards the elm as pathogens and are strongly associated in Europe with their two most efficient bark beetle vectors *S. scolytus* and *S. multistriatus* (53), some elm bark beetles such as *S. scolytus* and *S. pygmaeus* may occasionally feed on other hardwoods (43). Casual vectors such as phoretic mites regularly cross between elms and other tree genera. Such behavior may provide the occasional opportunity for interactions between, for example, *O. ulmi* and the OPH form of *O. piceae*.

In view of this possibility, and also because it has been suggested that an *O. piceae*-like fungus might be involved in the sudden appearance of both *O. ulmi* and *O. novo-ulmi* in Europe earlier this century (17), the formation of perithecia between *O. ulmi* or *O. novo-ulmi* and *O. piceae* (Table 1) is of special interest. If fertilization is involved rather than a sexual morphogen, then, even though no ascospores have been obtained, these perithecia could indicate a potential for rare genetic exchange between *O. ulmi* or *O. novo-ulmi* and 'O. piceae'; either in the past or in the future. Rare genetic exchanges between species could also occur asexually, via sporadic 'illegitimate' hyphal fusion followed by nuclear fusion, as well as via illegitimate sexual fusions. While such exchanges might be of little importance in local populations of fungi exposed to routine selection [*sensu* Brasier, (11,14)], they might be of great importance if there is an unusual opportunity for evolutionary development, such as occurs under episodic selection (11,14). In the latter circumstances, they might sometimes fuel unusual speciation events.

LITERATURE CITED

1. Bates, M.R. 1990. DNA polymorphism in the Dutch elm disease fungus *Ophiostoma ulmi*. Ph.D thesis, Imperial College, London.

2. Bates, M.R., Brasier, C.M. and Buck, K.W. 1991. Molecular relationships of the *O. ulmi* subgroup. Rep. For. Res. 1990. Pages 53-59. HMSO, London.

3. Bates, M.R., Buck, K.W. and Brasier, C.M. 1990. Molecular variation in the Dutch elm disease fungus. in: Molecular Evolution. M.T. Clegg and S.J. O'Brian, eds. UCLA Symp. Mol. Cell. Biol., n.s. 122:171-178.

4. Brasier, C.M. 1977. Inheritance of pathogenicity and cultural characters in *Ceratocystis ulmi*. Hybridisation of protoperithecial and non-aggressive strains. Trans. Br. Mycol. Soc. 68:45-52.

5. Brasier, C.M. 1978. Mites and reproduction in *Ceratocystis ulmi* and other fungi. Trans. Br. Mycol. Soc. 70:81-89.

6. Brasier, C.M. 1979. Dual origin of recent Dutch elm disease outbreaks in Europe. Nature 281:78-79.

7. Brasier, C.M. 1981. Laboratory investigation of *Ceratocystis ulmi*. Pages 76-79 in: Compendium of Elm Diseases. R.J. Stipes and R.J. Campana, eds. American Phytopathological Society, St. Paul, MN. 96 pp.

8. Brasier, C.M. 1982. Occurrence of three sub-groups within *Ceratocystis ulmi*. Pages 298-321 in: Proceedings of the Dutch elm disease Symposium and Workshop, Winnipeg, Manitoba, October 5-9, 1981. E.S. Kondo, Y. Hiratsuka and W.B.C. Denyer, eds. Manitoba Department of Natural Resources, Manitoba. 517 pp.

9. Brasier, C.M. 1983. Dutch elm disease. The origin of Dutch elm disease. Rep. For. Res. 1983 p.32. HMSO, London.

10. Brasier, C.M. 1984. Inter-mycelial recognition systems in *Ceratocystis ulmi*: their physiological properties and ecological importance. Pages 451-497 in: The ecology and physiology of the fungal mycelium. D. Jennings and A.D.M. Rayner, eds. Cambridge University Press, Cambridge. 564 pp.

11. Brasier, C.M. 1986. The population biology of Dutch elm disease: its principal features and some implications for other host-pathogen systems. Pages 55-118 in: Advances in Plant Pathology. D.S. Ingram and P.H. Williams, eds. Academic Press, London and New York. 220 pp.

12. Brasier, C.M. 1986. Dutch elm disease - *Ophiostoma (Ceratocystis) ulmi*. The emergence of EAN and NAN hybrids in Europe. Rep. For. Res. 1986 p.37. HMSO, London.

13. Brasier, C.M. 1987. Recent genetic changes in the *Ophiostoma ulmi* population: the threat to the future of the elm. Pages 213-226 in: Populations of Plant Pathogens. M.S. Wolfe and C.E. Caten, eds. Blackwells, Oxford. 280 pp.

14. Brasier, C.M. 1987. The dynamics of fungal speciation. Pages 231-260 in: Evolutionary biology of the fungi. A.D.M. Rayner, C.M. Brasier and D. Moore, eds. Cambridge University Press, Cambridge. 465 pp.

15. Brasier, C.M. 1988. *Ophiostoma ulmi*, cause of Dutch elm disease. Pages 207-223 in: Genetics of Plant Pathogenic Fungi. G.S. Sidhu, ed. Advances in Plant Pathology Vol. 6. Academic Press, London and New York. 566 pp.

16. Brasier, C.M. 1988. Rapid changes in genetic structure of epidemic populations of *Ophiostoma ulmi*. Nature 332:538-541.

17. Brasier, C.M. 1990. China and the origins of Dutch elm disease: an appraisal. Plant Pathol. 39:5-16.

18. Brasier, C.M. 1991. *Ophiostoma novo-ulmi* sp. nov., causative agent of the current Dutch elm disease pandemics. Mycopathologia 115:151-161.

19. Brasier, C.M. 1991. Current questions in *Phytophthora* systematics: the role of the population approach. Pages 104-128 in: *Phytophthora*. J.A. Lucas, R.C. Shattock, D.S. Shaw and L.R. Cooke, eds. Cambridge University Press, Cambridge. 447 pp.

20. Brasier, C.M. and Gibbs, J.N. 1976. Inheritance of pathogenecitiy and cultural characters in *Ceratocystis ulmi*. I. Hybridisation of aggressive and non-aggressive strains. Ann. Appl. Biol. 83:31-37.

21. Brasier, C.M. and Kirk, S.A. 1989. European oak decline. Identity of *Ophiostoma roboris*. Rep. For. Res. 1989 p.47. HMSO, London.

22. Brasier, C.M. and Kirk, S.A. 1989. European oak decline. Status of *O. piceae* on hardwoods and conifers. Rep. For. Res. 1989 pp. 47-48. HMSO, London.

23. Brasier, C.M. and Rayner, A.D.M. 1987. Whither terminology below the species level in the fungi? Pages 379-388 in: Evolutionary Biology of the Fungi. A.D.M. Rayner, C.M. Brasier and D. Moore, eds. Cambridge University Press, Cambridge. 465 pp.

24. Buisman, C.J. 1932. *Ceratostomella ulmi*, de geslachtelijke vorm van *Graphium ulmi* Schwarz. Tijd. Plantenziek. 38:1-5.

25. Buisman, C.J. 1934. Über die Biologie und den Prasitismus der Gattung *Ceratostomella* Sacc. Phytopathol. Z. 4:429-439.

26. Burnett, J.H. 1975. Mycogenetics. John Wiley and Son, London. 375 pp.

27. Burnett, J.H. 1983. Speciation in fungi. Trans. Br. Mycol. Soc., 81:1-14.

28. Champe, S.P., Rao, P. and Chang, A. 1987. An endogenous inducer of sexual development in *Aspergillus nidulans*. J. Gen. Microbiol. 133:1383-1387.

29. Croft, J.H. and Jinks, J.L. 1977. Aspects of the population genetics of *Aspergillus nidulans*. Pages 339-360 in: Genetics and Physiology of *Aspergillus*. J.E. Smith, and J.A. Pateman, eds. Academic Press. London and New York. 552 pp.

30. Dobzhansky, T. 1937. Genetics and the Origin of Species. New York: Columbia University Press, New York. 364 pp.

31. Elias, K.S. and Schneider, R.W. 1991. Vegetative compatibility groups in *Fusarium oxysporum f. sp. lycopersici*. Phytopathology 81:159-162.

32. Georgescu, C.C., Teodoru, I. and Badea, M. 1948. Uscarea in massa a stejarului. Anal. Inst. Cerc. For. Rom. 11:185-223.

33. Georgevitch, M.P. 1926. *Ceratostomella quercus* n.sp. Acad.

Sci. Compt. Rend. Paris 183:759.

34.   Gibbs, J.N. 1981. European Forestry and *Ceratocystis* species. EPPO Bull. 11:193-197.

35.   Grant, V. 1971. Plant Speciation. Columbia University Press, New York. 435 pp.

36.   Harrington, T.C. and Cobb, F.W. 1984. Host specialization of three morphological variants of *Verticicladiella wagenerii*. Phytopathology 74:286-290.

37.   Harrington, T.C. and Cobb, F.W. 1986. Varieties of *Verticicladiella wagenerii*. Mycologia 78:562-567.

38.   Hunt, J. 1956. Taxonomy of the genus *Ceratocystis*. Lloydia 19:1-58.

39.   Kile, G.A. and Brasier, C.M. 1990. Inheritance and inter-relationship of fitness characters in progeny of an aggressive x non-aggressive cross of *Ophiostoma ulmi*. Mycol. Res. 94:514-522.

40.   Korhonen, K. 1987. Breeding units in the forest pathogens *Armillaria* and *Heterobasidion*. Pages 301-310 in: Evolutionary Biology of the Fungi. A.D.M. Rayner, C.M. Brasier and D. Moore, eds. Cambridge University Press, Cambridge. 465 pp.

41.   Kowalski, D. and Butin, H. 1989. Taxonomie bekannter und neuer *Ceratocystis*-Arten an Eiche (*Quercus robur* L.) Phytopathol. Z. 124:236-248.

42.   Loos, W. 1932. Über eine buchenholzbewohnende *Ceratostomella*, *Ceratostomella fagi* n. sp. Arch. Mikrobiol. 3:370-383.

43.   Maslov, A.D. 1970. Pests of elms and how to control them. Lesnaya Promyshlennost, Moscow.

44.   Mitchell, A.G. 1988. Interaction between the aggressive and non-aggressive subgroups of *Ophiostoma ulmi*. Ph.D thesis, University of Bath.

45.   Münch, E. 1907. Die Blaufäule des Nadelholzes. Naturw. Z. Forst. Landw. 5:531-573.

46.   Oleskyn, J. and Przybyl, K. 1987. Oak decline in the Soviet Union - scale and hypotheses. Eur. J. For. Pathol. 17:321-336.

47.   Przybyl, K. and de Hoog, G.S. 1989. On the variability of *Ophiostoma piceae*. Antonie van Leeuwenhoek 55:177-188.

48.   Puhalla, J.E. 1979. Classification of isolates of *Verticillium dahliae* based on incompatibility. Phytopathology, 69:1186-1189.

49.   Puhalla, J.E. 1985. Classification of strains of *Fusarium oxysporum* on the basis of vegetative incompatibility. Can. J. Bot. 63:179-183.

50.   Schafer, T. and Liming, O.N. 1952. *Ceratostomella ulmi* mating types in relation to the development and identification of perithecia. Phytopathology 40: 1035-1042.

51.   Schwarz, M.B. 1922. Das zweigensterben der olmaen, trauerweiden und pfirschbaume. Med. Phytopathol. Lab. Willie Commelin Scholten 5:1-73.

52.   Siddiq, A.A., Ingram, D.S., Johnstone, K., Freind, J. and Ashby, A.M. 1989. The control of sexual development by morphogens in fungal pathogens. Asp. Appl. Biol. 23:417-426.

53.   Webber, J.F. 1990. Relative effectiveness of *Scolytus scolytus*, *S. multistriatus* and *S. kirschi* as vectors of Dutch elm disease. Eur. J. For. Pathol. 20:184-192.

54.   Webber, J.F. and Brasier, C.M. 1984. The transmission of Dutch elm disease: a study of the processes involved. Pages 271-306 in: Invertebrate-microbial interactions. J.M. Anderson., A.D.M. Rayner and D. Walton, eds. Cambridge University Press, Cambridge. 350 pp.

55.   Webber, J.F. and Brasier, C.M. 1991. Status of *Ophiostoma piceae* on hardwoods and conifers. Rep. For. Res. 1990, pp. 54-55. HMSO, London.

56.   Webber, J.F., Brasier, C.M. and Mitchell, A.G. 1988. The role of the saprophytic phase in Dutch elm disease. Pages 298-313 in: Fungal infections of plants. G.F. Pegg and P.G. Ayres, eds. Cambridge University Press, Cambridge. 320 pp.. U.K.

57.   Upadhyay, H.P. 1981. A monograph of *Ceratocystis* and *Ceratocystiopsis*. University of Georgia Press, Athens, GA. 176 pp.

58.   Zambino, P.J. and Harrington, T.C. 1989. Isozyme variation among host-specialized varieties of *Leptographum wagenerii*. Mycologia 81:122-123.

Chapter 10

GROUPING OF ISOLATES AND SPECIES OF *CERATOCYSTIS SENSU LATO* ON THE BASIS OF MOLECULAR AND MORPHOLOGICAL CHARACTERS

G. HAUSNER, J. REID and G.R. KLASSEN

INTRODUCTION

Grouping large numbers of strains into a particular fungal species is often difficult because of morphological variation. *Ceratocystis ips* is one of the more pleomorphic species of *Ceratocystis sensu lato*, possessing at least three distinct synanamorphs (27). We have strains of *C. ips* from New Zealand, North America and Scandinavia that exhibit considerable variation in perithecial production in culture, length of perithecial necks, perithecial base pigmentation, presence of ornamenting hyphae on the bases and nature of their synanamorphs. In fact, the only constant feature among them is the size and shape of their ascospores when perithecia do form.

Molecular taxonomy provides independent data sets that can be used to objectively evaluate the phylogenetic significance of morphological features. Ribosomal genes comprise highly conserved sequences that offer a means of assessing affinities above the species level (18). Although such genes are highly conserved, the intergenic region (IGR), also known as the intergenic spacer, is highly variable even among closely related taxa (3,22,29). Therefore, the ribosomal (r) DNA repeat unit is ideal for studying relatedness among both distantly and closely related species.

Mitochondrial (mt) DNA has also been employed with considerable success to investigate phylogenetic relationships between closely related organisms (7,24,25,26). Mitochondrial polymorphisms appear to arise relatively quickly due to both deletions and insertions. The lack of a mtDNA repair mechanism may allow mtDNA to evolve 10 fold more rapidly than nuclear DNA (5). Thus, the use of mtDNA in taxonomy is limited to the phylogenetic study of very closely related species.

The morphological variations we observed in our *C. ips* strains offered an ideal case to test whether such variations could be correlated with significant intraspecific differences at either the rDNA or mtDNA levels. And the possibility that some of our strains might represent new species or distinct varieties could also be tested. We also included strains of species synonymized with *C. ips* (27) to test those decisions. Generally, it was our intent to illustrate that restriction enzyme analysis of rDNA and mtDNA could be a fairly fast and reliable method of grouping strains and species of *Ceratocystis s.l.*

CULTURING METHODS AND DNA EXTRACTION

All strains (Table 1) were cultured in petri dishes containing 2% malt extract agar (13). A 4 mm mycelial plug was removed from the colony margin of a strain and transferred aseptically to a Roux bottle containing 100 ml peptone - yeast extract - glucose medium (PYG) containing ($g \ell^{-1}$): glucose, 3; peptone, 1; yeast extract, 1. Cultures were incubated in standing culture at 20°C for 48 to 96 h. Mycelia were harvested by vacuum filtration onto Whatman No. 1 filter paper (Whatman Laboratory Products, Clinton, N.J.) and thoroughly washed with 1 ℓ of distilled water. The contents of 2 to 4 Roux bottle cultures (100 to 500 mg wet weight of mycelia) was usually sufficient for DNA extraction. A rapid DNA isolation procedure based on the methods of Murray & Thompson (19) and Rogers *et al.* (22) as modified by Kim *et al.* (15) was employed.

ENDONUCLEASE RESTRICTION, ELECTROPHORESIS, AND SOUTHERN BLOTTING:

Restriction endonucleases obtained from BRL (Bethesda Research Laboratories, Gaithersburg, MD) were used according to the manufacturer's recommendations. The procedures for electrophoresis and Southern blotting were as described by Klassen *et al.* (16), except for rDNA restriction fragment length polymorphism (RFLP) profiles generated by *Hha*I, *Rsa*I, *Mbo*I, *Hae*III, and *Alu*I; these required 1.8% agarose gel for resolution of small DNA fragments.

RFLP ANALYSIS OF *C. IPS* AND RELATED SPECIES:

Ribosomal DNA restriction profiles were genera-

TABLE 1. List of fungal strains studied.

Designated Species	Accession Code	Host	Country of origin or supplier
Cephaloascus fragrans	ATCC 36174 (CBS 12129)	Unknown	ATCC
	ATCC 60760	*Pseudotsuga menziesii*	
Ceratocystiopsis falcata	WIN(M)82-23d	*Larix* sp.	New Zealand
Ceratocystiopsis minuta	CBS 145.59 (NYBG)	Unknown	CBS
Ceratocystis adiposa	CBS 127.27	Unknown	CBS
Ceratocystis adjuncta	ATCC 34942	*Pinus ponderosa*	ATCC
Ceratocystis autographa	CBS 670.75	*Juniperus communis*	CBS
Ceratocystis coerulescens	WIN(M) 98	*Picea abies*	Norway
Ceratocystis fimbriata	DAOM 195303	*Kerma japonica*	DAOM
Ceratocystis hyalothecium	ATCC 28825	*Pinus contorta*	ATCC
Ceratocystis ips	WIN(M)82-57b	*Pinus radiata*	New Zealand
	WIN(M)82-58	*P. radiata*	"
	WIN(M)82-70a	*P. elliotii*	"
	WIN(M)82-70b	*P. elliotii*	"
	WIN(M)82-77b	*P. radiata*	"
	WIN(M)82-83a	*P. radiata*	"
	WIN(M)82-83d	*P. radiata*	"
	WIN(M)82-85b	*P. radiata*	"
	WIN(M)82-87a	*P. radiata*	"
	WIN(M)88-100B	*P. radiata*	"
	WIN(M)88-105	*P. radiata*	"
	WIN(M)88-131	*P. radiata*	"
	WIN(M)88-134	*P. radiata*	"
	WIN(M)88-135	*P. radiata*	"
	WIN(M)88-138	*P. radiata*	"
	WIN(M)88-141	*P. radiata*	"
	WIN(M)88-185	*Pinus* sp.	"
	WIN(M)88-508	*P. contorta*	"
	WIN(M)92	*Pinus sylvestris*	Norway
	WIN(M)96	*P. sylvestris*	"
	WIN(M)114	*P. sylvestris*	"
	WIN(M)182 (F.P.NOR59-44/3)	*P. sylvestris*	"
	WIN(M)391	Unknown	A. Mathiesen-Käärik
Ceratocystis major	CBS 138.34	Isolated from air	CBS
Ceratocystis montia	CBS 151.78	*P. ponderosa*	CBS
	C450	*P. contorta*	CFB
Ceratocystis ossiformis	WIN(M)82-52 (69-17)	*Abies balsamea*	WIN(M)
Ceratocystis paradoxa	CBS 107.22	*Cocos nucifera*	CBS
Ceratocystis penicillata	CBS 210.67 (ATCC 18082)	*P. abies*	CBS
Ceratocystis piceaperda	WIN(M)82-14b	*Pinus nigra*	New Zealand
Ceratocystis pilifera	WIN(M)82-129d	*P. radiata*	New Zealand
	B-94	Unknown	A. Mathiesen-Käärik

TABLE 1 Continued

Designated Species	Accession Code	Host	Country of origin or supplier
Ceratocystis radicicola	CBS 114.47 (IMI 36479)	*Phoenix dactylifera*	CBS
Ceratocystis sp.	DAOM 191892	*Ulmus* sp.	DAOM
Chalara sp.	WIN(M)82-141a	*Podocarpus* sp.	New Zealand
Endomyces decipiens	ATCC 11647	Unknown	ATCC
Europhium aureum	CBS 438.69 (ATCC 16936)	*Pinus contorta* var. *latifolia*	CBS
Europhium clavigerum	CBS 493.77	*P. ponderosa*	CBS
Europhium triancriforme	C.527	*P. monticola*	CFB
Neosartorya fischeri var. *fischeri*	CBS 525.65 (ATCC 16904)	Unknown	CBS
Ophiostoma flexuosum	WIN(M)88-445 (NFRI 81-79/10)	*P. abies*	H. Solheim
Sphaeronaemella fimicola	WIN(M)82-55a	*P. radiata*	New Zealand

ATCC	American Type Culture Collection, Rockville, Maryland, U.S.A.
CBS	Centraalbureau voor Schimmelcultures, Baarn, The Netherlands
CFB	Northern Forest Research Centre, Edmonton, Canada
DAOM	Centre for Land and Biological Resources Research, Ottawa, Canada
WIN(M)	The author's (J.R.) own collection

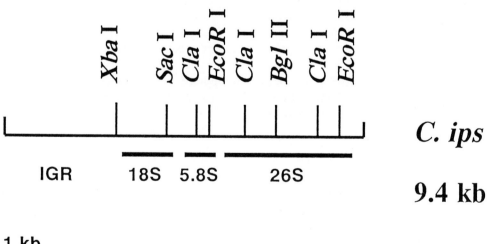

Fig. 1. Restriction enzyme site map of the 9.4 Kb rDNA repeat unit of *C. ips* [WIN(M) 82-57b].

ted using endonucleases that recognize sites comprised of either six base pairs (six-cutters) or four base pairs (four-cutters), to investigate the intraspecific variability within the *C. ips* strains and the interspecific variability between them and strains of various closely related species.

The profiles generated with *Cla*I (a six-cutter) for all *C. ips* strains show three DNA fragments (Fig. 1). These comprise common 1.2 kb and 1.8 kb fragments from the coding regions and a larger, variable-sized

TABLE 2. Sizes of the rDNA fragments that hybridized to the pMF$_2$ probe following restriction with *Cla*I.

	kb
Isolates of *C. ips*	
WIN(M) 92	6.0, 1.8, 1.2
WIN(M) 96	5.7, 1.8, 1.2
WIN(M) 114	6.0, 1.8, 1.2
WIN(M) 182	6.0, 1.8, 1.2
WIN(M) 391	5.7, 1.8, 1.2
WIN(M) 88-100B	5.7, 1.8, 1.2
WIN(M) New Zealand[1]	6.4, 1.8, 1.2
C. montia CBS 151.78	8.7, 2.4, 1.2
C. montia C 450	6.6, 2.9, 1.2
C. pilifera WIN(M) 82-129d	8.2, 2.5, 1.2
S. fimicola	3.7, 1.6, 0.5
C. penicillata	4.6, 1.6, 1.0

[1] The following New Zealand strains identified as *C. ips* all yielded identical fragment sizes: 82-57b, 82-70a, 82-70b, 82-77b, 82-83a, 82-83d, 82-85b, 82-87a, 88-105, 88-131, 88-134, 88-135, 88-138, 88-141, 88-185, 88-508.

fragment (Table 2). Based on the restriction map (Fig. 1), the large fragment contains the intergenic regions and this fragment is useful for grouping our *C. ips* strains geographically. Except for 88-100B, all of the New Zealand strains yielded a 6.4 kb large *Cla*I fragment, while our Scandinavian strains yielded either a 5.7 or a 6.0 kb large *Cla*I fragment.

The *Cla*I profiles do not provide enough information to estimate the degree of relatedness amongst *C. ips*, *C. montia*, *C. pilifera*, *S. fimicola*, or *C. penicillata* (Table 2), and the only fragment shared with the *C. ips* strains by the others is the 1.2 kb fragment of the *C. montia* and *C. pilifera* strains. Six-cutter profiles generate insufficient numbers of fragments for relatedness appraisal.

While six-cutter endonucleases usually generate only two or three fragments, four-cutters (eg. *Rsa*I, *Msp*I) have a much higher digestion frequency, yielding up to 10 or more fragments per digestion. Thus, four-cutter profiles represent a more thorough sampling of sequences and yield more information. The *Msp*I (Fig. 2) and *Rsa*I profiles of all *C. ips* strains were identical. Each profile comprised eight recognizable fragments, indicating that a total of 16 sites had been restricted in each strain by the two endonucleases. Because the sizes and position of the fragments on the gels depend upon the distance

between two adjacent restriction sites, the identity of the profiles suggests that there are no insertions or deletions. The results further suggest that the tested strains are all the same species and that four-cutter profiles can be useful in evaluating sequence divergence between closely related species.

Restriction fragments were visualized by Southern blotting and hybridization with pMF2. This plasmid contains the entire coding region plus 300 bases of the IGR flanking either side of the coding region of the rDNA repeat of *Neurospora crassa* (8). As it is unlikely that pMF2 would hybridize to IGR fragments unless they included parts of the adjacent coding regions, the four-cutter profiles probably represent fragments at least partially within the coding region of the rDNA repeat unit of *C. ips*.

The relationship of *C. montia*, *C. adjuncta*, *C. ossiformis*, *O. flexuosum* and *C. hyalothecium* to *C. ips* was evaluated by generating four-cutter profiles with *Msp*I and *Mbo*I. The fraction of common bands or F-values [F = 2(number of fragments common to two isolates) ÷ the total number of restriction fragments from the two isolates] between strains of all species was determined (17). Although F-values were calculated for each pair of strains with each endonuclease, only the combined F-values for each pair with both endonucleases are reported. The two data sets were consistent with each other for all comparisons.

F-values reflect sequence divergence due to mutations at particular restriction sites. Sites may be lost or gained and fragments may change in size due to insertions and deletions. Thus high F-values, supported by independent data sets, are useful measures of relatedness because they indicate evolutionary change at the DNA sequence level.

The combined four-cutter F-values (Table 3) suggest that *C. montia*, *C. adjuncta*, *O. flexuosum*, *C. ossiformis* and *C. hyalothecium*, all of which would be members of the Ips group (20) or section Ips (27), are distinct genetic entities and likely distinct species. The four non-Ips group species were included here as outgroups to determine F-values for morphologically distinct species not expected to be closely related to *C. ips*. Of these, *C. pilifera* does show a high degree of similarity to *C. ips* and the other *C. ips*-like species, but *C. fimbriata*, *C. penicillata*, and *S. fimicola* share only low F-values with *C. ips* and related species. While the *Cla*I profiles had earlier suggested our two strains of *C. montia* were distinct, the four-cutter profiles confirmed that, although closely related, they are discrete genetic entities.

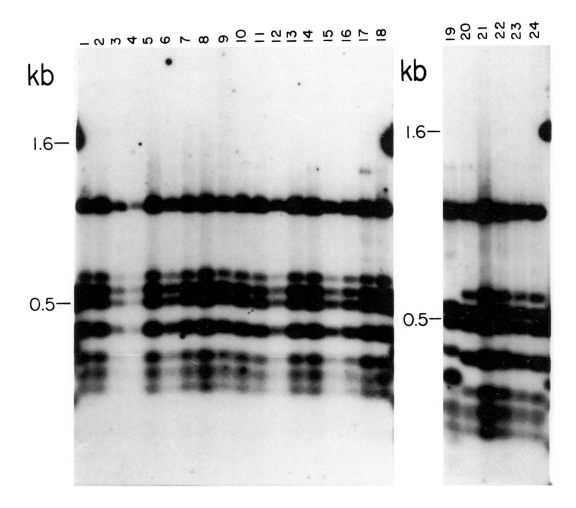

Fig. 2. Southern hybridization of *Msp*I digested whole-cell DNAs with radiolabelled, rDNA-containing plasmid pMF2 showing identical patterns among different isolates of *C. ips*. *C. ips* isolates, all WIN(M): Lanes 1 & 24, 88-100B; 2, 88-105; 3, 88-131; 4, 88-134; 5, 88-138; 6, 88-508; 7, 88-141; 8, 88-135; 9, 88-185; 10, 82-83d; 11, 92; 12, 82-77b; 13, 96; 14, 82-83a; 15, 82-70b; 16, 82-85b; 17, 82-87a; 18, 82-57b; 20, 391; 21, 82-70a; 22, 182; 23, 114; 19, *C. montia*, CBS 151.78.

The possibility of using mitochondrial profiles as molecular characters was investigated by analyzing intraspecific variability at the mtDNA level in the *C. ips* isolates, plus those of *C. adjuncta*, *C. montia*, and *C. pilifera* (B-94) as outgroups. Two four-cutter profiles were generated by digesting total DNA samples with *Hae*III and *Msp*I and hybridizing

Southern blots with a probe consisting of radiolabelled pure mtDNA prepared from strain 82-57b. The combined F-values (Table 4) determined from these mtDNA restriction profiles (Fig. 3) distinguish between *C. ips* strains from New Zealand and Scandinavia, except for strain 88-100b which clusters with the Scandinavian strains. The F-values

TABLE 3. Combined F-values (fraction of common bands between two tested species) following restriction of rDNA with *Mbo*I and *Msp*I for twelve presumed species of the Ophiostomataceae.

	C.i.[1]	C.a.	C.m. 151 78	C.m. 450	C.o.	O.f.	C.h.	C.p.	C.f.	C.p.
C. ips WIN(M)82-57b										
C. adjuncta	0.73									
C. montia CBS 151.78	0.71	0.76								
C. montia C450	0.71	0.76	0.93							
C. ossiformis	0.76	0.81	0.85	0.73						
O. flexuosum	0.71	0.76	0.67	0.67	0.61					
C. hyalothecium	0.81	0.83	0.73	0.73	0.73	0.58				
C. pilifera WIN(M) 82-129d	0.71	0.83	0.93	0.80	0.79	0.65	0.65			
C. fimbriata	0.13	0.14	0.14	0.21	0.13	0.07	0.07	0.07		
C. penicillata	0.27	0.36	0.41	0.34	0.31	0.27	0.27	0.28	0.21	
S. fimicola	0.07	0.08	0.07	0.07	0.07	0.07	0.07	0.07	0	0.08

[1]As the *Msp*I and *Rsa*I profiles of all *C. ips* strains tested earlier had been the same, only one representative strain was included here.

that resulted from comparing the New Zealand strains with the Scandinavian strains range from 0.50 to 0.62, while F-values within the Scandinavian strains ranged from 0.70 to 0.93. Within the New Zealand strains, except for 88-100B, F-values ranged from 0.82 to 1.0. In addition, the New Zealand strains appear to represent at least two clusters [(88-105, 88-131, 88-138, 88-141, 88-134, 82-185) and (88-105, 82-83d, 82-70a, 82-83a, 82-87a, 82-70b, 82-57b, 82-85b)] corresponding to the two separate geographical regions of New Zealand from which they originated. The F-values for the outgroups included within this survey ranged from 0.07 to 0.24. For the restriction profiles of *C. adjuncti, C. montia,* and *C. pilifera,* when compared to those of the *C. ips* strains, the F-values never exceeded 0.2. The two *C. montia* strains shared an F-value of 0.58, which is within the range

observed for the *C. ips* strains. Overall, the mtDNA profiles were quite diverse, suggesting that mtDNA might be useful for DNA typing of strains.

No classification system for fungi assigned to *Ceratocystis s.l.* is yet fully accepted, although *C. ips* is often considered the central species of the Ips spore-group (4,20,27). This group is characterized by species with ascospores that appear rectangular, ossiform, or pillow-shaped in side or plan view, spherical in end view, and are never curved (20). These spore characters still seem to set this group of species apart regardless of the taxonomic treatment followed (2,11,27).

Our results suggest that the only reliable morphological characters that should be used to identify strains as *C. ips* are ascospore size and shape. Even strains showing consistent significant differences

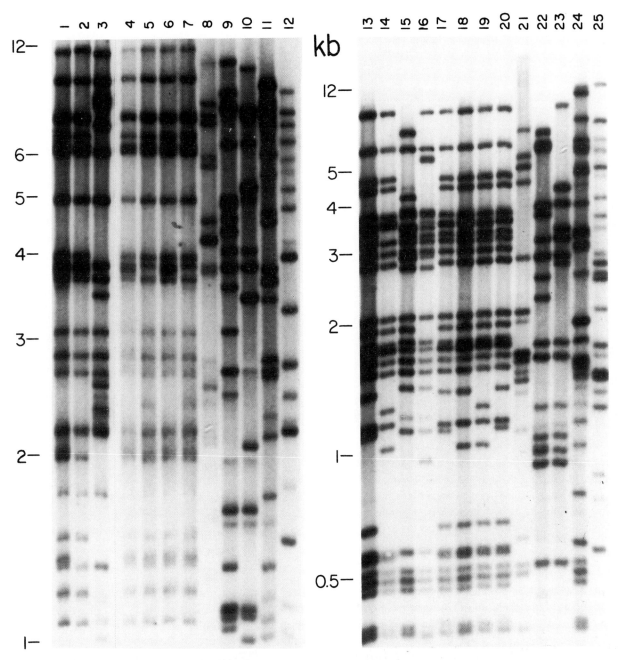

Fig. 3. Southern hybridizations of *Hae*III (lanes 1-12) and *Msp*I (lanes 13-25) digested whole cell DNAs with radio labelled, mtDNA from *C. ips* isolate 82-57b showing different patterns between species. Twelve isolates representing five species were tested. *C. ips* isolates, all WIN(M): Lanes 1 & 16, 82-87a; 2 & 13, 88-134; 3 & 14, 88-100B; 4 & 17, 82-57b; 5 & 18, 82-70a; 6 & 19, 82-85b; 7 & 20, 82-70b; 15, 96; 8 & 12, *C. adjuncta*; 9 & 22, *C. montia*, CBS 151.78; 10 & 23, *C. montia*, C-450; 11 & 24, *Ceratocystis* sp.; 12 & 25, *C. pilifera*, B-94. NOTE: There is no *Hae*III digestion for WIN(M) 96.

in the secondary characters noted earlier were confirmed as *C. ips* by the molecular techniques employed when their ascospores were similar in shape and

size. Further, the molecular characters of the two *C. montia* strains tested suggest that this species is distinct from *C. ips*. Upadhyay (27) synonymized

TABLE 4. Combined F-values (fraction of common bands between two tested strains) following restriction of mtDNA with *Hae*III and *Msp*I of twenty-seven isolates of six species of the Ophiostomataceae.

	88[1]-100B	182	92	114	96	88-105	88[2]-131	88-135	82-77b	88[3]-508	82-83a	82[4]-87a	82[5]-57b	C.a	C.m 151.78	C.m 450
WIN(M)																
88-100B																
182	0.84															
92	0.84	0.88														
114	0.84	0.93	0.92													
96	0.80	0.75	0.70	0.73												
88-105	0.56	0.57	0.52	0.52	0.60											
88-131	0.56	0.54	0.52	0.52	0.54	0.98										
88-135	0.55	0.58	0.53	0.56	0.62	0.81	0.83									
82-77b	0.55	0.55	0.54	0.55	0.61	0.86	0.90	0.95								
88-508	0.55	0.52	0.52	0.50	0.54	0.88	0.88	0.86	0.91							
82-83a	0.55	0.54	0.53	0.52	0.55	0.87	0.87	0.85	0.90	0.99						
82-87a	0.55	0.54	0.54	0.52	0.56	0.88	0.88	0.86	0.88	0.89	0.97					
82-57b	0.53	0.54	0.54	0.52	0.56	0.92	0.92	0.82	0.92	0.94	0.93	0.96				
C. adjuncta	0.14	0.15	0.15	0.15	0.15	0.18	0.18	0.19	0.18	0.18	0.17	0.11	0.17			
C. montia CBS 151.78	0.16	0.17	0.17	0.17	0.17	0.17	0.17	0.17	0.17	0.17	0.16	0.16	0.16	0.12		
C. montia C450	0.19	0.18	0.18	0.18	0.18	0.18	0.18	0.19	0.18	0.18	0.17	0.17	0.17	0.13	0.58	
C. pilifera B-94	0.09	0.09	0.09	0.09	0.09	0.09	0.18	0.11	0.09	0.09	0.09	0.09	0.09	0.14	0.11	0.09

[1] Strain 391 had an F-value identical to strain 88-100b.
[2] Strain 88-134, 88-138, and 88-141 had F-values identical to strain 88-131.
[3] Strain 82-70a and 82-83d had F-values identical to strain 88-508.
[4] Strain 82-70b had an F-value identical to strain 82-87a.
[5] Strain 82-85b had an F-value identical to strain 82-57b.

C. montia with *C. ips* because their ascocarp bases overlapped in size. Rumbold (23) distinguished the two species on characters such as ascospore size, temperature range for growth and anamorph complexity. Such differences do exist, and their significance is confirmed by the molecular separation of *C. montia* from *C. ips*.

All *C. ips* strains tested yielded identical four-cutter rDNA restriction profiles, but those of the *C. montia* isolates differed from each other. However, the mtDNA divergence between the *C. montia* strains was within the range observed among the *C. ips* strains. Thus if both strains are *C. montia*, the ribosomal sequences would appear to be evolving faster relative to the mtDNA sequences than is the case in *C. ips*. This would be most unusual. Unfortunately, neither *C. montia* strain produced perithecia in culture so their identities could not be verified. Only a study of authentic strains of *C. montia* will clarify the nature of this case of apparent intraspecific variation.

These results illustrate the importance of examining both rDNA and mtDNA when morphologically similar strains or species are studied (7,24,25,26). As mitochondrial polymorphisms appear to arise very rapidly (5), mtDNA is not very useful when more distantly related species are studied (24,26,30).

TABLE 5. Combined F-values (fraction of common bands between two tested species) following restriction of rDNA with *Mbo*I, *Rsa*I, *Msp*I, *Hha*I, and *Alu*I for fifteen presumed species of the Ophiostomataceae and two unrelated species.

	C. fi.	C. pa.	C.r.	C.a.	Ch. sp.	C. au.	C. fa.	C.i.	C.p	S.f.	N.f.	C. pe.	C. pi.	C. mi.	E.a.	E.c.
C. fimbriata																
C. paradoxa	0.78															
C. radicicola	0.82	0.86														
C. adiposa	0.76	0.75	0.76													
Chalara sp.	0.25	0.34	0.35	0.26												
C. autographa	0.25	0.25	0.25	0.27	0.38											
C. falcata	0.10	0.10	0.10	0.09	0.13	0.07										
C. ips WIN(M)82-57b	0.32	0.33	0.32	0.31	0.15	0.13	0.06									
C. pilifera B-94	0.29	0.27	0.22	0.26	0.01	0.10	0.03	0.64								
S. fimicola	0	0	0	0	0	0	0	0.03	0.03							
N. fischeri	0.12	0.12	0.12	0.15	0.06	0.03	0.06	0.20	0.15	0.02						
C. penicillata	0.29	0.30	0.29	0.31	0.12	0.06	0.06	0.41	0.36	0	0.25					
C. piceaperda	0.30	0.30	0.30	0.30	0.11	0.11	0.06	0.42	0.36	0	0.22	0.70				
C. minuta	0.21	0.21	0.21	0.23	0.05	0.08	0.03	0.32	0.27	0	0.12	0.45	0.49			
E. aureum	0.21	0.21	0.21	0.16	0.29	0.09	0.03	0.32	0.25	0	0.16	0.55	0.55	0.50		
E. clavigerum	0.22	0.22	0.22	0.22	0.05	0.08	0.03	0.30	0.26	0	0.15	0.54	0.55	0.51	0.89	
E. triancriforme	0.21	0.22	0.22	0.21	0.05	0.08	0.03	0.28	0.25	0	0.15	0.50	0.50	0.43	0.79	0.74

RFLP ANALYSIS OF SPECIES OF *CERATOCYSTIS SENSU LATO*

The position of *C. ips* within *Ceratocystis s.l.* was examined by a comparison of its four-cutter profiles with those of 14 other species. The latter were selected because collectively they illustrate many of the morphological features found within the genus. An isolate of *N. fischeri* and of a *Chalara* species were included as outgroups. The restriction profiles were generated with *Mbo*I, *Rsa*I, *Msp*I, *Hha*I, and *Alu*I, and Table 5 records the combined F-values obtained for all endonucleases with each strain pair compared. These values suggest *C. autographa* and *C. falcata* do not belong in *Ceratocystis s.l.*, and that *S. fimicola,* which also shares only low F-values with all other strains tested, has its true affinities elsewhere. *C. ips* shared a relatively high F-value (0.64) only with *C. pilifera*; this was expected from earlier results.

The four-cutter profiles suggest that *Ceratocystis s.l.* is heterogeneous but does include subgroups of related species. For example, the species having *Chalara* anamorphs and ascospores representative of the Fimbriata-spore group (20) shared high F-values but their F-values with other species were low (<0.30). This supports the contention that *Ceratocystis* species with *Chalara* anamorphs form a discrete group (1,11). Our results also support synonymizing *C. major* with *C. adiposa*; all restriction profiles were identical (F = 1.0).

The relatively high F-values among the *Europhium* species sets them apart from other species. Thus, *Europhium* is a discrete genus, not to be merged with either *Ceratocystis s.l.* (27) or *Ophiostoma* (9,11). The F-values also suggest the Europhium species are not conspecific as speculated by Harrington (10).

It has been proposed that yeasts with galeate ascospores could be related to the Ophiostomataceae (21; Kendrick *et al.* this volume), although this was discounted on several other grounds by Benny and Kimbrough (4). To test this hypothesis, *Hae*III and *Msp*I restriction profiles were generated for strains of *C. fragrans*, *E. decipiens* and four species of the Fimbriata-spore group (Fig. 4). The two yeast-species profiles have little in common with either those of the

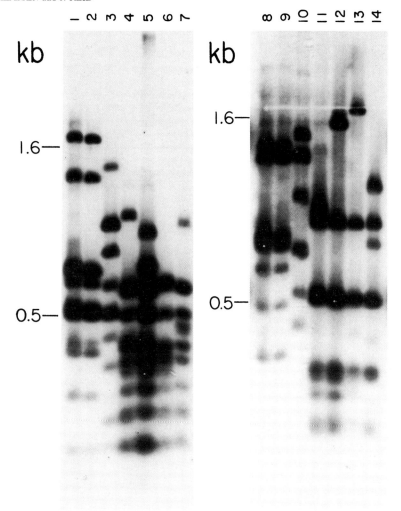

Fig. 4. Southern hybridizations of *Hae*III (lanes 1-7) and *Msp*I (lanes 8-14) digested whole cell DNAs with radiolabelled, rDNA-containing plasmid pMF2 showing differences between yeasts and species of *Ceratocystis s.l.* Lanes 1 & 8, *Cephaloascus fragrans*, ATCC 60760; 2 & 9, *C. fragrans*, ATCC 36174; 3 & 10, *E. decipiens*; 4 & 11, *Ceratocystis paradoxa*; 5 & 12, *C. adiposa*; 6 & 13, *C. fimbriata*; 7 & 14, *C. coerulescens*.

Ceratocystis species or with each other. However, *C. coerulescens*, which possesses an endoconidial anamorph, was also included here and it clustered with the species of *Ceratocystis* that have *Chalara* anamorphs. Our results are at variance with those of Upadhyay (27); he placed *C. adiposa* and *C. fimbriata* in section *Ceratocystis* of *Ceratocystis sensu* Upadhyay, but *C. coerulescens, C. paradoxa*, and *C. radicicola* in section *Endocondiophora*.

DISCUSSION

Although ascospore shape proved to be important in defining *C. ips*, our results do not support dividing *Ceratocystis s.l.* into the spore groups of Olchowecki and Reid (20). *Ceratocystis pilifera*, the central species of the Pilifera spore-group, appears closely related to

the Ips spore-group; thus, a clear separation between these groups is questioned. Conversely, recognition of the Fimbriata spore-group appears justified based on the F-values of *C. fimbriata, C. adiposa, C. paradoxa*, and *C. radicicola. C. coerulescens*, which Olchowecki and Reid (20) placed in their Pilifera spore-group, is actually closely related to the Fimbriata spore-group. All tested members of the Fimbriata spore-group have *Chalara* anamorphs; this supports de Hoog and Scheffer's (11) contention that only species with endoconidial anamorphs belong in *Ceratocystis sensu stricto*. Their contention is also supported by the cell wall chemistry and cycloheximide tolerance found in species of *Ceratocystis s.str.* (Samuels, this volume). However, based on our obtained F-values, *C. autographa*, which has a *Chalara* anamorph, should be excluded from *Ceratocystis s.str.* De Hoog and

Scheffer (11) also noted this anomaly; we believe currently available strains do not represent *C. autographa sensu* Bakshi.

Upadhyay and Kendrick (28) erected the genus *Ceratocystiopsis* for members of Olchowecki and Reid's (20) Minuta spore-group. However *Ceratocystiopsis falcata*, a species with two-celled ascospores and two *Chalara* synanamorphs (12), showed little relatedness to either *C. minuta*, the type species of *Ceratocystiopsis*, or to any other species of *Ceratocystis s.l.* If *C. falcata* is proven to be related to *Pyxidiophora* (11), then the suggestion that *Ceratocystis s.str.* also belongs in the Pyxidiophoraceae (2) appears inappropriate.

The fact that some yeast species produce galeate ascospores does not appear indicative of a relationship with galeate-ascospore-producing species of *Ceratocystis s.l.* The yeast profiles we obtained were quite different from those of the compared *Ceratocystis* species; this finding supports Benny and Kimbrough's (4) view that there is not a close relationship between the Ophiostomataceae and the Endomycetales.

Although restriction patterns are useful in studying closely related species, problems arise when more distant species are examined. Simple fragment comparisons should not be used once F-values fall below 0.25 because there is a possibility that two unrelated DNA samples could contain fragments of the same size even though cleavage sites are different (14). Complete restriction site maps could be constructed but this is a very time consuming process (6).

CONCLUSIONS

Four-cutter analysis of rDNA and mtDNA is a method for rapidly screening large numbers of strains. Because F-values are influenced by point mutations at restriction sites and insertions and deletions between sites, the F-values reflect evolutionary change. Although morphological change and molecular divergence are quite independent and respond to different evolutionary pressures (31,32), molecular taxonomy can be important in assessing the significance of morphological divergence.

From our limited study, it would appear that the following represent discrete genera: *Ceratocystis s.str.* (excepting strains currently identified as *C. autographa*); *Ceratocystiopsis* (excluding *C. falcata*); *Ophiostoma* (for the Ips and Pilifera spore groups); *Europhium*; and *Sphaeronaemella*. We doubt that

either *Ceratocystiopsis* (28) or *Ophiostoma* (11,9) represent natural groupings, but this will be resolved only when more species of *Ceratocystis s.l.* have been studied using molecular techniques.

Ultimately, proper assessment of relationships within *Ceratocystis s.l.* will require DNA sequencing of the rDNA genes. However the genus is very large and sequencing appropriate strains of all of its species will be very time consuming and expensive. Therefore, our approach could be useful in screening and grouping strains to determine which species are of sufficient phylogenetic interest to warrant full DNA sequence analysis.

LITERATURE CITED

1. Arx, J.A. von 1987. Plant Pathogenic Fungi. J. Cramer, Stuttgart Berlin. 288 pp.

2. Arx, J.A. von and van der Walt, J.P. 1987. Ophiostomatales and Endomycetales. Pages 167-176 in: The Expanding Realm of Yeast-Like Fungi. G.S. de Hoog and A.C.M. Weijman, eds. Stud. Mycol. 30.

3. Appels, R. and Dvorak, J. 1982. Relative rates of divergence of spacer and gene sequences within the rDNA in the Triticeae: Implications for the maintenance of homogeneity of a repeated gene family. Theor. Appl. Gen. 63:361-365.

4. Benny, G.R. and Kimbrough, J.W. 1980. A synopsis of the orders and families of Plectomycetes with keys to genera. Mycotaxon 12:1-91.

5. Brown, W.M., George, M., Jr. and Wilson, A.C. 1979. Rapid evolution of animal mitochondrial DNA. Proc. Nat. Acad. Sci. USA. 76:1967-1971.

6. Dowlin, T.E., Moritz, C. and Palmer, J.D. 1990. Nucleic Acids II: Restriction site analysis. Pages 250-317 in: Molecular Systematics. D.M. Hillis and C. Moritz, eds. Sinauer Associates, Sunderland, MA. 588 pp.

7. Förster, H., Kinscherf, T.G., Leong, S.A. Maxwell, D.P. 1988. Estimation of relatedness between *Phytophthora* species by analysis of mitochondrial DNA. Mycologia 80:466-478.

8. Free, S.J., Rice, P.W. and Metzenberg, R.L. 1979. Arrangement of the genes coding for ribosomal ribonucleic acids in *Neurospora crassa*. J. Bacteriol. 137:1219-1226.

9. Harrington, T.C. 1987. New combinations in *Ophiostoma* of *Ceratocystis* species with *Leptographium* anamorphs. Mycotaxon 28:39-43.

10. Harrington, T.C. 1988. *Leptographium* species, their distributions, hosts and insect vectors. Pages 1-39 in: Leptographium Root Diseases on Conifers. T.C. Harrington and F.W. Cobb, Jr. eds. American Phytopathological Society Press, St. Paul, MN. 149 pp.

11. Hoog, G.S. de and Scheffer, R.J. 1984. *Ceratocystis* versus *Ophiostoma*: A reappraisal. Mycologia 76:292-299.

12. Hutchison, L.J. and Reid, J. 1988. Taxonomy of some potential woodstaining fungi from New Zealand. 1. Ophiostomataceae. N. Z. J. Bot. 26:63-81.

13. Johnston, A. and Booth, C. (ed.) 1983. Plant Pathologist's

Pocketbook. Commonwealth Mycological Institute, Kew.

14. Kessler, L.G. and Avise, J.C. 1985. A comparative description of mitochondrial differentiation in selected avian and other vertebrate genera. Mol. Biol. Evol. 2:109-126.

15. Kim, W.K., Mauthe, W., Hausner, G. and Klassen, G.R. 1990. Isolation of high molecular weight DNA and double-stranded RNAs from fungi. Can. J. Bot. 68:1898-1902.

16. Klassen, G.R., McNabb, S.A. and Dick, M.W. 1987. Comparison of physical maps of ribosomal DNA repeating units in *Pythium*, *Phytophthora* and *Apodachlya*. J. Gen. Microbiol. 133:2953-2959.

17. Kozlowski, M. and Stepien, P.P. 1982. Restriction enzyme analysis of mitochondrial DNA of members of the genus *Aspergillus* as an aid to taxonomy. J. Gen. Microbiol. 128:471-476.

18. Kurtzman, C.P. 1985. Molecular taxonomy of the fungi. Pages 35-63 in: Gene Manipulations in Fungi. J.W. Bennett and L.L. Lasure, eds. Academic Press. Orlando, FLA. 558 pp.

19. Murray, M.G. and Thompson, W.F. 1980. Rapid isolation of high molecular weight plant DNA. Nucleic Acids Res. 8:4321-4325.

20. Olchowecki, A. and Reid, J. 1974. Taxonomy of the genus *Ceratocystis* in Manitoba. Can. J. Bot. 52:1675-1711.

21. Redhead, S.A. and Malloch, D.W. 1977. The Endomycetaceae: new concepts, new taxa. Can. J. Bot. 55:1701-1711.

22. Rogers, S.O., Rehner, S., Bledsoe, C., Mueller, G.J., and Ammirati, J.F. 1989. Extraction of DNA from Basidiomycetes for ribosmal DNA hybridizations. Can. J. Bot. 67:1235-1243.

23. Rumbold, C.T. 1941. A blue stain fungus, *Ceratostomella montium* n.sp., and some yeasts associated with two species of *Dendroctonus*. J. Agric. Res. 62:589-601.

24. Smith, M.L. and Anderson, J.B. 1989. Restriction fragment length polymorphisms in mitochondrial DNAs of *Armillaria*: identification of North American biological species. Mycol. Res. 93:247-256.

25. Taylor, J.W. 1986. Fungal evolutionary biology and mitochondrial DNA. Exp. Mycol. 10:259-269.

26. Taylor, J.W. and Natvig, D.O. 1989. Mitochondrial DNA and evolution of heterothallic and pseudohomothallic *Neurospora* species. Mycol. Res. 93:257-272.

27. Upadhyay, H.P. 1981. A monograph of *Ceratocystis* and *Ceratocystiopsis*. University of Georgia Press, Athens, GA. 176 pp.

28. Upadhyay, H.P. and Kendrick, W.B. 1975. Prodromus for a revision of *Ceratocystis* (Microascales, Ascomycetes) and its conidial states. Mycologia 67:798-805.

29. Varma, A. and Kwong-Chung, K.J. 1989. Restriction fragment polymorphism in mitochondrial DNA of *Cryptococcus neoformans*. J. Gen. Microbiol. 135:3353-3362.

30. Weber, C.A., Hudspeth, M.E.S., Moore, G.P. and Grossman, L.I. 1986. Analysis of the mitochondrial and nuclear genomes of two basidiomycetes, *Coprinus cereus* and *Coprinus stercorarias*. Curr. Gen. 10:515-525.

31. Wilson, A.C., Sarich, V.M. and Maxson, L.R. 1974. The importance of gene rearrangement in evolution: Evidence from studies of rates of chromosomal, protein, and anatomical evolution. Proc. Nat. Acad. Sci. 72:5061-5065.

32. Wilson, A.C., Carlson, S.S. and White, T.J. 1977. Biochemical Evolution. Ann. Rev. Biochem. 46:473-639.

Chapter 11

CONSIDERATION OF HIGHER TAXONOMIC RELATIONSHIPS INVOLVING *PYXIDIOPHORA*

M. BLACKWELL, J.W. SPATAFORA, D. MALLOCH and J.W. TAYLOR

INTRODUCTION

Pyxidiophora is a genus of Ascomycetes with long- to short-necked ascomata, early evanescent basal asci and ascospores that undergo extreme morphological changes during maturation. Ontogeny of late-maturing ascospores has led to taxonomic confusion at the generic level. Lundqvist's important work (17) placed five genera *(Mycorhynchus, Treleasia, Copranophilis, Ascolanthanus, and Acariniola)* into synonymy with *Pyxidiophora* and clarified the generic limits. Lundqvist (17) also noted that ascospores of *Pyxidiophora* become attached to phoretic mites of bark beetles. The ascospores previously had been described as minute thalli of *Thaxteriola* and *Acariniola* but ascospores did not produce conidia and were not thought at that time to have a connection with *Thaxteriola*.

The relatively recent transfer of *Ceratocystis* to the Pyxidiophoraceae and inclusion of the family in the Ophiostomatales (28) make a discussion of *Pyxidiophora* relevant here. We will review life history details of the genus and emphasize usefulness of nuclear encoded small subunit ribosomal DNA sequence data in confirming an anamorph connection; these data also corroborate removal of one species from the genus.

Life History of *Pyxidiophora*

Not long after *Pyxidiophora* was described in Europe (12), Thaxter (27) provided beautiful illustrations of a minute fungus on beetles in North America; he was uncertain of its disposition, but included it as an undescribed species of *Amphoromorpha*. Spegazzini (26) described two similar fungi as species of *Thaxteriola*. Thaxter (28) realized his fungus belonged in this genus and provided a formal description of the third species. Only two additional species of *Thaxteriola* and a similar form, *Acariniola*, with two species have been described since 1920 (19,23). However, the presence on phoretic mites of ascospores of *Pyxidiophora* and the anamorphs developing directly from them,

provides evidence for many undiscovered species, particularly in wood where several species are known to be associated with bark beetles (11).

The astute observations of Thelma Perry, U.S. Forest Service, Southern Forest Experiment Station, Pineville, Louisiana, led to the discovery that, indeed, *Pyxidiophora* and *Thaxteriola* are related (9,10). Examination of hundreds of phoretic mites on bark beetles yielded a few fungal specimens in which the ascospores of *Pyxidiophora kimbroughii* had undergone direct development and become conidium-producing *Thaxteriola* thalli. The rarity of the conidium-producing thalli from phoretic mites is probably a collection artifact because beetles are collected as they leave the habitat carrying mites only recently infested with the young ascospores. Additional species of *Pyxidiophora* have been observed with similar life cycles (5) and *P. lundqvistii* has been shown to produce an *Acariniola*-type ascospore that also adheres to mites (8). Arthropod dispersal in the life history of *P. lundqvistii* probably is representative of most species of *Pyxidiophora*.

More recently, Blackwell and Malloch (5,6) have concentrated on studying *Pyxidiophora* species in dung substrates. Beetles and their phoretic mites can be trapped as they arrive at the new substrates with mature ascospores or newly developed anamorphs and, because they can be observed on the substrate, it has been easier to make critical observations on the life histories of all the associated organisms. These studies (5-8) indicate that many species of fungi in quickly decomposing habitats, including *Pyxidiophora* spp., rely upon arthropod dispersal (See Malloch and Blackwell, this volume).

Classification of *Pyxidiophora*

Here we discuss the phylogenetic relationship of *Pyxidiophora* to other fungi. A phylogenetic classification requires that an attempt be made to place the genus in a monophyletic group, not merely grouped with other arthropod dispersed fungi, including the Ophiostomatales, that are suspected of being the result of convergent evolution (14). *Pyxidiophora*, in all its incarnations, has usually been placed in the Hypocreales (see 17). As Lundqvist pointed out, only Spegazzini (25), who described *Treleasia* and *Copranophilis*, now both synonymized with *Pyxidiophora*, had doubts about the relationship of the genus to the Hypocreales.

At a time when the Melanosporaceae was classified in the Hypocreales (1), Arnold (2) described the Pyxidiophoraceae, which he believed related to the Melanosporaceae. Rogerson (20) pointed out how poorly known many of these fungi were. In fact, of 104 genera (including *Pyxidiophora, Mycorhynchus,* and *Treleasia*) in his key to the Hypocreales, he considered only ten genera to be known well enough to be certain of their placement in the order. Lundqvist (17) expanded the Pyxidiophoraceae of Arnold to include the cleistothecial *Mycorhynchidium* Malloch and Cain with ascospores of the same distinct morphology as those of *Pyxidiophora*. However, recent radical changes have been suggested for the Pyxidiophoraceae (23).

Von Arx and van der Walt (3) defined four families in the Ophiostomatales primarily on the basis of anamorphs. The Pyxidiophoraceae (23) is comprised of four genera, three of which are reported to possess *Chalara* anamorphs: *Pyxidiophora, Cryptendoxyla,* and *Ceratocystis* Ellis and Halst., and the cleistothecial *Mycorhynchidium*. Genera in the other three families of the Ophiostomatales defined by von Arx and van der Walt, including the Ophiostomataceae, generally have *Sporothrix, Leptographium,* or *Acremonium* anamorphs. In their proposal, several yeasts also were aligned with ascomatal groups, including the Metschnikowiaceae with Pyxidiophoraceae.

Although the *Chalara* anamorphs give some credence to an ophiostomatalean relationship for *Pyxidiophora* and *Ceratocystis*, Blackwell and Malloch (5) were not convinced that the anamorph connections were proven. Moreover, the evanescent, ovoid asci of *Pyxidiophora* are arranged in a basal fascicle, unlike the evanescent spherical to ellipsoidal or ovoid asci arranged uniformly throughout the ascomatal cavity generally ascribed to the *Ophiostoma*-type centrum. A detailed comparison of the morphology of *Pyxidiophora* with that of the Ophiostomatales, Hypocreales, and Sordariales was inconclusive in determining relationships (5). It is clear from the discussion of the *Pyxidiophora* life cycle that species are closely associated with arthropods and have undergone strong selection for successful

dispersal. The morphological features of arthropod-dispersed Ascomycetes that we currently use as taxonomic characters are most likely the result of convergent evolution. Therefore, we have begun to investigate other types of characters that may be useful in the inference of relationships. Here we report several aspects of sequencing studies of nuclear encoded ribosomal DNA that have bearing on the problem of distinguishing convergent structural features.

Molecular Techniques

Whole genomic DNA was extracted from ground fungi using the techniques of Lee and Taylor (16). The DNA pellet isolated from each fungus was resuspended in TE buffer and frozen (-80°C) until use in polymerase chain reaction (PCR) amplifications. Primers used to amplify small subunit rDNA and internal transcribed spacer (ITS) are those of White *et al.* (29). Double stranded rDNA was obtained by symmetrical primer directed amplification, then asymmetrically amplified to provide single stranded fragments for sequencing (22). Purity of the amplified DNA and proper fragment length were verified at each step using agarose gels with a 123 bp ladder (BRL) as a molecular weight standard; gels were stained with ethidium bromide. Dideoxy sequencing with Sequenase 2.0 (29) was used with incorporation labelling of α-^{35}S-dATP. Sequence data were aligned with the University of Wisconsin Genetics Computer Group (UWGCG) software package (13).

Molecular Evidence in *Pyxidiophora* Systematics

Although Blackwell and Malloch (5) were hesitant to accept previous *Pyxidiophora-Chalara* connections, they described another non-hypocrealean presumptive anamorph for *Pyxidiophora* species from moose dung in Canada (6). Cultures established from conidia of the presumptive synnematous anamorph and the ascospore products of *Pyxidiophora* sp. were identical; however, neither synnemata nor perithecia were produced in culture. Because this anamorph was clearly non-hypocrealean in that it produced holoblastic conidia with sympodial or annellidic proliferation and because some species of the Ophiostomatales possess synnematous anamorphs with holoblastic conidia, we thought it important to establish the connection beyond doubt.

Comparison of over 500 nucleotide base positions of small subunit rDNA from *Pyxidiophora*

TABLE 1. Pairwise comparisons of percentage similarity of three nuclear rDNA regions (29). Numbers in parentheses give total bases compared between each pair.

	Synnematous anamorph			K. calyculata			K. analemmoides		
	ITS4	NS3	NS6	ITS4	NS3	NS6	ITS4	NS3	NS6
1. *Pyxidiophora* sp.	99.6 (324)	100 (207)	100 (233)	38.6[1] (317)	83.0[1] (316)	94.6 (207)	36.5[1] (397)	88.0 (239)	93.6 (254)
2. Synnematous anamorph				45.3[1] (264)	84.0[1] (315)	94.6 (207	45.2[1] (398)	88.0 (235)	93.6 (255)
3. *Kathistes calyculata*							93.0 (357)	95.0 (287)	99.0 (254)

[1] Differences in percentage similarity in comparisons are due to differences in number of nucleotides compared, not nucleotide composition.

sp. and its presumptive anamorph were identical (NS3, NS6) (29). This gene has been shown to be conserved evolutionarily in a variety of organisms (24). Identical sequences of the conserved region are an indication that the two isolates are not very different but we also examined a more variable region, the internal transcribed spacer (ITS). The pairwise comparison of over 300 bases showed only one difference, an inserted base in the ascospore isolate (Table 1). This is not unexpected below species level (15).

The molecular data provide good evidence for the synnematous anamorph connection. Furthermore, we have very recently found a *Chalara* anamorph from ascospore cultures of another *Pyxidiophora* species. This additional evidence firmly establishes that the genus has several known non-hypocrealean anamorphs (21), making its position in the order suspect. However, the combination of known anamorphs does not place *Pyxidiophora* unequivocally in a higher taxon, although similar anamorphs are found in, but not restricted to, species in the Ophiostomatales.

Pyxidiophora fimbriata was described from horse dung in Spain (4). In studies of moose dung in Ontario and New Brunswick, Canada, Malloch and Blackwell (18) described the genus *Kathistes* of the Kathistaceae with two species, *K. calyculata* and *K. analemmoides*; they also transferred *P. fimbriata* to *Kathistes*. All three species are characterized by long

dark ascomatal necks similar to those of *P. badiorostris* and evanescent basal asci. These fungi also are associated with arthropods. However, the ascospores are very different from those of *Pyxidiophora* and a unique structure, the sporidioma, is found associated with ascomata in all three species, including the holotype of *P. fimbriata*. Sporidiomata of this type are unknown in any other fungi.

While we do not have cultures of *K. fimbriata*, the two Canadian species grow well as yeasts and have provided DNA for sequencing in the rDNA regions already described for *Pyxidiophora* species Pairwise comparisons between the morphologically similar *K. calyculata* and *K. analemmoides* show that the sequences are divergent, especially in the ITS. More importantly, the comparisons of these two species with *Pyxidiophora* species (and its anamorph) show a high level of dissimilarity, especially in the ITS (Table 1). The recognition of *Kathistes* as distinct from *Pyxidiophora* on the basis of morphological characters (18) is supported by the degree of nucleic acid divergence; however, cladistic analysis may ultimately provide stronger evidence of the separation.

CONCLUSIONS

The application of PCR and sequencing techniques has provided important new clues in the study of the enigmatic genus *Pyxidiophora*. We have been able to make an anamorph connection with one species of *Pyxidiophora* and to show genetic divergence between *Pyxidiophora* and *Kathistes*. These techniques and the cladistic analysis of sequence data from carefully selected taxa should eventually provide an independent data set, the analysis of which will be important in assessing higher relationships among fungi with similar structural features resulting from convergent evolution.

ACKNOWLEDGEMENTS

We are grateful to Dr. Thomas J. White and Dr. Thomas D. Bruns for giving us primer sequences before publication. Dr. Donald H. Pfister has made numerous specimens available from the Farlow Herbarium, Harvard University, and participated in insightful discussions. Dr. Russell L. Chapman gave constructive criticism throughout this study. Essential field studies were carried out in Algonquin Park, Ontario and at the Huntsman Marine Centre, New Brunswick; we are grateful to the directors of these facilities for their help. We acknowledge the financial support of NSF (BSR-8604656 and BSR-8918157 to M.B.; NSF-BSR8516513 to J.W.T.), NIH (AI 28545-01 to J.W.T.), and NSERC (OGP0000145 to D.M.).

LITERATURE CITED

1. Alexpoulos, C.J. 1962. Introductory Mycology, 2nd ed. Wiley, New York. 613 pp.

2. Arnold, G.R.W. 1971. Über einige neue Taxa und Kombinationen de Sphaeriales. Z. Pilzk. 37:187-198.

3. Arx, J.A. von and Van der Walt, J.P. 1987. Ophiostomatales and Endomycetales. Pages 167-176 in: The expanding realm of yeast-like fungi G.S. de Hoog, M. Th. Smith and A.C.M. Weijman, eds. Stud. Mycol. 30.

4. Barrasa, J.M. and Moreno, G. 1982. *Pyxidiophora badiorostris* Lundq. y *Pyxidiophora fimbriata* sp. nov., in España (Pyrenomycetes). Crypt. Mycol. 3:41-49.

5. Blackwell, M. and Malloch, D. 1989a. *Pyxidiophora*: A link between the Laboulbeniales and hyphal ascomycetes. Mem. N.Y. Bot. Gard. 49:23-32.

6. Blackwell, M. and Malloch, D. 1989b. *Pyxidiophora*: Life histories and arthropod associations of two species. Can. J. Bot. 67:2552-2562.

7. Blackwell, M. and Malloch, D. 1989c. Similarity of *Amphoromorpha* and secondary capilliconidia of *Basidiobolus*. Mycologia 81:735-741.

8. Blackwell, M. and Malloch, D. 1990. Discovery of a *Pyxidiophora* with *Acariniola*-type ascospores. Mycol. Res. 94:415-417.

9. Blackwell, M., Bridges, J.R., Moser, J.C. and Perry, T.J. 1986a. Hyperphoretic dispersal of a *Pyxidiophora* anamorph. Science 232:993-995.

10. Blackwell, M., Perry, T.J., Bridges, J.R. and Moser, J.C. 1986b. A new species of *Pyxidiophora* and its *Thaxteriola* anamorph. Mycologia 78:607-614.

11. Blackwell, M., Moser, J.C. and Wisniewski, J. 1989. Ascospores of *Pyxidiophora* on mites associated with beetles in trees and wood. Mycol. Res. 92:397-403.

12. Brefeld, O. and von Tavel, F. 1891. Die Hemiasci und die Ascomyceten. Pages 1-7 in: Brefeld, O. Untersuchungen aus dem Gesammtgebiete der Mykologie 9. Leipzig, Germany. 156 pp.

13. Devereux, J., Haeberli, P. and Smithies, O. 1984. A comprehensive set of sequence analysis programs for the VAX. Nucleic Acids Res. 12: 387-395.

14. Harrington, T.C. 1987. New combinations in *Ophiostoma* of *Ceratocystis* species with *Leptographium* anamorphs. Mycotaxon 28:39-43.

15. Jorgensen, R.A. and Cluster, P.D. 1988. Modes and tempos in the evolution of nuclear ribosomal DNA: new characters for evolutionary studies and new markers for genetic and population studies. Ann. Mo. Bot. Gard. 75:1238-1247.

16. Lee, S.B. and Taylor, J.W. 1990. Isolation of total DNA from fungi for amplification by the polymerase chain reaction. Pages 282-287 in: PCR Protocols: A Guide to Methods and Applications. M.A. Innis, D.H. Gelfand, J.J. Sninsky and T.J. White eds. Academic Press, New York. 482 pp.

17. Lundqvist, N. 1980. On the genus *Pyxidiophora sensu lato* (Pyrenomycetes). Bot. Notiser 133:121-144.

18. Malloch, D. and Blackwell, M. 1990. *Kathistes*, a new genus of pleomorphic ascomycetes. Can. J. Bot. 58:1712-1721.

19. Majewski, T. and Wisniewski, J. 1978. New species of parasitic fungi occurring on mites (Acarina). Acta Mycol. 14:3-12.

20. Rogerson, C.T. 1970. The hypocrealean fungi (Ascomycetes, Hypocreales). Mycologia 62:865-910.

21. Samuels, G.J. and Seifert, K.A. 1987. Taxonomic implications of variation among hypocrealean anamorphs. Pages 29-56 in: Pleomorphic fungi: the diversity and its taxonomic implications. J. Sugiyama, ed. Kodansha, Tokyo and Elsevier, New York. 325 pp.

22. Saiki, R.K., Gelfand, D.H., Stoffel, S., Scharf, S.J., Higuchi, T., Horn, G.T., Mullis, K.B. and Erlich, H.A. 1988. Primer-directed enzymatic amplification of DNA with thermostable DNA polymerase. Science 239:487-491.

23. Simpson, J.A. and Stone, C. 1987. A new species of *Thaxteriola* associated with mites in Australia. Mycotaxon 30:1-4.

24. Sogin, M.L. and Gunderson, J.H. 1987. Structural diversity of eukaryotic small subunit RNAs: evolutionary implications. Endocytobiology III. Ann. N.Y. Acad. Sci. 503:125-139.

25. Spegazzini, C. 1909. Mycetes argentinenses. An. Mus. Nac. Hist. Nat. Buenos Aires 19:257-458.

26. Spegazzini, C. 1918. Observaciones microbiológicas. An. Soc. Cient. Argent. 85:311-323.

27. Thaxter, R. 1914. On certain peculiar fungus-parasites of living insects. Bot. Gaz. 58:235-253.

28. Thaxter, R. 1920. Second note on certain peculiar fungus-parasites of living insects. Bot. Gaz. 69:1-27.

29. White, T.J., Bruns, T.D., Lee, S.B. and Taylor, J.W. 1990. Analysis of phylogenetic relationships by amplification and direct sequencing of ribosomal DNA genes. Pages 315-322 in: PCR Protocols: A Guide to Methods and Applications. M.A. Innis, D.H. Gelfand, J.J. Sninsky and T.J. White, eds. Academic Press, New York. 482 pp.

Chapter 12

POTENTIAL VALUE OF CELLULAR LONG-CHAIN FATTY ACID COMPOSITION IN THE TAXONOMY OF THE OPHIOSTOMATOID FUNGI

J.L.F. KOCK, M.J. WINGFIELD and S.C. ERASMUS

INTRODUCTION

Lipids, which consist mainly of fatty acids and glycerol, occur in fungi as major constituents of membrane systems, cell wall components, storage material and as extracellular products. The most abundant fatty acids in fungi tend to be of carbon chain-lengths 16 and 18, with varying degrees of unsaturation (19).

In 1963, the first attempt to correlate lipid composition with microbial classification was made by Abel *et al.* (1). These authors showed that qualitative fatty acid analyses could be used to differentiate between various bacterial species. In surveys of the literature on the cellular long-chain fatty acid composition of plants, animals, yeasts and bacteria, various authors (15,24,25) have suggested that the distribution of fatty acids in these organisms may be useful in distinguishing taxonomic and phylogenetic relationships. Furthermore, many fatty acids may be synthesized by different pathways in different organisms and this provides an endless number of possible permutations and combinations for comparison.

The taxonomic significance of long chain fatty acid composition as a phenotypic character has been discussed by several authors (7,10,14,18,20). In these studies, however, no standardized cultivation procedures were employed. This is in spite of the fact that standardization of culture conditions has been shown to influence the fatty acid composition in yeasts (3,4,26). Recently, a standardized method for analyzing fatty acids for yeast identification has been developed in our laboratories (17,26) and has proved successful in differentiating between several yeast species and in the demarcation of new taxa. With the aid of this criterion, the new taxa *Waltiozyma* (21) and *Hasegawaea* (30) have been established. Furthermore, the genus *Nadsonia* has been revised by Golubev (9) using fatty acids as one of the taxonomic criteria. As the analysis of long chain fatty acid composition has proved to be a reasonably rapid and inexpensive means for identifying yeasts, the aim of this study was to determine whether this technique

might have practical application in the identification of *Ceratocystis* and *Ophiostoma* species, especially those believed to be related to the endomycetous yeasts (2,22).

Because no previous data were available to us, we initially considered the influence of culture age on fatty acid composition. For these experiments, an isolate of *Leptographium serpens* [anamorph of *Ophiostoma serpens*] was chosen. Once the ideal age at which to analyze cultures had been established, an attempt was made to determine the extent of variation within a species. Here, single conidial isolates from a culture of *L. serpens* were used. These studies were followed by fatty acid analyses of isolates of *L. serpens* from various geographic origins. A number of isolates identified as *L. serpens* but which, on morphological grounds, do not conform to the description of the species were included. Finally, the fatty acid composition of a number of different species of *Ceratocystis sensu stricto*, *Ophiostoma* and *Ceratocystiopsis* was analyzed in order to determine whether any differences in fatty acid composition existed between these apparently related genera.

FATTY ACID ANALYSES (FAA)

All isolates used in these studies were grown in liquid culture, harvested and lyophilized. The extraction and preparation of fatty acid methyl esters was performed according to the method described by Kock *et al.* (17), with final extraction of the esters done using n-hexane. Fatty acid methyl esters were analyzed by gas chromatography on a Hewlett-Packard model 5830A gas chromatograph equipped with dual flame-ionization detectors. Identification of the esters was performed by comparing retention times with known standards of C14:0 (myristic acid), C14:1 (myristoleic acid), C16:0 (palmitic acid), C16:1 (palmitoleic acid), C16:2 (9,12-hexadecenoic acid), C18:0 (stearic acid), C18:1 (oleic acid), C18:2 (linoleic acid) and C18:3 (linolenic acid) (Serva Chemicals). Analyses were performed

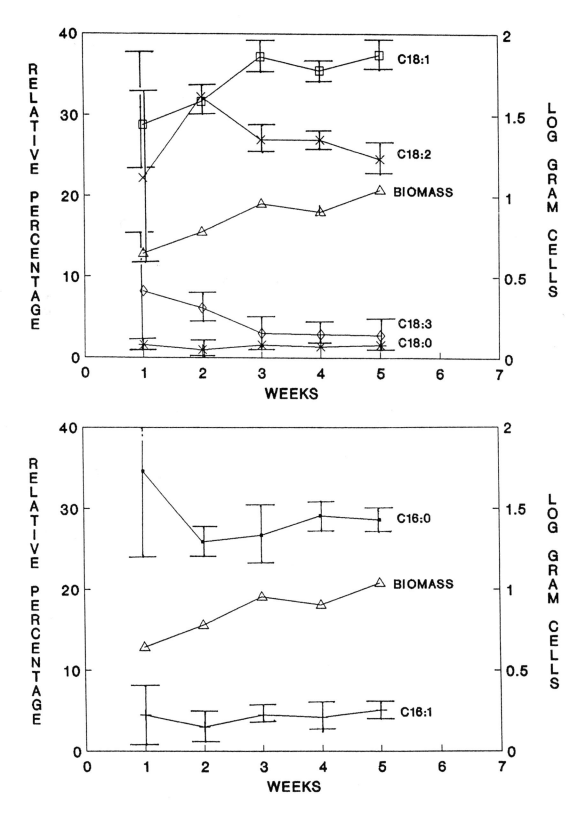

Fig.1. Changes in fatty acid composition in *L. serpens* (CMW 60). Statistical interpretation of the results were performed by using the Student's *t*-test. Each point represents the mean of triplicate results.

on a Supelco Wax 10 capillary column (30 m x 0.75 mm i.d.). The flow rate of the nitrogen carrier gas was 4 ml min^{-1} at a linear column temperature programming from 145°C to 230°C (final temperature) at a rate of 3°C min^{-1}.

An initial study evaluated the stability of fatty acid composition of *L. serpens* with culture age. An isolate of *L. serpens* obtained from insect-infested roots of *Pinus pinaster* in Grabouw, Cape Province, South Africa (CMW60, DAOM 17660) was evaluated. Stock cultures were maintained on 2% malt extract agar slants. Erlenmyer flasks (500 ml) were inoculated from slants and cultured for 6 days at 18°C on a rotary shaker at 160 r.p.m. (throw 50mm). Each flask contained 180 ml medium consisting of 80 gℓ^{-1} glucose (Merck) and 6.7 gℓ^{-1} yeast nitrogen base (YNB) (28). Samples (20 ml) of each culture were inoculated into each of 500 ml conical flasks containing the same medium. Inoculated flasks were incubated as before. Duplicate flasks were collected at the sampling times indicated. Growth was monitored by weighing the dry biomass.

All growth experiments were done in triplicate. After the appropriate time intervals, cells were harvested by centrifugation at 10,000 g for 5 min at 4°C, washed and recentrifuged three times, and resuspended in cold 0.85% NaCl. The cells were then stored at -15°C, lyophilized and their fatty acids determined.

Changes in biomass and fatty acid composition during cultivation of *L. serpens* are shown in Fig. 1. The fatty acids of *L. serpens* were predominantly esters of palmitic (C16:0), palmitoleic (C16:1), stearic (C18:0), oleic (C18:1), linoleic (C18:2) and linolenic (C18:3) acids in various proportions. Significant changes in fatty acid composition of *L. serpens* occurred only during exponential phase (1-3 weeks) (Fig. 1) in a manner similar to that found in yeasts (25). During late stationary phase (3-4 weeks), the relative composition of different fatty acids remained constant. An increase in oleic- and linoleic acid occurred for up to two weeks, while palmitic and linolenic acid decreased steadily. The other fatty acids studied remained constant during the entire growth period.

Based on these results, a culture age of three weeks was selected for the analyses of cellular fatty acids for identification purposes. This period of growth is much longer than that required for yeasts (48 h) to obtain reproducible fatty acid compositions (25).

FATTY ACID COMPOSITIONS OF SINGLE CONIDIAL ISOLATES

Variation in fatty acid composition among cultures of an individual fungal isolate was evaluated. Isolate CMW60 of *L. serpens* was grown on 2% MEA until sporulation commenced. The spore suspension was diluted serially and aliquots of

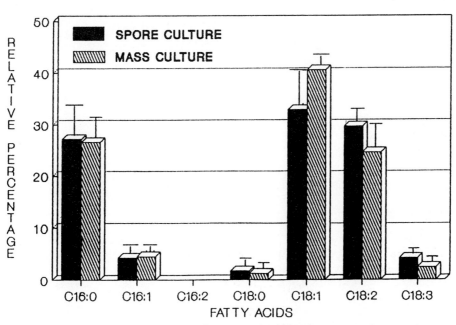

Fig. 2. Percentage fatty acid compositions of single conidial isolates and mass cultures of *L. serpens* CMW 60. Values represent the percentage of total contributed by specified fatty acid.

dilutions were spread on the surface of water agar. Ten single conidial isolates and the original isolate were cultivated and used in the fatty acid comparisons.

As might be expected, single conidial isolates contained similar cellular fatty acids to those of the mass culture from which they originated (Fig. 2). Similarly, no significant differences in the relative percentage fatty acid composition of the mass culture and the single conidial isolates were detected. The variation in fatty acid composition between single conidial isolates and between different mass cultures was sometimes as high as 20% (Fig. 2), which was considerably higher than that observed in yeasts (17). This might be explained by the fact that the growth conditions of yeasts can be standardized more easily and accurately without disturbing growth using optical instruments (colorimeter), while clearly, this is not possible in the case of *Ophiostoma* species, which have a mycelial growth habit.

COMPARISON OF ISOLATES FROM DIFFERENT GEOGRAPHIC ORIGINS

On the basis of fatty acid composition, the isolates of *L. serpens* from different geographic origins and those purportedly belonging to this species could be divided into three groups (Table 1).

The first group (Group A) was characterized by the presence of a C16:2 fatty acid and had a higher percentage C18:2 than C18:1. Two isolates fell into this group. One of these isolates originated in Italy and is the type culture of the species isolated by Goidànich (8) and later studied by various researchers (6,16,29), while the other isolate in this group originated in France and was isolated by Dr. M. Morelet. The second group of isolates (Group B) was also comprised of two isolates. These were from *Pinus strobus* roots in North Carolina, U.S.A. (CMW1138) and Virginia, U.S.A. (CMW41). Although they were both originally identified as *L.*

TABLE 1. Fatty acid composition of *L. serpens* isolates from different geographic origins and two isolates incorrectly identified as this species.

Group[1]	Isolate no[2]	\multicolumn{7}{c}{Fatty acids[3]}						
		C16:0	C16:1	C16:2	C18:0	C18:1	C18:2	C18:3
A	CMW 305	+	+	+	+	+	+ +	+
	CMW 746	+	+	+	+	+	+ +	+
B	CMW 1138	+	+	+	+	+ +	+	+
	CMW 41	+	+	+	+	+ +	+	+
C	CMW 853	+	+	-	+	+ +	+	+
	CMW 191	+	+	-	+	+ +	+	+
	CMW 290	+	+	-	+	+ +	+	+
	CMW 623	+	+	-	+	+ +	+	+
	CMW 37	+	+	-	+	+ +	+	+
	CMW 60	+	+	-	+	+ +	+	+
	CMW 382	+	+	-	+	+ +	+	+
	CMW 745	+	+	-	+	+ +	+	+

[1] Group A includes *L. serpens* isolates from Italy (Type strain - CMW 305) and France (CMW 746). Group B comprises isolates from North Carolina, U.S.A. (CMW 1138) and Virginia, U.S.A. (CMW 41), originally identified as *L. serpens* but believed to be of a recently undescribed species (Wingfield and Harrington, unpublished). Group C includes *L. serpens* from England (CMW 853), Italy (CMW 191, 290), Portugal (CMW 623), South Africa (CMW 37, 60, 382) and Spain (CMW 745).

[2] Isolate numbers refer to those in the culture collection of M.J. Wingfield.

[3] C18:1 and C18:2 were present in all isolates but in differing concentrations. Fatty acids were either absent (-), present in low concentrations (+), or high concentrations (+ +).

serpens, they are morphologically identical but distinct from *L. serpens* (Wingfield and Harrington, unpublished). These differences are further confirmed by their unique fatty acid profile characterized by the presence of a C16:2 fatty acid and a relatively lower percentage C18:2 than C18:1 (Table 1).

The third group (Group C) consisted of the majority of *L. serpens* isolates studied and is characterized by a relatively higher percentage C18:1 than C18:2 (Table 1).

In this study, the two isolates incorrectly identified as *L. serpens* could be distinguished from authenticated isolates of the species, suggesting that analysis of cellular long chain fatty acids holds promise for distinguishing between species. These findings are in agreement with those of Ferreira and Augustyn (5) who distinguished two ascomycetous fungi (i.e. *Eutypa lata* and *Cryptovalsa* cf *ampelina*) with fatty acid analyses.

Most authenticated isolates of *L. serpens* could be grouped together using this technique. We cannot explain the fact that the type culture and the isolate from France fell in a different group than most other isolates. However, the type culture of the species is known to be morphologically different, although according to iso-enzyme studies similar to other other isolates (12,29). These morphological differences could also be reflected in the composition of the cellular long chain fatty acids. Such variability suggests that the taxonomic value of fatty acid compositions in this group of fungi should be viewed with a degree of circumspection.

FATTY ACID COMPOSITION OF SELECTED SPECIES OF *CERATOCYSTIS*, *CERATOCYSTIOPSIS* AND *OPHIOSTOMA*

Reproducible results were obtained when 12 species (Table 1) representing the genera *Ophiostoma*, *Ceratocystiopsis* and *Ceratocystis* were grown under standard conditions (Table 2). The species were mainly characterized by the presence of C16:0, C16:1, C18:0, C18:1, C18:2 and C18:3 fatty acids. They could be divided into three groups according to the presence of C18:3 and the relative percentages of C18:1 and C18:2.

Group I, characterized by the absence of C18:3, consisted of only one species, ie. *Ceratocystiopsis fasciata*. Group II was comprised of *O. piceae, O. valdivianum, Ceratocystiopsis minuta, O. araucariae, O. cucullatum, O. davidsonii, Ceratocystis adiposa* and *C. fimbriata*. These species were characterized by the presence of C18:3 and a higher percentage of C18:2

TABLE 2. Long-chain fatty acid composition of species representing *Ceratocystis, Ceratocystiopsis* and *Ophiostoma*.

Group	Isolates	Isolate no.[b]	% Fatty Acids of total lipid[a]					
			C16:0	C16:1	C18:0	C18:1	C18:2	C18:3
1	*Ceratocystiopsis fasciata*	CMW138	20.54±1.27	3.46±3.15	2.89±0.48	29.58±7.70	43.37±0	0 0
2	*Ceratocystiopsis minuta*	CMW1458	17.64±6.02	3.49±0.30	1.21±0.54	20.85±1.47	42.61±5.06	14.21±1.34
	C. adiposa	CMW121	10.69±1.87	1.32±0.46	3.58±1.33	13.65±3.00	40.69±0.30	30.07±6.94
	O. araucariae	CMW706	15.84±1.45	1.25±0.56	2.04±1.00	15.84±0.44	35.38±1.72	29.66±5.17
	O. cucullatum	CMW1141	15.55±4.12	5.10±0.35	0.81±0.27	26.22±3.85	39.79±0.38	12.52±0.19
	O. davidsonii	CMW799	20.27±0.10	1.94±0.49	1.94±0.67	15.79±0.49	41.14±3.31	18.92±2.89
	O. fimbriata	CMW78	13.73±0.22	1.204±1.70	3.30±0.56	21.91±0.07	49.34±1.40	10.51±0.53
	O. piceae	CMW215	23.06±0.33	1.33±0.08	5.90±1.52	1.73±2.39	36.81±3.02	1.17±0.64
	O. valdivianum	CMW449	14.53±0.56	2.29±0.45	2.20±0.41	26.85±3.31	49.17±0.67	5.00±3.25
		range	10.69-23.06	1.25-5.10	0.81-5.9	13.65-31.73	35.38-49.34	5.00-30.07
3	*C. coerulescens*	CMW81	9.47±0.67	0.49±0.08	2.97±0.23	42.75±5.03	22.48±2.33	21.83±8.17
	O. galeiformis	CMW653	10.63±4.24	1.62±0.33	1.55±0.39	51.49±2.70	32.50±6.73	2.46±0.14
	O. serpens	CMW60	26.60±4.31	4.47±0.43	1.22±0.38	40.54±1.75	24.61±4.74	2.36±0.71
		range	9.47-26.60	0.49-4.47	1.22-2.97	40.54-51.49	22.48-32.50	2.36-21.83

[a]   Values are the mean of three repetitions ±standard deviation.

[b]   Isolate numbers refer to the culture collection of M.J. Wingfield.

than C18:1. Species in group III were characterized by the presence of C18:3 and a higher percentage of C18:1 than C18:2. These included *O. galeiformis, C. coerulescens* and *O. serpens.*

Ophiostoma and *Ceratocystis sensu stricto* differ in terms of their cell wall composition, ecology, anamorphs and tolerance to cycloheximide (11,13,24,27, Samuels this volume). We thus consider these genera to be distantly related; their morphological similarities can be ascribed to convergent evolution. Analysis of cellular long chain fatty acids showed no obvious differences between species belonging to these genera. From this preliminary study, we conclude that this technique holds no promise in distinguishing genera of the ophiostomatoid fungi.

CONCLUSIONS

Cellular long chain fatty acid composition appears to be a useful technique for taxonomic studies in the yeasts. From the preliminary studies presented here, there appears to be a great deal of variability between isolates of species from different geographic origins. Moreover, these fatty acid compositions of single conidial isolates of a species also vary. This is possibly the result of difficulties in standardizing culture conditions and would reduce the applicability of this technique to the taxonomy of the ophiostomatoid fungi.

In comparisons between isolates of a single species, there were some indications that fatty acid analyses could be used in taxonomic studies. Different fatty acid compositions could at least provide justification for further study of the isolates concerned. In future studies, many isolates of different origins should be compared.

Fatty acid analyses appeared to have no function in distinguishing between well established groups within ophiostomatoid fungi. This is consistent with the fact that the technique is best applied at the species and not the generic level in yeasts.

LITERATURE CITED

1. Abel, K., De Schmertzing, H. and Peterson, J.I. 1963. Classification of micro-organisms by analysis of chemical composition. J. Bacteriol. 85:1039-1044.
2. Arx, J.A. von and Van der Walt J.P. 1987. Ophiostomatales and Endomycetales. Pages 167-177 in: Proceedings of an international symposium on the perspectives of taxonomy, ecology and phylogeny of yeasts and yeast-like fungi. G.S. de Hoog, M.T. Smith and A.C.M. Weijman, eds. Stud. Mycol. 30.
3. Dawson, P.S. and Craig, B.M. 1966. Lipids of *Candida utilis*: changes with growth. Can. J. Microbiol. 12: 775-785.
4. Deinema, M.H. 1961. Intra- and extracellular lipid production by yeasts. Ph.D. thesis. Laboratory of Microbiology, Agricultural University, Wageningen, The Netherlands.
5. Ferreira, J.H.S. and Augustyn, O.P.H. 1989. Differentiation between *Eutypa lata* and *Cryptovalsa* c.f. *ampelina* by means of cellular fatty acid analysis. S. A. J. En. Vit. 10:18-22.
6. Gambogi, P. and Lorenzini, G. 1977. Conidiophore morphology in *Verticicladiella serpens.* Trans. Br. Mycol. Soc. 69:217-223.
7. Gangopadhyay, P.K., Thadepalli, H., Roy, I. and Ansari, A. 1979. Identification of species of *Candida, Cryptococcus* and *Torulopsis* by gas-liquid chromatography. J. Infect. Dis. 140:952-958.
8. Goidànich, G. (1936). Il genere di Ascomiceti "*Grosmannia*" G. Goid. Boll. Staz. Patol. Veg. Roma 16: 26-60.
9. Golubev, W.I., Smith, M.T., Poot, G.A. and Kock J.L.F. 1989. Species delineation in the genus *Nadsonia* Sydow. Antonie van Leeuwenhoek 55:369-382.
10. Gunasekaran, M. and Hughes, W.T. 1980. Gas-liquid chromatography: a rapid method for identification of different species of *Candida.* Mycologia 72:505-511.
11. Harrington, T.C. 1981. Cycloheximide sensitivity as a taxonomic character in *Ceratocystis.* Mycologia 73: 1123-1129.
12. Harrington, T.C. 1988. *Leptographium* species, their distributions, hosts and insect vectors. Pages 1-39 in: *Leptographium* root diseases of conifers. T.C. Harrington and F.W. Cobb, Jr., eds. American Phytopathological Society Press, St. Paul, MN. 149 pp.
13. Hoog, G.S. de and Scheffer, R.J. 1984. *Ceratocystis* versus *Ophiostoma:* A reappraisal. Mycologia 76:292-299.
14. Kaneko, H., Hosohara, M., Tanaka, M. and Itoh, T. 1976. Lipid composition of 30 species of yeast. Lipids 11:837-844.
15. Kates, M. 1964. Bacterial lipids. Adv. Lipid Res. 2:17-90.
16. Kendrick, W.B. 1962. The *Letographium* complex. *Verticicladiella.* Hughes. Can. J. Bot. 40:771-779.
17. Kock, J.L.F., Lategan, P.M., Botes, P.J. and Viljoen B.C. 1985. Developing a rapid statistical identification process for different yeast species. J. Microbiol. Meth. 4:147-154.
18. Kock, J.L.F. 1988 Chemotaxonomy and yeasts. S. Afr. J. Sci. 84:735 - 740.
19. Lösel, D.M. 1988. Microbial lipids. Pages 699-794 in: Microbial Lipids. C. Ratledge and S.G. Wilkinson, eds. Academic Press, London. 963 pp.
20. Moss, C.W., Shinoda, T. and Samuels, J.W. 1982. Determination of cellular fatty acid composition of various yeasts by gas-liquid chromatography. J. Clin. Microbiol. 6:1073-1079.
21. Muller, H.G. and Kock, J.L.F. 1988. *Waltiozyma* gen. nov. (Saccharomycetaceae), a new genus of the Endomycetales. S. Afr. J. Sci. 82:491-492.
22. Redhead, S.A. and Malloch, D.W. 1977. The Endomycetaceae: new concepts, new taxa. Can. J. Bot. 55:1701-1711.
23. Rosinski, M.A. and Campana, R.J. 1964. Chemical analysis of the cell wall of *Ceratocystis ulmi.* Mycologia 56:738-744.
24. Shaw, N. 1974. Lipid composition as a guide to the classification of bacteria. Adv. Appl. Microbiol. 17: 63-108.
25. Suzuki, K-I. and Komagata, K. 1983. Taxonomic significance of cellular fatty acid composition in some coryneform bacteria. Int. J. Syst. Bacteriol. 33:188-200.
26. Viljoen, B.C., Kock, J.L.F. and Lategan, P.M. 1986. The

influence of culture age on the cellular fatty acid composition of four selected yeasts. J. Gen. Microbiol. 132:1895-1898.

27. Weijman, A.C.M. and Hoog, G.S. de 1975. On the subdivision of the genus *Ceratocystis*. Antonie van Leeuwenhoek. 41:453-460.

28. Wickerham, L.J. 1951. Taxonomy of yeasts. Tech. Bull. No. 1029. USDA, Washington, D.C.

29. Wingfield, M.J. and Marasas, W.F.O. 1981. *Verticicladiella alacris,* a synonym of *V. serpens.* Trans. Br. Mycol. Soc. 76:508-570.

30. Yamada, Y. and Banno, I. 1987. *Hasegawaea gen. nov.,* an ascosporogenous yeast genus for the organisms whose asexual reproduction is by fission and whose ascospores have smooth surfaces without papillae and which are characterized by the absence of CoQ and by the presence of linoleic acid in cellular fatty acid composition. J. Gen. Microbiol. 33:295-298.

Chapter 13

VOLATILE METABOLITES PRODUCED BY SPECIES OF *OPHIOSTOMA* AND *CERATOCYSTIS*

H.-P. HANSSEN

INTRODUCTION

Many species of ophiostomatoid fungi produce intense, characteristic odors under defined culture conditions. These odors were described by Hunt (16) as similar to banana oil, fruity, sweet, slightly acid or reminiscent of radish. Strains of species considered members of *Ceratocystis sensu stricto*, in particular, often produce volatile metabolites with fruity odors.

The development of modern analytical techniques such as gas chromatography (GLC) and mass spectrometry (MS) has facilitated the identification of such volatiles, even when they occur in small quantities. Their possible role in the interaction between fungal pathogens, as well as an increasing interest in these compounds as commercial flavor and fragrance chemicals, has stimulated research on these metabolites. This strong economic interest has made certain *Ceratocystis* and *Ophiostoma* species model organisms for terpene biosynthesis in fungi or for biotechnological production of flavor chemicals. Besides the chemistry and biosynthesis of volatile metabolites, questions have arisen concerning:

(a) strain-dependent formation of certain volatiles within a single species and the influence of culture conditions on the production of these metabolites,

(b) the potential for biotechnological production of certain volatiles,

(c) the possible use of volatiles for chemosystematic studies, and

(d) the reasons why these organisms produce volatiles and their possible function in vector systems.

CHEMISTRY AND BIOSYNTHESIS OF VOLATILES BY OPHIOSTOMATOID FUNGI

To date, volatile metabolites isolated from cultures of *Ceratocystis* and *Ophiostoma* strains comprise mainly short-chain alcohols and esters, and mono- and sesquiterpenes (Table 1). In addition, several miscellaneous compounds have been detected that are derived via other metabolic pathways (Table 1).

Short-chain alcohols and esters

Collins and Morgan (5) were the first researchers to apply gas chromatography to the analysis of fungal volatiles. Using this technique, they identified several short-chain alcohols and esters in cultures of *C. coerulescens, C. moniliformis, C. major* (= *C. adiposa*) and *C. fimbriata*. Later, other authors confirmed their results and extended their findings to related compounds and additional species and strains (9,13,18,25).

The esters, also called fruit esters, are important aroma chemicals and are often responsible for the fruity odor emanating from fungal cultures. These substances may be important odor ingredients, especially in *Chalara* and *Ceratocystis* cultures. The odor of many *Ceratocystis* strains was described as reminiscent of banana oil by Hunt (16). In fact, the characteristic impact compound of banana oil is isoamyl acetate (3-methylbutyl acetate), which has also been identified as a constituent of some *Ceratocystis* cultures. Isobutanol, 3-methyl-l-butanol and 3-methyl-2-butanol are derived from amino acid metabolism; their corresponding precursors valine, leucine and isoleucine, respectively, are decarboxylated and deaminated. The subsequent step in the biosynthetic pathway, the acetylation of the alcohols resulting in the acetate derivatives, has been characterized as a strain-dependent marker in *C. coerulescens* (24).

Terpenes

Monoterpenes (C10) and sesquiterpenes (C15) are formed via the isoprenoid pathway; a C5-unit is derived from acetate with mevalonate as a key intermediate. The first volatile terpenoid, 6-methyl-5-hepten-2-one and its corresponding alcohol, were isolated from cultures of *C. coerulescens* (4). These methyl heptenyl compounds were originally described as degradation products from monoterpenes in higher plants. It seems possible, however, that they

TABLE 1. Volatile metabolites identified in *Ceratocystis* and *Ophiostoma* cultures.

Compound[a]	Species[b]	Reference
1. Short-chain alcohols and esters		
ethanol (1)	1, 2, 3, 4	5
ethyl acetate	1, 2, 3, 4	5
n-propyl acetate (2)	3, 4	5, 18
isobutanol (3)	1, 2, 3, 4	5
isobutyl acetate	1, 2, 3, 4	4, 5
3-methyl-1-butanol (4) (= isoamyl alcohol)	1, 2, 3, 4	5
3-methylbutyl acetate (= isoamyl acetate)	2, 3, 4	5, 24
2-methyl-1-butanol (5) (= amylalcohol)	2	5
2-methylbutyl acetate (= amyl acetate)	4	18
2. Terpenoids and terpenes		
6-methyl-5-hepten-	2	4
2-one (6)	5	24
-ol; (R= -OH)		
-acetate (R=-O-COCH3)		
linalool (7)	2	26
	3	6, 13
	4	17
	7	10
citronellol (8)	2	26
	3	6, 13
	4	17
citronellyl acetate	2	26
	3	6, 13
geraniol (9)	2	26
	3	6, 13
	4	17
geranial	2	9
	6	
	4	17
geranyl acetate	2	26
	3	6, 13
nerol (10)	2	26
	4	17
neral	2	9
	3	6
	4	17
neryl acetate	2	26
cyclic monoterpenes	2	26
(hydrocarbons, alpha-terpineol linalool oxides)		
(artifacts?, non-enzymatically derived products?)	3	27, 13
	4	17
farnesol (11)	2	26
2,3-dihydro-6-farnesol (12)	2	26
dihydrofarnesyl	2	26
nerolidol (13)	2	26
dihydronerolidol; tetrahydronerolidol	2	26
α-amorphene (14)	7	10
γ-amorphene (15)	7	10
δ-cadinol (16)	7	10
τ-muurolol (17)	7	10
6-protoilludene (18)	6	14
cerapicol (19)	6	12
cerapicanol (20)	6	12
leptographiol (21)	8	1
isoleptographiol (22)	8	1
isoafricanol (23)	8	1

Compound[a]	Species[b]	Reference
3. **Miscellaneous compounds**		
2-phenethyl acetate (24) (2-phenylethanol)	2	9
τ-decalactone (25)	3	27
δ-decalactone (26)	3	27
1-octen-3-ol (27)	7	10

[a] Numbers in parentheses refer to chemical formulae shown in Fig. 2.

[b] For species: 1= *C. adiposa* 2= *C. coerulescens* 3= *C. fimbriata* 4= *C. moniliformis* 5= *C. virescens* 6= *O. piceae* 7= *O. populinum* 8= *Leptographium lundbergii* (Note: *C. adiposa* reported as *C. major* in 5 and *C. fimbriata* reported as *C. variospora* in 6,13 and 27).

can also be formed in an anabolic reaction via a by-pass of the mevalonate pathway. In 1970, Collins and Halim (6) reported the occurrence of acyclic monoterpenes in fungal cultures for the first time. Among the constituents isolated from *C. variospora* (*C. fimbriata*) were the alcohols linalool, geraniol and citronellol, the esters geranyl and citronellyl acetate and the aldehydes neral and geranial. Acyclic mono- and sesquiterpenes were later identified from cultures of other *Ceratocystis* species (13,17,26). Sesquiterpenes described include farnesol, nerolidol and derivatives of these compounds (9,26). Lanza and Palmer (17) demonstrated that the biosynthesis of fungal monoterpenes, studied with *C. moniliformis*, follows the same pathway as in higher plants.

Acyclic mono- and sesquiterpene alcohols, like the fruit esters, are also important flavor and fragrance chemicals; geraniol has a flowery-roselike odor, while linalool produces a more flowery-fresh impression and citronellol a sweet rose-like note (3). Geraniol and nerol are *cis-trans* isomers; the farnesols and nerolidols are sesquiterpene analogs of geraniol/nerol and linalool. Farnesol, with a linden blossom odor, and nerolidol, possessing a mild, flowery flavor impression, are often used for perfume compositions (3). The aldehydes and acetates are also frequently used by the perfumery industries.

However, unlike the acyclic monoterpenes, it seems that species of *Ceratocystis* lack the enzymatic equipment to synthesize cyclic monoterpenes; the few cyclic compounds hitherto reported as *Ceratocystis* 'metabolites' are probably artifacts of inappropriate separation conditions, or they may be formed non-enzymatically from unstable precursors in an acidic culture environment (11).

In contrast to monoterpenes, numerous fungal constituents with various cyclic sesquiterpene skeletons have been isolated. A number of different sesquiterpenes have been described, particularly from the *Ophiostoma* group. Predominant compounds in

the steam distillates of *O. populinum* (strain RWD 835C) were hydrocarbons and alcohols with a bicyclic 1,7-dimethyl-4-isopropyldecaline skeleton (cadines and related compounds, 10). Besides the alcohols τ-muurolol and δ-cadinol, two hydrocarbons with an amorphane structure (α- and τ-amorphene) were identified as major constituents. Whereas cadinenes are ubiquitous in higher plants, the occurrence of compounds with the antipodic amorphane skeleton has been reported only rarely.

From cultures of *O. piceae* (strain Ha 4/82), we isolated three tricyclic sesquiterpenes with a protoilludane structure. These included the hydrocarbon 6-protoilludene (15), a key intermediate in the biosynthesis of compounds with a protoilludane, illudane, marasmane, hirsutane, sterpurane, lactaranes or isolactarane skeleton. Interestingly, with the exception of *O. piceae*, reports describing natural products with these structures have been restricted to basidiomycetous fungi. Using solid media, we identified two additional alcohols, cerapicol and cerapicanol, which are derived from 6-protoilludene (12).

An isolate of *Leptographium lundbergii* (Ha 2/82) produced tricyclic components with an africanane skeleton (1). Compounds with similiar structures have been described so far only from soft corals and a few higher plants (Compositae, Verbenaceae). It has been assumed that they are derived from humulene; we have named these new natural products leptographiol, isoleptographiol and isoafricanol (1).

Miscellaneous compounds

In addition to the compounds noted above, several constituents of other chemical classes have been identified from *Ceratocystis* or *Ophiostoma* cultures. 2-Phenylethanol and especially 2-phenethyl acetate have been found in the steam distillates of *C.*

119

coerulescens strains (9,25). This ester has a fine rose scent with a sweet honey-note and is also called sherry ester.

Two lactones, γ- and δ-decalactone, have been isolated from *C. variospora* (*C. fimbriata*) cultures (27). γ-Decalactone is an especially important flavor compound used in perfume and aroma compositions because of its intensely fruity peach odor.

In *O. populinum*, small quantities of l-octen-3-ol have also been detected (10). This constituent, with a typical mushroom-like odor, is derived from fatty acid metabolism and is ubiquitously found among fungi, especially in Basidiomycetes.

Biotechnology - presuppositions, possibilities and limitations

The demand in food industries for natural flavor and fragrance chemicals is increasing steadily. The current trend towards the use of natural products and the decreasing availability of these substances from traditional sources has encouraged biotechnological approaches towards finding a new generation of aroma chemicals. The strategies currently adopted include: (i) de novo-biosynthesis of individual compounds or mixtures of chemically related substances, (ii) bioconversion of low-priced precursors or substrates, and (iii) production of aroma chemicals as by-products of other fermentation processes.

The development of a biotechnological process requires two initial steps: the selection of a high-yielding strain and the optimization of the culture medium. The formation of volatiles may vary enormously between different strains within a single species (11,13,25). One such example is the strain-dependent biosynthesis of terpenes in *C. coerulescens* and *C. fimbriata*. Varying culture conditions may influence not only the yields of volatile metabolites, but the composition of an aroma extract or distillate (9, 14). For example, the yields of terpene mixtures obtained from agar or shaken broth *Ceratocystis* cultures can amount to as much as 100 mg/ℓ, depending on the strain, the culture conditions and culture age. Accumulating terpenes may have toxic effects on the producing organism and feedback inhibition and evaporation effects may likewise act as limiting factors on further productivity. To counteract these negative effects, Schindler and Bruns (23) developed a fermentation process using XAD-2 as a lipophilic adsorber (21,22). Using this method in a 20 ℓ fermentation with *C. variospora* (*C. fimbriata*) ATCC 12866, terpene production was enhanced to

TABLE 2. Comparison of a fungal terpene mixture from *C. fimbriata* with industrially used citronell and palmarosa oil (modified from 21).

Compound(s)	Composition (%)[a]		
	C. fimbriata	citronell oil	palmarosa oil
alcohols and esters			
geraniol and esters	40-75	60-80	70-95
citronellol and esters	10-43	15	+
linalool	1-2	-	+
nerol	1-6	+	-
aldehydes			
citronellal	5-35	5-10	-
neral	1-2	-	-

[a] (+) indicates minor traces and (-) indicates absence of compound

1.9 g/ℓ (including 1.6 g geraniol) within five days. Table 2 shows a comparison of this terpene mixture with industrially used citronell oil and palmarosa oil. Although the constituents of the fungal aroma concentrate may broadly agree with traditional products of plant origin and optimization of the fermentation process could result in increased yields, it is uncertain whether such fungal products will ever enter the market. The yields obtained are so far economically uncompetitive and the extracts are unconvincing to commercial perfumers (21). In general, fine chemicals produced by fermentation must achieve a selling prize of US $200-500 per kg and possibly as much as US $2,000 per kg, to be competitive with commercially available compounds (11).

CHEMOSYSTEMATICS AND ECOPHYSIOLOGY

Because the formation of fungal volatiles is frequently a strain-dependent feature, it is difficult to use these metabolites for chemosystematic purposes (25). It is clear that different chemotypes occur within certain fungal species and that species concepts should generally be based on other characters, such as morphology in association with more conservative biochemical data such as nucleic acid composition.

Nevertheless, chemosystematic approaches can provide a useful insight for groupings beyond the

FEATURE [1]
OPHIOSTOMATOID FUNGI

ENDOMYCETALES

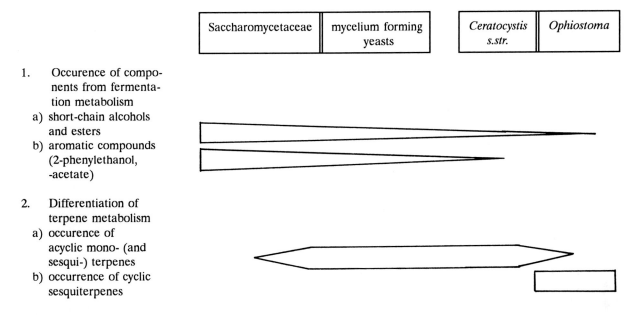

| Saccharomycetaceae | mycelium forming yeasts | | *Ceratocystis s.str.* | *Ophiostoma* |

1. Occurence of compo-
   nents from fermenta-
   tion metabolism
   a) short-chain alcohols
      and esters
   b) aromatic compounds
      (2-phenylethanol,
      -acetate)

2. Differentiation of
   terpene metabolism
   a) occurence of
      acyclic mono- (and
      sesqui-) terpenes
   b) occurrence of cyclic
      sesquiterpenes

Fig. 1. Comparison of volatile compunds produced by *Endomycetales* and ophiostomatoid fungi.

[1] Decreasing and increasing shapes indicate relative abundance of each class of volatiles produced by the different fungal groups.

species level and also lead to 'intelligent' approaches for screening programs. In the past, several authors have suggested that there might be a relationship between members of the ophiostomatoid fungi and certain filamentous and unicellular yeasts (Kendrick *et al.*, this volume). On the other hand, a subdivision of the genus *Ceratocystis sensu lato* was proposed on the basis of conidium formation and biochemical data (29,30, Samuels, this volume). Although information on volatile metabolites produced by these fungi is still fragmentary, a comparison of the findings hitherto obtained does show certain trends. True yeasts are predominantly producers of aliphatic and aromatic alcohols and, even more importantly, esters; acyclic mono- and sesquiterpenes are formed only as side components. Significant amounts of monoterpenes have been found in several yeast-like fungi [*Ambrosiozyma* spp. (15), *Ascoidea hylecoeti* (7,8), *Eremothecium ashbyi* (20)] and in certain members of *Ceratocystis s. str.* (see above). However, the biosynthesis of cyclic sesquiterpenes is restricted to *Ophiostoma* species (Fig. 1).

The biological significance of volatiles in fungi is still unknown in most cases. A summary of hypotheses concerning why secondary metabolites like these are synthesized has recently been put forward by Williams *et al.* (31). A convincing hypothesis is that these compounds 'are a measure of the fitness of the organism to survive; the ability to synthesize an array of secondary metabolites which may repel or attract other organisms has evolved as one facet of the organisms's strategy for survival'. This seems especially likely for more complicated molecules that require much metabolic energy and genetic information for their manufacture.

Because the conidia of many blue-staining fungi are disseminated by insects, especially by scolytid beetles, it has been assumed that volatiles might play a role in the interspecific communication of these organisms. A number of the volatiles (e.g. the monoterpene alcohols citronellol and geraniol) reported from cultures of ophiostomatoid fungi are also described as plant chemicals attractive as insect kairomones (19). In this context, Upadhyay (28) mentions the attraction of sap-feeding beetles to the fruity odor of *C. fagacearum*. Other volatiles, such as the terpene alcohols linalool and nerolidol act as insect pheromones (2). A repellent effect of certain

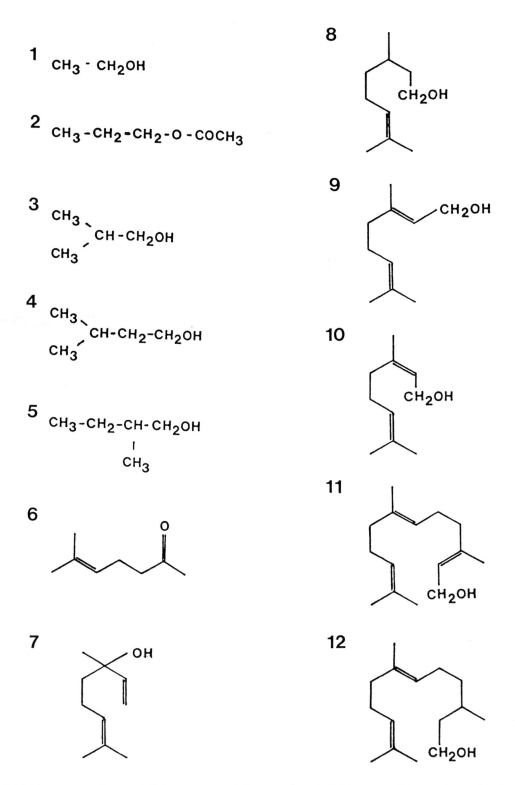

Fig. 2. Volatile compounds reported from species of *Ceratocystis* and *Ophiostoma*. The numbers with the chemical formulae correspond to those following the compound name in Table 1.

13

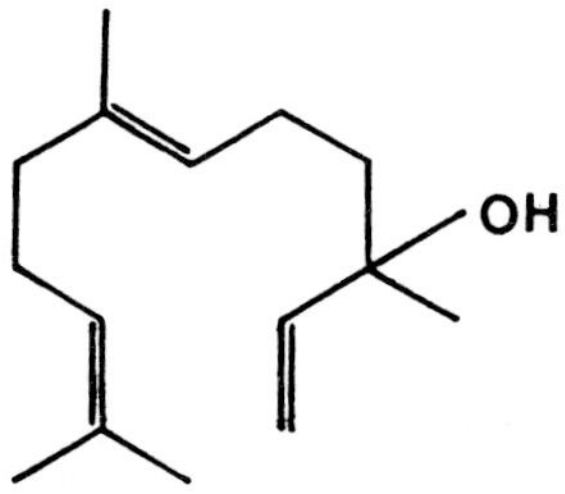

18

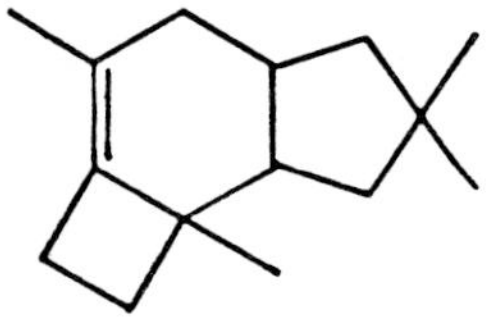

22

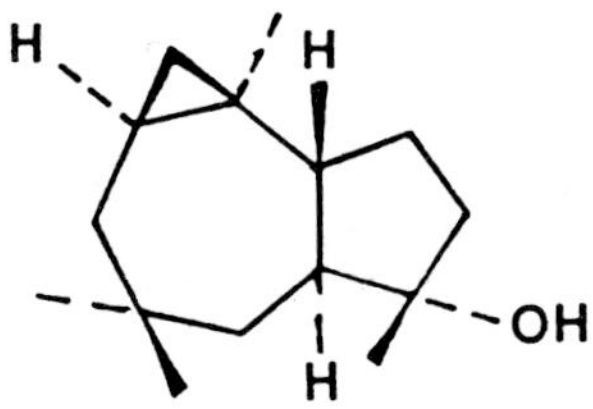

14

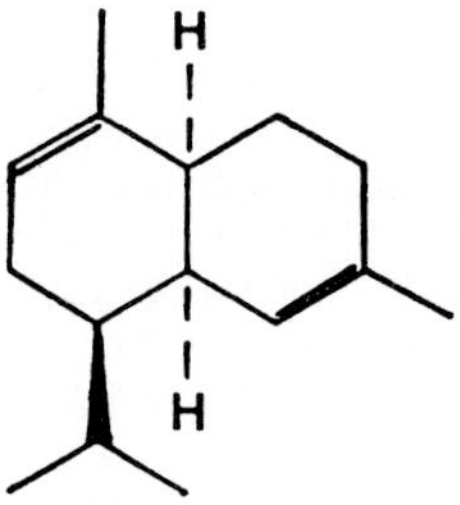

19

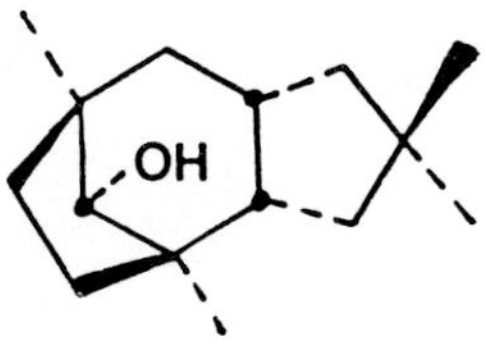

23

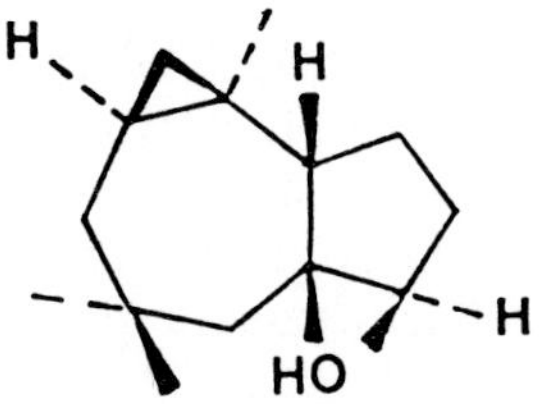

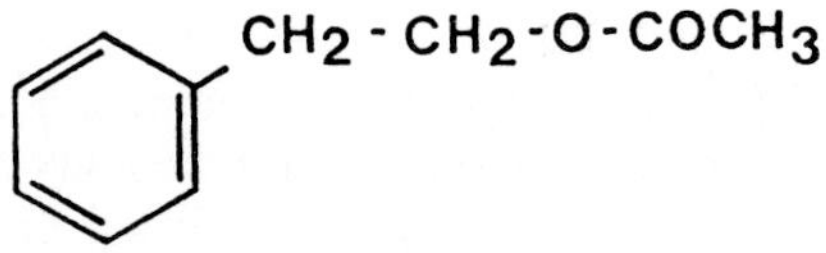

15

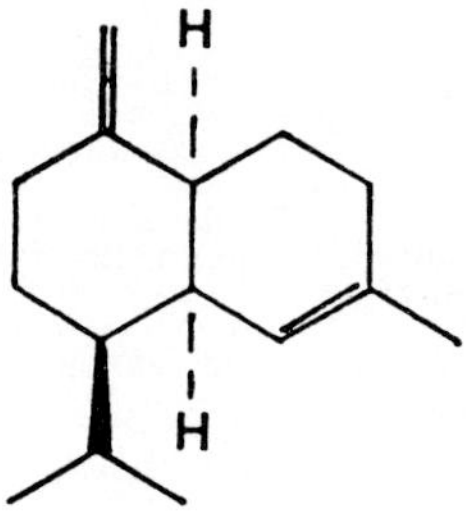

20

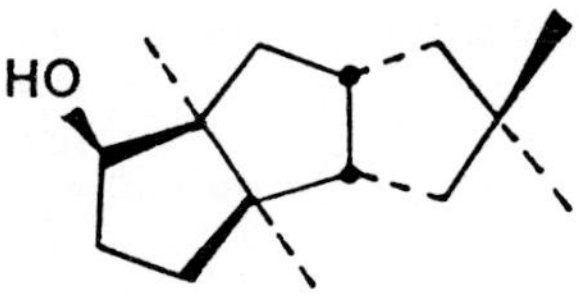

24

$CH_2-CH_2-O-COCH_3$

25

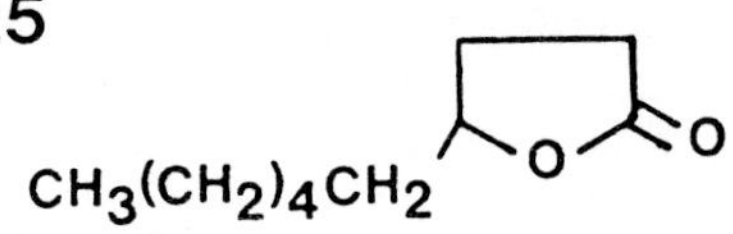

$CH_3(CH_2)_4CH_2$

16

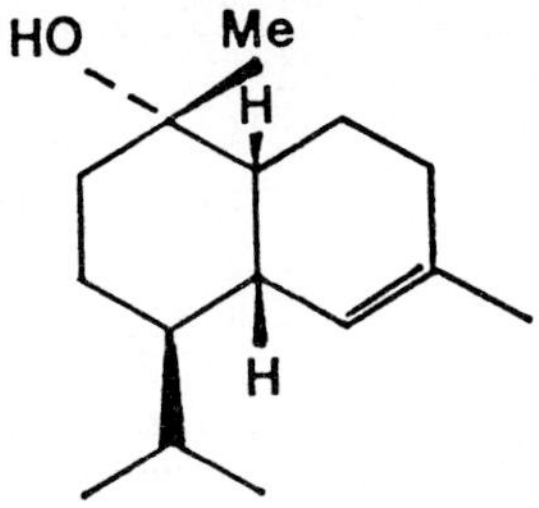

21

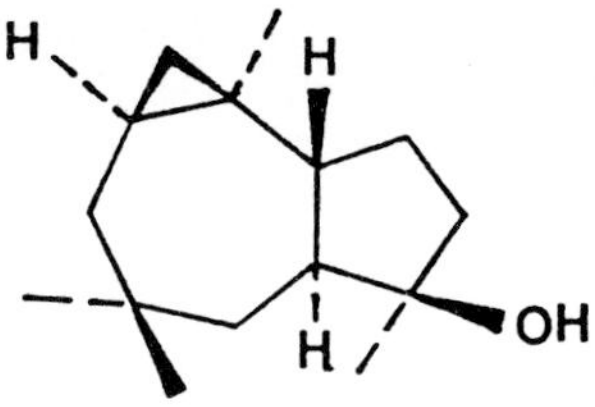

26

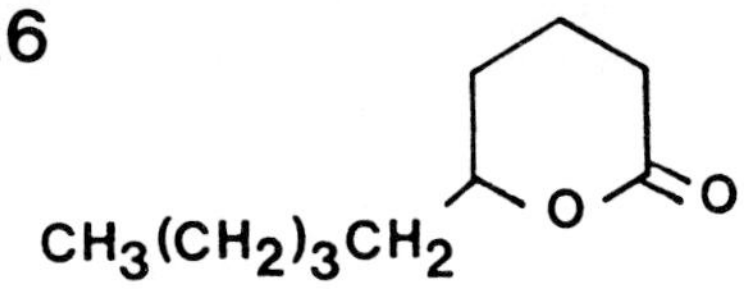

$CH_3(CH_2)_3CH_2$

17

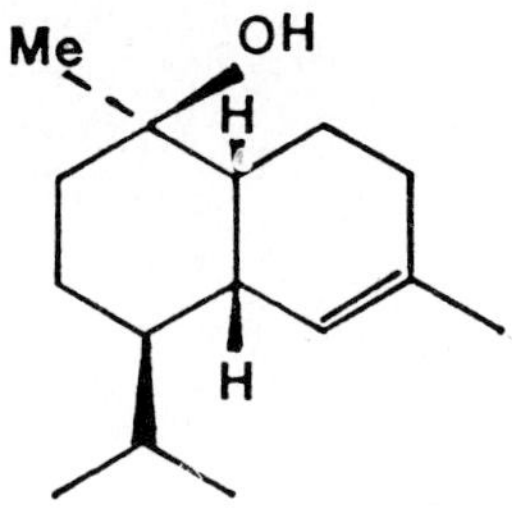

27 $CH_2=CH-CH-CH_2-CH_2-CH_2-CH_2-CH_3$
$\quad\quad\quad\quad\quad OH$

Fig. 2. (continued)

volatiles is also conceivable, as is a facilitated elimination of toxic metabolites by conversion to volatiles (e.g. formation of acetates). A more thorough investigation of the function of these metabolites in vector systems could lead to a better understanding of the ecology of certain pathogenic fungi and increase prospects for biological pest control.

CONCLUSIONS

1. *Ceratocystis* and *Ophiostoma* strains provide a rich source of chemically different volatile metabolites. The ophiostomatoid fungi seem to be a particularly interesting fungal group because of their ability to producing unique sesquiterpenes.

2. The formation of volatiles is frequently a strain-dependent feature and is influenced by the culture conditions applied.

3. The role of volatiles in intra- and interspecific communication is poorly understood. Further work on their functions in vector systems could lead to a better understanding of certain diseases caused by ophiostomatoid fungi.

LITERATURE CITED

1. Abraham, W.-R., Ernst, L., Witte, L., Hanssen, H.-P. and Sprecher, E. 1986 . New trans-fused africanols from *Leptographium lundbergii*. Tetrahedron 42:4475-4480.

2. Aldrich, J.R. 1988. Chemistry and biological activity of pentatomoid sex pheromones. Pages 417-431 in: Biologically Active Natural Products: Potential Use in Agriculture. H. G. Cutler, ed. American Chemical Society Symposium Series 380. 483 pp.

3. Bauer, K. and Garbe, D. 1985. Common Fragrance and Flavor Materials. VCH Verlagsgesellschaft mbH, Weinheim, Germany. 213 pp.

4. Birkinshaw, J.H. and Morgan, E.N. 1950. Biochemistry of the wood-rotting fungi. 6. Volatile metabolic products of species of *Endoconidiophora*. Biochem. J. 47:55-59.

5. Collins, R.P. and Morgan, M.E. 1962. Identity of fruit-like aroma substances synthesized by endoconidial-forming fungi. Phytopathology 52:407-409.

6. Collins, R.P. and Halim, A.F. 1970. Production of monoterpenes by the filamentous fungus *Ceratocystis variospora*. Lloydia 33:481-482.

7. Francke, W. and Brümmer, B. 1978a. Flüchtige Stoffwechselprodukte aus *Ascoidea hylecoeti*. Planta med. 34:332-334.

8. Francke, W. and Brümmer, B. 1978b. Terpene aus *Ascoidea hylecoeti*. Planta med. 34:426-429.

9. Hanssen, H.-P. 1976. Der Einfluß des Nährmediums auf das Wachstum und die Bildung flüchtiger Stoffwechselprodukte von *Ceratocystis coerulescens* Bakshi (Münch). Diploma thesis, University of Hamburg.

10. Hanssen, H.-P. 1985. Sesquiterpenes and other volatile metabolites from liquid cultures of *Ceratocystis populina* (Ascomycota) - Essential oil compounds from fungi. Pages 173-177 in: Essential Oil and Aromatic Plants. A. Baerheim Svendsen and J.J.C. Scheffer, eds. W. Junk Publishers, Dordrecht, Netherlands. 246 pp.

11. Hanssen, H.-P. 1986. Volatile terpenes from sapwood staining fungi. Pages 331-341 in: Progress in Terpene Chemistry. D. Joulain, ed. Editions Frontières, Gif-sur-Yvette, France. 452 pp.

12. Hanssen, H.-P. and Abraham, W.-R. 1988. Sesquiterpene alcohols with novel skeletons from the fungus *Ceratocystis piceae* (Ascomycotina). Tetrahedron 44:2175-2180.

13. Hanssen, H.-P. and Sprecher, E. 1981. Flüchtige Terpene aus *Ceratocystis fimbriata*. Z. Naturforsch. 36c:1075-1076.

14. Hanssen, H.-P., Sprecher, E. and Abraham, W.-R. 1986. 6-Proto-illudene, the major volatile metabolite from *Ceratocystis piceae* liquid cultures. Phytochem. 25:1979-1980.

15. Hanssen, H.-P., Sprecher, E. and Klingenberg, A. 1986. Screening for volatile terpenes in yeasts. Pages 395-399 in: Progress in Essential Oil Research. E. J. Brunke, ed. De Gruyter, Berlin, Germany. 668 pp.

16. Hunt, J. 1956. Taxonomy of the genus *Ceratocystis*. Lloydia 19:1-58.

17. Lanza, E. and Palmer, J.K. 1977. Biosynthesis of monoterpenes by *Ceratocystis moniliformis*. Phytochem. 16:1555-1560.

18. Lanza, E., Ko, K.H. and Palmer, J.K. 1976. Aroma production by cultures of *Ceratocystis moniliformis*. J. Agric. Food Chem. 24:1247-1250.

19. Metcalf, R.L. 1987. Plant volatiles as insect attractants. CRC Crit. Rev. Plant Sci. 5:251-301.

20. Mironov, V.A., Tsibulskaya, M.I. and Yanotovsky, M.T. 1982. Synthesis of monoterpenes by the ascomycete *Eremothecium ashbyi*. Prikladnaya Biokhim. Mikrobiol. 18:343-345.

21. Schindler, J. 1982a. Mikrobielle Gewinnung von Terpenen. Henkel-Referate 18:24-27.

22. Schindler, J. 1982b. Terpenoids by microbial fermentation. Ind. Eng. Chem. Prod. Res. Dev. 21:537-539.

23. Schindler, J. and Bruns, K. 1978. Verfahren zur fermentativen Gewinnung monoterpenhaltiger Riechstoffe. DOS 2 840 143. Henkel KG, Germany.

24. Sprecher, E. 1968. Stammesspezifische Acetylierungen verschiedener Alkohole bei der Gattung *Ceratocystis*. Arch. Mikrobiol. 60:24-34.

25. Sprecher, E. and Hanssen, H.-P. 1983. Distribution and strain-dependent formation of volatile metabolites in the genus *Ceratocystis*. Antonie van Leeuwenhoek 49:493-499.

26. Sprecher, E., Kubeczka, K.-H. and Ratschko, M. 1975. Flüchtige Terpene aus Pilzen. Arch. Pharm. 308:843-851.

27. Tressl, R., Apetz, M., Arrieta, R. and Grünewald, K.G. 1978. Formation of lactones and terpenoids by microorganisms. Pages 145-168 in: Flavor of Food and Beverages. G. Charalambous & G.E. Inglett, eds. Academic Press, New York. 422 pp.

28. Upadhyay, H.P. 1981. A Monograph of *Ceratocystis* and *Ceratocystiopsis*. University of Georgia Press, Athens, GA. 176 pp.

29. Weijman, A.C.M. 1976. Cell-wall composition and taxonomy of *Cephaloascus fragrans* and some Ophiostomataceae. Antonie van Leeuwenhoek 42:315-324.

30. Weijman, A.C.M. and Hoog, G.S. de 1975. On the subdivision of the genus *Ceratocystis*. Antonie van Leeuwenhoek 41:353-360.

31. Williams, D.H., Stone, M.J., Hauck, P.R. and Rahman, S.K. 1989. Why are secondary metabolites (natural products) biosynthesized? J. Nat. Prod. 52:1189-1208.

Chapter 14

IMMUNOLOGICAL DETECTION OF SOME OPHIOSTOMATOID FUNGI

C. BREUIL and K.A. SEIFERT

INTRODUCTION

Detection of fungi before the appearance of symptoms is an important component of treating and controlling diseases or degradation. Immunological methods are attractive because they are potentially sensitive and specific. Widely used in medicine for several decades, immunological methods are now being applied in forest and wood products pathology (25). To date, these applications have been largely for experimental purposes, primarily studying the mechanisms of plant disease, but it is possible to foresee more practical diagnostic applications. In this paper, we will review published work on immunological detection of some members of the Ophiostomataceae in trees and on lumber and discuss its impact on our knowledge of these fungi.

THE TECHNOLOGY

Producing antisera

Most biologists are now familiar with polyclonal and monoclonal antibodies. Both types of antibodies are produced by injecting an animal with a substance (known as an antigen) that induces an immune response. For polyclonal antibodies, the blood serum of the inoculated animal, usually a rabbit, is harvested. The serum contains a mixture of different antibodies that react with the original antigen (27,28). For monoclonal antibodies, individual lymphocytes are harvested from the spleen of the inoculated animal, usually a mouse. Each cell produces only one kind of antibody. The cells are fused with myeloma cell lines to produce hybridomas. Each hybridoma can be grown as tissue culture and will produce a single kind of antibody (6,11,20,27).

The specificity of the resulting antibodies often depends on the nature of the antigen or antigen mixture that is originally used to inoculate the animals. A purified antigen should result in polyclonal or monoclonal antibodies that are specific to that antigen. Small molecules that would not themselves elicit an immune response can be conjugated with proteins for use as antigens. In many cases, however, it is not possible to utilize a purified antigen because

of our scant knowledge of fungal proteins. In these situations, mixtures of antigens, either whole mycelia, spores or purified cell walls, are used to inoculate the animal.

Screening of polyclonal and monoclonal antibodies is laborious, particularly if mixed antigens are used. The screening process involves testing the cross reactivity of the antisera with other related and unrelated fungi. Usually, the goal is to obtain an antiserum that reacts specifically with the fungus of interest, although less specific sera may be useful in detecting problems caused by more than one species. Especially with polyclonals, the heterogeneity of antisera produced *in vivo* can be reduced by adsorbing the serum onto other fungi to remove antibodies reacting with antigens common to both fungi (15,31). This is a useful strategy in *in vitro* experiments where the fungi present are known, but is less unequivocal for detecting fungi in the field where species with unknown reactivity are present. We have used such pre-adsorbed polyclonal antisera raised to a specific *Ophiostoma* strain, for example, for quantifying a number of different *Ophiostoma* species in mixed species experiments on wood (Seifert and Breuil, unpublished).

Assays

Polyclonal and monoclonal antisera can be utilized in several ways to provide quantitative, qualitative or visual information about the presence, abundance or location of a fungus or its components. The assays are based on the same principle. Antibodies produced by a rabbit, for example, can themselves be used for antigens in another animal, such as a goat. The resulting anti-rabbit antibodies then will react with the experimental antibodies. The anti-rabbit serum is then conjugated with an enzyme, for colorimetric or histochemical detection, to a heavy metal for immunogold or ISSG detection by microscopy, or to a radioactive compound for detection by autoradiography.

For the enzyme-linked immunosorbent assay (ELISA), antibodies are conjugated with an enzyme (such as horse radish peroxidase) that catalyzes a colorimetric reaction. The enzyme reacts with antigen in the test solution, allowing quantification of that antigen with reference to a standard curve. ELISAs can be very simple if the antigen to be detected is soluble (such as a metabolite), but complicated extraction procedures are sometimes necessary for insoluble antigens, or antigens that are components of living cells in a solid matrix (such as a fungus growing in wood). A similar assay, the radio immunoassay (RIA), utilizes a radioisotope conjugated to the antibody rather than an enzyme. To date, its use to detect members of the Ophiostomataceae has been limited to *Sporothrix schenckii* (see below).

For immunolabelling, the antibodies are conjugated with other molecules that can be detected microscopically. Specific binding of these complexes allows localization of the antigens of interest with either light or electron microscopy (Figs. 1-4). For light microscopy, the conjugant can be a heavy metal such as gold, a fluorescent molecule, or an enzyme substrate (17). For electron microscopy, heavy metals or enzyme substrates are used (14,33).

Immunodiffusion is a simple technique in which the reference polyclonal antiserum is placed in a well in the middle of an agar plate. Test antigens are placed in wells surrounding the central well. Usually, these antigens are cell-free antigens, known as exoantigens. The antibodies in the reference antiserum diffuse outwards from the central well and react with compatible antigens that diffuse out from the sample wells. The antibody-antigen complexes precipitate out and will form a discrete band when stained. Using this method, it is possible to determine the number of antigens that the reference organism and test organism have in common simply by counting the bands formed in the agar plate.

CONTRIBUTIONS TO OUR KNOWLEDGE OF THE OPHIOSTOMATACEAE

Ophiostoma ulmi and *O. novo-ulmi*

Immunological methods have been used to study various aspects of the pathogenicity and population biology of the Dutch elm disease fungi, *Ophiostoma ulmi* and *O. novo-ulmi*. *Ophiostoma ulmi* is non-aggressive, and *O. novo-ulmi* (formerly designated the non-aggressive subgroup of *O. ulmi*) occurs as Eurasian (EAN) and North American (NAN) races (7, Brasier, this volume). Although the EAN and NAN races can be distinguished by mating tests, the occurrence of hybrids complicates identification.

Therefore, Dewey and Brasier (12) and Dewey *et al.* (13) attempted to raise polyclonal and monoclonal antibodies that would distinguish the two races easily. Using mycelium extracts as antigens, two hybridomas were raised that distinguished mycelial antigens of aggressive and non-aggressive isolates, but only distinguished EAN and NAN isolates quantitatively. Other monoclonals were genus specific (ie. they reacted with both *O. ulmi* and *O. piceae* but not *Ceratocystis* species). The polyclonal antibodies tended to cross react with host tissue, a problem avoided with some of the monoclonal lines.

Several toxins have been implicated in the pathogenicity of *O. ulmi* and *O. novo-ulmi*. Antibodies raised to these toxins have been used to demonstrate toxin production by various strains. Antibodies have also been utilized to demonstrate the distribution of the toxins in fungal cultures and in infected plants.

Scheffer and Elgersma (29) produced a polyclonal antiserum to a phytotoxic glycopeptide produced by *O. novo-ulmi*. An ELISA was able to detect the compound at 1 nM and was used to demonstrate its accumulation in xylem sap 2 weeks after inoculation of *Ulmus hollandica*. A concentration of 5 μg/ml in wood sap was recorded after 4 weeks. Benhamou *et al.* (2,3) produced two monoclonal antibodies to the same glycopeptide, using purified toxin as an antigen. Using immunohistochemical and immuno-gold labelling, they demonstrated high concentrations of this toxin in the conidia and much lower concentrations in subtending hyphae. The toxin could be detected inside the vessel walls of infected tissue 24 hr after inoculation, before any disease symptoms were noted. After three and four days, it was detected in many different tissues of the infected plant, and specifically localized over pit membranes, the innermost wall layer of paratracheal parenchyma cells, and in intracellular spaces and lamellae.

Immunoassays for a different proteinaceous phytotoxin produced by *O. novo-ulmi*, known as cerato-ulmin (CU), have also been produced. Nordin *et al.* (24) produced a polyclonal antiserum using purified CU as an antigen. An ELISA was developed and shown to detect as little as 20 μg toxin per assay well. A variety of bacteria and fungi were screened for CU production but no other producers of this toxin were found. Svircev *et al.* (32) used a polyclonal antiserum for immuno-gold and immunohistochemical labelling and demonstrated the uniform distribution *in vitro* of CU on vegetative, perithecial and synnematal structures of an *O. novo-ulmi* isolate. Much lower concentrations were detected in *O. ulmi*

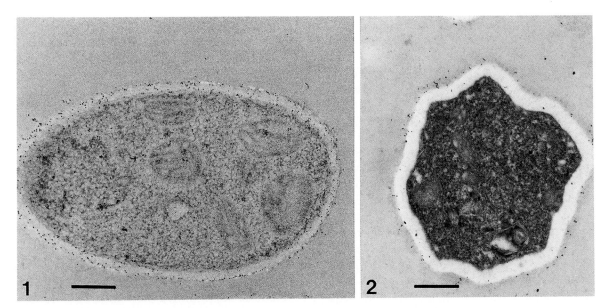

Figs. 1-2. Immunogold labelling of *Ophiostoma piceae* cells fixed with glutaraldehyde and embedded in LR White medium. Fig. 1. Thin section labelled with polyclonal serum against *Ophiostoma* sp. C28 adsorbed with *Gliocladium roseum* mycelia. The label is mainly over the entire cell wall, with some gold particles over the protoplasm. Fig. 2. Thin section incubated with a monoclonal antibody (MAb) against an *O. piceae* cell wall preparation. The label is localized on the outer surface of the cell wall; the protoplasm contains background levels of gold particles. Scale bars = 0.5 μm.

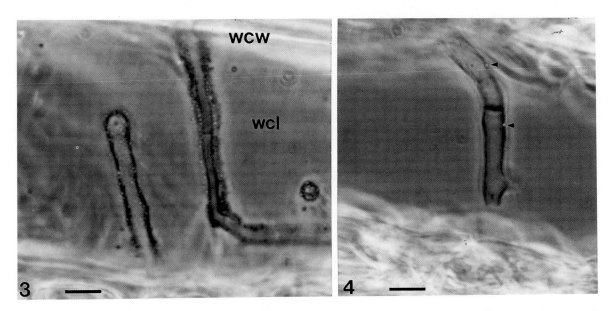

Figs. 3-4. Immunogold silver staining of semi-thin sections of *Pinus banksiana* infected with *O. piceae* after 6 weeks incubation. Fig. 3. The primary antibody was a MAb against *O. piceae* cell walls. The fungal mycelium is heavily labelled with silver-gold particles and easily identified in the wood cell lumen (wcl). wcw = wood cell wall. Fig. 4. Control section with omission of the primary antibody. The fungal mycelium has a few gold-silver particles (arrowheads) and is outlined by a dense cell wall. Scale bars = 5 μm. (Figs. 1-4 courtesy B. T. Luck and D. L. Brown).

isolates.

Jeng and Svircev (18) raised a polyclonal antiserum to the polypeptide QP1, isolated from *O. ulmi* using two dimensional SDS-PAGE gels. This protein was produced only by *O. ulmi* and not by aggressive *O. novo-ulmi* isolates. It was localized in the cell walls of conidia and vegetative hyphae using protein A-gold immunolabelling. Its biological significance is unknown.

The d²-factor in *O. novo-ulmi* was originally detected in the NAN subgroup. It has since been found in EAN aggressive subgroup and in the non-aggressive *O. ulmi* (8). The disease is caused by transmissible dsRNA. Benhamou *et al.* (4) raised monoclonal antibodies able to detect 5-20 ng of dsRNA. They demonstrated the occurrence of dsRNA in an isolate of *O. ulmi*, but were unable to detect dsRNA in an isolate of *O. novo-ulmi*.

Ceratocystis fagacearum

Serological recognition of *Ceratocystis fagacearum*, the cause of oak wilt, was first attempted by Amos and Burrell (1), who wanted to identify spores found in wounds of infected oaks. Polyclonal antisera were prepared using killed spores as antigens. Adsorption of the antisera onto spores of other *Ceratocystis* or *Ophiostoma* species removed most of the cross reactivity, allowing spores of *C. fagacearum* fixed onto microscope slides to be distinguished using immunofluorescence. Not surprisingly, no differences were demonstrated between the A and B mating types of *C. fagacearum*.

Hausler (16) reported on the application of monoclonal antibodies for the detection of *C. fagacearum* but details of the work have yet to be published.

Sapstaining *Ophiostoma* species

In order to detect sapstain of lumber before visible symptoms occurred, Breuil *et al.* (9) developed a polyclonal antiserum to *Ophiostoma* sp. C28 using whole mycelium as an antigen source. This strain was chosen for its ability to quickly produce sapstain on blocks of *Pinus banksiana* in the laboratory. The resulting serum reacted strongly with other *Ophiostoma* species and to unrelated species such as *Gliocladium roseum* but most cross reactivity to *G. roseum* was readily eliminated by adsorbing the serum onto mycelium of this species. Using an ELISA, *Ophiostoma* sp. C28 could be detected in as little as 1 mg of wood, before any visible sapstain was

apparent (10). Using similarly adsorbed polyclonal serum, it was possible to detect *Ophiostoma piceae* at concentrations as low as 0.25 μg dry weight/ml. Immunogold labeling and electron microscopy demonstrated that most antigens were located in the cell wall (21, Figs. 1, 2). Recently, we have produced monoclonal antibodies to *O. piceae* using purified cell walls as an antigen (Figs 3, 4). Sixteen hybridomas were obtained after screening but these exhibited high cross reactivity with *G. roseum*. Presently, we are using proteins extracted from cell walls as antigens. Preliminary results indicate that monoclonal bodies can be selected that will discriminate between the *Ophiostoma* and *Gliocladium* species.

Sporothrix schenckii

A variety of immunological methods have been used for the rapid detection of *Sporothrix schenkii*, the cause of sporotrichosis in humans (Summerbell *et al.*, this volume). Many of these tests utilize polyclonal antisera derived from infected human patients, rather than experimental animals. The antigens are detected by their reaction with cells or cell components of the pathogen, usually in some form of agglutination reaction.

Because of the medical importance of the fungus and the difficulty in the diagnosis of the disease, tests based on immunological principles were attempted as early as 1910 (34). Since then, many studies have been published involving agglutination tests (19,23,33). Agglutination tests involve the reaction of the patient serum with *S. schenckii* yeast cells. The mixture is incubated at 37°C for one hour, refrigerated overnight, then centrifuged. A qualitative estimation is then made of the agglutination of cells induced by the test serum (33).

Blumer *et al.* (5) compared the effectiveness of five different immunological assays for detecting this pathogen. They developed a slide agglutination test that could be performed in 5 minutes and detected 94% of the *Sporothrix* infections in the study group. The test involved reaction of the test serum with latex particles "sensitized" by binding with antigens from an anti-*Sporothrix* serum. A tube agglutination assay had similar sensitivity (96%) but took longer to perform. However, immunodiffusion and complement fixation assays were less effective at detecting the presence of *S. schenkii*.

Later, Scott *et al.* (30) developed ELISA and RIA procedures that were even more sensitive than the slide agglutination tests, detecting 98% of infected patients. Although some cross reactivity occurred with other mycotic infections, the titers for these patients were much lower.

A rapid identification protocol for clinical isolates of *S. schenckii* was developed by Polonelli and Morace (26). Using immunodiffusion, they identified isolates within three days.

In an effort to clarify the infection process leading to sporotrichosis, Nishikawa *et al.* (22) made an immunological comparison between clinical strains of *S. schenkii* and strains isolated from soil. Considerable serological variation was observed within the species and the authors were unable to prove or disprove the idea that infection could result from inoculation of wounds by strains associated with soil or plants.

Taxonomic usefulness

Although immunological methods have occasionally been used for taxonomic purposes in fungi, they have not been employed to a great extent in the Ophiostomataceae. In general, studies have demonstrated shared antigens among *Ophiostoma* species. Detection of antigens unique to a particular species or strain has been difficult.

Amos and Burrell (1) studied the serological relationships of eight species included at that time in *Ceratocystis*, based on their agglutination reactions with polyclonal sera raised to two species. The relationships postulated do not correspond with the taxonomic distribution of the species generally accepted today. For example, *O. ulmi* was considered more closely related to *C. fagacearum* than either *C. adiposa* and *C. fimbriata* (referred to as *C. variospora*). *Ophiostoma pluriannulatum* was considered more closely related to *C. adiposa* than to *O. piliferum*, *O. ulmi* or *O. ips*.

The taxonomic relationship between *S. schenkii* and various *Ophiostoma* species has been explored several times using immunological techniques (Summerbell *et al.*, this volume). Polonelli and Morace (26) also examined this relationship using immunodiffusion. They found that isolates of *O. minus* and *Graphium penicillioides* produced homologous precipitin bands with their reference antiserum to *S. schenckii*, suggesting a close relationship between these three species. No homologous bands were produced by other species of fungi tested.

CONCLUSIONS

The power of immunological techniques lies in their ability to detect, quantify and localize specific molecules (antigens). Useful information concerning the production and localization of toxins produced by a few species of *Ophiostoma* and *Ceratocystis* has been obtained using immunological techniques. Monoclonal antibodies remain the method of choice for dealing with specific molecules.

In some cases, detection of organisms in plants or infected patients has also been achieved. Immunological detection of *S. schenckii* is an important clinical procedure. However, detection of pathogens in plants using polyclonal and monoclonal sera usually has been problematic because of cross reactivity. In the future, detection of specific organisms *in vivo* may be better served using DNA probes.

Taxonomic applications of immunological techniques are limited because the large number of similar antigens shared by closely related species makes detection of unique antigens difficult.

LITERATURE CITED

1. Amos, R.E. and Burrell, R.G. 1967. Serological differentiation in *Ceratocystis*. Phytopathology 57:32-34.
2. Benhamou, N., Ouellette, G.B., Lafontaine, J.G. and Joly, J.R. 1985a. Use of monoclonal antibodies to detect a phytotoxic glycopeptide produced by *Ophiostoma ulmi*, the Dutch elm disease pathogen. Can. J. Bot. 63:1177-1184.
3. Benhamou, N., Lafontaine, J.G., Joly, J.R. and Ouellette, G.B. 1985b. Ultrastructual localization in host tissues of a toxic glycopeptide produced by *Ophiostoma ulmi*, using monoclonal antibodies. Can. J. Bot. 63:1185-1195.
4. Benhamou, N., Parent, J.G., Garzon, S., Asselin, A., Ouellette, G.B. and Joly, J.R. 1987. Use of monoclonal antibody against poly[I]:poly[C] acid for detecting mycoviruses and potential applications to potato spindle tuber viroid and animal seroviruses. Can. J. Pl. Pathol. 9:106-114.
5. Blumer, S.O., Kaufman, L., Kaplan, W., McLaughlin, D.W. and Kraft, D.E. 1973. Comparative evaluation of five serological methods for the diagnosis of sporotrichosis. Appl. Microbiol. 26:4-8.
6. Boonekamp, P.M. ed. 1988. Monoclonal antibodies and immunological techniques to detect plant pathogens. Pudoc, Wageningen, Netherlands. 86 pp.
7. Brasier, C.M. 1979. Dual origin of recent Dutch elm disease outbreaks in Europe. Nature 281:78-79.
8. Brasier, C.M. 1986. The d-factor in *Ceratocystis ulmi*- Its biological characteristics and implications for Dutch elm disease. Pages 177-208 in: Fungal Virology. K. W. Buck, ed. CRC Press, Boca Raton, FL. 306 pp.
9. Breuil, C., Yamada, J., Seifert, K.A and Saddler, J.N. 1988a. An enzyme linked immunisorbent assay (ELISA) for detecting staining fungi in unseasoned wood. J. Inst. Wood Sci. 11:132-134.
10. Breuil, C., Seifert, K.A., Yamada, J., Rossignal, L. and Saddler, J.N. 1988b. Quantitative estimation of fungal

colonization of wood using an enzyme-linked immunosorbent assay. Can. J. For. Res. 18:374-377.

11. Campbell, A.M. 1984. Laboratory Techniques in Biochemistry and Molecular Biology, vol. 13: Monoclonal Antibody Technology. R. H. Burdon and P. H. van Knippenberg, eds. Elsevier, Amsterdam, New York and Oxford.

12. Dewey, F.M. and Brasier, C.M. 1988. Development of an ELISA for *Ophiostoma ulmi* using antigen-coated wells. Plant Pathol. 37:28-35.

13. Dewey, F.M., Munday, C.J. and Brasier, C.M. 1989. Monoclonal antibodies to specific components of the Dutch elm disease pathogen *Ophiostoma ulmi*. Plant Pathol. 38:9-20.

14. Faulk, W.P. and Taylor, G.M. 1971. An immunocolloidal method for the electron microscope. Immunochem. 8:1081-1083.

15. Gerik, J.S., Lommel, S.A. and Huisman, O.C. 1987. A specific serological staining procedure for *Verticillium dahliae* in cotton root tissue. Phytopathology 77:261-265.

16. Hausler, C.J. 1988. Application of monoclonal antibodies in the detection of oak wilt (Abstr.). Am. Soc. Adv. Sci., Abstr. Papers, 1988 Nat. Meeting p. 116.

17. Holgate, C.S., Jackson, P., Cown, P.N. and Bird, C.C. 1983. Immunogold-silver staining: new method of immunostaining with enhanced sensitivity. J. Histochem. Cytochem. 31:928-944.

18. Jeng, R.S. and Svircev, A.M. 1990. Isolation and ultrastructural localization of a soluble protein from *Ophiostoma ulmi*. Can. J. Bot. 68:2517-2524.

19. Karlin, J.V. and Nielsen, H.S. Jr. 1970. Serologic aspects of sporotrichosis. J. Infect. Dis. 121:316-327.

20. Kennett, R.H., Bechtol, K.B. and McKearn, T.J. 1984. Monoclonal antibodies and functional cell lines. Progress and applications. Plenum Press, New York, London. 426 pp.

21. Luck, B.T., Breuil, C. and Brown, D.L. 1990. Immunological discrimination between a sapstaining fungus and a biological control fungus. Can. J. Bot. 68:1578-1588.

22. Nishikawa, T., Harada, T., Harada, S. and Hatano, H. 1975. Serologic differences in strains of *Sporothrix schenckii*. Sabouraudia 13:285-290.

23. Nordin, A. 1951. Sporotrichosis. Clinical and laboratory features and a serologic study in experimental animals and humans. Acta Pathol. Microbiol. Scand. Suppl. 89:1-119.

24. Nordin, J.H., Mason, T.L., Smith, L.L., Willmann, P.A., Richards, W.C. and Takai, S. Use of an enzyme-linked immunosorbent assay with murine ascitic antibodies to screen microorganisms for production of cerato-ulmin, a toxin of *Ceratocystis ulmi*. Phytopathology 77:96-100.

25. Ouellette, G.B. and Benhamou, N. 1987. Use of monoclonal antibodies to detect molecules of fungal plant pathogens. Can. J. Plant Pathol. 9:167-176.

26. Polonelli, L., and Morace, G. 1982. Exoantigen studies of *Sporothrix schenckii*, *Ceratocystis minor* and *Graphium penicillioides* cultures. J. Clin. Microbiol. 15:362-365.

27. Roitt, I., Brostoff, J. and Male, D. 1988. Antibodies: a laboratory manual. Cold Spring Harbour. Laboratory Press. 726 pp.

28. Roitt, I., Brostoff, J. and Male, D. 1989. Immunology, 2nd. ed. Gower Medical Publishing, London, New York.

29. Scheffer, R.J. and Elgersma, D.M. 1981. Detection of a phytotoxic glycopeptide produced by *Ophiostoma ulmi* in elm by enzyme-linked immunospecific assay (ELISA). Physiol. Plant Pathol. 18:27-32.

30. Scott, E.N., Muchmore, H.G. and Parkinson, A.J. 1982. Enzyme and radioimmunoassays in human sporotrichosis. Pages 212-215 in: Proc. VIIIth Congress Int. Soc. Human and Animal Mycology. Michael Baxter, ed. Massey University, New Zealand.

31. Sudesh, B.M. 1988. Evaluation of antisera raised against *Phytopthora fragariae* for detecting the red core disease of strawberries by enzyme-linked immunosorbent assay (ELISA). Plant Pathol. 37:206-216.

32. Svircev, A.M., Jeng, R.S. and Hubbes, M. 1988. Detection of cerato-ulmin on aggressive isolates of *Ophiostoma ulmi* by immunocytochemistry and scanning electron microscopy. Phytopathology 78:322-327.

33. Waele, M.de, de Wey, J., Moeremans, M., de Brabander, M. and van Camp, B. 1983. Immunogold staining methods for the detection of cell surface antigens with monoclonal antibodies. Pages 1-24 in: Techniques in immunocytochemistry, vol. 2. G. R. Bullock and P. Petruz eds. Academic Press, New York. 290 pp.

34. Welsh, R.D. and Dolan, C.T. 1973. *Sporothrix* whole yeast agglutination tests. Low-titer reactions of sera of subjects not known to have sporotrichosis. Am. J. Clin. Pathol. 59:82-85.

Chapter 15

ULTRASTRUCTURE OF CENTRUM AND ASCOSPORE DEVELOPMENT IN SELECTED *CERATOCYSTIS* AND *OPHIOSTOMA* SPECIES

P.W.J. VAN WYK, M.J. WINGFIELD and P.S. VAN WYK

INTRODUCTION

Ceratocystis sensu lato includes the genera *Ceratocystis sensu stricto, Ophiostoma* and *Ceratocystiopsis*. These fungi include important plant pathogens (2,4,13,19, Kile, Harrington, Smalley *et al.,* this volume) and have well documented mutualistic relationships with insects (3,10,22). The classification of *Ceratocystis* within the Ascomycetes (1,16,22, Upadhyay and Samuels, this volume) and the generic concept in this group of fungi (8,22) have been widely debated. In this chapter, we follow the taxonomic scheme of de Hoog & Scheffer (8, Seifert *et al.,* this volume), where *Ceratocystis s.str.* and *Ophiostoma* are treated as distinct genera.

Centrum organization is considered an important characteristic in the taxonomy of Ascomycetes (11,12). Despite this, centrum organization in *Ceratocystis s.l.* has received little attention. The few ultrastructural studies that have been made of these fungi have reported on various aspects of the ultrastructure of *O. stenoceras*. (5), *O. ulmi* (9), *C. fimbriata* (21), and *C. moniliformis* (26). Of these, only the study of *C. moniliformis* (26) includes consideration of centrum organization.

Wright and Cain (27) emphasized the importance of ascospore shape in the taxonomy *of Ceratocystis* species and subsequently, the morphology of ascospores has been considered of prime importance in many studies (6,15,18,20,22,23). Griffin (8) recognized three basic ascospore forms, including those with (i) uniform shapes, (ii) hat-shapes, and (iii) rectangular/quadrangular shapes. Species with hat-shaped ascospores, examined by Griffin (8), included those with bowler-hat shapes (e.g. *C. fimbriata)* and ascospores that are triangular in end view (e.g. *O. penicillatum*). Subsequent to the study of Griffin (6), the morphology of hat-shaped ascospores received little attention. Species with a variety of different morphologies, therefore, have been grouped together in *Ceratocystis s.l.* (14,20,22). It is surprising that the ultrastructure of hat-shaped ascospores has been neglected, despite their apparent diversity.

In this review, we will discuss the results of our recent studies on the ultrastructure of centrum and ascospore development in *C. moniliformis, O. davidsonii* and *O. cucullatum*. We will also compare these results with those of previous studies where applicable. Although the species under consideration have hat-shaped ascospores, they belong to two distinct genera (1,7,8,16).

CENTRUM ORGANIZATION

Luttrell (11) proposed that the development of the centrum and its mature components was particularly important in the taxonomy of Ascomycetes. The centrum organization of many genera has been studied and a comprehensive review has been provided elsewhere (17). However, very little is known of the centrum development in *Ceratocystis s.l.* (24). No information was provided on centrum development in the few ultrastructural studies of members of this group (5,9,21).

In a study of *C. moniliformis,* Van Wyk *et al.* (26), reported that asci lined the inner ascomatal wall of this fungus and did not occur near the base of the neck (Fig. 1). Rather, mature ascospores were released towards the center of the ascoma, through the apparent lysis of the mature asci. In contrast, in *O. davidsonii* (25) and *O. cucullatum* (Van Wyk and Wingfield, unpublished), young asci were arranged in a cluster at the base of the ascoma (Fig. 2). In both the latter species, mature ascospores were released above the developmental area, towards the ascomatal neck.

Distinct differences in patterns of centrum development appear to be present in *C. moniliformis* and the *Ophiostoma* species studied. Such differences confirm the importance of centrum organization in the taxonomy of Ascomycetes and substantiate subdivision of *Ceratocystis s.l.* into *Ophiostoma* and *Ceratocystis.* Clearly, ultrastructural studies of centrum organization in additional species of *Ceratocystis s.l.* are necessary and could provide useful new criteria in the taxonomy of *Ceratocystis s.l.*

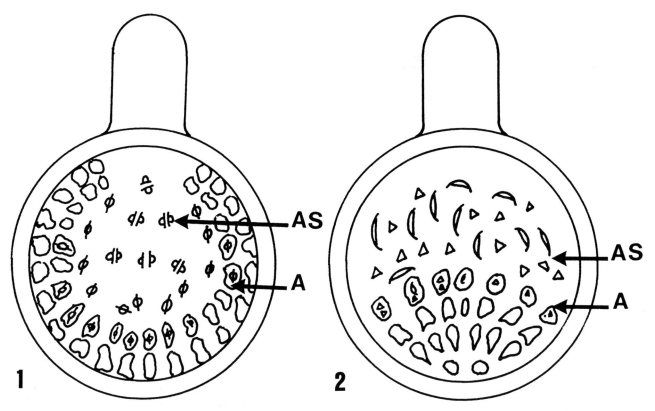

Figs. 1-2. Diagrammatic representation of centrum organization in *Ceratocystis* and *Ophiostoma*. Fig. 1. Centrum type of *Ceratocystis*. Developing asci (A) arranged in a lining adjacent to perithecium wall and ascospores (AS) released towards perithecium centre. Fig. 2. Centrum type of *Ophiostoma*. Developing asci (A) arranged at perithecium base and ascospores (AS) released towards neck.

ASCOSPORE MORPHOLOGY IN *CERATOCYSTIS SENSU LATO*

Ascospores in *Ceratocystis s.l.* have been characterized by the presence or lack of hyaline gelatinous sheaths (14,20,22). Previous ultrastructural studies on hat-shaped ascospores reported to have gelatinous sheaths have been made on only two species: *C. fimbriata* (21) and *C. moniliformis* (26). Other ultrastructural studies have been made on species that apparently do not have sheaths, including *O. stenoceras* (5) and *O. ulmi* (9).

Ascospores in *Ceratocystis*

Ascospore development appears to be similar in *C. fimbriata* (21) and *C. moniliformis* (26). The only apparent difference between these two species is in the initial delimitation of the ascospore nuclei within the ascus. In *C. fimbriata* (21), the nuclei are delimited by two membranes that enclose each nucleus. After delimitation, the ascospore wall is deposited between the delimiting membranes. In contrast, in *C. moniliformis* the delimitation of the nuclei by membranes occurs simultaneously with the deposition of the ascospore wall (26).

There is no evidence of hyaline gelatinous sheaths being present in ascospores of *C. fimbriata* and *C. moniliformis*. In these species, electron microscopic examination indicates the walls of the ascospores consist of at least three distinct layers (Fig. 3). The inner wall layer, or primary wall, surrounds the ascospore cytoplasm; the secondary wall consisted of two layers (21,26). The outer two wall layers form distinct appendages that give the ascospores their hat-shaped appearance. Thus, what have been previously referred to as hyaline gelatinous sheaths are apparently distinct wall layers.

A unique feature of *C. moniliformis* and *C. fimbriata* is that the ascospores develop in pairs in the ascus. Brim appendages form in the region where the ascospores are in contact (Fig. 4) and the ascospores separate during their release into the ascomatal cavity. Development in pairs results in the

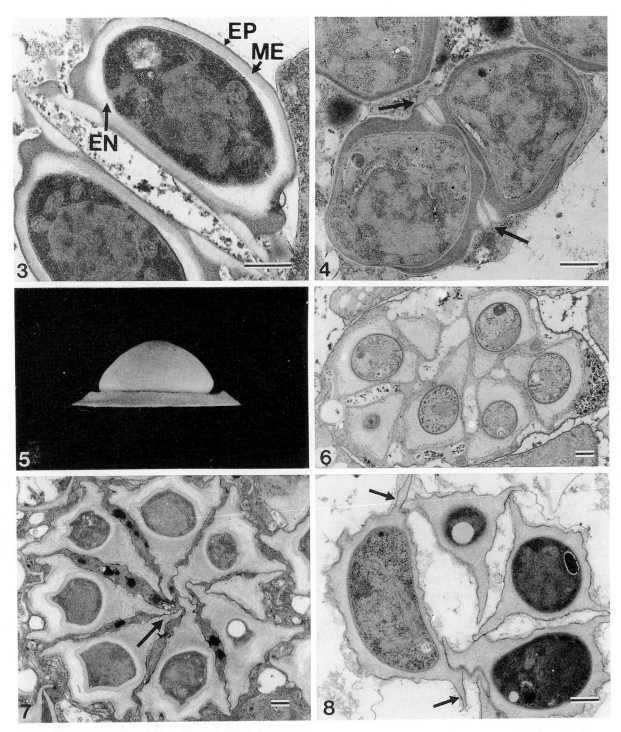

Figs 3-8. Transmission electron micrographs (TEM) of ascospores in *C. moniliformis, O. davidsonii* and *O. cucullatum* and sculptured model of a bowler-hat shaped ascospore. (Bar = 500 nm). Fig. 3. Mature hat-shaped ascospore of *C. moniliformis* showing three-layered wall (EP, ME = secondary walls and EN = primary wall). Fig. 4. Young paired ascospores in *C. moniliformis* showing brim development (arrows). Fig. 5. Sculptured model of a bowler-hat shaped ascospore. Fig. 6. Young ascospores of *O. davidsonii*, formed singly and randomly arranged in ascus. Fig. 7. Young ascospores of *O. cucullatum*, formed singly in the ascus with one ridge on each ascospore (arrow) oriented towards middle. Fig. 8. Transverse and longitudinal section through mature ascospores in *O. davidsonii*. Transverse section showing triangular appearance of the ascospores. Longitudinal section showing hat-shaped appearance with appendages at rounded ends of the ascospore (arrows).

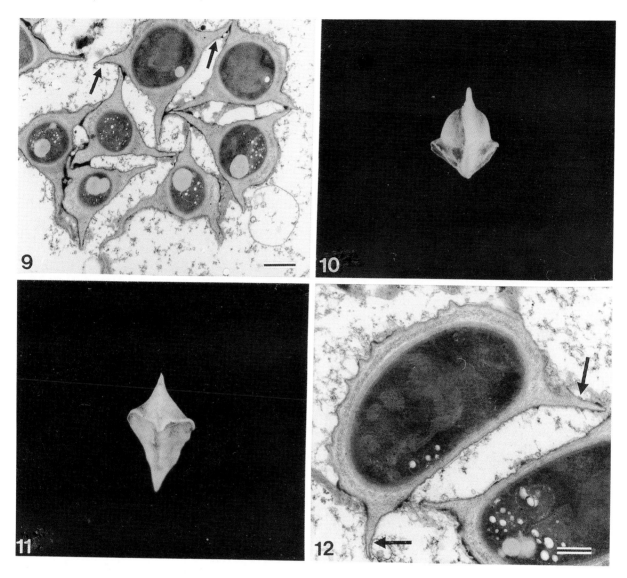

Figs 9-12. TEM and sculptured models of ascospores in *O. davidsonii* and *O. cucullatum*. (Bar = 500 nm). Fig. 9 Transverse section through mature ascospores of *O. cucullatum* showing triangular shape due to ridges (arrows). Fig. 10. Sculptured model of *O. davidsonii* ascospore in end view showing triangular shape. Fig. 11. Sculptured model of *O. cucullatum* ascospore in end view showing triangular shape. Fig. 12. Longitudinal section of mature hat-shaped ascospore in *O. cucullatum* showing appendages at rounded ends of ascospore (arrows).

cytoplasm of each of the paired ascospores having a hemispherical form with prominent appendages. Hence they can be described as 'bowler-hat' shaped (Fig. 5).

Ascospores in *Ophiostoma*

Development of hat-shaped ascospores in *O. davidsonii* (25) and *O. cucullatum* (Van Wyk and Wingfield, unpublished) is similar to that of *C. fimbriata* (21) and *C. moniliformis* (26) with the delimitation of nuclei by membranes followed by the

deposition of wall material. However, the ascospores in *O. davidsonii* and *O. cucullatum* form singly in the asci (Figs 6, 7). In the latter species, the secondary wall layers are selectively deposited along the length of the ascospore to form three prominent and equidistant ridges. This results in ascospores that are triangular in appearance in transverse sections (Figs 8, 9) or end view (Figs 10, 11).

The ridges along the ascospore walls converge at the rounded ends of the reniform primary wall layer to form brim-like appendages (Figs 8, 12).

The arrangement of the ascospores in the asci of

O. cucullatum (Van Wyk and Wingfield, unpublished) and *O. davidsonii* (25) also differ from each other. In *O. davidsonii*, ascospores are randomly arranged in the ascus (Fig. 6). In contrast, ascospores in *O. cucullatum* are arranged with one of the ridges on each ascospore oriented towards the center of the ascus (Fig. 7).

No evidence of gelatinous sheaths was found in ascospores of the *Ophiostoma* species studied. Thus, in both *Ceratocystis* and *Ophiostoma*, ascospores had distinct and rigid walls comprised of three layers.

DISCUSSION

From a relatively small number of recent ultrastructural studies, there appear to be significant differences in centrum organization between species of *Ceratocystis s.str.* and *Ophiostoma*. Additional ultrastructural studies should, however, be undertaken to confirm whether centrum organization might be used as a reliable characteristic in the taxonomy of these fungi.

Turning to ascospore structure, taxonomic literature on species of *Ceratocystis s.l.* commonly refers to gelatinous sheaths surrounding ascospores. From studies treated in this review, the "sheaths" surrounding the ascospores are clearly wall layers. Reference to gelatinous sheaths in early light microscopic studies is erroneous and has probably resulted from an inaccurate interpretation of the hyaline outer wall layers. We suggest that the term "sheath" should be avoided when describing wall layers in *Ceratocystis s.l.* Reference to hat-shaped outer secondary wall and ornamentation would be more appropriate. Similarly, the term primary wall would accurately describe the outline of the ascospore cytoplasm.

The appendages of the two outer wall layers of hat-shaped ascospores in *Ceratocystis s.str.* and *Ophiostoma* are distinctly different. The ascospores of *Ceratocystis s.str.*, characterized by *C. moniliformis* and *C. fimbriata*, are bowler-hat shaped in side view, apparently characteristic of this genus. The hat-shaped ascospores in *Ophiostoma* species appear characteristically triangular in end view. Therefore, they would appear hat-shaped only in side view.

From these observations it appears that, contrary to previous belief, hat-shaped ascospores in *Ceratocystis* and *Ophiostoma* differ completely from each other. This also calls to question whether inferences about the relatedness of yeasts and *Ceratocystis* based on hat-shaped ascospores hold any merit (16). Future ultrastructural studies of ascospores in *Ceratocystis* and *Ophiostoma* promise to be most rewarding.

Ceratocystis s.l. includes a wide variety of ascospore forms. These may be hat-, pillow-, inequilateral shaped or falcate. There are also species that have ascospores with uniform secondary wall layers (i.e. without "sheaths"). From the limited number of ultrastructural studies available, it is clear that ascospores previously thought to be similar in form can be quite distinct. We believe that additional ultrastructural studies on species of *Ceratocystis s.l.* that have diverse ascospore forms may reveal exciting new taxonomic information. Finally we suggest that characters of ascospore shape, based solely on light microscopic observations, should be applied cautiously.

LITERATURE CITED

1. Benny, L. and Kimbrough J.W. 1980. A synopsis of the orders and families of Plectomycetes with keys to genera. Mycotaxon 12:1-91.
2. Boyce, J.S. 1961. Forest pathology 3rd ed. McGraw-Hill, New York. 572 pp.
3. Bridges, J.R. and Moser, J.C. 1983. Role of two phoretic mites in transmission of the bluestain fungus, *Ceratocystis minor*. Ecol. Entomol. 8:9-12.
4. Clark, C.A. and Moyer, J.W. 1988. Compendium of sweet potato diseases. American Phytopathological Society Press. St Paul, MN. 75 pp.
5. Garrison, R.G., Mariat, F., Boyd, K.S. and Fromentin, H. 1979. Perithecial ultrastructure and formation of ascospores of *Ceratocystis stenoceras* (Robak) C. Moreau. Ann. Microbiol. 130:3-21
6. Griffin, H.D. 1968. The genus *Ceratocystis* in Ontario. Can. J. Bot. 46:689-718.
7. Hoog, G.S. de 1974. The genera *Blastobotrys, Sporothrix, Calcarisporum* and *Calcarisporiella* gen. nov. Stud. Mycol. 7:1-84.
8. Hoog, G.S. de and Scheffer, R.J. 1984. *Ceratocystis* versus *Ophiostoma*: A Reappraisal. Mycologia 76:292-299.
9. Jeng, R.S. and Hubbes, M. 1980. Ultrastructure of *Ceratocystis ulmi*. II. Ascogenous system and ascosporogenesis. Eur. J. For. Pathol. 10:104-116.
10. Juzwik, J. and French, D.W. 1983. *Ceratocystis fagacearum* and *C. piceae* on the surface of free-flying and fungus mat-inhabiting nitidulids. Phytopathology 73:1164-1168.
11. Luttrell, E.S. 1951. Taxonomy of the Pyrenomycetes V. The *Ophiostoma* type. Univ. Mo. Stud. 24:55-120.
12. Malloch, D. 1981. The Plectomycete centrum. Ascomycete systematics. Pages 73-91 in: The Luttrellian Concept. D.R. Reynolds, ed. Springer-Verlag, New York. 242 pp.
13. Marion, P.D. and French, D.W. 1967. *Nectria galligena* and *Ceratocystis fimbriata* cankers of aspen in Minnesota. For. Sci. 123:23-28.
14. Olchowecki, A. and Reid, J. 1974. Taxonomy of the genus *Ceratocystis* in Manitoba. Can. J. Bot. 52:1675-1711.

15. Parguey-Leduc, A. 1977. Les asques des Pyrénomycetes. Rev. Mycol. (Paris) 41:281-338.

16. Redhead, S.A. and Malloch, D.W. 1977. The Endomycetaceae: new concepts, new taxa. Can. J. Bot. 55:1701-1711.

17. Reynolds, D.R. 1981. Ascomycete systematics. The Luttrellian concept. Springer-Verlag, New York. 242 pp.

18. Rosinsky, M.A. 1961. Development of the ascocarp of *Ceratocystis ulmi*. Am. J. Bot. 48:285-293.

19. Smith, R.S. Jr. 1967. *Verticicladiella* root disease of pines. Phytopathology 57:935-938.

20. Solheim, H. 1986. Species of Ophiostomataceae isolated from *Picea abies* infested by the bark beetle *Ips typographus*. Nord. J. Bot. 6:199-207.

21. Stiers, D.L. 1976. The fine structure of ascospore formation in *Ceratocystis fimbriata*. Can. J. Bot. 54:1714-1723.

22. Upadhyay, H.P. 1981. A monograph of *Ceratocystis* and *Ceratocystiopsis*. University of Georgia Press. Athens, GA. 176 pp.

23. Upadhyay, H.P. and Kendrick, W.B. 1975. Prodromus for a revision of *Ceratocystis* (Microascales, Ascomycetes) and its conidial states. Mycologia 117:798-805.

24. Van Wyk, P.W.J. and Wingfield, M.J. 1990. Ascospore development in *Ceratocystis sensu lato* (Fungi): a review. Bothalia 20:141-145.

25. Van Wyk, P.W.J. and Wingfield, M.J. 1991. Ultrastructure of ascosporogenesis in *Ophiostoma davidsonii*. Mycol. Res. 95:725-730.

26. Van Wyk, P.W.J., Wingfield, M.J. and Van Wyk, P.S. 1991. Ascospore development in *Ceratocystis moniliformis*. Mycol. Res. 95:96-103.

27. Wright, E.F. and Cain, R.F. 1961. A new species of the genus *Ceratocystis*. Can. J. Bot. 39:1215-1230.

PART III

PATHOLOGY AND ECOLOGICAL ASPECTS

Chapter 16

SAPSTAIN OF COMMERCIAL LUMBER BY SPECIES OF *OPHIOSTOMA* AND *CERATOCYSTIS*

K.A. SEIFERT

INTRODUCTION

Sapstain is a grey, black or bluish discoloration of sapwood caused by the presence of pigmented fungal hyphae. It is also referred to as blue stain, which is something of a misnomer as the color is usually more grey, black or brown. The damage to wood is cosmetic, in contrast to the structural damage produced by soft-rot fungi or decay fungi. Sapstain of lumber is generally caused by three groups of fungi:

1. Species of *Ceratocystis, Ophiostoma* and *Ceratocystiopsis*.

2. Black yeasts such as *Hormonema dematioides, Aureobasidium pullulans, Rhinocladiella atrovirens* and *Phialophora* spp.

3. Dark molds such as *Alternaria alternata, Cladosporium sphaerospermum* and *C. cladosporioides*, which produce abundant conidia on the surface of the wood but also stain the wood tissue. *Penicillium* and *Trichoderma* species frequently occur on sapwood and their abundantly-produced conidia cause green discolorations. However, they are not generally considered sapstain organisms because their growth is superficial and they do not usually discolor the wood tissue.

Sapstain is the phenomenon that first brought species of *Ophiostoma* and *Ceratocystis* to light as economically important microorganisms. The term 'sapstain' refers to a series of related phenomena. As noted by Gibbs (this volume), there is a continuum from truly pathogenic sapstaining organisms that occur in living trees, through pathogenic fungi that grow on weakened trees and may also have a saprobic phase, to truly saprobic fungi. With lumber, discolorations are caused mostly by saprobic fungi growing in and staining the sapwood after the wood is cut (Fig. 1). Sapstain caused by pathogenic or endophytic fungi may be less important economically to the lumber industry because infected wood can be discarded before or during processing. Growth of saprobic fungi or opportunistic pathogens is more insidious because colonization of the wood can occur at any time after the tree is felled. Sapstain then becomes evident only when the wood is exposed to favorable conditions for fungal growth.

The use of one term for a series of related phenomena leads to complications. For example, Käärik (36) enumerated more than 250 fungal species associated with sapstained wood. Fifty-eight species of *Ceratocystis* and *Ophiostoma* were included but many of these are pathogenic fungi associated with stain of living trees. If sapstain of lumber is considered to be primarily a saprobic phenomenon, then the magnitude of the problem for the protection of lumber is reduced.

This paper reviews some aspects of the biology and the control of *Ceratocystiopsis, Ophiostoma* and *Ceratocystis* species and their anamorphs that cause sapstain. Historically, these fungi have been most often implicated as sapstaining organisms but it is clear that moulds and black yeasts are often important. Many general reviews on sapstain have been published (1,16,27,54).

Generalizations about the solid wood products industry are difficult to make because each lumbering region has its own unique combination of wood species, indigenous fungal pests, accepted mill standards and government imposed regulations. A consequence of this is that much of the literature is published in limited circulation journals or brochures published by regional laboratories for the local industry, often in languages other than English. This review will concentrate on work done in North America and Europe, where the bulk of sapstain research has been done. Sapstain also occurs in the tropics, but ophiostomatoid fungi are less important. An attempt has been made to provide a universal rather than regional perspective whenever possible.

BIOLOGY

Hartig (29), who proved that fungi caused wood decay, was also the pioneer in the study of sapstain, demonstrating that the discolorations were caused by darkly pigmented fungal hyphae. Hartig assumed that all staining of coniferous wood was caused by one species now known as *Ophiostoma piliferum*. Hedgcock (30) and Münch (47) isolated fungi from

Fig. 1. Typical sapstain on *Pinus banksiana* lumber. The dark stain on the end of the center board is *Trichoderma harzianum*. The rest of the stain is caused primarily by *Ophiostoma piceae*. x 0.4.

sapwood and confirmed that they were the cause of the stain by inoculating them onto unstained wood. Hedgcock (30) considered six species of *Ophiostoma*, including four species still considered important sapstainers on North American lumber today: *O. piliferum, O. pluriannulatum, O. minus* and *O. moniliformis*. Münch (47) isolated four species from lumber in Germany: *O. piliferum, O. piceae, O. canum* and *O. minus* and demonstrated that they could discolor unstained pine or spruce sapwood. His explanation that the blue or dark grey discoloration of the wood is an optical effect of the brown pigmented hyphae growing in the cells is still widely accepted.

Many fungi are now known to cause sapstain in nature and on unseasoned lumber. It is not unusual to find several different species growing in close proximity on a single piece of wood (15,23,49). Different sapstain species predominate in different geographical areas and although some species are limited to certain timbers, most are generalists. In the southern United States, *O. piliferum* and *Ophiostoma ips* are the most common species on conifers (26,65), while in Canada, *O. piceae* is by far the most common sapstain fungus. The species of *Ophiostoma* and *Ceratocystis* that have most frequently been reported from lumber in north temperate regions are listed in Table 1. Many other species have been isolated, but they are of minor importance or of unknown significance.

Causes of discolorations

As long ago as 1907, Münch (47) demonstrated

TABLE 1. Frequently reported species of *Ceratocystis* and *Ophiostoma* implicated in sapstain of lumber.

Species	Observations	References
C. coerulescens[1]	Penetrating dark stain Conifers North America and Europe	23, 36
C. moniliformis	Superficial grey or brown stain Angiosperms Common in southern USA	23, 36
C. virescens[1]	Penetrating dark stain Angiosperms Common in Southern USA	14, 23
O. ips	Dark stain Conifers Very common in USA, less so in Sweden. Introduced to Southern hemisphere Some strains cause weight loss	23, 26, 36
O. minus	Grey to black stain Conifers North America, Europe	31

O. piceae	Superficial or penetrating
	  light grey stain
	Abundant sporulation
	Conifers and angiosperms
	Very common in Canada, common
	  in USA, Europe
	Some strains cause weight loss
		14, 26, 36, 47

O. piliferum	Penetrating grey to black stain Conifers and angiosperms Very common USA, less so Canada, Europe Some strains cause weight loss	23, 26, 28, 29 36, 47, 56
O. pluriannulatum	Penetrating grey to black stain Conifers and angiosperms Common in USA, less so in Canada, Europe	14, 23, 26, 36

[1]See Gibbs (this volume) for an explanation for accepting *C. coerulescens* and *C. virescens* as distinct species.

that hyphae of *Ophiostoma* species were concentrated in the ray parenchyma and resin ducts of infected wood (Fig. 2). No actual staining of the wood cell walls occurs. Although hyphae of sapstaining fungi are often found in tracheids, they are generally unable to penetrate wood cell walls but penetrate from cell to cell through bordered pits. Some sapstain species can also produce minute boreholes; swollen appressoria are formed on the lateral surface of the wood cell wall and a penetration peg physically forces its way through the wall (68). The other microscopic effects of sapstaining ophiostomatoid fungi on wood are slight. Electron microscopic studies have demonstrated some mechanical breakdown of the torus of bordered pits of *Pinus* wood by a species of *Lepto-*

graphium (41) but no visible effects by *O. piceae* (43).

The pigment responsible for the stain is usually considered to be fungal melanin (polymers of 1,8-dihydroxynaphthalene, see 67) but few precise studies have been made. Ayer and coworkers identified 2,3-dihydroxybenzoic acid (4) and ceratenolone (3) chelated in a complex with iron as possible causes of stain caused by some *Ophiostoma* species in diseased lodgepole pine. Despite the apparent involvement of iron in the staining, however, no differences were noted in the trace element compositions of infected trees (5). According to some reports, it is possible to remove the stain from the wood using oxidizing agents such as sodium chlorite or hydrogen peroxide (37,45).

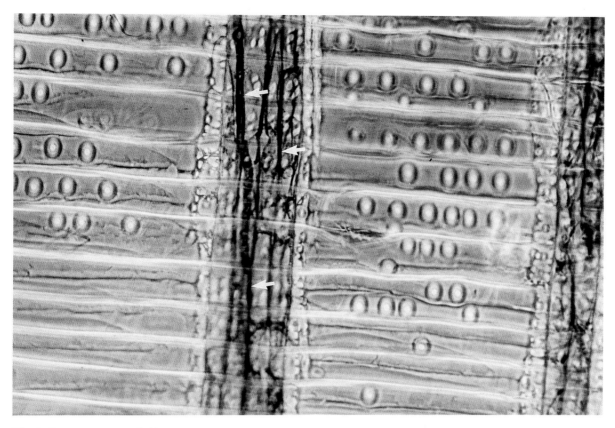

Fig. 2. Dark hyphae of *Ophiostoma* sp. strain FTK C28 (arrows) growing in *Pinus banksiana* sapwood. About 500 x.

Although sapstain is generally considered unsightly, acceptance of stained products depends on the specifications of the consumer. For example, stained wood is frequently used for its artistic effects by Swedish wood workers. Shitova and Biryukova (61,62), investigating the possibility that such stained wood could be used to produce attractive violins, demonstrated that light infections did not alter the acoustic properties of the material.

Effects on wood properties

The effects of sapstain fungi on wood properties have been reviewed by Campbell (14), Findlay (27) and Scheffer (54) and are summarized here in Table 2. Sapstain fungi generally cause only small losses in dry weight. Weight losses caused by various *Ophiostoma* species on conifer wood after 3 months vary between 1-4%, although weight losses as high as 25% have been reported on angiosperm wood after 3 months (26). Although sapstain does not dramatically alter the strength properties of wood, some species do cause strength loss. Toughness is the

property most seriously affected, being reduced up to 30% in heavily stained pine (18,28). Chapman and Scheffer (18) found losses of 1-2% in specific gravity, 2-10% in surface hardness, and 1-5 % in bending and crushing strength in heavily stained pine but did not find any correlation between intensity of staining and strength loss. Generally, these strength losses are considered insignificant unless the wood is intended for applications requiring shock resistance (54). Scheffer (53) noted that stained wood has better drying properties than unstained timber. The belief, prevalent in lumber markets, that stained wood is more susceptible to subsequent decay has not been adequately proven or disproven.

Conditions for growth

The nutrient, moisture and oxygen contents of wood influence the development of sapstain, as does the ambient temperature. Sapstain generally occurs during seasoning or transportation of green lumber before the wood is dried and is enhanced at relative humidities above 90% (10). Fully water saturated

TABLE 2. Effect of common sapstaining ophiostomatoid fungi on wood properties.

Species	Wood	Property	Reduction	Reference
O. ips	*Nyssa*	Weight loss	4.3%	26
	Pinus	Weight loss	0%	26
		Toughness	9.4-47.1%	18
O. minus[1]	*Pinus*	Bending	minor	63
		Compression	minor	63
		Impact bending	30%	63
O. piceae	*Betula*	Weight loss	11.4%	26
	Acer	Weight loss	17.3%	26
	Picea	Weight loss	0%	8, 9
	Pinus	Weight loss	0%	8, 9
	Pinus[2]	Specific gravity	0-2%	17, 18
		Compression parallel to grain	0-3%	18
		Modulus of rupture	0-4.4	17, 18
		Total work to bend	8-16	17
		Total work to maximum load	5.8-24.3	18
		Toughness	18-25%	17, 18
O. piliferum	*Nyssa*	Weight loss	5.6%	26
	Pinus	Weight loss	0%	26
		Specific gravity	0-2.1%	17, 18
		Compression parallel to grain	0-6.2%	18
		Modulus of rupture	0-3.3	17, 18
		Total work to bend	51	17
		Total work to maximum load	25.1-29%	18
		Toughness	41.8-44.9%	17, 18
O. pluriannulatum	*Nyssa*	Weight loss	3.8%	26
	Pinus	Weight loss	0%	26

[1] as *C. pini*.
[2] as *Graphium rigidum*

wood will not stain because of the very low oxygen concentrations. Liese and Peek (42), for example, reported that a water content of 100-120% was necessary to prevent sapstain in pine. The minimum moisture percentage widely reported as necessary for fungal growth in wood is 20% (19), a value that is usually exceeded in green timber. Von Schrenk (56) and Lagerberg *et al.* (38) reported that the intensity of the stain is influenced by the moisture content of the wood. The optimum water content for maximum stain development is 60-80% (38). When the moisture content of the wood is lowered beyond a critical threshold, sapstain is not a problem unless the wood is rewetted. Even so, some ophiostomatoid fungi will

not grow on wood that has been dried and then rewetted (57).

Scheffer (55) studied the *in vitro* oxygen requirements of several sapstaining *Ophiostoma* species. *O. piliferum* and *O. minus* (as *Ceratocystis pini*) grew fairly well at oxygen concentrations as low as 0.8%, but had much reduced growth at lower concentrations. *Ophiostoma minus, O. piliferum* and *Graphium rigidum*[1] recovered after 1-3 months without oxygen and *O. ips* revived after 3-6 months. In general, sapwood-inhabiting fungi were less able to survive long periods without oxygen than were heartwood-inhabiting fungi. Solheim (this volume) also reports on the ability of some *Ophiostoma* species to grow at low oxygen tensions.

Sapstain fungi grow best on wood at temperatures between 22 and 30°C (46,50,51, 52). Under suitable conditions, sapstain fungi will grow 10-15 mm/wk radially in wood and up to 50 mm/wk longitudinally (34). Fluctuating temperatures reduce the rate of growth (52) but there is evidence that serious staining can occur on wood stored at lower temperature, in the range 3-8°C (46). Some of this staining, however, may be caused by psychrotolerant molds such as *Cladosporium* and *Penicillium* species, not by *Ophiostoma* species (39). Pechmann (50) demonstrated that some bluestain fungi exposed to short periods of freezing grew at greater than normal rates when the temperature rose. Only *Ophiostoma clavatum* has been shown to grow at temperatures above 40°C (31).

If the relative humidity is 100%, most staining fungi will stop growing at 40-50°C. At 10-20% RH, temperatures of up to 130°C are required before some species are killed (69). Seehan (57) showed that some *Ophiostoma* species were able to withstand one hour at 200 °C. Some species can survive up to ten years in wood stored at 30-40% RH (68). Air and kiln drying may alter the nutrient content of the wood such that some staining fungi are unable to grow. In these cases, fungi that are normally considered secondary colonizers, such as *Aureobasidium pullulans* and *Sclerophoma pithyophila*, predominate when the wood is remoistened (57).

Nutrition

Most studies of sapstain have been concerned with conifer wood, although the phenomenon also occurs on angiosperm wood (14). Certain wood species are particularly prone to sapstain. Most species of *Pinus*, for example, are susceptible, as are *Tsuga* and *Pseudotsuga* species. Species of *Picea* are relatively less prone to sapstain. Sapstain of hardwood is a problem for some commodities (14) but the literature on this subject is sparse. The differences in susceptibility to stain may be attributed to the presence of inhibitory compounds in the different wood species, or to differences in available nutrients.

As sapwood inhabiting organisms, sapstain fungi are generally thought to utilize the easily assimilable nutrients and not to damage structural carbohydrates.

Lagerberg *et al.* demonstrated that *O. piliferum* and *O. piceae* grew on agar with glucose, maltose, dextrin, starch or olive oil as carbon sources. Histochemical studies to determine whether these species and *O. pluriannulatum* could deplete starch and lipids in pine and spruce wood were inconclusive.

Käärik (34) studied the growth and sporulation of many different *Ophiostoma* species on synthetic media. Carbon and nitrogen source data are summarized in Table 3. On agar media, mycelial conidia were produced at a wide variety of concentrations. Production of synnemata or perithecia occurred over a narrower nutrient range and was best on media with high C/N ratios. In liquid culture, only mycelial conidia were formed. With citrate as a carbon source, growth was usually yeast-like. Most *Ophiostoma* species required the vitamins thiamine, pyridoxine and/or biotin for growth but there was some variation between strains of a species. The optimum pH for growth was usually 3.5-6.5.

Unsaturated fatty acids stimulate the production of perithecia and macronematous anamorphs in *Ophiostoma* species (21,22,48).

Origins and development of sapstain in the lumber yard

The origin of the fungi that stain lumber has been the subject of numerous studies. Land *et al.* (39) refer to several categories: sapstain that occurs during stacking (including sticker and cross stain, which are associated with the small pieces of wood that are used to separate the rows in a pile), insect-borne sapstain, air-borne sapstain, end stain and log stain. Few studies have considered more than one of these possibilities. Sapstain is often assumed to develop from inoculum at the mill site but this may not always be the case. Wood may be colonized but not yet stained when it arrives at the mill.

Some wood clearly arrives at sawmills infected with sapstain fungi. Conspicuously infected logs can be discarded before processing. The piling of logs together before processing, and the stacking of wood after milling, tends to concentrate inoculum and increase the risk of cross infection. Davidson (23) reported that unstained lumber can become stained within three weeks after stacking in the southern U.S. Solid-piled pine can become badly stained in only four to five days.

Species of *Ophiostoma* and *Ceratocystis* and their anamorphs are often among the first fungi to appear on freshly cut wood. According to Dowding (25), species of *Ophiostoma* and *Ceratocystis* colonize

---

[1]The taxonomic identity of *Graphium rigidum* is unknown (58). Most references in the sapstain literature result from Hedgcock's use of this name for a fungus that probably represents the anamorph of *Ophiostoma piceae* (30).

TABLE 3. General patterns of carbon and nitrogen source utilization by *Ophiostoma* spp. (summarized from 34).

	Good growth	Poor growth (or variable)
Carbon sources		
Hexoses	Glucose	Sorbose
	Fructose	
	Mannose	
	Galactose	
Pentoses	Xylose	Ribose
	Arabinose	
	Rhamnose	
Disaccharides	Maltose	Sucrose
	Cellobiose	Lactose
		Raffinose
Polysaccharides	Starch	Inulin
	Pectin	Glycogen
		Cellulose
Sugar alcohols	Glycerol	
	Sorbitol	
	Mannitol	
Nitrogen sources		
Amino acids	Asparagine	
	Glutamine	
	Alanine	
Inorganic	Ammonium sulfate	Nitrate
	Ammonium tartrate	

freshly exposed pine wood on tangential surfaces that are protected from light and dessication. Surfaces exposed to a greater extent are colonized by molds. Some species occur only on relatively uncolonized wood and apparently disappear after 3-6 months as other fungi colonize the wood. However, some of the important sapstaining species of *Ophiostoma*, namely *O. piceae* and *O. piliferum*, can be isolated readily from wood for up to eighteen months after felling (35).

Many experiments intended to determine the source of mold and sapstain inoculum in lumber yards have not considered the possibility of insect dispersal. Therefore open petri dishes containing agar media or sterile wood disks have been placed at various points in the yard at different times of the day at selected times throughout the year; fungi growing on the plates have been isolated or counted, and identified (64).

The association of slimy spored sap-staining fungi with insects, including bark beetles, ambrosia beetles, powder post beetles and mites, was mentioned by Hartig (29), Münch (47), and since has been well documented (see contributions by Gibbs, Harrington, Paine *et al.*, Malloch and Blackwell, this volume). Not only do bark beetles introduce sapstain fungi into standing trees but they visit lumber yards and infest cut logs before processing, sometimes even attacking wood that has been processed into lumber. Davidson (23), for example, reported that *Ips* beetles were always found on *Pinus* lumber infected with *O. ips*. Freshly cut lumber is host to a variety of insects that may be involved in the vectoring and inoculation of sapstain. Experiments to determine the role of these insects in the development of sapstain have been carried out on several occassions. Leach *et al.* (40) prevented infection of logs by *O. ips* by sealing the ends with a fungicidal wax coating and excluding insects using a cage. Dowding (25) reported that treatment of pine wood with a 1% solution of the insecticide Lindastan significantly reduced but did not prevent sapstain caused by *Ophiostoma* and *Ceratocystis* species. Henningsson and Lundström (31) reported that *Ophiostoma clavatum*, normally vectored in Sweden by the beetle *Ips acuminatus*, would not grow if pure cultures were inoculated directly onto lumber and the beetles were excluded. If the wood was placed in the presence of infected beetles, however, stain developed rapidly.

In addition to the association between the fungi and the beetles, it is clear that sapstaining fungi are dispersed by other means. Dowding (24) studied dispersal in a wind tunnel of slimy spores of eight species of *Ophiostoma* and *Ceratocystis* or their anamorphs. He discovered that while these species released none or only a few conidia in dry air, large numbers of conidia were released in misty air. Also, even in still air, propagules were splash-dispersed up to 4 m from a petri dish by 3 mm diam. water droplets dropped from a height of 3 m. The propagules dispersed in these experiments were primarily conidia; ascospores generally remained in intact masses. Such dispersal appears to be only a short-range strategy, however. Liberated conidia die quickly after dessication begins (24). Spores of *Ophiostoma* and *Ceratocystis* species are rarely isolated from the air (25).

Lumber yards are complex, man-made environments and we have much to learn about the ecological strategies of sapstain fungi in this ecosystem. Few comparisons have been made between fungi staining wood at different stages during processing, or between those found on the mill site and in surrounding areas. In a study of one German mill site, Butin (13) noted that several fungi colonized cut, unprocessed trunks, including *Leptographium lundbergii*, and *Ophiostoma* spp. Freshly cut lumber was more often colonized by molds and painted planks by black yeasts. Aufsess (2) concluded that the fungi causing stain of freshly cut Scots Pine logs were different from those prevalent in the surrounding forest debris.

CONTROL

Sapstain control should be an integrated process involving careful harvesting and storage of timber, judicious chemical treatment and efficient delivery to the customer. In practical terms, however, protection of lumber from sapstain is fraught with difficulties.

Harvest and storage

Many forest products companies harvest trees in the winter, when fungal inoculum and insect activity are lowest, as one means of retarding sapstain during transportation (50). Harvested trees are often floated down river to lumber mills, or stored in ponds for up to a year before processing (11). A similar, widely-used practice involves saturating log piles by sprinkling (66). Water storage is usually effective because saturated wood is not prone to sapstain due to the lowered oxygen content (1,10). Portions of the log that float above the surface during ponding, however, may become stained. It is also important that pond water be exchanged. If the storage water is stagnant, serious sapstaining may occur, caused mainly by black yeasts (10).

Reviews of air-seasoning practices are given by Hubert (32) and Findlay (27). The surface of freshy processed lumber is always damp and therefore suitable for fungal growth. To minimize sapstain, lumber mills stack the wood with stickers between the planks, ensuring maximize air exchange and promoting rapid drying. Ideally, the stacks are protected from precipitation by a roof, but this is not always feasible (1,60).

Protective treatments

Wood preservation and protection have been active research areas for much of this century. Many reviews have been published, including those by Cartwright and Findlay (16), Findlay (27) and Levi (44). The most up to date information is presented at annual meetings of national wood preservation societies and associations (for example, the American Wood Preservation Association), the proceedings of which are often published.

Currently, lumber manufacturers are in a crisis situation in their efforts to control sapstain. For more

than fifty years, the industry has relied on chlorinated phenols to prevent growth of sapstain fungi and molds, principally sodium pentachlorophenol and sodium tetrachlorophenol, applied either by surface spraying or dipping. These chlorinated phenols are effective fungicides and, except for occasional problems caused by resistant species such as *Cephaloascus fragrans* (20), the industry has been very satisfied with their action. Unfortunately, the compounds are quite toxic to fish, potentially carcinogenic and are sometimes contaminated with extremely toxic dioxins, as biproducts of the manufacturing process (12,33). For these reasons, the use of chlorinated phenols has been discontinued in most lumber producing countries.

In the past, antisapstain chemicals were expected to protect lumber for up to two years. Because of improved distribution networks and better lumber management, protection may be required for only six months to a year. This reduction in the necessary protection time may provide an opportunity for shorter life pesticides that were previously unable to compete with the extended effectiveness of chlorinated phenols. Moreover, many alternative chemical preservatives are being tested in the laboratory for sapstain prevention. When pentachlorophenol fell into disfavour in Canada, only three alternative fungicides were registered for commercial use, incorporated in a variety of formulations: TCMTB (2- 2-thiocyanomethyl-thiobenzothiozole), borax (sodium borate) and copper-8-quinolinolate. In the last year, two additional chemicals have received temporary registration, namely 3-iodo-2-propynyl-butyl-carbamate and quaternary ammonium compounds. Formulations incorporating these two compounds are now dominating the antisapstain market in both the United States and Canada. Unfortunately, none of these preservatives completely satisfy an industry that had become used to the very effective chlorinated phenols. They suffer from a combination of the following problems: reduced efficacy, higher effective concentrations, unwanted discoloration of the wood, increased costs, corrosion of equipment, high fish toxicity, skin sensitivity and worker resistance.

Kiln drying is an effective means of preventing sapstain (60) but it is not yet economical to dry all lumber for export or domestic use. In addition, some consumers prefer to purchase undried lumber for particular end uses. Refrigeration is not a satisfactory preservation method (46).

Because of the suspicion directed towards chemical preservatives by the general public, several initiatives are underway for environmentally acceptable means of controlling sapstain. A number of biological control organisms, including other sapwood inhabiting fungi, mycorrhizal fungi or bacteria, have been investigated (6,7,59). To date, none of these alternative antisapstain treatments is available for industrial use.

CONCLUSIONS

Despite a century of concern, sapstain of conifer wood remains a serious problem for the lumber industry. Most research has concentrated on chemical protection of lumber and information on the basic biology and ecology of sapstaining fungi is scattered, often in obscure journals, often lacking scientific rigor. There are many unsolved problems, including:

1. The vectoring of sapstain fungi in a lumber mill. What is the role of scolytid beetles and other insects in dispersal in mills? What is the relative importance of the fungi that colonize the wood before it arrives in the mill? What roles do air-borne, mist-borne, water film-borne and rain splash inocula have? Does the mill site and mill equipment become heavily contaminated with sapstaining inoculum?

2. The role of different fungi in sapstain of lumber. How much sapstain can be attributed to pathogenic species that attack standing trees, opportunistic pathogens that attack fallen trees, and saprobic species? Are there synergistic interactions between sapstain fungi? What is the relative importance of different fungal species on different commodities in different geographical regions?

3. The relationship of mill ecology with other ecosystems. Is the fungal biota in a lumber mill different from that of the surrounding environment? Is sapstain that develops during transit (in wrapped packages in a ship's hold) comparable to sapstain developing during seasoning in a lumber yard?

4. Effects on wood properties. Does sapstain make the wood more susceptible to subsequent decay?

The use of broad spectrum, highly toxic fungicides to control sapstain is no longer an option. Effective wood protection will be impossible without a more thorough understanding of the biology of sapstaining fungi than we presently have.

ACKNOWLEDGEMENT

I am grateful to John Gibbs for his critical review of the manuscript.

LITERATURE CITED

1. Anonymous. 1955. Sapstain in timber. Its cause, recognition and prevention. Dept. Sci. Ind. Res. Leaflet no. 2. For. Prod. Res. Lab., Princes Riseborough, England.
2. Aufsess, H. von. 1980. Untersuchungen über das Auftreten der 'Innenbläue' im Kiefernschnittholz. Forstwissen. Cbl. 99:233-242.
3. Ayer, W.A., Attah-Poku, S.K., Browne, L.M. and Orszanska, H. 1987. The chemistry of the blue stain fungi: Part 3. Some metabolites of Ceratocystis minor (Hedgcock) Hunt. Can. J. Chem. 65:765-769.
4. Ayer, W.A., Browne, L.M., Feng, M.C., Orszanska, H., and Saeed I-Ghomi, H. 1986a. The chemistry of the blue stain fungi: Part 1. Some metabolites of Ceratocystis species associated with mountain pine beetle infected Lodgepole Pine. Can. J. Chem. 64:904-909.
5. Ayer, W.A., Kratochvil, H., Allen, E., Browne, L.M., Dufresne, C. Figueroa, D. and Szenthe, A. 1986b. The chemistry of the blue stain fungi: Part 2. Some essential metal levels of diseased and healthy Lodgepole Pine. Can. J. Chem. 64:910-913.
6. Benko, R. 1987. Antagonistic effect of some mycorrhizal fungi as biological control of sap-stain. Int. Res. Group on Wood Preserv., Document No. IRG/WP/1314.
7. Benko, R. 1988. Bacteria as possible organisms for biological control of blue stain. Int. Res. Group on Wood Preserv., Document No. IRG/WP/1339.
8. Bergman, O. and Nilsson, T. 1968. On outside storage of birch chips at Morrum's sulfate mill. Res. Notes Dept. For. Prod. Roy. Coll. Forest., Stockholm R60:1-56.
9. Bergman, O. and Nilsson, T. 1971. Studies on outside storage of sawmill chips. Res. Notes Dept. For. Prod. Roy. Coll. Forest., Stockholm R71:1-54.
10. Björkman, E. 1946a. Om uppkomsten av stockblånad och lagrinsröta i furusågtimmer i samband med flotting. Med. Stat. Skogsforsk. Tidskr. 35:1-56.
11. Björkman, E. 1946b. Om betingelserna för uppkomsten av brädgårdsblånade samt denna bekämpande. Med. Stat. Skogsforsk. Tidskr. 35:1-46.
12. Bray, A.R. 1981. Hazard warning: Pentachlorophenol. Canada Safety Council, Ottawa, Canada.
13. Butin, H. 1965. Untersuchungen zur Ökologie einiger Bläuepilze an verarbeitetem Kifernholz. Flora (Jena) 155:400-440.
14. Campbell, R.N. 1959. Fungus sap-stains of hardwoods. Southern Lumberman, Dec. 15 1959:115-120.
15. Campbell, R.N. 1960. Some sap-stain fungi found in Minnesota. Plant Dis. Rep. 44:625-628.
16. Cartwright, K.St.G. and Findlay, W.P.K. 1958. Decay of timber and its prevention. H. M. Stationary Office, London. 332 pp.
17. Chapman, A.D. 1933. Effect of steam sterilizing on susceptibility of wood to blue-staining and wood-destroying fungi. J. Agric. Res. 47:369-374.
18. Chapman, A.D. and Scheffer, T.C. 1940. Effect of blue stain on specific gravity and strength of southern pine. J. Agric. Res. 61:125-133.

19. Colley, R.H. and Rumbold, C.T. 1930. Relation between moisture content of the wood and blue stain in Loblolly pine. J. Agric. Res. 41:389-399.

20. Csjeresi, A.J. 1967. The adaptation of fungi to pentachlorophenol and its biodegradation. Can. J. Microbiol. 13:1243-1249.

21. Dalpé, Y. and Neumann, P. 1976. L'effet d'acides gras sur la stimulation des périthèces de Ceratocystis ips, C. minor et C. capillifera. Eur. J. For. Pathol. 6:335-342.

22. Dalpé, Y. and Neumann, P. 1977. L'induction chez Ceratocystis de fructifications de types Graphium et Leptographium par des acides gras insaturés. Can. J. Bot. 55:2159-2167.

23. Davidson, R.W. 1935. Fungi causing stain in logs and lumber in the southern states, including five new pecies. J. Agric. Res. 50:789-807.

24. Dowding, P. 1969. The dispersal and survival of spores of fungi causing bluestain in pine. Trans. Br. Mycol. Soc. 52:125-137.

25. Dowding, P. 1970. Colonization of freshly bared pine sapwood surfaces by staining fungi. Trans. Br. Mycol. Soc. 55:399-412.

26. Eslyn, W.E. and Davidson, R.W. 1976. Some wood-staining fungi from pulpwood chips. Mem. N. Y. Bot. Gard. 28:50-57.

27. Findlay, W.P.K. 1959. Sapstain of timber. For. Abstr. 20:1-14.

28. Findlay, W.P.K. and Pettifor, C.B. 1937. Effect of sapstain on the properties of timber. I. Effect of sapstain on the strength properties of Scots Pine wood. Forestry 11:40-52.

29. Hartig, R. 1878. Die Zersetzungserscheinungen des Holzes, der Nadelbaüme und der Eich. Julius Springer, Berlin. 151 pp.

30. Hedgcock, G.C. 1906. Studies upon some chromogenic fungi which discolour wood. Ann. Rep. Mo. Bot. Gard. 17:59-114.

31. Henningsson, B. and Lundström, H. 1974. Insect-borne blue stain. Growth and effects caused by water immersion of the wood. Some laboratory tests. Roy. Coll. For., Dept. For. Prod. Rep. R 92.

32. Hubert, E.E. 1929. Sap stains of wood and their prevention. U. S. Dept. Comm. Wood Util. Rep. no. 10:1-77.

33. Jones, P.A. 1981. Chlorophenols and their impurities in the Canadian environment. Environmental Protection Service, Environment Canada, E.P.S.-3-EC-81-2.

34. Käärik, A. 1960. Growth and sporulation of Ophiostoma and some other blueing fungi on synthetic media. Symb. Bot. Upsal. 16:1-168.

35. Käärik, A. 1968. Colonisation of pine and spruce poles by soil fungi after twelve and eighteen months. Mat. und Org. 3:185-198.

36. Käärik, A. 1980. Fungi causing sap stain in wood. Swed. Univ. Agric. Sci, Dept. For. Prod. Rep. no. R 114.

37. Kai, Y. 1985. Bleaching of blue stain in aspen wood. Bull. Fac. Agric. Shizuoka Univ. 35:43-47.

38. Lagerberg, T., Lundberg, G. and Melin, E. 1927. Biological and practical researches into blueing of pine and spruce. Svenska Skogsför. Tidskr. 25:145-272, 561-691.

39. Land, C.J., Banhidi, Z.G. and Albertsson, A.-C. 1985. Surface discoloring and blue staining by cold tolerant filamentous fungi on outdoor softwood in Sweden. Mat. und Org. 20:133-156.

40. Leach, J.G., Orr, L.W. and Christensen, C.M. 1934. The interrelationship of bark beetles and bluestaining fungi in felled Norway pine timber. J. Agric. Res. 49:315-342.

41. Liese, W. and Hartmann-Fahnenbrock, M. 1953. Licht-und elektronenmikroskopische Untersuchungen über das Wachstum von Blauepilzen in Kiefern- und Fichtenholz. Holzforschung 7:97-102.

42. Liese, W. and Peek, R. 1984. Experiences with wet storage of conifer logs. Skovtek. Dansk. Skov. Tidsskr. (Sonderheft): 73-91.

43. Liese, W. and Schmid, R. 1961. Licht- und electronen-mikroskopische Untersuchungen über das Wachstum von Blaüepilzen in Kiefern- und Fichtenholz. Holz Roh u. Werkstoff 19:329-337.

44. Levi, M.P. 1973. Control methods. Pages 183-216 in: Wood Deterioration and Its Prevention by Preservative Treatments. Vol. 1. Degradation and Protection of Wood. D.D. Nicholas, ed. Syracuse University Press, Syracuse, NY. 380 pp.

45. Luchi, G. 1971. "Bleaching of wood affected by bluestain fungi". Contr. Sci. Prat. Migl. Conosc. Util. Legno 14:55-60 (in Italian, cited in For. Abstr. 34:224. 1973).

46. Miller, D.J. and Goodell, B. 1981. Blue staining in Ponderosa pine sapwood at moderate and low temperatures. For. Prod. J. 31:54-59.

47. Münch, E. 1907. Die Blaufäule de Nadelholzes I. Naturw. Z. Forst. Landw. 5:531-573.

48. Neumann, P. and Hubbes, M. 1972. Terpenes and unsaturated fatty acids trigger coremia formation by Ceratocystis ulmi. Eur. J. For. Pathol. 5:129-137.

49. Olchowecki, A. and Reid, J. 1974. Taxonomy of the genus Ceratocystis in Manitoba. Can. J. Bot. 52:1675-1711.

50. Pechmann, H. von. 1965. Der Einfluss der Temperatur auf das Wachstum von Bläuepilzen. Mat. und Org. Suppl. 1:237-250.

51. Pechmann, H. von, Graessle, E. and Wutz, A. 1964. Untersuchungen über Bläuepilze an Kifernholz. Forstwissen. Cbl. 83:290-314.

52. Reynolds, P.E., Smith, W.H. and Jensen, K.F. 1972. Effect of constant and fluctuating temperatures on the in vitro growth of Ceratocystis species. Trans. Br. Mycol. Soc. 59:1-9.

53. Scheffer, T.C. 1941. Drying rates of blue stained and bright lumber. Southern Lumberman 162:46.

54. Scheffer, T.C. 1973. Microbiological degradation. Pages 31-106 in: Wood Deterioration and Its Prevention by Preservative Treatments. Vol. 1. Degradation and Protection of Wood. D.D. Nicholas, ed. Syracuse University Press, Syracuse, NY. 380 pp.

55. Scheffer, T.C. 1986. O_2 requirements for growth and survival of wood-decaying and sapwood-staining fungi. Can. J. Bot. 64:1957-1963.

56. Schrenck, H. von. 1903. The blueing and red rot of the western yellow pine, with special reference to the Black Hill Forest Reserve. USDA Bur. Plant. Ind. Bull. no. 36.

57. Seehan, G. 1965. Über die Wirkung einer Trocknung und Erwärmung von Nadelholz auf das Wachstum von Bläuepilzen. Holz Roh u. Werkstoff 23:341-347.

58. Seifert, K.A. 1985. A monograph of Stilbella and some allied hyphomycetes. Stud. Mycol. 27:1-235.

59. Seifert, K.A., Breuil, C., Rossignol, L., Best, M. and Saddler, J.N. 1988. Screening for microorganisms with the potential for biological control of sapstain on unseasoned lumber. Mat. und Org. 23:81-96.

60. Shields, J.K., Thornber, W. and McKnight, T.S. 1971. How researchers are combatting eastern hardwood stain problem. Can. J. For. Res. 91:49-51.

61. Shitova, A.E. and Biryukova, T.S. 1972. "Effect of bluestain on the acoustic constant of spruce resonance wood." Derevoobrabatyvayuschaya Promyshlemost 1972:12-13 (in Russian).

62. Shitova, A.E. and Biryukova, T.S. 1973. "Effect of bluestain on some strength properties of resonance wood." Derevoobrabatyvayuschaya Promyshlemost 1973:16 (in

Russian).

63. Thunell, B. 1952. Einwirkung der Bläue auf die Festigkeiseigenschaften der Kiefer. Holz Roh u. Werkstoff 11:66-68.

64. Unligil, H.H., Shih, M.S.H. and Shields, J.K. 1974. Airborne fungal spores at lumber seasoning yards in the lower Ottawa Valley. Can. J. For. Res. 4:301-307.

65. Verral, A.F. 1939. Relative importance and seasonal prevalence of wood-staining fungi in the southern states. Phytopathology 29:1031-1051.

66. Webber, J. F. 1990. Guidelines for water storage of timber. For. Comm. Res. Inf. Note 175. Farnham, England.

67. Wheeler, M. H. 1983. Comparisons of fungal melanin synthesis in ascomycetous, imperfect and basidiomycetous fungi. Trans. Br. Mycol. Soc. 81:29-36.

68. Wilcox, W.W. 1973. Degradation in relation to wood structure. Pages 107-148 in: Wood Deterioration and Its Prevention by Preservative Treatments. Vol. 1. Degradation and Protection of Wood. D. D. Nicholas, ed. Syracuse University Press, Syracuse, NY. 380 pp.

69. Zimmermann, G. and Butin, H. 1973. Untersuchungen über Hitzeund Trockenresistenz holzbewohnender Pilze. Flora (Jena) 162:393-419.

Chapter 17

THE BIOLOGY OF OPHIOSTOMATOID FUNGI CAUSING SAPSTAIN IN TREES AND FRESHLY CUT LOGS

J.N. GIBBS

Sapstain is defined as the blue-black discoloration of sapwood caused by deeply penetrating fungi that do not cause decay. As the general features of sapstain have been summarized by Seifert (this volume), this paper will concentrate on the biology of ophiostomatoid fungi (including species of *Ophiostoma* and *Ceratocystis*) that cause stain in the wood of trees and fresh logs, i.e. wood that is comprised, at least in part, of living host cells and that has not previously been colonized by other organisms. In such material, the stain is typically triangular or wedge-shaped in cross-section. This is the result of a pattern of host invasion that involves much growth along the medullary rays (see Fig. 1).

DIVERSITY OF RELATIONSHIP BETWEEN FUNGUS AND TREE

The relationship between sapstaining ophiostomatoid fungi and their hosts is varied. In some combinations, virtually no pathogenic activity is involved; the fungi only develop in trees where active host-resistance mechanisms, such as resin accumulation and phenol production, are greatly impaired. This may happen if the tree is suppressed by its neighbours or if it comes under some adverse environmental influence such as drought. It is brought about in an extreme form by felling. In contrast, some members of the group cause serious

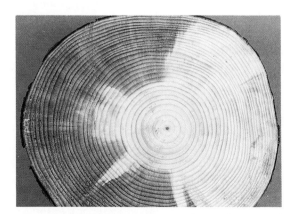

Fig. 1. Blue stain in a windblown Scots pine caused by *Leptographium wingfieldii.*

diseases in which the fungus is fully capable of overwhelming the resistance of a healthy tree. This range of behaviour is illustrated in the following paragraphs.

A good example of a system within which the sapstain fungus acts non-pathogenically is provided by *Ceratocystis coerulescens* on Scots pine *(Pinus sylvestris)* and Corsican pine *(P. nigra* var. *calabrica)* in Europe. Here, stain is common in recently cut logs and has also been recorded penetrating into the butts of windblown trees from broken roots. There are, however, no records of attack on healthy trees.

Distinctly more pathogenic activity is demonstrated by *C. coerulescens* on Norway spruce *(Picea abies)*. In Sweden, Lagerberg *et al.* (19) reported that when a number of 80-120 year old trees were felled, 28% were stained with *C. coerulescens*; the infection was traceable back to 'blazes' made on the stems 20 months earlier. The maximum linear extent of stain was 3.8 m - representing an impressive average linear growth rate of 3 mm/day. In Norway, Solheim and Selas (36) have produced similar data.

A somewhat comparable example of differential behavior on two host genera is provided by *C. virescens*, a fungus which has been synonymized erroneously with *C. coerulescens* by several authors (18). *Ceratocystis virescens* causes serious sapstain of freshly cut logs of certain hardwoods such as oak and sweetgum in the southern United States (6,8,9); but on sugar maple *(Acer saccharum)* it can be a lethal pathogen, causing the disease 'sapstreak' (see Kile, this volume).

In considering the kind of situation outlined above, it is important to recognize that with the ophiostomatoid fungi (as with many other fungal groups), species defined on classical morphological grounds may contain a number of genetically distinct entities associated with certain hosts. This is clearly the case with *O. piceae* as defined by Hunt (17), which causes sapstain on logs of both conifers and broadleaves. Brasier (this volume) has shown that two groups, based on characters such as fertility barriers, can be recognized: one is found only on hardwoods, the other principally on conifers. These differences may well reflect varying abilities to cause

TABLE 1. Comparison of two *Ophiostoma* spp. associated with *Ips typographus*. Modified from Solheim (34,35).

	O. polonicum	O. penicillatum
Percentage of Norway spruce sapwood showing desiccation 10 wk. after inoculation of standing trees (based on a section through the inoculation zone)	27.5	8.7
Growth rate (mm/day) on malt agar at 22°C	8.3	10.6

TABLE 2. Effect of inoculum density on blue stain development in Norway spruce inoculated with *Ophiostoma polonicum*. Modified from Christiansen (7).

Number of inoculation points per 100 cm^2	Percentage bluestaining of peripheral sapwood in the inoculation zone 4 months after inoculation of trees of different vigor categories[1]		
	1	2	3
1	3.2	0.0	4.8
2	3.6	4.2	13.6
4	12.6	57.0	78.0
8	99.0	93.0	98.6

[1] Trees in category 1 = very vigorous, 2 = moderately vigorous, 3 = suppressed vigor

sapstain on their respective hosts.

A very interesting contrast in the degree of pathogenic behaviour exhibited by two ophiostomatoid fungi on the same host is found with *O. polonicum* and *O. penicillatum* on Norway spruce in Norway. In nature, these two fungi may be introduced together by the bark beetle, *Ips typographus*, but *O. polonicum* has a much greater ability to develop and cause bluestain in healthy trees than has *O. penicillatum* (35, see also Solheim, this volume). This is illustrated by the data in Table 1, which show the degree of sapwood desiccation caused by the two fungi 10 weeks after multiple inoculations to the cambium. That this difference is not due to the intrinsic growth rate of the fungus is shown by data for growth on malt agar from Solheim (34), also presented in Table 1. Solheim commented that since *O. penicillatum* has been recorded as one of the dominant species on logs, it might be better adapted to this material. It would be valuable if the two fungi could be inoculated both into standing and freshly felled Norway spruce and their invasive capacity in the two substrates compared.

It seems that the ability of *O. polonicum* to overcome the active host resistance of a healthy tree depends upon a sufficient density of infection points being established. Thus, Christiansen (7) showed that when the density of inoculation points in very vigorous trees was increased from 4 to 8 per 100 cm^2, a dramatic increase in sapwood invasion took place (Table 2).

The kind of behaviour shown by *O. polonicum* on Norway spruce may be common among sapstaining ophiostomatoid fungi that are introduced to their hosts via mass attacks by bark beetles. A contrasting situation is provided by canker stain of London plane in southern Europe. Here the fungus *Ceratocystis fimbriata* var. *platani* develops from a single infection point, such as a small wound, and spreads through the tree by mycelial growth in the medullary rays and mycelial growth and passive spore transport in the vessels. Vigorous trees can be killed within a few months (see Kile, this volume). In considering this disease, it is important to recognize that it has probably resulted from the introduction of the causal fungus from North America. Other ophiostomatoid

TABLE 3. Degree of association of various *Ophiostoma* species with European pine bark beetles. Modified from Mathiesen-Käärik (28).

Bark beetle	*Ips sexdentatus*	*Ips acuminatus*	*Tomicus minor*	*Tomicus piniperda*	*Hylastes ater*
No. beetles examined	30	86	244	91	30
Percentage beetles with:					
O. minus	0	46	11	36	13
O. brunneociliatum	50	0	0	0	0
O. canum	0	1	52	4	0
O. clavatum	6	78	0	1	0

fungi, currently causing only minor sapstain, may well have the potential to become serious vascular stain pathogens on allied host species in other parts of the world if they were to be introduced there (see 16).

DISPERSAL AND THE INFECTION PROCESS

It has long been known that many of the sap-staining ophiostomatoid fungi are intimately linked with bark beetles that act as vectors. Von Schrenk (37) seems to have been the first to suggest this association. He suspected that *Dendroctonus ponderosae* carried a bluestain fungus and introduced it to *Pinus ponderosa* during breeding attacks. However, he was unsuccessful in isolating the fungus from the beetle. This led him to suggest that the fungal spores were wind-borne and entered the tree through the holes made by the beetles. Subsequent workers returned to the idea of insect-vectoring but it was not until the work of Leach *et al.* (21) in Minnesota that critical experiments were carried out to prove the link between insects and fungi. Leach (20) later summarized the work on the role of *Ips pini* and *I. grandicollis* in transmitting *Ophiostoma ips* as follows: Freshly cut logs of Norway pine (*Pinus resinosa*) were exposed under a variety of conditions in experiments designed to determine the degree of interdependence between the beetles and the bluestain fungi. The ends of some of the logs were sealed and others were left without sealing. The logs were exposed in such a way as to exclude insects from some and to exclude wind-blown spores from others. These experiments proved that the blue-staining

fungi, along with certain yeasts, were routinely introduced by the beetles and rarely, if ever, in any other way.

Leach *et al.* (21) went on to report that spores of the bluestain fungi were carried both externally on the body surface and internally within the intestinal tract. Mycangia, specialized organs for fungal transport, have never been identified in these two *Ips*, species. Indeed only *I. acuminatus*, a European pine bark beetle, is listed by Beaver (2) as possessing a mycangium.

As further work continued, most notably in Northern Europe, various patterns emerged. Some bluestain fungi were associated closely with specific bark beetles while others had much more haphazard relationships with insects. This is illustrated by the data from Mathiesen-Käärik (28) in Table 3, which show that while *O. minus* was recorded on several beetles; *O. canum*, *O. brunneociliatum* and *O. clavatum* were associated only with a single beetle species.

Despite the evidence for the importance of bark beetles as vectors, air dispersal was still considered important for the dissemination of these fungi. Thus, Mathiesen-Käärik (29) stated that species such as *C. coerulescens, O. minus* and *O. piliferum*, which frequently colonized mechanically injured or partially de-barked logs in the absence of beetle infestation, "were apparently distributed mostly by wind, although some secondary insects might be involved". This point was taken up by Dowding (10), who used various experimental approaches to examine the dispersal in dry air, mist and splash droplets of

TABLE 4. Linear growth rate on malt agar at optimum temperature of some ophiostomatoid fungi causing blue stain in pine and spruce.

Radial Growth Rate (mm/day)		
More than 10	Between 5 and 10	Less than 5
Ceratocystis coerulescens	Ophiostoma clavatum	Ophiostoma brunneociliatum
	Ophiostoma ips	Ophiostoma canum
Leptographium lundbergii	Ophiostoma minus	Ophiostoma piceae
Leptographium penicillatum	Ophiostoma polonicum	Ophiostoma piliferum
Leptographium wingfieldii	Leptographium huntii	Leptographium procerum
	Leptographium serpens	Graphium spp.
	Ambrosiella ips[1]	Ambrosiella tingens[1]

[1] The two *Ambrosiella* spp. are included because they will grow on agar amended with cycloheximide, suggesting affinities with the genus *Ophiostoma*.

conidia of *O. piceae*, *O. piliferum*, *O. minus* and *C. coerulescens*. Not surprisingly, he found that dry air was completely ineffective in causing conidium dispersal but that both mist-laden air and splash droplets would dislodge and disseminate conidia relatively easily. Ascospores could also be dislodged by splash droplets but only with difficulty; they usually remained as large spore masses. Even more important in dismissing the entrenched ideas of air dispersal, Dowding found that once separated, the conidia desiccated and died very rapidly, especially under the influence of ultra-violet light. He also drew attention to the fact that none of the studies on air dispersal of *Ophiostoma* and *Ceratocystis* species had been conducted with sufficient rigor to exclude insect transmission. When Dowding (11,12) carried out field studies on small Scots pine in eastern England, he found that much of the *O. piceae*, *O. piliferum*, *O. minus* and *C. coerulescens* infection occurred on logs without insecticide treatment but which had been wounded in such a way as to create sapwood wounds that were protected by residual flaps of bark. He argued that the most likely means of transmission was casual arthropod transfer, although water splash might be locally important.

Little subsequent research on the significance of arthropod vectors has been conducted, although Bridges and Moser (4,5) demonstrated that phoretic mites on the southern pine beetle, *Dendroctonus frontalis*, were important in transferring *O. minus* to *D. frontalis*-attacked pines. Recently, Levieux *et al.* (22) reported the presence of *O. brunneo-ciliatum* and *O. minus* on mites phoretic on *Ips sexdentatus* in France. Moser *et al.* (30) recorded *O. polonicum* on mites associated with *Ips typographus* in Sweden. Despite this work, it remains very doubtful if mites can be as effective as beetles as vectors for these fungi; they must always be largely, if not exclusively, dependent on beetle galleries for access to suitable host tissue.

GROWTH OF SAPSTAINING FUNGI WITHIN THE HOST

Intrinsic rates of fungal growth.

Table 4 describes linear growth rates on malt agar for some of the major bluestain species on pine in Europe. It is interesting to note that the fastest group comprises three species (*C. coerulescens*, *L. lundbergii*, *L. wingfieldii*) that apparently do not have intimate associations with any particular bark beetle.

By contrast, species like *O. canum* and *O. clavatum*, which are constantly linked to just one species of bark beetle, are relatively slow growing. It may be that for fungi in the former group, rapid growth rates confer real benefits by increasing the chance of contact with a suitable vector. This seems to be the case with *L. wingfieldii*. Recent work in both France and England (15,26) has shown that this species can be vectored by the pine shoot beetle, *Tomicus piniperda*, a beetle that has a single generation per year. The adult beetles emerge in mid-summer and survive until the following spring when they enter weakened trees or fresh logs of pine to breed. During this relatively long adult life, the percentage of beetles carrying the fungus declines significantly, with the result that *L. wingfieldii* is

TABLE 5. Percentage of *Tomicus piniperda* carrying *Leptographium wingfieldii* at two points in the life cycle.

Source		Percentage of overwintering adults with *L. wingfieldii* at the time of entry to breed	Percentage of young adults with *L. wingfieldii* at time of emergence[1]
Studies in France	1985	10	30
(26)	1986	5	30
Studies in England	1988	16	60
(15)			

[1] The higher figures obtained in the English work are likely to be due, at least in part, to the use of a selective medium for the isolation of *L. wingfieldii*.

present on only a small proportion of the adults when the time of breeding comes round. However, through its rapid growth in the tracheids, *L. wingfieldii* establishes links, not only with the larvae originating from the parent beetle which introduced it, but also with larvae in adjacent gallery systems. As a consequence, many of the callow adults carry the fungus when they emerge (Table 5). Rapid growth would have no equivalent adaptive significance for a fungus such as *O. canum*, which is routinely introduced to the *T. minor* gallery systems during gallery excavation.

Growth in the wood

The most careful investigations into the process of host invasion by sapstaining ophiostomatoid fungi were those conducted in Germany by Liese and Schmid (23,24) who studied both naturally-bluestained wood of pine and spruce and blocks of fresh pinewood that had been surface-sterilized with propylene oxide and then inoculated with *O. piliferum* and *O. piceae*. This particular sterilization process was used because it was less damaging to the host tissues than the treatments used by earlier workers, which led to coagulation of the ray parenchyma. On the basis of their light microscope studies, Liese and Schmid (23) commented that no real differences could be found between the two hosts. Tracheids, rays and resin canals were all colonized, but whereas the nutrient-rich ray cells were preferentially invaded, it was in the tracheids that the highest rates of growth occurred. Progress of the fungi from tracheid to tracheid was via bordered pits or through direct penetration of the wall (Fig. 2). Electron microscope studies of the former

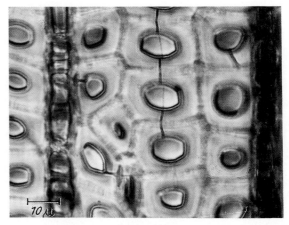

Fig. 2. Direct penetration of Scots pine tracheid wall by *Ophiostoma piliferum* (with permission from Liese and Schmid, 23).

process showed that penetration was usually through the torus of the pit membrane by means of a hole slightly smaller than the average diameter of the hyphae. There was no indication of any involvement of enzymes in the process. With the rarer process of wall penetration, an appressorium was formed, below which a narrow 'bore hypha', about one-fifth of the diameter of the normal hyphae, penetrated the wall (Fig. 3). Again there was no evidence from the electron micrographs to indicate any enzymatic dissolution or weakening of the host tissue. In the medullary rays, growth from cell to cell was almost entirely via the pits, which were found to be more commonly present than in the tracheids. Here, however, the photographs provided some evidence that enzymes were involved in the destruction of the pit membrane.

Some information on fungal growth in the host

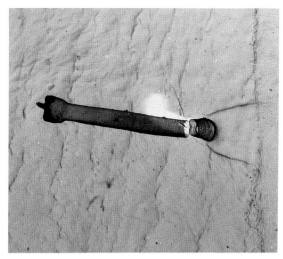

Fig. 3. Bore-hypha of *Ophiostoma piliferum* with a needle shaped point (with permission from Liese and Schmid, 24).

with one of the more pathogenic bluestains comes from the work of Ballard *et al.* (1) on *Pinus contorta* attacked by the mountain pine beetle *Dendroctonus ponderosae*. The particular fungi present were inadequately identified, although it seems likely that *O. clavigerum* was the principal species involved (see Yamaoka *et al.* 38). Ballard *et al.* reported that penetration of the walls of the ray parenchyma involved the production of appressorium-like structures and a penetration peg. The process was believed to be primarily mechanical but some evidence of secondary enzymatic activity was also detected. Relatively few observations were made on the mode of growth from one tracheid to another but, as with the work of Liese and Schmid (23), it appeared to be a mechanical process involving direct penetration through the torus of the pit membrane.

Little detailed research has been done on the nature of the enzymatic degradation that seems to occur in the non-lignified tissue. Working with *O. minus* in culture, however, Rosch *et al.* (32) detected cellulase, polygalacturonase, pectinesterase and phenoloxidase.

These studies suggest that all the sapstaining ophiostomatoid fungi are similar in their growth through the host cells. There are, however, some interesting lines of enquiry that could be pursued. Thus, Lagerburg *et al.* (19) suggested that *O. minus* might differ from some of the other species in being unable to penetrate cell walls directly.

Despite the earlier reference to the growth rate of *C. coerulescens* in Norway spruce trees, there are few good data on the rate of colonization by bluestain fungi in those situations in which pathogenic invasion

occurs; this is despite the large amount of work that has been done on the relationship between pathogenic bluestain fungi and their hosts (Lieutier and Paine, this volume). The lack of useful data on the rates of sapstaining in logs is even more striking. All too often the tests have been done on wood that has been so much altered by heat treatment or chemical sterilization that the results are of little relevance to the *in vivo* situation. One of the few worthwhile studies is that by Lindgren (27) on the growth of *O. piliferum* through blocks of fresh *Pinus echinata* sapwood. He reported a rate of longitudinal penetration of 4.5 mm/day at 25-28°C, which was as great as that on 2.5% malt agar at the same temperatures. Rates of radial and tangential colonization were appreciably slower, at 1.0 and 0.5 mm per day. This probably reflects, in part, the greater physical barriers to penetration in these directions but it may also reflect the fact that fungi often grow more rapidly in nutrient-poor than in nutrient-rich environments.

The influence of wood moisture content on colonization is another area deserving more study. One must often refer back to the work of pioneers like Münch (31), who investigated the rate of growth of *O. minus* into 5-10 cm disks cut from a 40-year-old Scots pine in April. In fresh sections, penetration was very slow. However, a loss of only 10% of this moisture through air drying was sufficient to allow complete penetration of the sapwood. It is interesting to note that this effect was recorded with *O. minus*. Later studies by Lagerberg *et al.* (19), albeit on wood that had been partially sterilized at 50°C, showed that *O. minus* was noticeably less inhibited by a high moisture content than were species such as *O. piliferum* and *L. lundbergii*. Essentially the same effect, measured in terms of tolerance of low oxygen levels, has been recorded by Scheffer (33). For most ophiostomatoid fungi, it seems that an appreciable loss of moisture may be necessary before invasion can occur. In this connection, it is important to note that with the bluestain fungi, as well as with many other parasitic fungi, a local drying of the sapwood is one of the first features of pathogenic attack on standing trees (see for example Table 1).

Humans have taken advantage of the inability of bluestain fungi to tolerate high wood moisture contents by developing water storage systems for logs, particularly those of pine (see Liese and Peek, 25). Recent experience in Britain has shown that even established bluestain infections can be arrested by these procedures and apparently rendered inviable

(Fig. 4). Under water storage conditions, it is likely that colonization of the wood by anaerobic bacteria supplements the effect of high moisture content on available oxygen levels.

SAPROTROPHIC SURVIVAL

Garrett (13) argued that poor saprophytic survival was a normal concomitant of specialized parasitic ability. This concept is well illustrated by the sapstaining ophiostomatoid fungi. Some 25 years ago, I noted how the benefits conferred on *L. lundbergii* from its ability to act as an early and rapid colonizer of heavily suppressed Scots pine were offset by the relentless and often speedy growth through the blue-stained wood of fungi such as *Trichoderma viride* or the wood-rotting basidiomycetes *Peniophora gigantea* and *Heterobasidion annosum* (14). *Trichoderma* spp., in particular, will race through blue-stained sectors of logs and render the isolation of ophiostomatoid fungi very difficult, if not impossible, even with the use of selective media. This is strikingly illustrated by some work carried out after the 1987 gale in southern England. Scots pine and Corsican pine logs were cut from windblown but stain-free trees in April 1988 and stacked in piles in the forest. After 8 months they were sawn up and extensive culture work was undertaken from blue-stained areas using malt agar with and without cycloheximide. Ophiostomatoid fungi (principally *Leptographium* and *Graphium*) were obtained from only 29% of the samples but *Trichoderma viride* was recovered from 88% (B.J.W. Greig and J.N. Gibbs, unpublished data). The restricted ability of the ophiostomatoid fungi to remain in occupation of colonized tissue must limit the range of wood- and bark-inhabiting insects that can act as vectors; although to some extent, the effect may be mitigated by the production of melanized perithecia that can withstand predation by mites and other animals (3).

CONCLUDING REMARKS

It is impossible to escape the conclusion that, in the past, the pursuit of the short-term objective of bluestain control has resulted in far too little effort being directed to an understanding of the biology of the causal organisms.

Further work is needed on most of the species mentioned here. In particular, much more information is required on the growth of the various fungi in the host and on the extent to which this is

Fig. 4. Section through Scots pine log after 2 years under water-sprinkling. The extent of the blue-stained area is the same as when water-sprinkling began. No blue-stained fungi could be reisolated.

influenced by environmental factors. More research on the saprotrophic survival of many of the fungi would also be valuable, particularly if it was coupled with consideration of the life cycle of possible vectors. Such work could lead to the development of new approaches to control, that will be very much needed in the post-pentachlorophenol era!

ACKNOWLEDGEMENTS

I would like to thank Prof. Walter Liese for the provision of two photographs.

LITERATURE CITED

1. Ballard, R.G., Walsh, M.A. and Cole, W.E. 1984. The penetration and growth of blue-stain fungi in the sapwood of lodgepole pine attacked by mountain pine beetle. Can. J. Bot. 62:1724-1729.
2. Beaver, R.A. 1989. Insect-fungus relationships in the bark and ambrosia beetles. Pages 121-143 in: Insect-fungus interactions. N. Wilding, N.M. Collins, P.M. Hammond and J.F. Webber, eds. Academic Press, London. 344 pp.
3. Brasier, C.M. 1978. Mites and reproduction in *Ceratocystis ulmi* and other fungi. Trans. Br. Mycol. Soc. 70:81-89.
4. Bridges, J.R. and Moser, J.C. 1983. Role of phoretic mites in transmission of blue stain fungi. Ecol. Entomol. 8:9-12.
5. Bridges, J.R. and Moser, J.C. 1986. Relationships of phoretic mites (*Acari tarsonemidae*) to the bluestaining fungus *Ceratocystis minor* in trees infected by southern pine beetle. Environ. Entomol. 15:951-953.
6. Campbell, R.N. 1959. Fungus sap-stains of hardwoods.

Southern Lumberman, Dec. 15, 1959. 115-120.

7. Christiansen, E. 1985. *Ceratocystis polonica* inoculated in Norway spruce: bluestaining in relation to inoculum density, resinosis and tree growth. Eur. J. For. Pathol. 15:160-167.

8. Davidson, R.W. 1935. Fungi causing stain in logs and lumber in the southern States, including five new species. J. Agric. Res. 50:789-807.

9. Davidson, R.W. 1944. Two American hardwood species of *Endoconidiophora* described as new. Mycologia 36:300-306.

10. Dowding, P. 1969. The dispersal and survival of spores of fungi causing blue stain in pine. Trans. Br. Mycol. Soc. 52:125-137.

11. Dowding, P. 1970. Colonisation of freshly bared pine sapwood surfaces by staining fungi. Trans. Br. Mycol. Soc. 55:399-412.

12. Dowding, P. 1973. Effects of felling time and insecticide treatment on the inter-relationships of fungi and arthropods in pine logs. Oikos 24:422-429.

13. Garrett, S.D. 1956. Biology of root infecting fungi. Cambridge University Press, Cambridge. 293 pp.

14. Gibbs, J.N. 1967. The role of host vigour in the susceptibility of pines to *Fomes annosus*. Ann. Bot., n.s. 31:803-815.

15. Gibbs, J.N. and Inman, A. 1991. The pine shoot beetle *Tomicus piniperda* as a vector of blue stain fungi to windblown pine. Forestry 64:239-249.

16. Gibbs, J.N. and Wainhouse, D. 1986. Spread of forest pests and pathogens in the northern hemisphere. Forestry 59:141-153.

17. Hunt, J. 1956. Taxonomy of the genus *Ceratocystis*. Lloydia 19:1-58.

18. Kile, G.A. and Walker, J. 1987. *Chalara australis* sp. nov. (Hyphomycetes), a vascular pathogen of *Nothofagus cunninghamii* (Fagaceae) in Australia and its relationship to other *Chalara* species. Austr. J. Bot. 35:1-32.

19. Lagerberg, T., Lundberg, G. and Melin, E. 1927. Biological and practical researches into blueing in pine and spruce. Svenska Skogsför. Tidskr. 25:145-691.

20. Leach, J.G. 1940. Insect transmission of plant diseases. McGraw-Hill, New York and London. 615 pp.

21. Leach, J.G., Orr, L.W. and Christensen, C. 1934. The inter-relationships of bark beetles and bluestaining fungi in felled Norway pine timber. J. Agric. Res. 9:315-341.

22. Levieux, J., Lieutier, F., Moser, J.C. and Perry, T.J. 1989. Transportation of phytopathogenic fungi by the bark beetle *Ips sexdentatus* Boerner and associated mites. J. Appl. Entomol. 108:1-11.

23. Liese, W. and Schmid, R. 1961. Licht-und elektronenmikroskopische Untersuchungen über das Wachstum von Bläuepilzen in Kiefern- und Fichtenholz. Holz Roh- u. Werkstoff 9:329-337.

24. Liese, W. and Schmid, R. 1964. Über das Wachstum von Bläuepilzen durch Verholzte Zellwände. Phytopathol. Z. 51:385-393.

25. Liese, W. and Peek, R. 1984. Experiences with wet storage of conifer logs. Skovtek. Dansk Skov. Tidsskr. (Sonderheft): 73-91.

26. Lieutier, F., Yart, A., Garcia, J., Ham, M.C., Morelet, M. and Levieux, J. 1989. Champignons phytopathogènes associés à deux Coleopteres scolytidae du pin sylvestre (*Pinus sylvestris*) et étude preliminarie de leur agressivite envers l'hote. Ann. Sci. For. 46:201-216.

27. Lindgren, R.M. 1942. Temperature, moisture and penetration studies of wood-staining *Ceratostomellae* in relation to their control. USDA, Tech. Bull. no. 807:35pp.

28. Mathiesen-Käärik, A. 1953. Eine Übersicht über die Gewöhnlichsten mit Borkenkäfern assoziierten Bläuepilze Schweden und einig für Schweden neue Bläuepilze. Meddn. St. Skogsforsk. Inst. 43:3-74.

29. Mathiesen-Käärik, A. 1960. Studies on the ecology, taxonomy and physiology of Swedish insect-associated blue stain fungi, especially the genus *Ceratocystis*. Oikos 11:1-25.

30. Moser, J.C., Perry, T.J. and Solheim, H. 1989. Ascospores hyperphoretic on mites associated with *Ips typographus*. Mycol. Res. 93:513-517.

31. Münch, E., 1907. Die Blaufäule des Nadelholzes. Naturw. Z. Forst. Landw. 5:531-573.

32. Rosch, R., Liese, W. and Berndt, H. 1969. Untersuchungen über die Enzyme von Blauepilzen I. Cellulase-, polygalakturonase-, pektinesterase-, undlaccase-Aktivität. Arch. Mikrobiol. 67:28-50.

33. Scheffer, T.C. 1986. Oxygen requirements for growth and survival of wood-decaying and sapwood-staining fungi. Can. J. Bot. 64:1957-1963.

34. Solheim, H. 1986. Species of Ophiostomataceae isolated from *Picea abies* infested by the bark beetle *Ips typographus*. Nord. J. Bot. 6:199-207.

35. Solheim, H. 1988. Pathogenicity of some *Ips typographus*-associated blue-stain fungi in Norway spruce. Medd. Nor. Inst. Skogforsk. 40:1-11.

36. Solheim, H. and Selas, P. 1986. Misfarging og mikroflora i ved etter saring av gran. 1. Utbredelser etter 2 år. Norsk Inst. Skogforsk. Rap. 7/86:16pp.

37. Von Schrenk, H. 1903. The 'blueing' and the 'red rot' of the western yellow pine, with special reference to the Black Hills forest reserve. USDA, Bur. Plant Ind. Bull. 36. 40pp.

38. Yamaoko, Y., Swanson, R.H. and Hiratsuka, Y. 1990. Inoculation of Lodgepole pine with four blue-stain fungi associated with mountain pine beetle, monitored by a heat pulse velocity (HPV) instrument. Can. J. For. Res. 20:31-36.

Chapter 18

DISEASES OF CONIFERS CAUSED BY SPECIES OF *OPHIOSTOMA* AND *LEPTOGRAPHIUM*

T. C. HARRINGTON

Compared to *Ceratocystis, Ophiostoma* and the anamorph genus *Leptographium* are large but relatively homogeneous genera. Most of the species are competitive saprophytes commonly found on woody plant tissues. Non-woody materials are unusual substrata for *Ophiostoma* species but some examples exist. For instance, *O. narcisi* is a weak pathogen on narcissus bulbs in western Europe (84) and has been reported from the U.S.A. and New Zealand (77,107).

Ophiostoma species have been found associated with numerous abiotic and biotic diseases and, in many cases, an etiological role of the *Ophiostoma* species was assumed. In some examples, the *Ophiostoma* did not prove to be the causal agent and in other examples the *Ophiostoma* species appeared to be a weak pathogen, perhaps contributing in a minor way to the disease syndrome. Examples where the role of *Ophiostoma* or *Leptographium* remains undefined include pole blight of western white pine, in which early studies (66,74) established pathogenicity of unidentified *Leptographium* species to roots of white pine (*Pinus monticola*). *Ophiostoma trinacriforme*, which has a *Leptographium* anamorph, was also associated with the disease; when inoculated into white pine, it caused lesions similar to those that developed with pole blight (92). It was not, however, believed to be the cause of the disease, which has been associated with poor site conditions in the inland forests of the Pacific Northwest and British Columbia, Canada.

Species of *Ophiostoma* have also been associated with pine wilt disease, which is caused by the pine wood nematode, *Bursaphelenchus xylophilus*. *Ophiostoma* species are vectored by *Monochamus carolinensis*, the vector of the pine wood nematode, but the sequence of colonization is unclear and the role of *Ophiostoma* in this disease has not been elucidated (64).

In addition, *Ophiostoma* species have been implicated in oak tracheomycosis in eastern Europe. However, many species of fungi have been associated with the disease (88,108), and the role of *Ophiostoma* species in causing the decline is far from clear. *Ophiostoma piceae*, or species closely related to it

(10), has been frequently isolated from these dying oak trees and fungal hyphae have been observed in the vessels of affected trees (121). Pathogenicity of the associated *Ophiostoma* species has yet to be established.

Many species associated with bark beetles have been shown to be pathogenic to conifers when artificially inoculated into seedlings or trees and are regarded as an important aid to stem-feeding bark beetles in killing mass-attacked trees. The pathogenicity of *Leptographium* species associated with root-feeding bark beetles and weevils has also received considerable attention. In spite of the pathogenicity of these *Ophiostoma* and *Leptographium* species, their role in the death of beetle-attacked trees remains unclear.

Only two species, *O. ulmi* and *L. wageneri*, have been studied extensively as causal agents of major plant diseases, Dutch elm disease and black stain root disease on conifers, respectively. A general review of black stain root disease will be given here, along with the similarities and contrasts with the better known Dutch elm disease.

BARK BEETLE SYMBIONTS

Because of the nearly invariable association of *Ophiostoma* species with coniferous bark beetles and the demonstrated pathogenicity of some of these fungi to conifers, it has been hypothesized that the beetles are dependent upon the fungi to kill trees. The evidence is circumstantial, however, and in many cases, it could be argued that *Ophiostoma* species confer no benefit to the beetle and, indeed, may be detrimental to the development of beetle brood.

Associations

The association of blue stain fungi (*Ophiostoma* species) with bark beetles has been noted since Hartig (57). Many reviews have discussed these associations (31,34,48,112) and most authors have supported the idea that the beetle and fungus are mutualistic symbionts. Clearly, the fungus benefits by being dispersed and the fruiting structures of the perfect and imperfect states of *Ophiostoma* are obvious adaptations for insect dispersal. Benefits to the beetle are less clear. Although some bark beetle species have evolved special fungal-carrying sacs, referred to as mycangia (5), these mycangia probably did not evolve to transport *Ophiostoma* species. Yeasts are more common inhabitants of bark beetle mycangia and the most developed of these mycangia appear to harbor fungi that are nutritionally beneficial to the beetle and competitive with *Ophiostoma* species.

Probably, spores of *Ophiostoma* are most commonly dispersed as they adhere to the exoskeleton of bark beetles or as they are eaten and passed through the digestive tract (34). In those bark beetles with special fungus-carrying structures, the mycangia are typically simple pits or pockets in the exoskeleton. Such fungus-filled punctures or pits are found in the head, pronotum or elytra of several species of *Hylurgops*, *Hylastes*, *Ips* and in *Scolytus ventralis* (33,75,78). Presumably, any fungal spore in the beetle gallery could find its way into such pits; species of both the Ophiostomataceae and yeasts have been found in these mycangia.

The maxillary mycangia of *Dendroctonus ponderosae* are perhaps more complex than the pits or punctures mentioned above but they are still not very specific in the fungi they carry. Both *O. clavigerum* and *O. montium* have been isolated from the mycangium but yeasts are more commonly present (114). Mandibular mycangia are found in *Ips accuminatus* (34) and *Dryocoetes confusus* (32), though the identity of the fungi occupying these mycangia is not clear.

Well-developed mycangia with secretory cells are found in only a few bark beetle species and *Ophiostoma* species are not the primary inhabitants of these mycangia. The pronotal mycangia of *D. brevicomis*, *D. frontalis* and *D. adjunctus* have gland cells capable of secretions that apparently select for certain fungal associates (34). An unidentified *Leptographium* species was found in the mycangium of *D. adjunctus* (3), and *O. nigrocarpum* was reported in the mycangium of *D. brevicomis* (90). More recently, however, careful isolation yielded only unidentified Basidiomycetes or *Ceratocystiopsis ranaculosus* in the mycangia of *D. brevicomis* and *D. frontalis* (56, Harrington, unpublished). These mycangial fungi are nutritionally beneficial to the beetle and inhibit the development of *O. minus*, a common bluestain fungus that is also vectored by the bark beetle but is detrimental to the development of

the beetle brood (11,15,44).

Species of *Ophiostoma* typically inhabit the phloem and sapwood of beetle-attacked trees, where they live primarily on readily available carbohydrates and other nutrients (2,69). Alteration of these constituents may favor the nutritional development of beetle larvae (21), though this benefit may not be as important as with yeasts (34) or may be detrimental to beetles. For example, larval feeding by *D. ponderosae* is generally in advance of yeasts and blue stain fungi (111). During oviposition, *Ips* bark beetles avoid tissues colonized by *O. ips* (124). As already mentioned, *O. minus* is detrimental to the development of *D. frontalis* (15); larvae and egg-laying adults avoid areas of the phloem colonized by *O. minus* (35). Goldhammer *et al.* (44) have also suggested that the winding egg-gallery pattern of *D. frontalis* is a pattern of avoidance of *O. minus*, which generally forms dark, vertical streaks above and below the entrance to the egg gallery. The mycangial fungi of *D. frontalis*, which are effective competitors of *O. minus*, may also be an adaptation that helps ensure that bluestain fungi are excluded from the tissues containing developing larvae.

Fungus-feeding and predatory diptera, beetles, mites and other small animals are active in bark beetle galleries and may also be important vectors of *Ophiostoma* and *Leptographium* species (12,30, 31,75,83). Non-specific vectoring by arthropods contributes to the generally varied mycoflora found in old beetle galleries (34,104). Mites and other microfauna frequently feed upon *Ophiostoma* and may ensure dissemination through this activity (62, 72). Dowding (31) has suggested that the relationship between bark beetles and sticky-spored fungi (Ophiostomataceae) is in fact a relationship between the fungi and fungus-feeding arthropods, both of which are dependent upon the bark beetle.

As far as the bark beetles are concerned, *Ophiostoma* species may be weeds in the complex mycoflora found in beetle galleries. Although some *Ophiostoma* and *Leptographium* species are associated with specific bark beetles, it is more common for them to be associated with a number of bark beetle genera. *Ophiostoma ips*, *O. minus*, *O. huntii*, *L. terebrantis* and *L. abietinum* are good examples of such non-specific ophiostomatoid fungi (48). The constant association of Ophiostomataceae with bark beetles, in itself, is not a compelling argument for mutualism. Only the pathogenicity to trees would suggest that the *Ophiostoma* species are of benefit to bark beetles.

Pathogenicity to conifers

Münch (85) suggested that *Ophiostoma* species were weakly pathogenic and the early work of Nelson and Beal (87) demonstrated that the fungal associates of a number of bark beetles of the southeastern United States were able to kill trees in the absence of their insect vectors. Nelson (86) concluded that bluestain fungi induced aspiration of pits in the tracheids of beetle-attacked trees and rendered the xylem non-conducting. Others (e.g., 34) have suggested that *Dendroctonus* species are able to kill the host tree by their girdling of the cambium and that the association with pathogenic *Ophiostoma* species is facultative. Christiansen *et al.* (20) have made some generalizations on the resistance of conifers to beetle attack and the role of *Ophiostoma* in overcoming this resistance. However, the pathogenicity of the fungi involved varies greatly and the significance of the fungal symbionts to beetle biology must also vary. Only a few beetle-fungus systems have been studied, so extrapolations are tenuous, but it would appear that not all bark beetles are dependent upon *Ophiostoma* species to kill trees.

Many, but not all, of the *Ophiostoma* species associated with tree-killing bark beetles are pathogenic. By causing phloem lesions that expand around the points of beetle attack and by colonizing the sapwood, the fungi are thought to contribute to tree death, arrest host defense reactions and create an environment conducive to beetle brood development (6,97). Sapwood occlusion and stoppage of water flow may be the ultimate cause of death of beetle-attacked trees. In *Pinus contorta* var. *latifolia*, hyphae of bluestain fungi are found in the ray parenchyma but not the tracheids as the sapwood dries (101). Resistance to water flow in the sapwood and a drop in foliar water potential also occurs in inoculated trees (17,93), but this may occur before the sapwood is colonized (100).

One could speculate that death of the phloem tissue is intimately related to the drying of the sapwood. If sufficient phloem tissue is destroyed over a large portion of the bole, it may somehow signal the ray parenchyma tissue of the sapwood to respond by producing gases that aspirate the tracheid pits or otherwise induce the drying of the sapwood. Successfully colonized trees show little resinosis as the phloem tissue dies; a general drying of the sapwood with little resinosis is typically found. On the other hand, in inoculated trees, heavy resinosis is generally found near the cambium; drying of the sapwood is in the outer growth rings and proceeds radially in a wedge-shaped pattern. Smaller, resinous lesions in the phloem are associated with weaker pathogenicity or greater host resistance in artificially inoculated trees (26,95,96), although this relationship may not be consistently observed (94). The resinous phloem tissue resulting from fungal inoculation alone or in association with unsuccessful beetle attacks is not conducive to egg-laying (91).

Obvious difficulties in simulating bark beetle galleries in live trees have led to numerous inoculation techniques for determining pathogenicity of bark beetle-associated fungi. One of the earliest studies to show that a beetle-associate was able to kill trees with a reasonable inoculum load was conducted by Molnar (81), who was able to kill subalpine fir trees by inoculation with *Ophiostoma dryocoetidis*, an associate of *Dryocoetes confusus*. The fungus proved to be highly pathogenic and caused lesions in the phloem similar to those that develop around *D. confusus* attacks. Patch kills of the bark or death of the tree resulted when lesions coalesced.

Two fungi associated with *Scolytus* species on true fir, *Spicaria anomala* and *Trichosporium symbioticum*, may be more appropriately placed in the genera *Sporothrix* and *Hyalorhinocladiella*, respectively, which would suggest that they are related to the anamorphs of *Ophiostoma* species. They are both pathogenic when inoculated into fir (95,122) and have a biology that appears to be similar to that of the other fir pathogen *O. dryocoetidis*.

Amongst the numerous *Ophiostoma* species associated with *Ips typographus* on spruce (104), *O. polonicum* is the most pathogenic; *Ophiostoma bicolor*, *O. penicillatum* and *Graphium* sp. are less pathogenic associates (105). When inoculated into trees at a density similar to that occurring under natural attack, *O. polonicum* is capable of killing trees (19,65). Besides density of inoculation, water stress appears to be an important determinant in whether the lesions coalesce and complete sapwood occlusion occurs.

There are numerous reports of pathogenicity of *Ophiostoma* species to pines, but the degree of pathogenicity varies greatly, and some of the reports are conflicting. *Ophiostoma clavigerum*, associated with *Dendroctonus ponderosae*, is a noteworthy pathogen (90,101). Yamaoka *et al.* (123) found it to be more pathogenic than *O. huntii*, *O. montium* and *O. minus* in *Pinus contorta*. In contrast, *O. ips* does not appear to be particularly pathogenic in artificial inoculations (93,100), although others have reported substantial pathogenicity (4,64,98). Two fungal associates of *Ips sexidentatus*, *O. brunneo-cilatum* and

O. ips, were only weakly pathogenic (76). *Leptographium wingfieldii* and *O. minus* were not consistently associated with *Tomicus piniperda*, but they were more pathogenic than the more commonly found fungal associates of this European bark beetle (76). *Ophiostoma minus* has been associated with a number of bark beetle species but has been most studied in relation to *D. brevicomis* and *D. frontalis*. *Ophiostoma minus* causes larger lesions than the other associates of these beetles when seedlings or larger trees are inoculated (7,90,93, Harrington, unpublished). Hemingway *et al.* (58) and DeAngelis *et al.* (28) have suggested that toxic metabolites of *O. minus* may be important in killing southern pine beetle-attacked trees. Strobel and Sugawara (106) found *O. minus* to be a weak pathogen on *Pinus contorta* but Nelson (86), Mathre (80) and Basham (4) have reported that *O. minus* can kill inoculated pine saplings.

If *O. minus* is important in killing trees attacked by *D. frontalis*, it is surprising that in some epidemic populations of *D. frontalis*, few of the beetles carry this bluestain fungus (14,13,62). Even where *O. minus* is found associated with beetle-attacked trees, it occurs as scattered patches on the bole (113), generally in association with the beetle entrance holes (86). *Ophiostoma nigrocarpum*, a species more commonly associated with *D. brevicomis* and *D. frontalis*, is not pathogenic (90,93, Harrington, unpublished). Of all the aggressive bark beetles studied to date, *D. brevicomis* and *D. frontalis* appear the least dependent upon *Ophiostoma* species for killing their host trees.

Although a great deal of attention has been given to *Leptographium* species from roots of conifers (53), there is little evidence to suggest that the biology of most of these root-inhabiting species is fundamentally different from that of the *Ophiostoma* species associated with stem-attacking bark beetles. Wingfield *et al.* (117) recently reviewed the role of *Leptographium* species in root diseases on conifers and questioned the role of *L. serpens* as a primary root disease agent in Italy and South Africa. *Leptographium procerum* has been associated with disease on a number of *Pinus* species but it is also a good saprophyte and was not very pathogenic in tests on seedlings and older trees (49,100,116). The fungus has been associated with a disease syndrome known as procerum root disease, which was recently reviewed by Alexander *et al.* (1). In inoculation studies with common *Leptographium* species from conifer roots, Harrington and Cobb (49) found that only *L. wageneri* was capable of causing significant

root disease, with black stain root disease being the only well-characterized disease caused by a *Leptographium* species.

Leptographium terebrantis has been found to be capable of causing large lesions in 15 yr old *Pinus strobus* and other pines and kills inoculated seedlings (49,90,93,99,100,116). It may be the most pathogenic of all of the bark beetle-associated fungi, perhaps because of the attacking strategies of its vector species *D. terebrans* and *D. valens*, the black and red turpentine beetles, respectively. Both beetle species attack living pines (often unsuccessfully) at the base of the trees, where moisture content of the wood is high, oleoexudation pressures are strong and the resinosis response is heavy. A competitive fungus colonizing such tissues might be expected to be a fast growing pathogen, able to invade and kill the host tissue before the host response is fully activated.

The question remains, however, why bark beetle-associated *Ophiostoma* and *Leptographium* species would be pathogenic if pathogenicity is not important in killing beetle-attacked trees? One aspect of the biology of *Ophiostoma* that has received little attention is interspecific competition (90,93). Generally, *Ophiostoma* species are more tolerant of the terpenes found in conifer resin than are other fungi colonizing beetle-attacked trees (23,29). Certainly, early colonists would need to be adapted to survive in the relatively resistant and resinous tissue formed in response to beetle attack, but pathogenic species should have an added advantage in being able to colonize the tissue while it is still alive. Thus, terpene tolerance and pathogenicity may have been strongly selected for in those pioneer *Ophiostoma* that are associates of bark beetle species attacking living trees. Although competitive saprophytic abilities and other strategies can be important factors in successful colonization, pathogenicity of species like *L. terebrantis* may have been selected through competition with *Ophiostoma* species and other microbes rather than through coevolution with bark beetles.

BLACK STAIN ROOT DISEASE

Root diseases caused by species of *Leptographium* were recently reviewed (53). In those proceedings, Cobb (22) gave a detailed account of black stain root disease, and chapters by Hansen *et al.* (47) and Morrison and Hunt (82) detailed the disease in the Pacific Northwest and British Columbia. Disease management will not be discussed in detail here, but the basic biology of the disease will be outlined, particularly to illustrate how it contrasts with Dutch elm disease.

The causal agent of black stain root disease, *Leptographium wageneri* (syn. *Verticicladiella wageneri*), is native to western North America, where it is restricted to members of the Pinaceae. This disorder was first recognized as a unique disease of conifers in the early 1960s (73,109), with similarities to the vascular wilts of hardwoods such as Dutch elm disease. In contrast to *O. ulmi*, *L. wageneri* is genetically depauperate, perhaps due to the lack of a functional sexual state. The mode of spread with and without insect vectors is strikingly similar in the two pathogens but the character of the epidemics of black stain root disease and Dutch elm disease are decidedly different.

Host specialization

Wagener and Mielke (109) recognized variation in *L. wageneri* and three host-specialized varieties of the fungus with overlapping geographic distributions are now known (50,51,52,125). The species was originally described from singleleaf pinyon *(Pinus monophylla)* and var. *wageneri* is specialized to *P. monophylla* and *P. edulis* in the southwestern U.S.A. and north to southern Idaho. Very rarely, ponderosa pine *(Pinus ponderosa)* may be infected by var. *wageneri* in diseased pinyon stands (70).

Leptographium wageneri var. *pseudotsugae* is a pathogen on Douglas-fir *(Pseudotsuga menziesii)* throughout the western U.S.A. and British Columbia. This variety is very restricted in host range; except for the report of infection of two western hemlock trees *(Tsuga heterophylla)* in a diseased Douglas-fir stand (82), *P. menziesii* is the only known host.

Variety *ponderosum* occurs on the hard pines *(P. ponderosa, P. contorta,* and *P. jeffreyi)* in the Pacific Coast states, Idaho, Montana and British Columbia. The host range of this variety appears to be greater than that of the other two varieties. In addition to the primary hosts, Goheen and Hansen (43) and Hansen *et al.* (47) found infected hemlocks *(T. heterophylla* and *T. mertensiana)* in the Pacific Northwest and Morrison and Hunt (82) recorded spruce *(Picea glauca* and *P. engelmannii)* as rare hosts. White pines *(Pinus strobus* and *P. monticola)* have also been recorded as rare hosts of var. *ponderosum* (51).

Ophiostoma wageneri (syn. *Ceratocystis wageneri)* was described as the teleomorph before the varieties of *L. wageneri* were named (38), but it is most likely the teleomorph of *L. wageneri* var. *ponderosum* (51).

However, because the anamorph-teleomorph connection has not been firmly established for each variety, the use of the teleomorph name is not recommended (48).

Host specialization of the three varieties has been demonstrated with inoculations of seedlings and mature trees (50). Morphologically, the three varieties differ only slightly in the pigmentation of the mycelial mat and in the size of the swelling at the apex of conidiophore stipes (51,52). Temperature maxima for growth and survival of var. *ponderosum* is slightly lower than that of the other two varieties (50,51).

Variants of the Dutch elm disease pathogen (known as strains) are also recognized, and although they do differ in pathogenicity, these variants do not differ substantially in host range. Because of reproductive isolation, Brasier (this volume) believes these variants should be recognized as distinct species. The role of humans in dispersing *O. ulmi* has greatly complicated the unraveling of the evolution of this important pathogen (10) but one factor that may play a major role in the development of variants of *O. ulmi* is an active sexual state (9). Compared to *O. ulmi*, there is very little in the way of genetic variation in *L. wageneri* and evolution appears to be proceeding at a surprisingly slow rate.

Genetics

Despite the fact that a sexual state has been reported for *L. wageneri*, problems with the holotype specimen (48), an inability to produce the sexual state in culture (125) and the relatively low level of variation found in the species (89,125,126) all suggest that there is no functional sexual state. The fungus forms multinucleate hyphal tips and is capable of forming heterokaryons when auxotrophic mutants are forced on minimal media (126). Although parasexual recombination was not demonstrated, this could still be a potential source of variation in the fungus. No heterokaryon formed when auxotrophic mutants of the three varieties were paired with each other. All tested isolates of *L. wageneri* var. *wageneri* formed heterokaryons with other isolates of this variety, suggesting one vegetative compatibility (VC) group for var. *wageneri*. However, three VC groups were detected in var. *ponderosum* and 10 in var. *pseudotsugae*.

Vegetative compatibility has been used as a measure of genetic variability in *O. ulmi* (8,9). In stark contrast to the variation found in *L. wageneri*, a single piece of elm bark could contain more VC groups of *O. ulmi* than what we could find in our collection of 76 isolates of *L. wageneri* from across its known range (126).

Isozyme analysis (89,125) also indicated limited variation in *L. wageneri* and confirmed the delineation of three infraspecific taxa. Most of the variation in isozyme electromorphs was explained by the variation among the three varieties, and within-variety variation was explained geographically (125). Consistent with the number of VC groups, var. *wageneri* was the least variable in isozyme electromorphs and var. *pseudotsugae* was the most variable.

Variation in electromorphs was found where the pathogen is uncommon and relative homogeneity was found where the pathogen is well established. In the latter areas, a single (perhaps, well-adapted) genotype apparently predominates, as might be expected in the evolution of an asexual organism (27). These common electrophoretic types are found in the southwestern extremes of the known distribution of varieties *ponderosum* and *pseudotsugae*, where refuge populations may have survived past glaciations. In the more northerly and easterly ranges of these varieties, where the pathogens may still be expanding their geographic ranges, different selection pressures may exist and unique genotypes still constitute a significant proportion of the populations. Perhaps less selection has occurred in these more recently-colonized regions and the most ideal genotypes have not yet predominated.

Host Colonization

Once in a living root, hyphae of *L. wageneri* colonize only the tracheids, moving systemically through the host xylem (22,61,103,109). The hyphae are orange-brown in the host xylem and a dark brown to black staining is macroscopically visible wherever the fungus grows. Radial spread from one growth ring to the next is limited compared to longitudinal growth but there is substantial tangential growth within an annual ring (59). Other *Ophiostoma* and *Leptographium* species are also capable of causing dark staining of the xylem of infected hosts but their stain preferentially follows the rays and thus forms a macroscopic pattern that is typically wedge-shaped in cross sections of the host xylem (22,49).

No vessel elements are found in the Pinaceae, whose water-conducting cells are of only one type, the relatively short tracheids. Thus, budding spores would not travel far within the xylem of these hosts. Aside from the predominance of hyphal growth in the living xylem, the pathogenesis of black stain root disease is similar to that of the vascular wilt diseases on angiosperms (22,103). The black stain fungus, however, moves relatively slowly, only a few millimeters per day or a couple of meters per year within a susceptible host (59). This contrasts sharply with the Dutch elm disease pathogen, which can passively move through vessel elements that are longer than 5 meters (18).

Aspects of host physiology are discussed by Cobb (22) but relatively little is known of the effects of black stain root disease on conifers. Plugging tracheids may be a major mechanism of inducing water stress but a phytotoxin may also be involved (22). This speculation, however, is not nearly as well supported as is the case for phytotoxins in Dutch elm disease (102).

In nature, only a proportion of infected trees are killed solely by *L. wageneri* and both bark beetles and other root diseases may obscure black stain root disease (42). Diseased ponderosa pine trees are typically attacked and killed by *D. brevicomis, D. ponderosae*, other bark beetles or wood borers (24,39,41); *Ips* species frequently attack diseased pinyons (109); and Douglas-fir trees infected with the fungus may also be attacked by bark beetles and wood borers (43). Trees with black stain root disease are also predisposed to other root diseases. For instance, *Armillaria* root rot is commonly associated with black stain root disease on Douglas-fir (16,43,82).

Infection of Adjacent Trees

Like *O. ulmi, L. wageneri* may spread to adjacent trees via root grafts but grafts are not necessary for root to root spread. The fungus may grow from diseased roots for short distances (5 cm) through the soil to infect small-diameter roots of neighboring trees (60,63). Infection typically takes place in relatively small roots (less than 3 mm diam.), whereas the inoculum emanates from larger roots (37). A variety of wounds may serve as infection courts (61).

High soil moisture levels favor infection (40) and spread to adjacent trees (115) and soil temperatures are also important. In greenhouse studies (50,60,103), no infection occurred with soil temperatures of 27°C and higher and indeed the fungus did not survive on the inoculum blocks at such temperatures. Warm soil temperatures are believed to be a limiting factor in the distribution of *L. wageneri* var. *wageneri* and var. *ponderosum* (50,51). Unlike the other common root disease fungi on conifers, *L. wageneri* does not survive long in killed host tissue (37,67,103,109).

Discrete infection centers of a few to hundreds of trees may develop from clonal spread of the pathogen (25,46). One of the important factors determining expansion of such infection centers is the density of mature, susceptible host trees in the stand (25,67). Spread rates averaging 1 m per year were found in ponderosa pine stands (25) but spread in pinyon stands of about 2 meters per year were reported (109). Spread rates of less than a meter per year were noted in Douglas-fir stands (46) but these lower rates may be more indicative of the size of the Douglas-fir trees studied, than in an inherently low spread rate. Even if the expansion of infection centers is slower in Douglas-fir than in pine, the higher incidence of new infection centers in young stands makes the disease more threatening in Douglas-fir.

Manipulation of the species composition of the stand is an important control for black stain root disease and, with the knowledge that each variety of the pathogen has a narrow host range, alternative crop species are generally available. In mixed stands, susceptible host species should be kept to a stocking level that is not conducive to underground spread through root systems. However, the small target of a seedling root system and the poor survival of *L. wageneri* in cut stumps may allow replanting of susceptible species after clear cutting, providing that vector activity is low.

Vector Relationships

Leptographium wageneri is vectored in a manner similar to the majority of *Ophiostoma* and *Leptographium* species. However, it is not consistently associated with any particular insect and vectoring is apparently a rare event (54). Conidia are produced in sticky drops on top of conidiophores within beetle galleries for passive acquisition. The pathogen must have some competitive saprophytic ability to compete with the *Ophiostoma* and other fungi more commonly associated with the vectors (48) but this critical aspect of the biology has not been studied. The poor survival of *L. wageneri* in stumps would suggest that it is a poor competitor compared to *O. ulmi* (110) and growth and sporulation in beetle galleries may be a major limiting factor in dispersal by insects.

Root-feeding bark beetles have been suggested as important agents of overland spread of the pathogen (38,54,119). Of the two weevils proposed as important vectors of *L. wageneri* var. *pseudotsugae*,

Pissodes fasciatus does not feed commonly on living trees and *Steremnius carinatus* is flightless, which does not preclude it from initiating new satellite centers in an infested stand, but may limit its role in establishing the pathogen in new stands. Wood boring insects may also come in contact with propagules of *L. wageneri* (38) but it is unknown if they are capable of introducing these propagules into a suitable infection court.

Leptographium species have been associated with many species of *Hylastes* (48), which have been the most studied of the potential vectors of *L. wageneri*. Their feeding and breeding behavior are conducive for vectoring. Breeding of *H. nigrinus* takes place in the major roots and base of stumps or in dead or dying trees, to which they are strongly attracted (120,127). Black-stained trees are suitable breeding material (38,118) and a small percentage of brood of *H. nigrinus* acquire propagules of *L. wageneri* (54, 119). Upon emergence, new adults may feed on roots of healthy trees before breeding and egg-laying (127) and this so-called maturation feeding has been proposed as a crucial stage for introduction of *L. wageneri* into a living host (54). Most of the feeding wounds on living trees do not penetrate to the xylem and are delimited by wound periderm, which presumably prevents the pathogen from invading xylem tissues (54).

Insect vectoring of *O. ulmi* also involves feeding on healthy trees before breeding in diseased or weakened trees (71), but a high proportion of the potential vectors breed in diseased trees (110). In contrast, most of the *Hylastes* beetles probably breed in uninfected stumps left after logging rather than in diseased trees. Therefore, only a small fraction of the population would be expected to carry propagules of *L. wageneri*, even in an area with a relatively high incidence of black stain root disease (54,119).

Epidemics

Local epidemics of the disease in Douglas-fir are strongly associated with stand disturbances such as roadside construction, tractor logging or stand thinning (45,47,55). Precommercial thinning of young Douglas-fir stands can lead to high levels of mortality (55) and it has been shown that one of the important vectors of *L. wageneri* var. *pseudotsugae*, *Hylastes nigrinus*, is strongly attracted to these thinned stands and will feed on the living, residual trees (54). The attraction persists at least one year after the thinning, so avoidance of vector activity by thinning after the flight period does not appear to be a viable control option in northern California (54). Studies in Oregon (119) confirmed the attraction of *H. nigrinus* to thinned stands. Chemical thinning may be a feasible way to avoid attraction of potential vectors but it has not been fully tested (54).

The population dynamics of vectors of *L. wageneri* needs further study. Populations of *H. nigrinus* may be artificially high in some managed Douglas-fir forests; the annual harvesting and thinning of stands in a local area may be ideal for the maintenance of high vector populations. In fact, it may prove feasible to decrease the incidence of the disease by concentrating thinning and harvesting practices in a single year. Thinning over a large area would dilute the population of vectors and thus result in fewer infection centers per hectare. Also, too few vectors would be able to utilize the high number of fresh stumps and in subsequent years, the vector population could crash before the next stand disturbance.

Black stain root disease in pinyon and in hard pines is also associated with disturbances, although the associations do not appear as strong as with the disease in Douglas-fir (22). A less efficient vector system or much lower vector population levels may explain the relatively rare initiation of new infection centers in pines. Even in the California mixed conifer zone of the central Sierra Nevada, where the disease may be particularly damaging to ponderosa pine, new infection centers arise very rarely (25). However, the infection centers found in this area and in the adjacent southern Cascades can be quite large in pure stands. Pure stands of ponderosa pine may develop in this normally mixed conifer ecosystem from fire, mud slides or stand management practices (22) and these stands are subject to local epidemics. Because of the narrow host range of the pathogen, black stain root disease reduces the ponderosa pine component and creates openings for the more shade-tolerant conifer species, which helps return the stand to the mixed-conifer forest type.

Overmature pinyon stands with little or no juniper can be created through fire suppression; when these stands occur on cool sites with deep and moist soils (70,109), local epidemics of black stain root disease can be found. These stands can support high stocking levels of large pinyon trees with large root systems and infection centers can expand rapidly under such conditions (109).

Although there is no reason to suspect that human activities have spread *L. wageneri* to new locations, black stain root disease may well be more common today than in previous years. Harvesting of trees and the creation of stumps has likely built up the population of insect vectors to unprecedented levels. Local disturbances, too, may concentrate the vectors into particular stands and thus intensify the incidence of infection centers. The preference for monocultures of susceptible species in some regions can also enhance tree-to-tree spread through root systems.

Even with an increase in monocultures and vector populations, black stain root disease remains only locally important and appears to have little capacity to expand its range in North America. It has a limited genetic base so a genetic bottleneck would likely occur wherever it might be introduced. Also, poor saprophytic survival and a highly inefficient vector system would tend to limit its potential in a new ecosystem. The history of local epidemics of black stain root disease and the restricted geographic range of the pathogen are in sharp contrast to the terrific pandemics reported for Dutch elm disease, which has been introduced into many regions throughout the world (10). The sexual state of *O. ulmi*, its saprophytic capabilities and its potential for establishing highly effective vector relationships in new ecosystems all contribute to its devastating potential as an introduced pathogen.

The local epidemics of black stain root disease are more similar to the epidemics of oak wilt in eastern North America than to those of Dutch elm disease (54). Oak wilt, caused by *Ceratocystis fagacearum*, differs from black stain root disease in that sap-feeding beetles (Nitidulidae) are believed to be the primary vectors and these vectors require fresh wounds for introducing the pathogen (36,68). Like *L. wageneri*, however, *C. fagacearum* is a poor saprophyte and has an extremely inefficient vector system in which only a small percentage of the vector population is infectious and few of them visit suitable infection courts. Because of limitations in the vector relationship, it has been speculated that *C. fagacearum* does not have the capacity of *O. ulmi* for introduction into new forest ecosystems (79). It could be argued that new, unforeseen vector relationships could become established on new continents and that new host species could have increased susceptibility. In North America, however, *C. fagacearum* and *L. wageneri* are believed to be indigenous pathogens of limited geographic distribution, causing only periodic and localized epidemics.

LITERATURE CITED

1. Alexander, S.A., Homer, W.E., and Lewis, K.J. 1988. *Leptographium procerum* as a pathogen on pines. Pages 97-112 in: Leptographium Root Diseases on Conifers. T. C. Harrington and F.W. Cobb, Jr., eds. American Phytopathological Society Press, St. Paul, MN. 149 pp.

2. Barras, S.J., and Hodges, J.D. 1969. Carbohydrates of inner bark of *Pinus taeda* as affected by *Dendroctonus frontalis* and associated microorganisms. Can. Entomol. 101:489-493.

3. Barras, S.J., and Perry, T. 1971. Gland cells and fungi associated with prothoracic mycangium of *Dendroctonus adjunctus* (Coleoptera: Scolytidae). Ann. Entomol. Soc. Am. 64:123-126.

4. Basham, H.G. 1970. Wilt of loblolly pine inoculated with blue-stain fungi of the genus *Ceratocystis*. Phytopathology 60:750-754.

5. Batra, L.R. 1963. Ecology of ambrosia fungi and their dissemination by beetles. Trans. Kansas Acad. Sci. 66:213-236.

6. Berryman, A. 1972. Resistance of conifers to invasion by bark beetle-fungus associations. Bioscience 22:598-602.

7. Bramble, W.C., and Holst, E.C. 1940. Fungi associated with *Dendroctonus frontalis* in killing shortleaf pines and their effect on conduction. Phytopathology 30:881-899.

8. Brasier, C.M. 1984. Intermycelial recognition systems in *Ceratocystis ulmi*: their physiological properties and ecological importance. Pages 451-497 in: The Ecology and Physiology of the Fungal Mycelium. D.H. Jennings and A.D. Rayner, eds. Cambridge University Press, Cambridge. 350 pp.

9. Brasier, C.M. 1988. Rapid changes in the genetic structure of epidemic populations of *Ophiostoma ulmi*. Nature 332:538-541.

10. Brasier, C.M. 1990. China and the origins of Dutch elm disease: an appraisal. Plant Pathol. 39:5-16.

11. Bridges, J.R. 1983. Mycangial fungi of *Dendroctonus frontalis* (Coleoptera: Scolytidae) and their relationship to beetle population trends. Environ. Entomol. 12:858-861.

12. Bridges, J.R., and Moser, J.C. 1983. Role of phoretic mites in transmission of bluestain fungus, *Ceratocystis minor*. Ecol. Entomol. 8:9-12.

13. Bridges, J.R., and Moser, J.C. 1986. Relationship of phoretic mites (Acari: Tarsonemidae) to the bluestaining fungus, *Ceratocystis minor*, in trees infested by southern pine beetle (Coleoptera: Scolytidae). Environ. Entomol. 15:951-953.

14. Bridges, J.R., Nettleton, W.A., and Connor M.D. 1985. Southern pine beetle (Coleoptera: Scolytidae) infestations without the bluestain fungus, *Ceratocystis minor*. J. Econ. Entomol. 78:325-327.

15. Bridges, J.R., and Perry, T.J. 1985. Effects of mycangial fungi on gallery construction and distribution of bluestain in southern pine beetle-infested pine bolts. J. Entomol. Sci. 20:271-275.

16. Byler, J.W., Harrington, T.C., James, R.L., and Haglund, S. 1983. Black stain root disease in Douglas-fir in western Montana. Plant Dis. 67:1037-1038.

17. Caird, R.W. 1935. Physiology of pines infested with bark beetles. Bot. Gaz. 96:709-733.

18. Campana, R.J. 1978. Inoculation and fungal invasion of tree. Pages 17-20 in: Dutch Elm Disease. Perspectives after 60 Years. W.A. Sinclair and R.J. Campana, eds. Cornell University Agricultural Experiment Station, Ithaca, N. Y., Search Agriculture vol. 8, no. 5. 52 pp.

19. Christiansen, E. 1985. *Ips/Ceratocystis*-infection of Norway spruce: what is a deadly dosage? Z. Ang. Entomol. 99:6-11.

20. Christiansen, E., Waring, R.H., and Berryman, A.A. 1987. Resistance of conifers to bark beetle attack: searching for general relationships. For. Ecol. Man. 22:89-106.

21. Clark, E.W., and Richmond, J.A. 1977. Variations of free and triglyceride fatty acids in phloem of *Pinus taeda* infected by *Ceratocystis minor*. Turrialba 27:377-383.

22. Cobb, F.W., Jr. 1988. *Leptographium wageneri*, cause of black-stain root disease: a review of its discovery, occurrence and biology with emphasis on pinyon and ponderosa pine. Pages 41-62 in: Leptographium Root Diseases on Conifers. T.C. Harrington and F.W. Cobb, Jr., eds. American Phytopathological Society Press, St. Paul, MN. 149 pp.

23. Cobb, F.W., Jr., Kristic, M., Zavarin, E., and Barber, H.W., Jr. 1968. Inhibitory effects of volatile oleoresin components on *Fomes annosus* and four *Ceratocystis* species. Phytopathology 58:1327-1335.

24. Cobb, F.W., Jr., Parmeter, J.R., Jr., Wood, D.L., and Stark, R.W. 1974. Root pathogens as agents predisposing ponderosa pine and white fir to bark beetles. Pages 8-15 in: Proceedings of the Fourth International Conference on *Fomes annosus*. E.G. Kuhlman, ed. USDA For. Serv., Washington, D.C. 289 pp.

25. Cobb, F.W., Jr., Slaughter, G.W, Rowney, D.L., and DeMars, C.J. 1982. Rate of spread of *Ceratocystis wageneri* in ponderosa pine stands in the central Sierra Nevada. Phytopathology 72:1359-1362.

26. Cook, S.P., and Hain, F.P. 1987. Four parameters of the wound response of loblolly and shortleaf pines to inoculation with the blue-staining fungus associated with the southern pine beetle. Can. J. Bot. 65:2403-2409.

27. Crow, J.F., and Kimura, M. 1965. Evolution in sexual and asexual populations. Am. Nat. 99:439-450.

28. DeAngelis, J.D., Hodges, J.D., and Nebeker, T.E. 1986. Phenolic metabolites of *Ceratocystis minor* from laboratory cultures and their effects on transpiration in loblolly pine seedlings. Can. J. Bot. 64:151-155.

29. DeGroot, R.C. 1972. Growth of wood-inhabiting fungi in saturated atmospheres of monoterpenoids. Mycologia 64:863-870.

30. Dowding, P. 1973. Effects of felling time and insecticide treatment on the interrelationships of fungi and arthropods in pine logs. Oikos 24:422-429.

31. Dowding, P. 1984. The evolution of insect-fungus relationships in the primary invasion of forest timber. Pages 133-135 in: Invertebrate-microbial Interactions. J. M. Anderson, A.D.M. Rayner, and D.W.H. Walton, eds. Cambridge University Press, Cambridge. 350 pp.

32. Farris, S.H. 1969. Occurrence of mycangia in the bark beetle *Dryocoetes confusus* (Coleoptera: Scolytidae). Can. Entomol. 101:527-532.

33. Francke-Grosmann, H. 1963. Some new aspects in forest entomology. Annu. Rev. Entomol. 8:415-438.

34. Francke-Grosmann, H. 1967. Ectosymbiosis in wood-inhabiting insects. Pages 141-205 in: Symbiosis. Vol II. S.M. Henry, ed. Academic Press. New York. 443 pp.

35. Franklin, R.T. 1970. Observations on the blue stain-

southern pine beetle relationship. J. Georgia Entomol. 5:53-57.

36. Gibbs, J.N., and French, D.W. 1980. The transmission of oak wilt. USDA For. Serv. Res. Pap. NC-185. Washington, D.C. 17 pp.

37. Goheen, D.J. 1976. *Verticicladiella wagenerii* on *Pinus ponderosa*: epidemiology and interrelationships with insects. Ph.D. Thesis. University of California, Berkeley.

38. Goheen, D.J., and Cobb, F.W., Jr. 1978. Occurrence of *Verticicladiella wagenerii* and its perfect state, *Ceratocystis wageneri* sp. nov., in insect galleries. Phytopathology 68:1192-1195.

39. Goheen, D.J., and Cobb, F.W., Jr. 1980. Infestation of *Ceratocystis wageneri*-infected ponderosa pines by bark beetles (Coleoptera: Scolytidae) in central Sierra Nevada. Can. Entomol. 112:725-730.

40. Goheen, D.J., Cobb, F.W., Jr., and McKibbin, G.N. 1978. Influence of soil moisture on infection of ponderosa pine by *Verticicladiella wagenerii*. Phytopathology 68:913-916.

41. Goheen, D.J., Cobb, F.W., Jr., Wood, D.L., and Rowney, D.L. 1985. Visitation frequencies of some insect species on *Ceratocystis wageneri* infected and apparently healthy ponderosa pines. Can. Entomol. 117:1535-1543.

42. Goheen, D.J., and Filip, G.M. 1980. Root pathogen complexes in Pacific Northwest forests. Plant Dis. 64:793-794.

43. Goheen, D.J., and Hansen, E.M. 1978. Black stain root disease in Oregon and Washington. Plant Dis. Rep. 62:1098-1102.

44. Goldhammer, D.S., Stephen, F.M., and Paine, T.D. 1990. The effect of fungi *Ceratocystis minor* (Hedgecock) Hunt, *Ceratocystis minor* (Hedgecock) var. *barrasii* and SJB 122 on reproduction of the southern pine beetle, *Dendroctonus frontalis* Zimmermann (Coleoptera: Scolytidae). Can. Entomol. 122:407-418.

45. Hansen, E.M. 1978. Incidence of *Verticicladiella wagenerii* and *Phellinus weirii* in Douglas-fir adjacent to and away from roads in western Oregon. Plant Dis. Rep. 62:179-181.

46. Hansen, E.M., and Goheen, D.J. 1988. Rate of increase of black-stain root disease in Douglas-fir plantations in Oregon and Washington. Can. J. For. Res. 18:942-946.

47. Hansen, E.M., Goheen, D.J., Hessburg, P.F., Witcosky, J.J., and Schowalter, T.D. 1988. Biology and management of black stain root disease in Douglas-fir. Pages 63-80 in: Leptographium Root Diseases on Conifers. T.C. Harrington and F.W. Cobb, Jr., eds. American Phytophathological Society Press, St. Paul, MN. 149 pp.

48. Harrington, T.C. 1988. *Leptographium* species, their distributions, hosts and insect vectors. Pages 1-39 in: Leptographium Root Diseases on Conifers. T.C. Harrington and F.W. Cobb, Jr., eds. American Phytopathological Society Press, St. Paul, MN. 149 pp.

49. Harrington, T.C., and Cobb, F.W., Jr. 1983. Pathogenicity of *Leptographium* and *Verticicladiella* spp. isolated from roots of western North American conifers. Phytopathology 73:596-599.

50. Harrington, T.C., and Cobb, F.W., Jr. 1984. Host specialization of three morphological variants of *Verticicladiella wageneri*. Phytopathology 74:286-290.

51. Harrington, T.C., and Cobb, F.W., Jr. 1986. Varieties of

Verticicladiella wageneri. Mycologia 78:562-567.

52. Harrington, T.C., and Cobb, F.W., Jr. 1987. *Leptographium wageneri* var. *pseudotsugae*, var. nov., cause of black stain root disease on Douglas-fir. Mycotaxon 30:501-507.

53. Harrington, T.C., and Cobb, F.W., Jr., eds. 1988. *Leptographium* Root Diseases on Conifers. American Phytopathological Society Press, St. Paul, MN. 149 pp.

54. Harrington, T.C., Cobb, F.W., Jr., and Lownsbery, J.W. 1985. Activity of *Hylastes nigrinus*, a vector of *Verticicladiella wageneri*, in thinned stands of Douglas-fir. Can. J. For. Res. 15:519-523.

55. Harrington, T.C., Reinhart, C., Thornburgh, D.A., and Cobb, F.W., Jr. 1983. Association of black-stain root disease with precommercial thinning of Douglas-fir. For. Sci. 29:12-14.

56. Harrington, T.C., and Zambino, P.J. 1990. *Ceratocystiopsis ranaculosus*, not *Ceratocystis minor* var. *barrasii*, is the mycangial fungus of the southern pine beetle. Mycotaxon 38:103-115.

57. Hartig, R. 1878. Die Zersetzungserscheinungen des Holzes, der Nadelbäume und der Eiche in forstlicher, botanischer und chemischer Richtung. Berlin. 151 pp.

58. Hemmingway, R.W., McGraw, G.W., and Barras, S. J. 1977. Polyphenols in *Ceratocystis minor* infected *Pinus taeda*: fungal metabolites, phloem and xylem phenols. J. Agric. Food Chem. 25:717-722.

59. Hessburg, P.F., and Hansen, E.M. 1986a. Soil temperature and rate of colonization of *Ceratocystis wageneri* in young Douglas-fir. Phytopathology 76:627-631.

60. Hessburg, P.F., and Hansen, E.M. 1986b. Mechanisms of intertree transmission of *Verticicladiella wageneri* in young Douglas-fir. Can. J. For. Res. 16:1250-1254.

61. Hessburg, P.F., and Hansen, E.M. 1987. Pathological anatomy of black stain root disease of Douglas-fir. Can. J. Bot. 65:962-971.

62. Hetrich, L.A. 1949. Some overlooked relationships of southern pine beetle. J. Econ. Entomol. 42:466-469.

63. Hicks, B.R., Cobb, F.W., Jr., and Gersper, P.L. 1980. Isolation of *Ceratocystis wageneri* from forest soil with a selective medium. Phytopathology 70:880-883.

64. Himelick, E.B. 1982. Pine blue-stain associated with the pine wilt syndrome. J. Abor. 8:212-216.

65. Horntvedt, R., Christiansen, E., Solheim, H., and Wang, S. 1983. Artificial inoculation with *Ips typographus*-associated blue-stain fungi can kill healthy Norway spruce trees. Rep. Norw. For. Res. Inst. 38:1-20.

66. Hubert, E.E. 1953. Studies on *Leptographium* isolated from western white pine. Phytopathology 43:637-641.

67. Hunt, R.S., and Morrison, D.J. 1986. Black-stain root disease on lodgepole pine in British Columbia. Can. J. For. Res. 16:996-999.

68. Juzwik, J., and French, D.W. 1983. *Ceratocystis fagacearum* and *C. piceae* on the surface of free-flying and fungus-mat-inhabiting nitidulids. Phytopathology 73:1164-1168.

69. Käärik, A. 1960. Growth and sporulation of *Ophiostoma* and some other blueing fungi on synthetic media. Symb. Bot. Upsal. 16:1-159.

70. Landis, T.D., and Helburg, L.B. 1976. Black stain root disease of pinyon pine in Colorado. Plant Dis. Rep. 60:713-717.

71. Lanier, G.N. 1978. Vectors. Pages 13-17 in: Dutch Elm Disease. Perspectives after 60 Years. W. A. Sinclair and

R.J. Campana, eds. Cornell University Agricultural Experiment Station, Ithaca, N. Y., Search Agriculture vol. 8, no. 5. 52 pp.

72. Leach, J.G., Orr, L.W., and Christensen, C. 1934. The inter-relationships of bark beetles and blue-staining fungi in felled Norway pine timber. J. Agric. Res. 49:315-341.

73. Leaphart, C.D. 1960. A root stain disease of eastern white pine. Plant Dis. Rep. 44:704-706.

74. Leaphart, C.D., and Gill, L.S. 1959. Effects of inoculations with the *Leptographium* spp. on western white pine. Phytopathology 49:350-353.

75. Levieux, J., Lieutier, F., Moser, J.C., and Perry, T.J. 1989. Transportation of phytopathogenic fungi by the bark beetle *Ips sexdentatus* Boerner and associated mites. J. Appl. Entomol. 108:1-11.

76. Lieutier, F., Yart, A., Garcia, J., Ham, M.C., Morelet, M., and Levieux, J. 1989. Champignons phytopathogènes associés à deux coléoptères scolytidae du pin sylvestre (*Pinus sylvestris* L.) et étude préliminaire de leur agressivité envers l'hôte. Ann. Sci. For. 46:201-216.

77. Limber, D.P. 1950. *Ophiostoma* on narcissus bulbs. Phytopathology 40:493-496.

78. Livingston, R.L., and Berryman, A.A. 1972. Fungus transport structures in the fir engraver, *Scolytus ventralis* (Coleoptera: Scolytidae). Can. Entomol. 104:1793-1800.

79. MacDonald, W.L., and Hindal, D.F. 1981. Life cycle and epidemiology of *Ceratocystis*. Pages 113-143 in: Fungal Wilt Diseases of Plants. M.E. Mace, A.A. Bell, and C.H. Beckman, eds. Academic Press, New York. 640 pp.

80. Mathre, D.E. 1964. Pathogenicity of *Ceratocystis ips* and *Ceratocystis minor* to *Pinus ponderosa*. Contr. Boyce Thompson Inst. 22:363-388.

81. Molnar, A.C. 1965. Pathogenic fungi associated with a bark beetle on alpine fir. Can. J. Bot. 43:563-570.

82. Morrison, D.J., and Hunt, R.S. 1988. *Leptographium* species associated with root disease of conifers in British Columbia. Pages 81-96 in: Leptographium Root Diseases on Conifers. T.C. Harrington and F.W. Cobb, Jr., eds. American Phytopathological Society Press, St. Paul, MN. 149 pp.

83. Moser, J.C. 1985. Use of sporothecae by phoretic tarsonemus mites to transport ascospores of coniferous bluestain fungi. Trans. Br. Mycol. Soc. 84:750-753.

84. Muller, P.J., and Bergman, B.H.B. 1966. The influence of cultural practices on the occurrence of head rot in *Narcissus*. Neth. J. Plant Pathol. 72:204-211.

85. Münch. E. 1907. Die Blaufäule des Nadelholzes II. Naturw. Z. Forst. Landw. 6:297-323.

86. Nelson, R.M. 1934. Effect of bluestain fungi on southern pines attacked by bark beetles. Phytopath. Z. 4:327-353.

87. Nelson, R.M., and Beal, J.A. 1929. Experiments with bluestain fungi in southern pines. Phytopathology 19:1101-1106.

88. Oleksyn, J., and Przybyl, K. 1987. Oak decline in the Soviet Union - scale and hypotheses. Eur. J. For. Pathol. 17:321-326.

89. Otrosina, W.J., and Cobb, F.W., Jr. 1987. Analysis of allozymes of three distinct variants of *Verticicladiella wageneri* isolated from conifers in western North America. Phytopathology 77:1360-1363.

90. Owen, D.R., Lindahl, K.Q., Wood, D.L., and Parmeter, J.R., Jr. 1987. Pathogenicity of fungi isolated from *Dendroctonus valens*, *D. brevicomis*, and *D. ponderosae* to pine seedlings. Phytopathology 77:631-636.

91. Paine, T.D., and Stephen, F.M. 1988. Induced defenses of loblolly pine, *Pinus taeda*: potential impact on *Dendroctonus frontalis* within-tree mortality. Entomol. Exp. Appl. 46:39-46.

92. Parker, A.K. 1957. The nature of the association of *Europhium trinacriforme* with pole blight lesions. Can. J. Bot. 35:845-856.

93. Parmeter, J.R., Jr., Slaughter, G.W., Chen, M.-M., Wood, D.L., and Stubbs, H.A. 1989. Single and mixed inoculations of ponderosa pine with fungal associates of *Dendroctonus* spp. Phytopathology 79:768-772.

94. Peterman, R.M. 1977. An evaluation of the fungal inoculation method of determining the resistance of lodgepole pine to mountain pine beetle (Coleoptera: Scolytidae) attacks. Can. Entomol. 109:443-448.

95. Raffa, K.F., and Berryman, A.A. 1982. Accumulation of monoterpenes and associated volatiles following inoculation of grand fir with a fungus transmitted by the fir engraver beetle, *Scolytus ventralis* (Coleoptera: Scolytidae). Can. Entomol. 114:797-810.

96. Raffa, K.F., and Berryman, A.A. 1983. Physiological aspects of lodgepole pine responses to a fungal symbiont of the mountain pine beetle, *Dendroctonus ponderosae* (Coleoptera: Scolytidae). Can. Entomol. 115:723-734.

97. Raffa, K.F., and Berryman, A.A. 1987. Interacting selective pressures in conifer-bark beetle systems: a basis for reciprocal adaptations? Am. Nat. 129:234-262.

98. Raffa, K.F., and Smalley, E.B. 1988a. Response of red and jack pines to inoculation with microbial associates of the pine engraver, *Ips pini* (Coleoptera: Scolytidae). Can. J. For. Res. 18:581-586.

99. Raffa, K.F., and Smalley, E.B. 1988b. Host resistance to invasion by lower stem and root infesting insects of pine: response to controlled inoculations with the fungal associate *Leptographium terebrantis*. Can. J. For. Res. 18:675-681.

100. Rane, K.K., and Tattar, T.A. 1987. Pathogenicity of blue-stain fungi associated with *Dendroctonus terebrans*. Plant Dis. 71:879-883.

101. Reid, R.W., Whitney, H.S., and Watson, J.A. 1967. Reactions of lodgepole pine to attack by *Dendroctonus ponderosae* Hopkins and blue stain fungi. Can. J. Bot. 45:1115-1126.

102. Scheffer, R.J., Liem, J.I., and Elgersma, D.M. 1987. Production *in vitro* of phytotoxic compounds by non-aggressive and aggressive isolates of *Ophiostoma ulmi*, the Dutch elm disease pathogen. Physiol. Mol. Plant Pathol. 30:321-335.

103. Smith, R.S., Jr. 1967. *Verticicladiella* root disease of pines. Phytopathology 57:935-938.

104. Solheim, H. 1986. Species of Ophiostomataceae isolated from *Picea abies* infested by the bark beetle *Ips typographus*. Nord. J. Bot. 6:199-207.

105. Solheim, H. 1988. Pathogenicity of some *Ips typographus*-associated blue-stain fungi to Norway spruce. Medd. Nor. Inst. Skogforsk. 40:1-11.

106. Strobel, G.A., and Sugawara, F. 1986. The pathogenicity of *Ceratocystis montia* to lodgepole pine. Can. J. Bot. 64:113-116.

107. Upadhyay, H.P. 1981. A Monograph of *Ceratocystis* and *Ceratocystiopsis*. University of Georgia Press, Athens, GA. 176 pp.

108. Urosevic, B. 1983. Tracheomycotic diseases in oak. Comm. Inst. For. Cechosl. 13:85-100.

109. Wagener, W.W., and Mielke, J.L. 1961. A staining-fungus root disease of ponderosa, Jeffrey and pinyon pines. Plant Dis. Rep. 45:831-835.

110. Webber, J.F., and Brasier, C.M. 1984. The transmission of Dutch elm disease: a study of the processes involved. Pages 271-306 in: Invertebrate-microbial Interactions. J.M. Anderson, A. D. M. Raynor, and D. Walton, eds. Cambridge University Press, Cambridge. 350 pp.

111. Whitney, H.S. 1971. Association of *Dendroctonus ponderosae* (Coleoptera: Scolytidae) with blue stain fungi and yeasts during brood development in lodgepole pine. Can. Entomol. 103:1495-1503.

112. Whitney, H.S. 1982. Relationships between bark beetles and symbiotic organisms. Pages 183-211 in: Bark Beetles in North American Conifers. A System for the Study of Evolutionary Biology. J.B. Mitton, and K. Sturgeon, eds. University of Texas Press, Austin. 539 pp.

113. Whitney, H.S., and Cobb, F.W., Jr. 1972. Non-staining fungi associated with the bark beetle *Dendroctonus brevicomis* (Coleoptera: Scolytidae) on *Pinus ponderosa*. Can. J. Bot. 50:1943-1945.

114. Whitney, H.S., and Farris, S.H. 1970. Maxillary mycangium in the mountain pine beetle. Science 167:54-55.

115. Wilks, D.S., Gersper, P.L., and Cobb, F.W., Jr. 1985. Association of soil moisture with spread of *Ceratocystis wageneri* in ponderosa pine disease centers. Plant Dis. 69:206-208.

116. Wingfield, M.J. 1986. Pathogenicity of *Leptographium procerum* and *Leptographium terebrantis* on *Pinus strobus* seedlings and established trees. Eur. J. For Pathol. 16:299-308.

117. Wingfield, M.J., Capretti, P., and MacKenzie, M. 1988. *Leptographium* spp. as root pathogens of conifers. An international perspective. Pages 113-128 in: Leptographium Root Diseases on Conifers. T.C. Harrington and F.W. Cobb, Jr., eds. American Phytopathological Society Press, St. Paul, MN. 149 pp.

118. Witcosky, J.J., and Hansen, E.M. 1985. Root-colonizing insects recovered from Douglas-fir in various stages of decline due to black-stain root disease. Phytopathology 75:399-402.

119. Witcosky, J.J., Schowalter, T.D., and Hansen, E.M. 1986. *Hylastes nigrinus*, (Coleoptera: Scolytidae), *Pissodes fasciatus*, and *Steremnius carinatus* (Coleoptera: Curculionidae) as vectors of black stain root disease of Douglas-fir. Environ. Entomol. 15:1090-1095.

120. Witcosky, J.J., Schowalter, T.D., and Hansen, E.M. 1987. Host-derived attractants for the beetles *Hylastes nigrinus* (Coleoptera: Scolytidae) and *Steremnius carinatus* (Coleoptera: Curculionidae). Environ. Entomol. 16:1310-1313.

121. Wozny, B. 1989. SEM-studies of the xylem of diseased oak trees growing in the Krotoszyn Plateau. Eur. J. For. Pathol. 19:385-388.

122. Wright, E. 1935. *Trichosporium symbioticum*, n. sp., a wood-staining fungus associated with *Scolytus ventralis*. J. Agric. Res. 50:525-539.

123. Yamaoka, Y., Swanson, R.H., and Hiratsuka, Y. 1990. Inoculation of lodgepole pine with four blue-stain fungi associated with mountain pine beetle, monitored by a heat pulse velocity (HPV) instrument. Can. J. For. Res. 20:31-36.

124. Yearian, W.C., Gouger, R.J., and Wilkinson, R.C. 1972. Effects of the bluestain fungus, *Ceratocystis ips*, on development of *Ips* bark beetles in pine bolts. Ann. Entomol. Soc. Am. 65:481-487.

125. Zambino, P.J., and Harrington, T.C. 1989. Isozyme variation within and among host-specialized varieties of *Leptographium wageneri*. Mycologia 8:122-133.

126. Zambino, P.J., and Harrington, T.C. 1990. Heterokaryosis and vegetative compatibility in *Leptographium wageneri*. Phytopathology 80:1460-1469.

127. Zethner-Moller, O., and Rudinsky, J.A. 1967. On the biology of *Hylastes nigrinus* (Coleoptera: Scolytidae) in western Oregon. Can. Entomol. 99:897-916.

Chapter 19

PLANT DISEASES CAUSED BY SPECIES OF *CERATOCYSTIS SENSU STRICTO* AND *CHALARA*

G.A. KILE

INTRODUCTION

Diseases caused by *Ceratocystis sensu stricto* and *Chalara* species occur on diverse, mainly angiosperm, hosts in both agricultural and natural ecosystems in temperate-tropical regions of the world. In this paper, I will compare some features of the better known pathogens of these genera [*Chalara australis, Ch. elegans, Ch. neocaledoniae, Ch. populi, Ch. thielavioides, Ceratocystis adiposa, C. fagacearum (Ch. quercina), C. fimbriata, C. paradoxa (Ch. paradoxa), C. radicola (Ch. punctulata), C. virescens*] and the diseases they cause. *Ceratocystis virescens* is accepted as distinct from *C. coerulescens* (69). *Chalara punctulata* is not discussed further as Nag Raj and Kendrick (94) considered it a synonym for the *Chalara* state of *C. radicola* (9) and Koch's postulates have not been established for it on the African host (*Lawsonia inermis*) from which it was isolated originally (53).

These organisms are necrotrophic plant pathogens of variable pathogenicity. *Chalara thielavioides* and *C. paradoxa* are, for example, generally considered weak pathogens. The latter species is restricted to monocots where it is known as an invader of parenchymatous tissue, particularly in stressed or scenescing plant parts.

In contrast, *Ch. australis, C. fagacearum* and *C. fimbriata* are examples of aggressive primary pathogens of various hardwood trees. In addition to their pathogenic behaviour, these fungi sometimes act in other roles. For example *Ch. elegans* is known as a stimulant of plant growth (116,149), as a carrier of viruses (12) and as a host of amoebae (96).

While the most severe disease often occurs in cultivated host populations, *Ch. australis, C. fagacearum, C. fimbriata, C. virescens* and *Ch. elegans* are known in native plant communities. *Chalara australis* may promote stand breakup and regeneration of *Nothofagus cunninghamii* in cool temperate rain forests in Tasmania (70, Kile unpublished). Tyron *et al.* (131) believed that the consequences of oak wilt in terms of regeneration of oak and other species was similar to that of selective logging, suggesting that it may also have a natural

ecological role. *C. fimbriata f. platani* has not been recognized as a cause of important losses in forests, perhaps because the native host may be less susceptible or natural spread inefficient (136), although occasionally local effects may be severe (85). *Chalara elegans* was common as a non-pathogen in association with many species in virgin and cultivated areas (148).

Several other *Chalara* species, while not known to cause plant disease, have been isolated in ecologically interesting situations where a parasitic role is possible. These include *Ch. heteroderae* (16) and *Ch. hyalina* (92), both associated with cysts of the soya bean cyst nematode, *Heterodera glycines*; and *Ch. vaccinii* (15), an endophyte of cranberry (*Vaccinium macrocarpon* Ait.) leaf and stem tissue.

MORPHOLOGICAL, PHYSIOLOGICAL AND BIOCHEMICAL FEATURES

Some morphological, physiological and biochemical features of these fungi are detailed in Table 1. In culture, the young mycelium may be light in color but most mature mycelia are dark (grey-brown-greenish black).

Temperature optima for growth in culture, where known, are generally in the range of 23-27°C, exceptions being *C. radicola* (30-31°C) and *Ch. australis* (17-20°C). The most favourable pH for growth in culture is normally 5-7. All species sporulate, forming at least one type of phialoconidium and all except *Ch. australis, Ch. neocaledoniae, C. fagacearum* and *C. virescens* produce macroconidia. Species are heterothallic (*C. fagacearum, C. paradoxa, C. radicola*) or homothallic (*C. fimbriata, C. virescens*).

These species produce volatile substances known collectively as fusel oils, which include mixtures of C1-5 aliphatic alcohols and their acetate esters (Table 2, see also Hanssen, this volume). Indeed, the common name for pineapple disease of sugar cane derives from the strong pineapple-like aroma (ethyl acetate) produced by *C. paradoxa*. The composition

TABLE 1. Some comparative morphological and physiological characteristics of pathogenic *Ceratocystis* and *Chalara* species.

Pathogen	Appearance in culture	Temperature optima (°C)	pH optima	Endoconidial forms	Macroconidia
Chalara australis	Dark greyish green	17.5-20	4-6	2	-
Ch. elegans	Brownish black	-	-	1	+
Ch. neocaledoniae	Grey to black	25	<5.5	1	-
Ch. populi	Greyish brown to black	-	-	1	+
Ch. thielavioides	White to grey	23-27	5.2-8.0	1	+
Ceratocystis adiposa	Dark grey brown	-	-	1	+
C. fagacearum	Olive green to greyish black	20-25	4-6.5	1	-
C. fimbriata	Brown, grey, dark green	22-26	-	2	+
C. paradoxa	Dingy white to greenish grey black	25-32	5-7	2	+
C. radicola	Dark grey green to black	30-31	-	1	+
C. virescens	Dark greenish grey	-	-	2	-

TABLE 2. Fusel oil components of pathogenic *Ceratocystis* and *Chalara* species.

Pathogen	Ethyl acetate	Ethyl alcohol	Isobutyl alcohol	Isobutyl acetate	Isobutyl propanoate	Isoamyl alcohol	Isoamyl acetate	Methyl acetate	Propyl acetate	Propyl alcohol	Reference
Chalara australis	-	-	-	+	+	-	+	-	-	-	Kile unpub.
Ch. elegans	+	+	+	+	-	+	+	+	+	+	27, 127
Ch. thielavioides	+	+	+	+	-	+	+	-	-	-	25
Ceratocystis adiposa	+	+	-	-	-	-	-	-	-	-	71
C. fagacearum	+	+	+	-	-	-	-	+	-	-	26
C. fimbriata f. platani	+	+	+	+	-	-	+	-	-	-	
C. paradoxa	+	+	-	-	-	-	-	-	-	-	
C. virescens[1]	+	+	+	-	-	+	-	-	-	-	27

[1] Isolate identified as *C. coerulescens* by Collins and Morgan (27) but geographical origin and host suggest it was *C. virescens*.

of these volatile mixtures has been assessed in the culture atmosphere or culture liquid for *Ch. australis, Ch. elegans, Ch. thielavioides, C. adiposa, C. fagacearum, C. fimbriata, C. paradoxa* and *C. virescens* (as *C. coerulescens*). Their presence has also been noted for *Ch. neocaledoniae* (34). The dominant compounds are typically ethyl acetate, ethyl alcohol and isobutyl acetate. For *Ch. australis* and *Ch. thielavioides*, approximately 95% and 58% respectively of volatile material is isobutyl acetate.

TYPES OF DISEASE, MAJOR HOSTS AND SYMPTOMS

Collectively, the species considered may cause disease in roots, stems, shoots, leaves, tubers, fruits and seed pods. Some of the species may infect different organs in different hosts and primary pathogenesis may be expressed in a number of ways. Important diseases caused by these organisms are shown in Table 3.

TABLE 3. Diseases, major hosts, common disease names and geographical occurrence of pathogenic *Chalara* and *Ceratocystis* species.

Pathogen	Disease Type	Major hosts	Common name	Geographical occurrence
Chalara australis	vascular stain	myrtle beech	myrtle wilt	Australia
Ch. elegans	root rot	tobacco, cotton, bean	black root rot	Temperate, Mediterranean areas world wide
Ch. neocaledoniae	vascular stain	coffee, guava		New Caledonia
Ch. populi	canker	poplar, willow	trunk scab, brown patch	Europe
Ch. thielavioides	root, graft rot	walnut, carrot, lupin	black mold	Europe, North America, Australia
Ceratocystis adiposa	root rot	sugar cane	black rot	India
C. fagacearum	vascular wilt	oak	oak wilt	USA
C. fimbriata	vascular stain	plane, cacao, mango	canker stain, mal de machete, wilt disease	USA, Europe, Central & South America, West Indies, Asia
	canker	aspen, almond, prune, pimento, rubber, coffee, *Gmelina*	mallet canker, llaga macana mouldy rot, *Ceratocystis* canker	USA, Central and South America, Indonesia
	root, tuber rot	sweet potato	black rot	world wide
C. paradoxa	root rot, stem rot	sugar cane, palms	pineapple disease, heart rot, stem bleeding disease	Sub tropical - tropical areas world wide
	fruit, pod rot	pineapple, banana, cacao	water blister, soft rot, stem-end rot	world wide
C. radicola	root rot	date palm	rhizosis	USA
C. virescens	vascular stain	sugar maple	sapstreak	USA

Vascular wilt

Vascular wilt diseases are distinguished by the preferential infection of the conductive elements of the xylem (vessels and tracheids), with colonization of the living ray and axial parenchyma only occurring as the host becomes moribund. In this sense, *C. fagacearum*, the cause of oak wilt in the United States, is a true vascular wilt pathogen.

Ceratocystis fagacearum occurs in at least 21 states in eastern and central USA and has been recorded infecting about 20 species of oak and also Chinese chestnut. Red oak species are particularly susceptible, although members of the white oak group are more or less resistant. The symptoms vary with oak species and region but they are usually first evident in the upper crown. Leaves discolor, curl and abscise and as discoloration and defoliation progress throughout the crown, twigs and branches die. Brown streaks develop in outer sapwood throughout the host coincident with foliar symptoms, marking vessel clusters colonized by the pathogen (118).

Vascular stain diseases

Chalara australis, Ch. neocaledoniae, C. fimbriata and *C. virescens* also infect woody xylem tissue but in contrast to a vascular wilt such as that caused by *C. fagacearum*, fungal growth in the rays and axial parenchyma is a major feature in the pathogenesis of these fungi. Movement through the vessels occurs but is more restricted than is the case with vascular wilts. These pathogens cause extensive discoloration of the sapwood, often as dark brown radial patches or streaks that may extend into the heartwood in some host species. Discoloration is often concentrated in the roots, lower stem or main branches. In some tree species, pathogen spread may result in distinctive discoloration and death of the bark as the fungus spreads outwards through the stem tissue from the initial infection court. Crown symptoms are often those of a wilt with discoloration - necrosis of foliage, defoliation and dieback. *C. fimbriata* also causes cankers in some tree species (see Canker diseases below).

Chalara australis causes myrtle wilt in *Nothofagus cunninghamii* in Australia (69), *Ch. neocaledoniae* produces wilt symptoms in *Coffea robusta* and *Psidium guajava* in New Caledonia (34) and *C. virescens* causes sapstreak of *Acer saccharum* in the north-eastern United States (54). *Ceratocystis fimbriata f. platani* causes canker stain of *Platanus x acerifolia* and *P. occidentalis* in the United States and Europe (99,136,138,), *Theobroma cacao* in Central and South America (see review in 62) and *Mangifera indica* in Brazil (7).

Canker Diseases

Ceratocystis fimbriata and *Ch. populi* may infect restricted areas of cambial and vascular tissue, resulting in perennial lesions of various types in woody hosts. Typically these pathogens cause discoloration and killing of bark and wood that results in stem or branch deformation or death of the affected part. Depending on the location of the infection and host susceptibility, symptoms may resemble those of a vascular stain.

Ceratocystis populi causes small cankers (trunk scab or brown patch disease) on *Populus* and *Salix* species in Europe (132). *Ceratocystis fimbriata* causes cankers on the following hosts: *Populus tremuloides* in North America; poplar hybrids in Poland (50,57,82,147,150); *Coffea arabica* in Central and South America and Indonesia (40,107,120,126,151); *Acacia decurrens* and *Gmelina arborea* in Brazil (93,111); *Pimenta officinalis* in Jamaica (75); *Hevea braziliensis* in most rubber growing regions (8,117); and *Prunus amygdalus, P. persica, P. armeniaca* and *P. domestica* in California (37, 38). Rates of canker development and effects on the host depend on the virulence of the isolate, interaction with host, and location of infection on the host.

Root and Stem rots

Chalara elegans, Ch. thielavioides, C. paradoxa, C. adiposa, C. fimbriata and *C. radicola* cause root and stem infections. Most infections occur in non-lignified

or lightly-lignified tissue but may result in blackening or browning of infected tissues and stunting, chlorosis or wilting of hosts.

Chalara elegans infects at least 137 species of plants, particularly those in the Solanaceae, Leguminosae and Cucurbitaceae (79); tobacco, cotton, beans, peanuts, citrus and poinsettia are some economically important hosts. The fungus can cause replant failure (115) and Stanghellini and Rasmussen (122) reported it as a pathogen of hydroponically grown corn-salad (*Valerianella locusta*). However, the Gramineae are regarded as non-hosts for this species (79).

Chalara thielavioides causes root rot or lower stem rot in *Ulmus pumila, U. parvifolia* (72) and *Lupinus albus* (101,106). Although occupying a specialized place in this category of diseases, *C. thielavioides* is also recognized as a cause of graft union failure (black mold) in both deciduous and evergreen hosts (5,52,56,77).

Ceratocystis paradoxa causes pineapple disease of sugar cane (*Saccharum officinarum*) cuttings (sets) and standing cane (83,141,145,146); black head disease of rhizomes, suckers and roots of banana (*Musa* sp.); and infection of the fibrous stem tissues of *Cocus nucifera* (coconut-stem bleeding disease, 29,105), *Elaeis guineensis* (oil palm-dry basal rot, 121), *Arecu cathecu* (date palm heart-rot) and other palms (stem rot, 124, 125). *Ceratocystis adiposa* also infects sugar cane sets (14). *Ceratocystis radicola* infects roots and stems of *Phoenix dactylifera* (10). *Ceratocystis fimbriata* causes a lower stem rot in *Crotolaria juncea* (31, 80) and also a root rot in sweet potato (*Ipomoea batatas*) seedlings (51,128).

Rots of fruits, tubers, seed pods, leaves and buds

Ceratocystis paradoxa has been associated with pineapple (*Ananas comosus*) leaf and fruit rot (55,74,76,112), main and finger stalk rot and black end in bananas (87,89), bitten leaf disease of cacao (98), soft rot of papaw (*Carica papaya*) leaves (22), and terminal bud and rachid rot in *Phoenix canariensis* (6). *Ceratocystis fimbriata* causes black rot of sweet potato (51,128). *Chalara thielavioides* and *Ch. elegans* infect carrot (*Daucus carota*) roots (11,45,52).

HOST RANGE OF PATHOGENIC STRAINS

Natural host range may be restricted to a single species (*Ch. australis, C. adiposa*), a few species or several species in one genus (*Ch. neocaledoniae, Ch.*

populi, C. fagacearum, C. radicola, C. virescens), or numerous species in a range of genera or plant families (*Ch. elegans, Ch. thielavioides, C. fimbriata, C. paradoxa*).

New host-pathogen combinations are possible when plant species are cultivated outside their natural environment, as for example with *C. fimbriata* on *Gmelina arborea* in the Amazon Basin of Brazil (93). Pathogens may also be introduced to previously unexposed but susceptible host populations, as has been the case with *C. fimbriata f. platani* on *Platanus* x *acerifolia* in Europe (44,99). *Platanus orientalis*, which occurs from south-east Europe to Asia Minor, could also be susceptible (136). *Ceratocystis fimbriata* was possibly introduced to Malaysian rubber growing areas about 1916 (117) and recently into Australia (135). Kile (67) suggested *Ch. australis* may pose a hazard to some *Nothofagus* species in New Zealand and South America if it were to spread from Australia. Awareness of these problems has led to the development of safeguards to minimize the risk of introducing *C. fagacearum* into European oak populations (47).

Development of strains or forms adapted to specific hosts or host groups could be expected for widely distributed polyphagous species. Physiological (pathogenic) specialization is indicated for *Ch. elegans* (3,123). Corbaz (30) allocated 24 isolates from eight different hosts into four partially overlapping groups on the basis of cross inoculation studies with *Nicotiana tabacum* and four other hosts. Other cross inoculation studies also indicate that pathogenic specialization is not definitive (73,143).

Evidence for pathogenic specialization is strong for *C. fimbriata* and indeed the designation *C. fimbriata f. platani* is derived from such observations (138). *C. fimbriata* isolates from different areas differ in colony type, growth rate, conidial states and pathogenicity (140). Isolates from diverse hosts and regions are, however, cross fertile (140). While pathogenicity is often greatest on the original host, cross inoculation experiments show a variety of interactions (32,38,57,75,107,109,111, see also Kojima, this volume).

For *C. paradoxa* and *Ch. thielavioides,* the situation is less clear. Sundararaman *et al.* (125) found an isolate of *C. paradoxa* from *Arecu cathecu* to be pathogenic on a number of hosts. Edgerton (41) and Wismer and Bailey (146) noted that the evidence for specialized strains in this species was not convincing. However, the cross inoculation results of Hamond (52) and Baker and Thomas (5) with *Ch. thielavioides* may indicate some degree of host specialization in that species.

INFECTION AND DISPERSAL

Wounds are a prerequisite for infection of above ground plant organs by these pathogens, although infections have been observed to develop in soft tissues under artificial conditions (150). In woody plants, exposure of the cambial-xylem tissue is usually necessary, although *C. fimbriata f. platani* can infect through small wounds in the outer bark (136,137). In contrast, wounds are not necessary for root infection by *Ch. elegans* in some plant species (21,142).

In spite of the importance of wounds in the epidemiology of this group of pathogens, the susceptibility of wounds to infection in relation to factors such as location, age and type has been studied only in detail for *C. fagacearum* and *C. fimbriata* (24,133,136,152). Wounds in oak and plane were only susceptible to infection by these pathogens for 2-5 days. Histological examination of the early stages of infection has been studied in most detail for *Ch. elegans, C. fagacearum* and *C. fimbriata* (21,142,150).

Dispersal occurs in a variety of ways and several pathogens have more than one means of dispersal (Table 4). Species forming thick walled macroconidia are typically soil-borne and most initial infections probably arise from such inoculum. One exception is *C. fimbriata*, which is difficult to isolate from soil in fruit orchards (91), although sweet potato strains may survive for extended periods in soil (23,128).

Species that sporulate on the aerial surfaces of infected hosts have the potential for dispersal by water or wind, which is potentially of some importance for the local spread of some vascular stains, cankers and diseases of roots, leaves and fruits (136). On the basis of limited data, Moller and De Vay (91) considered air currents unlikely to carry *C. fimbriata* propagules in fruit orchards. Vigouroux and Stojadinovic (134) showed *C. fimbriata f. platani* could be carried in water to infect wounded plane tree roots. *Chalara thielavioides* may also be dispersed in irrigation water (5).

Below ground spread by root grafts is important for local spread of vascular wilt and vascular stain diseases in perennial hosts. This form of dispersal has been demonstrated for *C. fagacearum* (see review in Gibbs and French, 46) and *C. fimbriata f. platani* (1) and probably accounts for the clumping of diseased *Nothofagus cunninghamii* in Tasmanian rainforest (42).

Insects are significant in the dispersal of *C.*

TABLE 4. Major methods of dispersal of pathogenic *Ceratocystis* and *Chalara* species.

Pathogen	Soil	Wind-water	Root-graft	Insect-animal (direct)	Insect frass	Pruning tools
Chalara australis	-	+	+?	-	+	-
Ch. elegans	+	-	-	-	-	-
Ch. neocaledoniae	-	+?	+?	-	+?	+?
Ch. populi	-	+	-	-	-	-
Ch. thielavioides	+	+	-	-	-	+
C. adiposa	+	-	-	-	-	-
C. fagacearum	-	+?	+	+	-	-
C. fimbriata	+	+	+	+	+	+
C. paradoxa	+	+?	-	+	-	+
C. radicola	+	-	-	-	-	-
C. virescens	-	+?	+?	+?	-	-

fagacearum, C. fimbriata, C. paradoxa and *Ch. australis.* Both sap feeding (nitidulids, drosopholid flies and other species) and tree wounding insects (bark beetles) are recognized as direct vectors contributing to the spread of the pathogens causing oak wilt, canker stain, mallet canker, and pineapple disease (19,33,46,58,110). For oak wilt, insect spread is not considered particularly efficient (46).

Insects may also be indirect agents of spread. Secondary ambrosia beetle attack on infected cacao and *Nothofagus cunninghamii* trees liberates frass contaminated with conidia and hyphal fragments of *C. fimbriata* and *Ch. australis*, respectively, which can be wind dispersed to wounds (62, Kile unpublished). A similar mechanism could operate for *C. neocaledoniae* and *C. virescens.* Dissemination of frass-borne propagules is not involved in the dispersal of oak wilt (104).

Human extractive and arboricultural activities contribute significantly to the spread of *C. fimbriata* in rubber, coffee, cacao and plane trees via pruning implements, tapping knives, wound sealants and clothing contaminated with fungal propagules or infected sawdust (13,117,136,137). Field mice are also known to contribute to the spread of black rot of sweet potato (49).

The volatiles emitted by these fungi may also be extremely attractive to some insect species, aiding insect dispersal. Insect vectors are attracted to the sporulating mycelial mats of *C. fagacearum* where the insects become contaminated with spores (46). Attraction of insects to infected tissue probably also assists insect dispersal of *C. fimbriata* and *C. paradoxa.* For *Ch. australis,* it is hypothesized that volatiles resulting from the host-pathogen interaction attract the ambrosia beetle *Platypus subgranosus* to infected stem tissue, which results in the liberation of infected frass (Kile, unpublished).

PATHOGENIC MECHANISMS

For a vascular wilt disease such as that caused by *C. fagacearum,* potential causes of wilting include physical blockage of the vascular system, vivotoxins, hydrolytic enzyme effects and disruption of hormonal regulation. McWain and Gregory (86) isolated an α-(1→6) linked mannan from *C. fagacearum* filtrates, which caused symptoms similar to oak wilt in red oak seedlings and cuttings. For vascular stains, cankers, and root and other rots, the causes of disease development are poorly understood but may involve one or more of these mechanisms.

Ethylene produced by *C. fimbriata* may play some role in pathogenesis (18). Tabachnik and De Vay (127) hypothesized that methyl acetate produced by *Ch. elegans* acted as a phytotoxin and induced swelling of cell walls and the discoloration of cotton (*Gossypium hirsutum*) root tissues. Ethyl acetate is a phytotoxin in sugar cane sets infected by *C. paradoxa* and *C. adiposa* (71). Isobutyl acetate, a major fusel oil component produced by *C. fimbriata,* may be toxic to almonds (127). However, this substance had no toxic effect when injected into *Nothofagus cunninghamii* (Kile, unpublished).

ECONOMIC IMPORTANCE

The economic importance of this group of pathogens is undoubtedly great. Collectively they infect a range of commercially important food plants (e.g. pineapple, banana, sweet potato, sugar, nut and stone fruits, beans, mangoes, dates), crops (e.g. cotton, tobacco, rubber, coffee, cacao) and timber and amenity species (e.g. plane, myrtle beech, sugar maple, aspen, *Gmelina*). In the absence of control practices, heavy losses would result in many situations. However, few quantitative assessments are available of the direct economic losses attributable to individual pathogens on particular host species in separate countries or regions.

In agricultural and horticultural crops, the losses are often immediate and well recognized. For *Ch. elegans* in tobacco, losses in some countries may account for up to 5% of total crop value (79). *Ceratocystis paradoxa* may cause devastating losses of pineapple fruit in transit and storage (112). In sugarcane, direct losses from *C. paradoxa* may necessitate replanting, and poor canopy development in infected crops hinders weed control (146). While black rot of sweet potato has become relatively uncommon in the USA because of the widespread implementation of an integrated control program, it is now more important in southeast Asia and Oceania (23). *Ceratocystis fimbriata* may reduce the tapping life of rubber trees from 30 to 10-15 years (84). In the late 1960's, mallet canker infected trees in more than 5000 ha of prune orchards in the Sacramento Valley, California. Thorold (130) reviewed the serious losses caused by this pathogen in cacao.

For forests or amenity plantings, losses are often more difficult to assess, although some attempts have been made at a local level to estimate them for canker stain of plane (136, 137) and sapstreak of sugar maple (88). Ohman and Spike (95) reported a 57% reduction in the value of lumber from sugar maple logs infected with sapstreak. Losses caused by *C. fimbriata* on *Gmelina arborea* in the Jari Valley, Brazil, may account for up to 40% of the potential production (Dianese, personal communication). Oak wilt is considered to cause relative minor timber losses in relation to the size of the timber resource (46).

CONTROL

Control procedures for these diseases in economically important crops have emphasized preventative measures including sanitation, cultural methods, chemical control, and to a lesser degree, the use of genetic resistance.

For species susceptible to infection by vascular stain or canker organisms, avoidance of wounds is a key preventative strategy. Wounds caused as a result of weeding, cultivation, pruning, harvesting machinery, animals or logging have been implicated as infection courts for diseases caused by *Ch. australis*, *Ch. neocaledoniae*, *C. fimbriata*, *C. paradoxa* and *C. virescens* (34,37,38,62,68,97,100,113,124,126,136,137, 145). Prevention of local root graft spread via physical barriers or root free zones has also been used or advocated for control of oak wilt (13) and canker stain (Vigouroux, personal communication).

Sanitation to destroy or minimize inoculum has been proposed or practised in situations from glasshouses to forests. Destruction of infected plants and disinfection of grafting facilities was used by Hamond (52) for control of *Ch. thielavioides*. Removal of dead and dying plants in orchards or forests has also been advocated for vascular stain and canker diseases caused by *Ch. neocaledoniae* (34), *C. fimbriata* (62,100,113,126, 136) and *C. virescens* (65,66). A major sanitation program involving felling, girdling or poisoning oak wilt infected trees to eradicate disease foci was conducted in West Virginia and Pennsylvania for more than a decade (48). Interestingly, the significant decline in the incidence of black rot of sweet potato in the USA has in part been due to sanitation procedures (23).

Cultural methods, including avoidance of hazardous sites and crop rotation, can assist management of diseases caused by *C. paradoxa* and *Ch. elegans*. Large sets and good drainage in well cultivated soils reduce pineapple disease losses (145). Cool, wet soils of high pH favour *Ch. elegans* growth and sporulation and inhibit seedling root development and should be avoided (36). Rotation with non-host plants also reduces disease severity to some extent (60,119). Improved drainage and better orchard aeration through weed control were advocated to assist control of *C. fimbriata* in coffee and rubber plantations (117,126). Pruning of infected shoots or branches has been used for eliminating *C. fimbriata* infection in plane, coffee, almond and stone fruits (38,136). Crop rotation also assists in control of black rot of sweet potato (23).

Chemicals have been used extensively for control of diseases caused by *Ch. elegans*, *C. fimbriata* and *C. paradoxa*. Soil or systemic fungicides assist control of *Ch. elegans* in a range of crops through direct effects on the pathogen or through improved establishment and early seedling growth (36). For many years, mercurial compounds were the main method for controlling pineapple disease of sugar cane (41,144,145), although less hazardous materials are now utilized (28,90,129). Fruit and storage disorders in pineapples, bananas and sweet potato have also been controlled chemically. Fungicidal wound dressings reduce infection by *C. fimbriata* in plane trees (35), pimento (75), almonds and stone fruits (38). Fungicides are also used to control moldy rot of rubber (8,102,103,117).

Selection or breeding for disease resistance is potentially the most effective control method in crops of economic importance. Effective control of *Ch. elegans* in tobacco has been obtained by the use of tolerant or resistant cultivars (59). Resistance to *C. fimbriata* is also utilized to limit disease impact in coffee, cacao and sweet potato (17,39,43,61,62,63, 64,78,81,153). Some poplar hybrids and rubber clones exhibit resistance to *C. fimbriata* (4,108) and breeding for oak wilt resistance may be feasible (114). Sugar cane clones vary in resistance to *C. paradoxa* (2,20,139). However, the effectiveness of other control methods has limited the interest in developing resistant cultivars in some crops (23).

CONCLUSION

Ceratocystis and *Chalara* species cause several types of disease on a wide range of angiosperm hosts. Collectively, they are of considerable economic importance. There is potential in the future for new host-pathogen combinations or introductions to healthy extant host populations. While necrotrophic, they are typically opportunists and largely dependent on wounds for entry and infection. For at least some species, natural mechanisms of dispersal appear inefficient. Nevertheless, agricultural, arboricultural and forestry activities contribute significantly to the economic importance of some species.

ACKNOWLEDGEMENTS

The assistance of Judy Sprent in obtaining reference material and Sheila Scott in typing the manuscript is greatly appreciated.

LITERATURE CITED

1. Accordi, S.M. 1986. Diffusione de *Ceratocystis fimbriata* f. *platani* attraverso le anastomosi radicali. Inftore. Fitopatol. 36:53-58.
2. Ahmed, H.U., Khan, M.A. and Mian, M.I.H. 1977. Screening sugarcane clones for resistance to pineapple disease. Sugar Pathol. Newsl. 18:8-9.
3. Allison, C.C. 1938. Physiologic specialisation of *Thielaviopsis basicola* on tobacco. Phytopathology 28:1. (Abstr.)
4. Anonymous. 1972. Mouldy rot. Planters Bull. Malay. Rubber Res. Inst. 118:3-6.
5. Baker, K.F. and Thomas, E.H. 1946. Failure of bud and graft unions of rose induced by *Chalaropsis thielavioides*. Phytopathology 36:281-291.
6. Barthelet, J. and Vinot, M. 1947. Notes sur les maladies des cultures méridionales. Annl. Epiphyt., n.s. 10: 11-23 (RAM 26:328-329)
7. Batista, A.C. 1960. *Ceratocystis fimbriata* Ell. and Halst, sobre *Mangifera indica* L. Inst. Micol. Univ. Recife, Pub. no. 244, 46pp.
8. Beeley, F. 1929. Fungi and diseases of the tapping panel. Malaya Rubber Res. Inst. Quart. J. 1:250-272.
9. Bliss, D.E. 1941a. A new species of *Ceratostomella* on the date palm. Mycologia 33:468-482.
10. Bliss, D.E 1941b. Relation of *Ceratostomella radicola* to rhizosis of the date palm. Phytopathology 31:1123-1129.
11. Boerema, G.H. 1959. *Chalaropsis thielavioides* Peyr. op wortelen verpakt in geperforeerde polyethyleen zakjes. Plantenziektkd Dienst. Versl. 134:158-161.
12. Bozarth, R.F. and Goenaga, A. 1976. A complex of virus-like particles from *Thielaviopsis basicola*. Proc. Am. Phytopathol. Soc. 3:250.
13. Bretz, T.W. 1951. Oak wilt. J. For. 49:169-171.
14. Butler, E.J. 1906. Fungus diseases of sugar-cane in Bengal. Mem. Dept. Agric. India (Bot. Ser.) 1:32-40.
15. Carris L.M. 1988. *Chalara vaccinii* sp. nov., a *Vaccinium* endophyte. Mycologia 80:875-879.
16. Carris, L.M. and Glawe, D.A. 1984. *Chalara heteroderae*, a new species isolated from cysts of *Heterodera glycines* in Illinois. Mycotaxon 21:441-448.
17. Castilla-Zapata, J. 1982. Produccion de una seleccion resistente a llaga macana *Ceratocystis fimbriata* (Ell. and Halst) Hunt con relacion a las variedades Tipica y Borbon. Cenicafe 33:53-66.
18. Chalutz, E. and De Vay, J.E. 1969. Production of ethylene in vitro and in vivo by *Ceratocystis fimbriata* in relation to disease development. Phytopathology 50:750-755.
19. Chang, V.C.S. and Jensen, L. 1974. Transmission of the pineapple disease organism of sugarcane by nitidulid beetles in Hawaii. J. Econ. Entomol. 67:190-192.
20. Chi, C.C. 1949. A preliminary report on the study of pineapple disease of sugar cane in Taiwan. J. Sugar Cane Res., Taiwan 3:71-102.
21. Christou, T. 1962. Penetration and host-parasite relationships of *Thielaviopsis basicola* in the bean plant. Phytopathology 52:194-198.
22. Ciferri, R. 1927. Notae mycologicae et phytopathologicae. Series II N. 1-15. Riv. Patol. Veg. 17:209-294 (RAM 7:229-230).
23. Clark, C.A. and Moyer, J.W. 1988. Compendium of sweet potato diseases. American Phytopathological Society Press, St. Paul, MN. 75 pp.
24. Cobb, F.W. Jr, Fergus, C.L. and Stambaugh, W.J. 1965. Factors affecting infection of red and chestnut oaks by *Ceratocystis fagacearum*. Phytopathology 55:1194-1199.
25. Collins R.P. and Morgan M.E. 1960. Esters produced by *Chalaropsis thielavioides*. Science 131:933-934.
26. Collins, R.P. and Kalnins, K. 1965. Volatile alcohols,

esters and acids produced by *Ceratocystis fagacearum* (Bretz) Hunt. Phyton 22:107-109.

27. Collins, R.P. and Morgan, M.E. 1962. Identity of fruit-like aroma substances synthesised by endoconidial-forming fungi. Phytopathology 52:407-409.

28. Comstock, J.C, Ferreira, S.A. Ching, S.A. and Hilton, H.W. 1984. Control of pineapple disease of sugarcane with propiconazole. Plant Dis. 68:1072-1075.

29. Cook, M.T. 1926. Report of the Division of Plant Pathology and Botany. Annl. Rep., Inst. Exp. Stat. Puerto Rico 1924-25.

30. Corbaz, R. 1985. Pathotypes et variations du pouvoir pathogéne chez *Chalara elegans* Nag Raj et Kendrick (= *Thielaviopsis basicola*). Phytopathol. Z. 113:289-299.

31. Costa, A.S. and Krug, H.P. 1935. Eine durch *Ceratostomella* hervorgerufene Welkekrankheit der *Crotalaria juncea* in Brazilien. Phytopathol. Z. 8:507-513.

32. Crone, L.J. 1962. Symptoms, spread, and control of canker stain of Plane trees. Diss. Abstr. 23:1857-1858.

33. Crone, L.J. and Batchelor, S. 1961. Insect transmission of canker stain fungus, *Ceratocystis fimbriata* f. *platani*. (Abstr.) Phytopathology 51:576.

34. Dadant, M.R. 1950. Sur une nouvelle maladie du *Coffea robusta* en Nouvelle-Calédonie. Rev. Gen. Bot. 57:168-176.

35. Davis, S.H. Jr and Peterson, J.L. 1973. A tree wound dressing to prevent spread of the *Ceratocystis* causing canker stain disease of the planetree. Plant Dis. Rep. 57:28-30.

36. Delon, R. and Kiffer, E. 1978. *Chalara elegans* (=*Thielaviopsis basicola*) et les espées voisines. Ingénéralités et pathologie. Ann. tab. Sect. 2, 15:159-186.

37. De Vay, J.E., English, H., Lukezic, F.L. and O'Reilly, H. J. 1960. Mallet wound canker of almond trees. Calif. Agric. 14:8-9.

38. De Vay, J.E., Lukezic, F.L., English, H., Trujillo, E.E. and Moller, W.J. 1968. *Ceratocystis* canker of deciduous fruit trees. Phytopathology 58:949-954.

39. Dominguez, R.P.F. and Velasquez, F. 1972. Seleccion de plantas de cacao (*Theobroma cacao* L.) por resistencia al hongo *Ceratocystis fimbriata*. Revta Fac. Agron. Univ. Cent. Venez. 6:57-73.

40. Echandi, E. 1955. Trunk and stem canker of coffee trees. Revta Biol. Trop. 3:237-241.

41. Edgerton, C.W. 1958. Sugarcane and its diseases. Louisiana State University Press, Baton Rouge. pp 103-106.

42. Elliott, H.J., Kile, G.A., Candy, S.G. and Ratkowsky, D.A. 1987. The incidence and spatial pattern of *Nothofagus cunninghamii* (Hook.) Oerst. attacked by *Platypus subgranosus* Schedl in Tasmania's cool temperate rainforest. Austr. J. Ecol. 12:125-138.

43. Enriquez, G.A. 1984. Resumen de las investigaciones sobre la mazorca negra y el mal de machete del cacao en Turrialba, Costa Rica. (Abstr.) Phytopathology 74:1014.

44. Ferrari, J-P. and Pichenot, M. 1974. *Ceratocystis fimbriata* Ellis et Halsted f. *platani* (Walter), responsable d'une grave maladie du Platane en France: [la tache chancreuse]. C. R. Hebdom. Séances Acad. Sci., D, 278:2787-2789.

45. Friedman, B.A., Barger, W.R. and Radspinner, W.A. 1954. *Thielaviopsis basicola* on carrot roots from California. Plant Dis. Rep. 38:855.

46. Gibbs, J.N. and French, D.W. 1980. The transmission of oak wilt. USDA For. Serv. Res. Pap. NC-185, 17pp.

47. Gibbs, J.N., Liese, W. and Pinon, J. 1984. Oak wilt for Europe. Outl. Agric. 13:203-207.

48. Gillespie, W.H. 1971. The oak wilt situation. Pages 124-128 in: Oak Symposium Proceedings, USDA NE For. Exp. Stn., Upper Darby, Pennsylvania.

49. Goto, K., Suzuki, N., Kondo, S. and Miyajima, M. 1954. On the soil infection of blackrot of sweetpotato and its transmission by fieldmouse. Bull. Div. Plant Breed. Cult., Tokai-Kinki Nat. Agric. Exp. Stn. 1:138-150.

50. Gremmen, J. and de Kam, M. 1977. *Ceratocystis fimbriata*, a fungus associated with poplar canker in Poland. Eur. J. For. Pathol. 7:44-47.

51. Halsted, B.D. 1890. Some fungus diseases of the sweet potato. N. J. Agr. Exp. Stn. Bull. 76:7-14.

52. Hamond, J.B. 1935. The morphology, physiology and mode of parasitism of a species of *Chalaropsis* infecting nursery walnut trees. J. Pomol. 13:81-107.

53. Hennebert, G.L. 1967. *Chalaropsis punctulata*, a new hyphomycete. Antonie van Leeuwenhoek 39:333-340.

54. Hepting, G.H. 1944. Sapsteak, a new killing disease of sugar maple. Phytopathology 34:1069-1076.

55. Hernandez, J., Gallo Llobet, L., Acosta, J., and Gonzalez, A. 1988. *Thielaviopsis paradoxa* (De Seyn.) Hoehn. en pina tropical (*Ananas comosus* L.) en la isla del Hierro. Pages 51-56 in: Comunicaciones del III Congreso Nacional de Fitopatologia. Llobet, L.G. Puerto de la Cruz ed. (Tenerife-Islas Canarias) 29 Oct-2 Nov 1984, La Laguna, Tenerife, Spain; Centro de Investigacion y Tecnologia Agrarias.

56. Hess, C.E, and Welch, D.S. 1954. *Chalaropsis thielavioides* Peyronel found on evergreen grafting stock. Plant Dis. Rep. 38:415.

57. Hinds, T.E. 1972a. *Ceratocystis* canker of aspen. Phytopathology 62:213-220.

58. Hinds, T.E 1972b. Insect transmission of *Ceratocystis* species associated with aspen cankers. Phytopathology 62:221-225.

59. Hoffbeck, L.J., Neas, M.O., Heggestad, H.E. and Skoog, H.A. 1965. Burley 49, a new disease resistant Burley tobacco. Univ. Tenn. Agric. Exp. Stn. Bull. 395, 18 pp.

60. Hsi, D.C.H. 1978. Effect of crop sequence, previous peanut blackhull severity, and time of sampling on soil populations of *Thielaviopsis basicola*. Phytopathology 68:1442-1445.

61. Ikehashi, H. 1986. New summer crop cultivars registered by the Ministry of Agriculture, Forestry and Fisheries in 1986. Japan. J. Breed. 36:438-439.

62. Iton, E.F. 1959. Studies on a wilt disease of Cacao at River Estate. A report on cacao research 1957-58, 55-64. Imperial College of Tropical Agriculture, Trinidad.

63. Iton, E.F. 1961. Studies on a wilt disease of cacao at River Estate. II. Some aspects of wind transmission. A report on cacao research 1959-60, 47-58. Imperial College of Tropical Agriculture, Trinidad.

64. Izquierdo, J.E. 1988. Comportamiento de genotipos de cafetas ante *Ceratocystis fimbriata*. Cienc. Tec. Agric. Cafe Cacao 1:53-59.

65. Kessler, K.J. Jr. 1972. Sapstreak disease of sugar maple. USDA For. Serv., Forest Pest Leaflet 128. 4 pp.

66. Kessler, K.J. Jr. 1978. How to control sapstreak disease of sugar maple. USDA For. Serv., N. Central For. Exp. Stn. Leaflet, 5 pp.

67. Kile, G.A. 1989. Infection of exotic and Tasmanian native tree and shrub species by the vascular stain fungus *Chalara australis*. Eur. J. For. Pathol. 19:98-104.

68. Kile, G.A. and Hall, M.F. 1988. Assessment of *Platypus subgranosus* as a vector of *Chalara australis*, causal agent of a vascular disease of *Nothofagus cunninghamii*. N.Z. J. For. Sci. 18:166-186.

69. Kile G.A. and Walker, J. 1987. *Chalara australis* sp.nov. (Hyphomycetes), a vascular pathogen of *Nothofagus cunninghamii* (Fagaceae) in Australia and its relationship to other *Chalara* species. Austr. J. Bot. 35:1-32.

70. Kile, G.A., Packham, J.M. and Elliott, H.J. 1989. Myrtle wilt and its possible management in association with human disturbance of rainforest in Tasmania. N.Z. J. For. Sci. 19:256-264.

71. Kuo, T., Chien, M. and Li, H. 1969. Ethyl acetate produced by *Ceratocystis paradoxa* and *C. adiposum* and its role in the inhibition of the germination of sugar cane buds. Can. J. Bot. 47:1459-1463.

72. Lamb, H., Wright, E. and Davidson, R.W. 1935. A root rot of Chinese elms. Phytopathology 25:652-654.

73. Lambe, R.C. and Wills, W.H. 1978. Pathogenicity of *Thielaviopsis basicola* to Japanese holly (*Ilex crenata*). Plant Dis. Rep. 62:859-863.

74. Larsen, L.D. 1910. Diseases of the pineapple. Hawaiian Sugar Plant. Assoc. Bull. 10:9-28.

75. Leather, R.I. 1966. A canker and wilt disease of Pimento (*Pimenta officinalis*) caused by *Ceratocystis fimbriata* in Jamaica. Trans. Br. Mycol. Soc. 49:213-218.

76. Lee, H.A. 1922. Observations on previously unreported or noteworthy plant diseases in the Philippines. Philipp. Agric. Rev. 14:422-434.

77. Longrée, K. 1940. *Chalaropsis thielavioides*, cause of 'black mold' of rose grafts. Phytopathology 30:793-807.

78. Lu, S.Y., Wu., C.G., Li, W.J. and Feng, Q.H. 1988. Irradiation of sweet potato (*Ipomoea batatas* (L.) Lam.) with gamma rays from ^{60}Co for black rot resistance. Acta Agron. Sinica 14:22-27.

79. Lucas, G.B. 1975. Diseases of tobacco. 3rd Edition. Biological Consulting Associates, Raleigh, North Carolina, USA. 621 pp.

80. Malaguti, G. 1952. Una podredumbre del tallo de *Crotalaria juncea*, causada por *Ceratostomella fimbriata*. Agron. Trop. 1:287-292.

81. Malaguti, G. 1956. La necrosis del tronco del Cacao en Venezuela. Agron. Trop. 5:207-226.(RAM 37: 271).

82. Manion, P.D. and French, D.W. 1967. *Nectria galligena* and *Ceratocystis fimbriata* cankers of aspen in Minnesota. For. Sci. 13:23-28.

83. Manzo, S.K. 1975. Pineapple disease on standing sugarcane in Nigeria. Sugarcane Pathol. Newsl. 13/14:3-4.

84. Martin, W.J. 1949. Moldy rot of tapping panels of *Hevea* rubber trees. USDA, Circular no 798, 23 pp.

85. McCracken, F.I. and Burkhadt, E.C. 1977. Destruction of sycamore by canker stain in the midsouth. Plant Dis. Rep. 61:984-986.

86. McWain, P. and Gregory, G.F. 1972. A neutral mannan from *Ceratocystis fagacearum* culture filtrate. Phytochemistry 11:2609-2612.

87. Meredith, D.S. 1961. Chemical control of transport and storage diseases of bananas. Trop. Agric. 38:205-223

88. Mielke, M.E. and Charette, D.A. 1989. The incidence of sapstreak of sugar maple in Menominee County, Wisconsin, and its relationship to wounds and season of logging. North. J. Appl. For. 6:65-67.

89. Mitchell, R.S. 1937. Stem end rot of bananas with special reference to the physiological relationships of *Thielaviopsis paradoxa* (De Seynes) Von Höhn. J. Coun. Sci. Ind. Res. Aust. 10:123-130.

90. Michell-Innes, L.E. and Thomson, G.M. 1974. Tests with some additional nonmercurial fungicides for the control of pineapple disease. Pages 85-87 in: Proceedings of the 48th South African Sugar Technologists Association Annual Congress, Durban and Mt Edgecombe, South Africa.

91. Moller, W.J. and De Vay, J.E. 1968. Insect transmission of *Ceratocystis fimbriata* in deciduous fruit orchards. Phytopathology 58:1499-1508.

92. Morgan-Jones, G., Gintis, O. and Rodriguez-Kabana, R. 1984. New species of *Chalara* and *Scytalidium* isolated from cysts of *Heterodera glycines*. Mycologia 76:211-217.

93. Muchovej, J.J., Albuquerque, F.C. and Ribeiro, G.T. 1978. *Gmelina arborea* - a new host of *Ceratocystis fimbriata*. Plant Dis. Rep. 62:717-719.

94. Nag Raj, T.R. and Kendrick, B. 1975. A monograph of *Chalara* and allied genera. Wilfred Laurier University Press, Waterloo, Ontario. 200 pp.

95. Ohman, J.H. and Spike, A.B. 1966. Effect of staining caused by sapstreak disease on sugar maple log and lumber values. USDA For. Serv. Res. Note NC-12, 4pp.

96. Old, K.M. and Patrick, Z.A. 1979. Giant soil amoebae, potential biocontrol agents. Pages 617-628 in: Soil-borne plant pathogens. B. Schippers and W. Gams, eds. Academic Press, New York. 686 pp.

97. O'Reilly, H.J. 1963. *Ceratocystis* canker of prunes, almonds and apricots. Calif. Agric. Exp. Stn. Ext. Serv., Circular 519, 7pp.

98. Orian, G. 1928. Le 'bitten leaf disease' du cocotier. Rev. Agric. Maurice 38:86-87 (RAM 7: 629).

99. Panconesi, A. 1972. I nostri platani soni in pericolo. Inftore. Fitopatol. 22:10-13.

100. Panconesi, A. 1981. *Ceratocystis fimbriata* of plane trees in Italy: biological aspects and control possibility. Eur. J. For. Pathol. 7:385-395.

101. Pape, H. 1927. Krankheiten und Schadlinge der Lupine. Illte. Landw. Ztg. 47:316-318.

102. Parnata, Y. and Asid, M. 1973. Evaluation of fungicides against mouldy rot in the field. Bull. Balai Penelitian Perkebunan Medan 4:5-11.

103. Pawirosoemardjo, S. 1977. Efficacy test of several fungicides against mouldy rot. Menara Perkebunan 45:81-84.

104. Peplinski, J.D. and Merrill, W. 1974. Nonsurvival of *Ceratocystis fagacearum* in frass of oak bark beetles and ambrosia beetles. Phytopathology 64:1528-1530.

105. Petch, T. 1909. The coconut stem disease. Trop. Agric. Suppl. 5:73-75.

106. Peyronel, B. 1916. Una nuova malattia del lupino prodotta da *Chalaropsis thielavioides* Peyr. nov. gen. et nova sp. Staz. Sper. Agric. Ital. 49:583-596.

107. Pontis, R.E. 1951. A canker disease of the coffee tree in Colombia and Venezuela. Phytopathology 41:178-184.

108. Przybyl, K. 1984. Development of the fungus *Ceratocystis fimbriata* in shoots of poplar clones with differing resistance. Eur. J. For. Pathol. 14:177-183.

109. Przybyl, K. 1988. The response of Populus 'NE42' (*P. maximowiczii* x *P. trochocarpa*) to infection by *Ceratocystis fimbriata* isolated from cacao-tree and plane. Eur. J. For. Pathol. 18:8-12.

110. Rexrode, C.O. 1977. Cacodylic acid reduces the spread of oak wilt. Plant Dis. Rept. 61:972-975.

111. Ribeiro, I.J.A., Ito, M.F., Parodela, F., Filho, O. and De

Castro, J.L. 1988. Gomose da acacia-negra causada por *Ceratocystis fimbriata* Ell. & Halst. Bragantia 47:71-74.

112. Roldan, E.F. 1925. The soft rot of pineapple in the Philippines and other countries. Philipp. Agric. 13:397-406.

113. Schieber, E. and Sosa, O.N. 1960. Cacao canker in Guatemala incited by *Ceratocystis fimbriata*. Plant Dis. Rep. 44:672.

114. Schreiber, L.R. and Townsend, L.M. 1981. Sources and genetics of host resistance in shade trees. Pages 413-429 in: Fungal Wilt Diseases of Plants. M.E. Mace, A.A. Bell and C.H. Beckman, eds. Academic Press. New York. 640 pp.

115. Sewell, G.W.F. and Wilson J.F. 1975. The role of *Thielaviopsis basicola* in the specific replant disorders of cherry and plum. Ann. Appl. Biol. 79:149-169.

116. Shanks, J.B. and Link, C.B. 1958. Cultural factors in the incidence of soil borne diseases of *Poinsettia*. Proc. Am. Soc. Hort. Sci. 71:522-536.

117. Sharples, A. 1936. Diseases and pests of the rubber tree. Pages 208-229. MacMillan, London.

118. Sinclair, W.A., Lyon, H. and Johnson, W.T. 1987. Diseases of trees and shrubs. Cornell University Press, Ithaca, London. 574 pp.

119. Smith, S.G. 1960. The influence of antagonistic fungi on *Thielaviopsis basicola*. Acta Bot. Neerl. 9:95-118.

120. Snyder, W.C., Trujillo, E.E., McOnie, K.C. and Berger, C.A. 1960. Trunk and branch canker of coffee trees in Guatemala. Plant Dis. Rep. 44:566-567

121. Staner, P. 1928. Belgian Congo. Some diseases of cultivated plants. Int. Bull. Plant Prot. 2:17.

122. Stanghellini, M.E. and Rasmussen, S.L. 1990. *Thielaviopsis* root rot of corn-salad. (Abstr.) Phytopathology 80:81.

123. Stover, R.H. 1950. The black root rot disease of tobacco. II. Physiologic specialisation of *Thielaviopsis basicola* on *Nicotiana tabacum*. Can. J. Res., Sect. C, 28:726-738.

124. Streets, R.B. 1933. Heart rot of the date palm caused by *Thielaviopsis paradoxa* (De Seynes) von Höhn. Ariz. Agric. Exp. Stn. Tech. Bull. 48:443-469.

125. Sundararaman, S., Krishnan Nayar, C. and Ramakrishnan, T.S. 1928. The stem-bleeding disease of arecanut (*Areca catechu*) caused by *Thielaviopsis paradoxa* von Höhn. Agric. Res. Inst. Pusa, Bull. 169. 12 pp.

126. Szkolnik, M. 1951. Coffee trunk and stem canker in Guatemala. Plant Dis. Rep. 35:500-501.

127. Tabachnik, M. and de Vay, J.E. 1980. Black root rot development in cotton roots caused by *Thielaviopsis basicola* and the possible role of methyl acetate in pathogenesis. Physiol. Plant Pathol. 16:109-117.

128. Taubenhaus, J. 1913. The black rots of the sweet potato. Phytopathology 3:159-166.

129. Taylor, P.W.J. and Ryan C.C. 1987. Assessment of prochloraz fungicide as a sett treatment for the control of pineapple disease of sugar cane. Plant Prot. Quart. 2:35-37.

130. Thorold, C.A. 1975. Diseases of cocoa. Clarendon Press, Oxford. 423 pp.

131. Tyron, E.H., Martin, J.P. and MacDonald, W.L. 1983. Natural regeneration in oak wilt centers. For. Ecol. Man. 7: 149-155.

132. Veldeman, R. 1971. "*Chalaropsis* sp." a new parasitic fungus on poplar, the cause of bark lesions. Med. Rijks. Land. Wetn. Gent 36:1001-1005.

133. Vigouroux, A. and Rouhani, H. 1987. Observation de sensibilities differentelles de quelques organes de *Platanus acerifolia* vis-a-vis de *Ceratocystis fimbriata f. platani*. Eur. J. For. Pathol. 17:181-184.

134. Vigouroux, A. and Stojadinovic, B. 1990. Possibilities d'infection du platane pour *Ceratocystis fimbriata f. platani* aprés contamination de l'eau ou se developpent des racines blessées. Eur. J. For. Pathol. 20:118-121.

135. Walker, J., Tesoriero, L., Pascoe, I. and Forsberg, L.I. 1988. Basal rot of *Syngonium* cultivars and the first record of *Ceratocystis fimbriata* from Australia. Australas. Plant Pathol. 17:22-23.

136. Walter, J.M. 1946. Canker stain of plane trees. USDA, Circular no. 742, 12 pp.

137. Walter, J.M., Mook, P.V. and May, C. 1940. Serious disease threatens the sycamore or plane tree. Arbor. News 5:49-55.

138. Walter, J.M., Rex, E.G. and Schreiber, R. 1952. The rate of progress and destructiveness of canker stain of planetrees. Phytopathology 42:236-239.

139. Waraitch, K.S. and Kumar, B. 1981. Relative behaviour of various sugarcane clones to *Ceratocystis paradoxa* (Dade) C. Moreau, causal organism of pineapple disease. Sugarcane Pathol. Newsl. 26:38-40.

140. Webster, R.K. and Butler, E.E. 1967. A morphological and biological concept of the species *Ceratocystis fimbriata*. Can. J. Bot. 45:1457-1468.

141. Went, F.A.F.C. 1896. Notes on sugar-cane diseases. Ann. Bot. 10:583-600.

142. Wick, R.L. and Moore, L.D. 1983. Histopathology of root disease incited by *Thielaviopsis basicola* in *Ilex crenata*. Phytopathology 73:561-564.

143. Wills, W.H. and Lambe, R.C. 1978. Pathogenicity of *Thielaviopsis basicola* from Japanese Holly (*Ilex crenata*) to some other host plants. Plant Dis. Rep. 62:1102-1106.

144. Wismer, C.A. 1951. Controlling pineapple disease of sugarcane. Hawaiian Planters' Rec. L111:23-53.

145. Wismer, C.A. 1961. Pineapple disease. Pages 224-245. in: Sugar cane diseases of the world. J.P. Martin, E.V. Abbott and C.G. Hughes, eds. Elsevier, New York.

146. Wismer, C.A. and Bailey, R.A. 1989. Pineapple disease. Pages 146-151 in: Diseases of sugar cane: Major diseases. C. Ricaud, B.T. Egan, A.G. Gillespie and C.G. Hughes, eds. Elsevier, New York. 410 pp.

147. Wood, F.A. and French, D.W. 1963. *Ceratocystis fimbriata*, the cause of a stem canker of quaking aspen. For. Sci. 9:232-235.

148. Yarwood, C.E. 1981. The occurrence of *Chalara elegans*. Mycologia 73:524-530.

149. Yarwood, C.E. and Karayiannis, I. 1974. *Thielaviopsis* may increase plant growth. Plant Dis. Rep. 58:490-492.

150. Zalasky, H. 1965. Process of *Ceratocystis fimbriata* infection in aspen. Can. J. Bot. 43:1157-1162.

151. Zimmerman, A. 1900. Über den Krebs von *Coffea arabica* verursacht *Rostrella coffeae* gen. et sp.n. Bull. Inst. Bot. Buitenzorg 4:19-22.

152. Zuckerman, B.M. 1954. Relation of type and age of wound to infection by *Endoconidiophora fagacearum* Bretz. Plant Dis. Rep. 38:290-292.

153. Zuluaga, V., Valencia, A.G. and Gonzalez, J. 1971. Contribucion al estudio de la naturaleza de la resistencia del cafeto a *Ceratocystis fimbriata* (Ell. Halst.) Hunt. Cenicafe 22:43-68.

Chapter 20

MEDICALLY IMPORTANT *SPOROTHRIX* SPECIES AND RELATED OPHIOSTOMATOID FUNGI

R.C. SUMMERBELL, J. KANE,
S. KRAJDEN and E.E. DUKE

INTRODUCTION

Species of *Ophiostoma* and related species known only as anamorphs (a group hereinafter referred to as 'ophiostomatoid' fungi, with that name used in a holomorphic, rather than a purely teleomorphic sense) include a single, prominent medically important member, *Sporothrix schenckii*. This paper will briefly discuss the etiology, pathology and treatment of human diseases caused by this fungus and will discuss the clinical significance of other morphologically similar *Sporothrix* species. The evidence regarding the proposed anamorph-teleomorph connection between *S. schenckii* and *Ophiostoma stenoceras* will also be reviewed and a case history of a possible *O. stenoceras* infection will be presented.

SPOROTHRIX SCHENKII

Sporothrix schenckii is one of the most important virulent, systemic fungal pathogens of humans. This relatively common, well-known species causes a variety of infections in humans. The most typical is a lymphocutaneous infection ('lymphocutaneous sporotrichosis') characterized by ulcerating, draining nodular lesions (37). Usually, such an infection follows a puncture wound or deep scratch involving soil or plant material bearing inoculum of the pathogen. The lesion initially appears as an indurated, non-painful subcutaneous nodule or as a superficial, suppurating ulcer. It may be accompanied by swelling of nearby lymph nodes. Healing of the primary lesion may occur but new subcutaneous nodules frequently appear nearby. In chronic cases, the combination of one or more subcutaneous nodules or suppurating ulcers with associated swollen lymph nodes is classic. In rare chronic cases, deep necrotic lesions reminiscent of gangrenous infection may develop (41).

Persons living in areas where *S. schenckii* is highly endemic, e.g., subtropical areas of Mexico, Argentina, Brazil, South Africa, Japan and Australia, not uncommonly develop single, localized sporotrichotic lesions after puncture or abrasion with contaminated plant material (37). These enduring lesions, which usually do not progress to further systemic infection, are referred to as 'fixed cutaneous sporotrichosis.'

More rarely, other sorts of sporotrichotic infections may occur, including a primary pulmonary infection predominantly affecting chronic alcoholics (37). This infection, unlike other types of sporotrichosis, is acquired by inhalation of conidia, often resulting from prolonged contact with debris or puddles on the ground. Aspiration of small quantities of contaminated soil or water may be a factor in this sort of infection. Other clinical manifestations of sporotrichosis have recently been reviewed (37).

Sporotrichosis has been recorded in numerous animal species, most commonly horses, dogs and cats (37). The disease usually occurs after traumatic implantation of inoculum, most likely from contaminated plant material, and resembles human lymphocutaneous or fixed cutaneous sporotrichosis. Dogs and cats are particularly susceptible to a general dissemination of the disease to the internal organs, generally with a fatal outcome (37).

Therapy for sporotrichosis has traditionally consisted of treatment with orally administered potassium iodide (KI). This is one of two fungal infections commonly treated with this compound. The other is entomophthoramycosis caused by *Basidiobolus*. The basis for the action of potassium iodide is unknown (37). Attempts to treat refractory cases of sporotrichosis with the standard antifungal antibiotics amphotericin B, 5-fluorocytosine and ketoconazole have met with mixed success (37) but the new agent itraconazole has shown much promise (4,36,49).

In tissue, *S. schenckii* is classically present in the form of yeast cells producing buds holoblastically from small denticles. Often, these yeasts are sparse in affected areas and are difficult to detect *in situ* unless special techniques, such as fluorescent antibody staining, are used (5,17). In some cases, depositions of eosinophilic host material in a stellate pattern around the yeast cells creates 'asteroid bodies' that are conspicuous when suitably stained (37). Hyphal elements rarely may be seen in sporotrichosis (21,23). The fungus is diagnosed in the laboratory by observation of its characteristic 'rosettes' of ovoid-apiculate, sympodially formed conidia in slide culture at 25°C and its conversion to the yeast phase on highly proteinaceous media, such as Difco Brain-Heart Infusion Agar superficially moistened with one or two drops of sterile 10% yeast extract. The presence of elongate 'cigar-shaped' buds arising on denticles is used to distinguish this yeast phase from potential contaminating yeast species.

Sporothrix schenckii is primarily associated with decaying plant material, particularly peat moss and various kinds of straw (37,47). Commercially processed peat moss has been responsible for extensive sporotrichosis outbreaks (9). Other materials associated with multiple cases of sporotrichosis include straw lined animal burrows, straw used commercially in basket weaving or as packing material, bromeliaceous (including pineapple) leaves in endemic sporotrichosis regions, fish scales, and various plant thorns (37, 47). Isolation from soil is not uncommon (37). Although *S. schenckii* is uncommon on decaying wood, it was reported to cause disease outbreaks in South African miners exposed to colonized mine timbers (10). In indoor environments, it may occur in such diverse habitats as potted plant soils (26) and damaged hospital intravenous fluid bottles (30). Other habitats and sources of infection arc summarized by Travassos and Lloyd (47) and Rippon (37).

Ophiostoma stenoceras (Robak) Nannf. and other species with anamorphs resembling *S. schenckii*

Ophiostoma stenoceras is infrequently seen in medical mycology laboratories (11) but may cause considerable confusion when isolated. Other closely related *Ophiostoma* and *Sporothrix* isolates may cause similar confusion (44). The nature of the relationship between *S. schenckii* and *O. stenoceras* has been debated for approximately 20 years. Mariat (27) greatly stimulated the debate in his studies of a *Ceratocystis* isolate (later revealed to be *O. stenoceras*) from scalp hair of a healthy African. This isolate, when inoculated into hamsters and reisolated from infected tissues, gave rise to isolates similar to classic *S. schenckii*. Although the original culture was pale and produced perithecia *in vitro*, the isolates from hamster tissues were dark-pigmented because of the

formation of typical *S. schenckii* secondary conidia and failed to reproduce sexually. Mariat suggested that the hamster isolates were mutants of the original and that *S. schenckii* might be an asexual variant of *O. stenoceras* that has adapted to pathogenicity.

Later studies have revealed that Mariat was almost certainly working with a mixed original culture. DNA extracted from a representative 'mutant' *S. schenckii* isolate showed 87% homology with reference *S. schenckii* DNA, while the purified *O. stenoceras* component of Mariat's original isolate showed only 30% homology (31). Also, mitochondrial restriction fragments of a 'mutant' isolate were compatible with *S. schenckii*, while those of the original were typical of *O. stenoceras* (43). Nonetheless, Mariat's experiments galvanized much useful research into the relationships between *Sporothrix, Ceratocystis,* and *Ophiostoma* species.

Morphological studies revealed that *S. schenckii* and the *Sporothrix* anamorph of *O. stenoceras* could not be separated by criteria such as conidial length (13). However, *O. stenoceras* lacks the pigmented, sessile secondary conidia possessed by most fresh isolates of *S. schenckii* (Fig. 1; 24,34). Other ophiostomatoid anamorphs resembling *S. schenckii* also lack dark secondary conidia and lack *S. schenckii*'s typical ability to degrade starch (44). The formation of perithecia has never been noted in *S. schenckii*, while *O. stenoceras* and some other *Ophiostoma* species often form perithecia *in vitro*. This does not occur on traditional medical mycology media (28) but does occur on many sporulation media such as wood macerate agars (28), dilute beer wort (28) or modified Leonian's agar (Summerbell, unpublished data). Finally, *Ophiostoma* species are nonpathogenic towards experimental animals (24).

In cases where *S. schenckii* is isolated from natural materials, non-pathogenic, non-perithecial isolates very similar to *S. schenckii* are also frequently obtained (24,28). These isolates, which do not fall within the circumscription of any currently well-characterized species, lack pigmented secondary conidia (24). In addition, their vitamin requirements may differ from *S. schenckii*'s characteristic requirement for thiamine (28,29). They may or may not convert to a yeast phase in protein-rich liquid media at 30-37°C, as both *S. schenckii* and *O. stenoceras* do (28). The exact affinities of these isolates are unknown and their identities constitute one of medical mycology's long-outstanding problems.

Further studies on the relationship between *S. schenckii* and *O. stenoceras* have revealed that *S. schenckii*, but not *O. stenoceras*, is able to resist

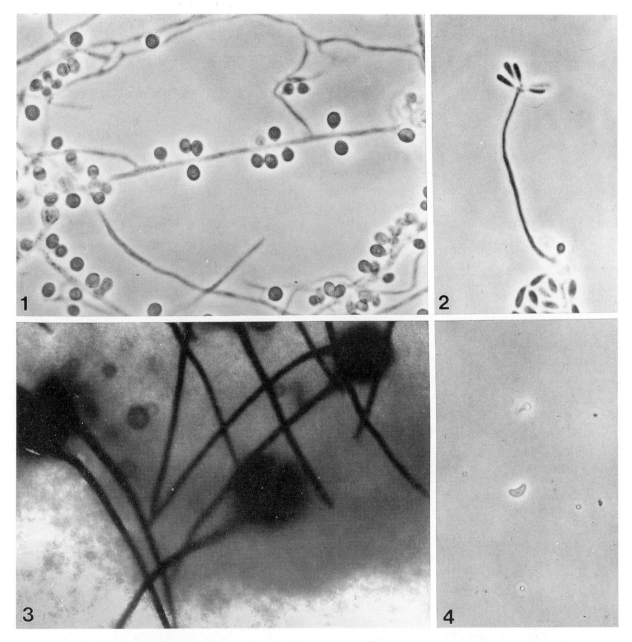

Figs. 1 - 4. *Sporothrix schenkii* and *Ophiostoma stenoceras*. Fig. 1. Pigmented secondary conidia of *Sporothrix schenckii*. (Phase contrast, 1050 x). Fig. 2. Sympodial 'rosette' of *Ophiostoma stenoceras* anamorphic state (Phase contrast, 1050 x). Fig. 3. Typical thick squash mount of *Ophiostoma stenoceras* ascomata immersed in a cloud of ascospores (150 x). Fig. 4. Orange-section-shaped ascospore of *Ophiostoma stenoceras* (Phase contrast, 1050 x).

digestion by macrophage cells of the mouse immune system (38). In terms of interaction with the humoral immune system, both species are similar. Indeed, a large number of *Ophiostoma* species cross-react significantly with *S. schenckii* in immunological studies (2,12,14,15,19,33,35). The rhamnomannan cell wall components, which act as major antigens for *S. schenckii*, cross-react with similar components of the *O. stenoceras* cell wall (22). The rhamnomannans of the two species are, however, chemically distinguishable, particularly when isolates grown at lower temperatures are examined (45,46). The relevant carbohydrate chemistry is comprehensively reviewed by Travassos and Lloyd (47). Quantitative studies of antigen/antibody precipitation indicate that *O. stenoceras* antigens are no more similar to *S. schenckii* antigens than are the antigens of several other rhamnomannan-producing *Ophiostoma* species (22). Antigens from ascomycetous *Sporothrix* species lacking rhamnose in the cell wall (50) cross-react only to a limited extent with *S. schenckii* (19).

Further biochemical studies on *S. schenckii* and *O. stenoceras* have shown that they are similar in neutral and polar lipid composition (7) but different in cellular carbohydrate composition (50) and in the acid phosphatase isoenzyme patterns of both mycelial and yeast phases (3).

Molecular genetic studies have had a great influence on our understanding of *S. schenckii* and related *Ophiostoma* species. The study of Mendonca-Hagler *et al.* (31) showed that *S. schenckii* DNA differs from that of several *Ophiostoma* species in guanine + cytosine content. The difference is significant but relatively slight. In DNA homology experiments (31), *S. schenckii* has a low level of binding affinity for *O. stenoceras* DNA (30% relative binding) but a relatively high (75%) affinity for the DNA of a representative isolate of *Ophiostoma minus* (=*Ceratocystis minor*). Such a degree of binding might be interpreted as an infraspecific, possibly varietal-level, degree of divergence in otherwise similar non-interbreeding fungi (8,20). However, the later restriction fragment study of Suzuki *et al.* (43) showed that mitochondrial DNA of *O. minus* differs considerably from that of *S. schenckii*. *Ophiostoma stenoceras* is distinguished from both species in mitochondrial DNA restriction fragment patterns.

Ophiostoma minus also differs profoundly in morphology and biology from *S. schenckii*. Its anamorph is not *Sporothrix* but rather *Hyalorhinocladiella* (48), and the species does not grow at 35-37°C *in vitro* (3,48). Taylor (44), anomalously, described a denticulate *O. minus* anamorph resembling a *Sporothrix* and capable of being cultivated in a yeast phase at 37°C. It is unlikely that the strain so described was a genuine representative of *O. minus*. Serological studies have shown that although *O. minus* cross-reacts strongly with *S. schenckii* in the exoantigen test (35), its purified rhamnomannan antigens react only weakly

with serum raised against *S. schenckii* cells grown at 25°C (47). *S. schenckii* rhamnomannans react strongly with the same serum. The multiple divergences between *S. schenckii* and *O. minus* suggest that the two organisms cannot be related at the infraspecific level. The DNA similarities observed by Mendonca-Hagler *et al.* (31) thus must be reevaluated in light of further work with additional isolates of *O. minus*.

OTHER *SPOROTHRIX* ISOLATES IN MEDICAL MYCOLOGY

Although typical *S. schenckii* is by far the most common *Sporothrix*-like fungus seen in the clinical laboratory, other similar fungi are seen on occasion. The most significant species are considered below.

Sporothrix schenckii var. *luriei* Ajello and Kaplan

The most medically important atypical *Sporothrix* is an unusual variant of *S. schenckii* described from South Africa by Ajello and Kaplan (1). *S. schenckii* var. *luriei* is an agent of sporotrichosis and is similar morphologically and antigenically to the type variety. It differs, however, in the production of inflated, irregular yeast-like cells in the tissue phase. These cells reproduce both by budding and by a process resembling fission (1,34). Unusual, sclerotium-like structures are produced by older colonies in pure culture (34).

S. schenckii var. *luriei* also differs from the type variety in failing to assimilate creatine, creatinine and guadinoacetic acid (40) and in possessing a mitochondrial restriction fragment profile dissimilar to all eleven types of profiles found among typical *S. schenckii* isolates (43). As has been suggested previously (40,43), it may deserve species status. It must be stated, however, that an anamorphic variety, a concept now supported as biologically meaningful by DNA relatedness studies (9,20), should be expected to possess a limited number of biochemical and genetic divergences from the type variety. Thus, any discussions of the species status of *S. schenckii* var. *luriei* may be premature when the degree to which it shares overall DNA homology with the type variety is unknown.

Ophiostoma piceae complex

Other ophiostomatoid anamorphs are occasionally isolated from medical specimens in our laboratory. These are probably common elsewhere as well, since they grow well on the cycloheximide-amended media used for selective isolation of many pathogenic fungi. They have not, however, been mentioned in medical mycology literature. Most common are *Ophiostoma piceae* and similar, synnema forming species. In our laboratory regimen, synnemata are regularly seen in fresh isolates subcultured on modified Leonian's agar (25), which we use as a general sporulation medium. Synnemata do not form on Sabouraud's peptone glucose agar, brain-heart infusion agar, or other protein-rich media traditionally used in medical mycology.

Ophiostoma piceae has been isolated from respiratory and dermatological samples. No link to infection has been found in the three isolations we have investigated to date. In the absence of synnemata, the anamorph is easily differentiated from *S. schenckii* by its elongate (8 - 15 µm) primary conidia and by the proliferative formation of secondary conidia from the primary conidia (8). In addition, our isolates failed to grow at 35-37°C, unlike all reported isolates of *S. schenckii*.

Sporothrix cyanescens de Hoog and de Vries

A *Sporothrix* species of non-ophiostomatoid affinity regularly seen from medical specimens is the basidiomycetous *S. cyanescens* (39). This fungus, which differs from *S. schenckii* by its cycloheximide sensitivity, benomyl tolerance, production of secondary conidia from the primary conidia and usual production of red to blue diffusing pigment, has been isolated from several cases suggestive of infection. Verification of pathogenicity has not been obtained and the fungus is non-pathogenic in normal and cortisone-treated mice (39). In our experience, Basidiomycetes are among the most abundant and pervasive contaminants seen in medical mycology laboratories. Like *S. cyanescens*, they tend as a group to be benomyl tolerant, an attribute that distinguishes them from most hyaline, medically-important molds with which they could be confused (Summerbell, unpublished data). Very few mycelial basidiomycetes have been isolated from well-documented infections (18).

Sporothrix cyanescens has recently been placed in the new genus *Cerinosterus* by Moore (32). This placement has been questioned by Sigler *et al.* (39), who noted that other members of Moore's genus are dacrymycetaceous anamorphs. *Sporothrix cyanescens*, with its simple dolipore septa lacking pore caps, has apparent affinities to members of the Filobasidiaceae or Ustilaginales. Sigler *et al.* (39) therefore opted to continue to use the name *S. cyanescens pro tem.*

PATHOGENICITY OF OPHIOSTOMATOID FUNGI OTHER THAN *S. SCHENCKII*

Some fungal species that do not cause marked infection in normal mice may nonetheless cause opportunistic human infections in certain circumstances, particularly in cases of immunosuppression (51). In the immunologically normal human, nail infections are commonly caused by normally nonpathogenic fungi (42). Although *O. stenoceras* and other ophiostomatoid fungi superficially resembling *S. schenckii* clearly differ from it biologically, the question of whether they may cause opportunistic infection is as yet unsettled. Most laboratories isolating such fungi from lesions would probably identify them as atypical isolates of *S. schenckii*. This might result either in: i) genuine infections caused by other ophiostomatoid fungi being falsely attributed to *S. schenckii* or ii) lesions without fungal etiology being treated as sporotrichosis because a contaminant resembling *S. schenckii* was isolated.

Animal studies with ophiostomatoid fungi other than *S. schenckii* have revealed that some isolates, usually members of the unclassified, non-perithecial, pale colored group, may produce persistent small abscesses in normal rodents (24, 28). Taylor (44) reported that several *Ceratocystis* species (now considered *Ophiostoma*) formed small, persistent lesions within the abdomens of intraperitoneally injected mice. Direct microscopy revealed the presence of typical yeast-phase cells. Species related to *S. schenckii* do not appear to have been tested in immunodepressed rodent models.

A human case suggestive of infection by O. stenoceras

We have recently observed a case of onychomycosis which was strongly suggestive of an *O. stenoceras* infection. Unfortunately for research purposes, a prompt cure of the infection prevented confirmatory re-isolation of the suspected agent. Nonetheless, the case is difficult to explain except as a valid infection and it is summarized here in the hope that it will stimulate critical observations of atypical *Sporothrix* isolations in other laboratories. It should be noted that in our own laboratory, an examination of records revealed several cases with features similar to the present one. In these cases, pale, atypical *S. schenckii*-like isolates were obtained from nails that were infested with fungal filaments but did not yield a dermatophyte or yeast.

In the current case, a 65-year-old woman presented with a 45-year history of recurrent inflammation of the base of the nails of both thumbs and the right middle finger. The infection was acquired during a period in 1943 when the patient was doing heavy manual labor in German forests and fields. An 'abscess' of one of the nails was drained in that year but the three involved nails have shown recurrent inflammation resembling a whitlow since that time. At the time of presentation, the infected nails were obviously disrupted and ridged, with some evidence of onycholysis. Also, an inflammation resembling paronychia, possibly caused by irritation of the nails, was evident.

The patient had no obvious risk factors for opportunistic infection; she was not diabetic and was not on steroidal or immunosuppressive treatment. She was, however, a relatively heavy alcohol user.

Nail scrapings sent for mycological analysis revealed the presence of fungal filaments. No evidence of yeast cells, conidia, or asteroid bodies was seen. A culture resembling *S. schenckii* was isolated, differing from typical isolates by pale coloration on Sabouraud agar, lack of secondary conidia and an unusually time-consuming (over 2 wk) and weak conversion to a yeast phase at 35 and 37°C on freshly prepared brain-heart infusion agar. A subculture on Leonian's agar had extensive dark areas and macroscopically resembled *S. schenckii*. The dark areas gave rise to perithecia typical of *O. stenoceras* after approximately 3 wk at 25°C.

Pending the results of mycological analysis, the infection was presumptively treated with Vioform Locacorten (Ciba-Geigy) drops, a combination of the iodine-based disinfectant pivalate-iodochlor hydroxyquin and the steroidal anti-inflammatory agent flumethasone. Application was one drop twice daily to the base and the end of each affected nail. Rapid improvement was seen, with near-complete resolution within one month. Upon follow up at 7 months, the nails appeared free of infection.

Because of the very rapid improvement, repeat culture was not attempted. Nor did the isolating laboratory preserve the original nail scrapings. Infection by *O. stenoceras*, therefore, cannot be definitively substantiated. However, the logical differential diagnosis, dermatophytosis, is rendered unlikely by a combination of circumstances. The first was the failure of the sample material to yield a dermatophyte, despite being obtained from a previously unmedicated, filament-positive lesion. Such failures do, however, occur in a minority of instances in samples taken from genuine dermatophyte infections.

The second and more intriguing factor was the rapid and apparently complete response to a topical iodine solution. Potassium iodide is a highly efficaceous, traditional therapeutic agent for sporotrichosis (37). Dermatophyte nail infections, especially persistent infections caused by anthropophilic dermatophytes such as *Trichophyton rubrum*, are notoriously resistant to all forms of treatment (37). Topical iodine disinfectants are considered ineffective against dermatophytic or non-dermatophytic agents of onychomycosis (42). On rare occasions, a therapeutic protocol has been attempted in which the patient is put on systemic griseofulvin therapy and affected nails are shaved paper-thin and painted with 1% iodine (16). In this case, the iodine is strictly an adjunct to the anti-dermatophytic griseofulvin.

The exclusive presence of hyphae in the putative *O. stenoceras* lesion is a feature that would not be expected in a typical *S. schenckii* lesion. *Sporothrix schenckii* forms filaments *in vivo* in some rodent models but only in necrotic lesions or in infections treated with griseofulvin or amphotericin B (29). There is no obvious explanation for the occasional report of an otherwise rather typical human *S. schenckii* infection, showing filaments in histological studies (21,23). Generally, *S. schenckii* grows in tissue as a yeast, sometimes attracting eosinophilic host materials in the form of an asteroid body (37). The yeast phase seen at 35-37°C *in vitro* is similar to the yeast in tissue. Our *O. stenoceras* isolate, however, was difficult to convert to a yeast phase and at best converted only partially. Indeed, most conidia germinated to form filaments at 35-37°C. Hence, we cannot rule out an *O. stenoceras* infection simply because yeast cells were not seen in ungual tissue. Further investigation of similar cases will be required to clarify the etiologic status of *O. stenoceras*.

CONCLUSIONS: DIFFERENTIATION OF *SPOROTHRIX SCHENCKII* AND OTHER OPHIO-STOMATOID FUNGI

Wherever atypical isolates resembling *S. schenckii* or *O. stenoceras* are obtained from infected skin or nails in the absence of classic signs of sporotrichosis, we recommend that detailed investigations be conducted in order to determine the etiologic and taxonomic status of the isolates. Also, isolates should be maintained for further study. (Our

O. stenoceras isolate is preserved in the University of Alberta Microfungus Collection and Herbarium as UAMH 6786.)

The taxonomic criteria currently available for rapid distinction of *S. schenckii* from *O. stenoceras* and unclassified, pale, non-pathogenic mimics should be an aid in this process. In brief synopsis, *S. schenckii* var. *schenckii* i) converts to a yeast phase at 35-37°C on protein-rich media such as brain-heart infusion agar; ii) requires thiamine but not biotin or other vitamins (29); iii) assimilates creatine and related compounds (40); iv) usually forms pigmented secondary conidia (Fig. 1) on inductive media such as corn meal agar (40), particularly when freshly isolated; v) fails to form perithecia or sclerotia on fungal sporulation media or media containing wood; and vi) manifests marked pathogenicity upon intraperitoneal injection into normal mice (24). *Ophiostoma stenoceras* may produce compressed sympodial 'rosettes' reminiscent of *S. schenckii* (Fig. 2), convert to a yeast phase, utilize creatine and related compounds and require thiamine, but will not form pigmented secondary conidia or evince strong pathogenicity towards normal rodents. In addition, on suitable media (see above), fresh isolates will reliably form characteristic perithecia (Fig. 3) with orange-segment shaped ascospores (Fig. 4) (6). Other ophiostomatoid isolates may differ from *S. schenckii* in any of the six characters mentioned above and those that grow at 35-37°C will reliably lack pigmented secondary conidia. In addition, they will lack *S. schenckii*'s characteristically strong animal pathogenicity.

ACKNOWLEDGEMENTS

The authors acknowledge the data collection efforts of Eleanor Leavitt and the valuable technical assistance of Maria Witkowska and Myrna de Castro. We thank Lynne Sigler and Dennis Dixon for providing useful information.

LITERATURE CITED

1. Ajello, L. and Kaplan, W. 1969. A new variant of *Sporothrix schenckii*. Mykosen 12:633-644.
2. Andrieu, S., Biguet, J. and Massamba, S. 1971. Étude immunologique comparée de *Sporothrix schenckii* et des souches saprophytes voisines. Sabouraudia 9:206-209.
3. Arnold, W.N., Mann, L.C., Coleman, P.D. and Garrison, R.G. 1987. Acid phosphatase isoenzyme patterns for *Sporothrix schenckii* and selected species of *Ceratocystis*. Microbios Lett. 34:143-146.
4. Baker, J.H., Goodpasture, H.C., Kuhns, H.R., Jr. and Rinaldi M.G. 1989. Fungemia caused by an amphotericin B resistant isolate of *Sporothrix schenckii*. Successful treatment with itraconazole. Archs. Pathol. 113:1279-1281.
5. Chuang, T.Y., Deng, J.S. *et al*. 1975. Rapid diagnosis of sporotrichosis by immunofluorescent methods. Chin. J. Microbiol. 8:259-261.
6. Davidson, R.W. 1942. Some additional species of *Ceratostomella* in the United States. Mycologia 34:650-662.
7. De Bieuvre, C. and Mariat, F. 1975. Composition en acides gras des lipides polaires et neutres de *Sporothrix schenckii* et de *Ceratocystis stenoceras*. Sabouraudia 13:226-230.
8. Ellis, J.J. 1989. An alignment of toxigenic *Gibberella* strains having anamorphs in Section *Liseola* of *Fusarium*. Mycologia 81:307-311.
9. England, T., Kasten M.J., Martin, R., Cote, T., Morse, D.L., David, R. and Davis, J.P. 1988. Multistate outbreak of sporotrichosis in seedling handlers, 1988. Mort. Morb. Wk. Rep. 37:652-653.
10. Findley, G.H. 1970. The epidemiology of sporotrichosis in the Transvaal. Sabouraudia 7:231-236.
11. Haines, J.H., Dixon, D.M., Salkin, I.F. 1989. A method for isolating ascospores of *Ophiostoma stenoceras*, the teleomorph of *Sporothrix schenckii*. Mycol. Soc. Am. Newsl. 40:30.
12. Harada, T., Nishikawa, T. and Hatano, H. 1976. Antigenic similarity between *Ceratocystis* species and *Sporothrix schenckii* as observed by immunofluorescence. Sabouraudia 14:211-215.
13. Hoog de, G.S. 1974. The genera *Blastobotrys, Sporothrix, Calcarisporium*, and *Calcarisporiella*, gen. nov. Stud. Mycol. 7:1-83.
14. Ishizaki, H., Nakamura, Y., Kariya, H., Iwatsu, T. and Wheat, R.W. 1976. Delayed hypersensitivity cross-reactions between *Sporothrix schenckii* and *Ceratocystis* species in sporotrichotic patients. J. Clin. Microbiol. 3:545-547.
15. Ishizaki, H., Wheat, R.W., Kiel, D.P. and Conant, N.F. 1978. Serological cross-reactivity among *Sporothrix schenckii, Ceratocystis, Europhium*, and *Graphium* species. Infect. Immunol. 21:585-593.
16. Jeremiasse, H.P. 1960. Treatment of nail infections with griseofulvin combined with abrasion. Trans. Rep. St. John's Hosp. Dermatol. Soc. (London) 45:92-93.
17. Kaplan, W. and Ivens, M.S. 1961. Fluorescent antibody staining of *Sporotrichum schenckii* in cultures and clinical material. J. Invest. Dermatol. 35:151-159.
18. Kern, M.E. and Uecker, F.A. 1986. Maxillary sinus infection caused by the homobasidiomycetous fungus *Schizophyllum commune*. J. Clin. Microbiol. 23:1001-1005.
19. Kurata, Y. 1981. Chemical composition and immunological properties of glycoproteins of *Sporothrix* species. Mycopathologia 76:45-53.
20. Kurtzman, C.P., Smiley, M.J., Robnett, C.J. and Wicklow, D.T. 1986. DNA relatedness among wild and domesticated species in the *Aspergillus flavus* group. Mycologia 78:955-959.
21. Lii, S.-L. and Shigemi, F. 1973. Demonstration of hyphae in human tissue of sporotrichosis, with statistics of cases reported from Tokushima. Tokushima J. Exp. Med. 20:69-92.

22. Lloyd, K.O. and Travassos, L.R. 1975. Immunochemical studies on L-rhamno-D-mannans of *Sporothrix schenckii* and related fungi by use of rabbit and human antisera. Carbohyd. Res. 40:89-97.

23. Maberry, J.D., Mullins, J.F. and Stone, O.J. 1966. Sporotrichosis with demonstration of hyphae in human tissue. Arch. Dermatol. 93:65-67.

24. Mackinnon, J.E., Conti Diaz, I.A., Gezuele, E., Civila, E., and Da Luz, S. 1969. Isolation of *Sporothrix schenckii* from nature and considerations on its pathogenicity and ecology. Sabouraudia 7:38-45.

25. Malloch, D. 1981. Moulds. Their isolation, cultivation, and identification. University of Toronto Press, Toronto, Ontario. 97 pp.

26. Mariat, F. 1968. The epidemiology of sporotrichosis. Pages 144-159 in: Systemic mycoses. G.E.W. Wolstenholme and R. Porter, eds. Churchill Publishing, London.

27. Mariat, F. 1971. Adaptation de *Ceratocystis* à la vie parasitaire chez l'animal—etude de l'acquisition d'un pouvoir pathogène comparable à celui de *Sporothrix schenckii*. Sabouraurdia 9:191-205.

28. Mariat, F. 1975. Observations sur l'écologie de *Sporothrix schenckii* et de *Ceratocystis stenoceras* en Corse et en Alsace, provinces françaises indemnes de sporotrichose. Sabouraurdia 13:217-225.

29. Mariat, F., Lavalle, P. and Destombes, P. 1962. Recherches sur la sporotrichose. Étude mycologique et pouvoir pathogène de souches mexicaines de *Sporotrichum schenckii*. Sabouraudia 2:60-79.

30. Matlow, A.G., Goldman, C.B., Mucklow, M.G. and Kane, J. 1985. Contamination of intravenous fluid with *Sporothrix schenckii*. J. Infect. Dis. 10:69-171.

31. Mendonca-Hagler, L.C., Travassos, L.R., Lloyd, K.O. and Phaff, H.J. 1974. Deoxyribonucleic acid base composition and hybridization studies on the human pathogen *Sporothrix schenckii* and *Ceratocystis* species. Infect. Immunol. 9:934-938.

32. Moore, R.T. 1987. Micromorphology of yeasts and yeast-like fungi and its taxonomic implications. Stud. Mycol. 30:203-226.

33. Nakamura, Y., Ishizaki, H. and Wheat, R.W. 1977. Serological cross-reactivity between group B *Streptococcus* and *Sporothrix schenckii*, *Ceratocystis* species, and *Graphium* species. Infect. Immunol. 16:547-549.

34. Nicot, J. and Mariat F. 1973. Characteres morphologiques et position systématique de *Sporothrix schenckii*, agent de la sporotrichose humaine. Mycopath. Mycol. Appl. 49:53-65.

35. Polonelli, L. and Morace, G. 1982. Exoantigen studies of *Sporothrix schenckii*, *Ceratocystis minor*, and *Graphium penicillioides* cultures. J. Clin. Microbiol. 15:362-365.

36. Restrepo, A., Robledo, J. and Gomez, I. 1986. Itraconazole therapy in lymphangitic and cutaneous sporotrichosis. Archs. Dermatol. 122:413-417.

37. Rippon, J.W. 1988. Medical mycology. The pathogenic fungi and the pathogenic actinomycetes. 3d ed. W. B. Saunders Co., Philadelphia. 797 pp.

38. Ryter, A. and Fromentin, H. 1985. Ultrastructural study of the interaction of the fungi *Sporothrix schenckii* and *Ceratocystis stenoceras* with bone-marrow-derived murine macrophages. Annls. Inst. Pasteur 136B:9-27.

39. Sigler, L., Harris, J.L., Dixon, D., Flis, A., Salkin, I.F., Kemna, M. and Duncan, R.A. 1990. Microbiology and potential virulence of *Sporothrix cyanescens*, a fungus rarely isolated from blood and skin. J. Clin. Microbiol. 28:1009-1015.

40. Staib, F. and Blisse A. 1974. Stellungnahme zu *Sporothrix schenckii* var. *luriei*. Ein Beitrag zum diagnostischen Wert der Assimilation von Kreatinin, Kreatin und Guanidinoessigsäure durch *Sporothrix schenckii*. Zbl. Bakt. Parasitkde., A 229:261-263.

41. Stroud, J.D. 1968. Sporotrichosis presenting as pyoderma gangrenosum. Archs. Dermatol. 97:667-670.

42. Summerbell, R.C., Kane, J. and Krajden, S. 1989. Onychomycosis, tinea pedis and tinea manuum caused by non-dermatophytic filamentous fungi. Mycoses 32:609-619.

43. Suzuki, K., Kawasaki, M. and Ishizaki, H. 1988. Analysis of restriction profiles of mitochondrial DNA from *Sporothrix schenckii* and related fungi. Mycopathologia 103:147-151.

44. Taylor, J.J. 1970. A comparison of some *Ceratocystis* species with *Sporothrix schenckii*. Mycopath. Mycol. Appl. 42:233-240.

45. Travassos, L.R., Gorin, P.A.J. and Lloyd, K.O. 1973. Comparison of the rhamnomannans from the human pathogen *Sporothrix schenckii* with those from *Ceratocystis* species. Infect. Immunol. 8:685-693.

46. Travassos, L.R., Gorin, P.A.J. and Lloyd, K.O. 1974. Discrimination between *Sporothrix schenckii* and *Ceratocystis stenoceras* rhamnomannans by proton and carbon-13 magnetic resonance spectroscopy. Infect. Immunol. 9:674-680.

47. Travassos, L.R. and Lloyd, K.O. 1980. *Sporothrix schenckii* and related species of *Ceratocystis*. Microbiol. Rev. 44:683-721.

48. Upadhyay, H.P. 1981. A monograph of *Ceratocystis* and *Ceratocystiopsis*. University of Georgia Press, Athens, GA. 176 pp.

49. Van Cutsem, J., Van Gerven, F. and Janssen, P.A.J. 1987. Activity of orally, topically and parenterally administered itraconazole in the treatment of superficial and deep mycosis:animal models. Rev. Infect. Dis. 9 (Suppl. 1): S15-S32.

50. Weijman, A.C.M. and de Hoog, G.S. 1985. Carbohydrate patterns and taxonomy of *Sporothrix* and *Blastobotrys*. Antonie van Leeuwenhoek 51:111-120.

51. Weitzman, I. 1986. Saprophytic molds as agents of cutaneous and subcutaneous infection in the immunocompromised host. Archs. Dermatol. 122:1161-1168.

PART IV

INSECT RELATIONS AND HOST RESPONSES

Chapter 21

DISPERSAL BIOLOGY OF THE OPHIOSTOMATOID FUNGI

D. MALLOCH and M. BLACKWELL

INTRODUCTION

The Ophiostomatales are generally recognized as Ascomycetes with long-necked perithecia, evanescent asci and hyaline ascospores lacking pores or slits. All of the species appear to be dispersed by arthropods. Beyond these generalizations there is little agreement.

The authors of chapters in the present volume do not uniformly agree on the taxonomic limits of the Ophiostomatales, nor even on whether the name should be accepted at all. These disagreements center on the relative taxonomic importance given to a variety of structural, ecological and biochemical features and will probably continue as long as such features are used as primary characters. Newer approaches to taxonomy and phylogeny, especially those utilizing molecular techniques, may lead to greater unanimity. Until this occurs, we prefer to avoid a clearly taxonomic bias in discussing the biology of these fungi and instead utilize the term "ophiostomatoid fungi." The ophiostomatoid fungi are those fungi that, regardless of their genetic relationships, fit the simple generalizations given above.

It has long been suspected or known that the ophiostomatoid fungi are dispersed by arthropods. It is difficult to determine who first suggested this; the connection between ambrosia beetles and fungi has been known since this system was described by Schmidberger in 1836 (64), although he did not recognize the ambrosia to be fungal. Although, as discussed below, not all ambrosia fungi are ophiostomatoid, some species of *Ophiostoma* appear to be involved in this symbiosis. Hartig (28) first recognized the ambrosial crusts to be fungi and later (29) described the association between a beetle and a bluestain fungus, clearly establishing the concept of insect dispersal in the ophiostomatoid fungi. In the twentieth century, the ophiostomatoid fungi became, along with the Phallales, the preferred examples for insect dispersal of fungi. In spite of this, insect dispersal is thought to be uncommon in fungi. Ingold (40), in his book on spore dispersal, stated that although there are some interesting examples of insect dispersal, fungi are largely wind-dispersed. The unexpected complexity of some insect associations in the ophiostomatoid and other fungi (49), as well as the variety of associates and mechanisms involved, suggests that this is untrue.

THE GENERA OF OPHIOSTOMATOID FUNGI AND THEIR LIFE CYCLES

The most familiar genera of ophiostomatoid fungi are *Ceratocystis* and *Ophiostoma*. These fungi are widely known because they are important crop or forest pathogens. There are, however, several other genera in this group, economically unimportant and thus neglected. Malloch and Blackwell (48) recognized 11 genera of ophiostomatoid fungi, noting that some of these may be synonymous. Each genus, and often the species within these genera, appear to have characteristic life cycles and all probably are dependent upon arthropods for their dispersal.

Ceratocystiopsis Upadhyay & Kendrick, Mycologia 67: 799. 1975.

Species of *Ceratocystiopsis* are mostly inhabitants of the tunnels and galleries of ambrosia and bark beetles in woody plants. They are characterized by relatively small ascomata, among the smallest of all ophiostomatoid fungi, and long, narrow ascospores. Anamorphs belong to the genera *Chalara*, *Hyalorhinocladiella*, *Knoxdaviesia*, *Sporothrix* and *Leptographium* (68,77). Current concepts in the ophiostomatoid fungi (for example, 38) suggest that the species with *Chalara* anamorphs belong elsewhere (see Wingfield this volume). Upadhyay (68) provided a key and descriptions of the species.

Reports on the dispersal of *Ceratocystiopsis* species are few. Hinds and Davidson (36) reported *C. retusi* from the larval chambers of *Typodendron retusum* (Scolytidae) in *Populus tremuloides* and isolated colonies of *C. crassivaginata* from young adults of this species. In his studies on aspen (*Populus tremuloides*) cankers, Hinds (34,35) found that *C. alba* and *C. crassivaginata* commonly occur on fresh wounds made in the stem of the tree and that the fungi are probably carried by several insects visiting these wounds. Because of difficulties in culturing *C. alba*, this species was not detected on cultures made from visiting insects but *C. crassivaginata* was found sparingly on nitidulid, rhizophagid and staphylinid beetles. In Hinds' (35) study, *C. alba* was the earliest of the ophiostomatoid fungi to appear on aspen wounds while *C. crassivaginata* was the latest (3-5 vs. 21 days). Hutchison and Reid (39) isolated *C. falcata* from bark beetle galleries in *Larix* sp. and *Pinus radiata* in New Zealand and stated that *Gliocladium roseum* stimulated perithecium production. Davidson (20) and Griffin (26) reported *C. minuta-bicolor* and *C. minuta* respectively from tunnels of *Ips* species. Moser *et al.* (53) tentatively identified ascospores of *C. minuta* from several mites phoretic on adults of *Ips typographus* (Scolytidae) captured in Sweden. Biel *et al.* (5) reported *Ceratocystis minor* var. *barrasii* to occur in the mycangia of *Dendroctonis frontalis* (Scolytidae) and to grow there as a yeast. According to Harrington and Zambino (31) this fungus is actually *Ceratocystiopsis ranaculosus*. These latter two records are the only ones reporting the direct observation of species of this genus on their vectors.

Ceratocystiopsis proteae is known only from flowers within inflorescences of *Protea repens* in South Africa (77). Although spores have not been observed attached to arthropods, the flowers of this plant become highly infested with a variety of insects and it is likely that some of them serve as vectors for the fungus.

Ceratocystis Ellis & Halstead, N.J. Agr. Exp. Sta. Bull. 97: 14. 1890.

In the restricted sense (38), *Ceratocystis* includes a few species having *Chalara*, *Chalaropsis* and *Thielaviopsis* anamorphs. The species are most frequently reported from habitats other than beetle galleries, such as herbaceous plants, rotting fruits, tree wounds, soil, etc. Nevertheless, a number of well-documented insect associations have been reported, particularly with the Nitidulidae.

Chang and Jensen (16) studied the dispersal of *C. paradoxa* by the nitidulids *Urophorus humeralis*, *Carpophilus hemipterus*, and *Haptoncus ocularis* in Hawaii. Field-trapped individuals of the three species were sealed into sugar cane stalks and disease incidence was assessed after 7 days. The transmission rate of the disease was 80, 75 and 55% for the three species respectively. *Urophorus humeralis*, the largest of the three beetles had the highest transmission rate, probably because of its larger size. Of artificially wounded stalks, 29.9% developed the disease in the field and 55% of these contained nitidulids or indications of their activities. No nitidulids were found in uninfected stalks. Feces from the beetles contained spores of the pathogen but the fungus apparently was not viable and could neither be cultured nor would it cause infection of the host. The results suggest that transmission of the disease is by spores on the surface of the vector.

To examine the efficiency of vectoring, beetles collected from diseased stalks were transferred to uninfected stalks serially at either 2 minute intervals or 24 hour intervals. The maximum number of disease transmissions was found to be 11 to 13, regardless of the length of the time intervals. Those transferred every 24 hours continued to transmit the disease for up to 12 days as compared to 26 minutes for the 2 minute group. Half of the beetles left in wounds for 24 hours made only four transmissions whereas those in wounds for 2 minutes made six transmissions. When larvae and adults were reared on 1) the fungus, 2) sugar cane juice, or 3) a combination of the two, the combination treatment yielded earlier pupation, higher percentage of pupation, and greater pupal weight. Clearly fungus and plant are both important to insect development. Traps baited with diseased stalks caught 9 times as many nitidulids as those baited with uninfected stalks. It is not clear whether ascospores or conidia were involved in the transmissions, although a photograph of a fecal sample showed only conidia.

Hinds (34,35) captured insects visiting wounds on *Populus tremuloides* in Colorado and allowed them to crawl over the surface of agar media in Petri dishes. Many of these carried *C. fimbriata*, a causative agent of aspen canker, as well as the non-pathogenic *C. moniliformis*. Both species were also recovered from surface-sterilized insects. Several orders and families of insects served as carriers for these species, including beetles, flies, aphids and moths, although the principal carriers were beetles of the families Nitidulidae, Staphylinidae and Rhizophagidae. *C. moniliformis* turned the sapwood pink then blue-black. The infected wounds emitted a strong ester odor typical of the two *Ceratocystis* species in pure culture. Both species appeared early in the succession of fungi on wounded trees (within a week). Hinds' observations suggest that these fungi are not highly selective in their arthropod vectors other than associating with populations of sap-feeding insects. The production of bright colors and fruity odors in these and other species of *Ceratocystis* (30) appears to reinforce attractants produced by the wounded host plant. Both species are also known from herbaceous plants and may not be strongly host-specific, although Hinds (34) found that an isolate of *C. fimbriata* from yams was not highly virulent in causing cankers on aspen. Nevertheless, the yam isolate grew for at least two years on aspen.

Juzwick and French (41), studying oak wilt caused by *C. fagacearum*, trapped nitidulid beetles and attempted to isolate the fungus from them. Success rate was low; only seven of 1043 beetles trapped actually carried the fungus. However, the spores of *C. fagacearum* were able to adhere to the beetles. Of 98 beetles collected from mats of the fungus, 80 yielded colonies of the fungus. Beetles carrying *C. fagacearum* also carried *Ophiostoma piceae*. These authors agreed with Gibbs (23) that *O. piceae* may serve as an effective competitor to *C. fagacearum*. Observations by Ruetze and Parameswaran (62) also supported this hypothesis.

Kathistes Malloch & Blackwell, Can. J. Bot. 68: 1712-1721. 1990.

Kathistes is a genus of coprophilous fungi characterized by small, long-necked perithecia bearing basally arranged clavate asci. The ascospores are hyaline, septate and germinate by yeast-like budding rather than the production of germ tubes. We have observed two species of *Kathistes* on a natural substrate and isolated them in pure culture (48). Both grew as yeasts and produced only a few hyphae. Ascospores have been seen attached to the bodies of phoretic mites and these may have developed a short foot-like attachment structure, although it is difficult to confirm this. Small pycnidium-like structures termed *sporidiomata* often accompany the ascomata on natural substrates but their function and arthropod associations are unclear.

The life cycle of *Kathistes* species is poorly understood. The ascomata appear on dung 3-4 weeks after deposition and often develop in areas of intense insect activity, especially those disturbed by larval Diptera. Maturation is later than that of most other fungi dispersed by phoretic coprophilous mites. However, the ascomata are very small, suggesting, as discussed below, that mites are likely vectors. Ascomata developing on dung in the field have never been observed; in all instances these have developed in moist chambers maintained in the laboratory.

Klasterskya Petrak, Ann. Mycol. 38: 227. 1940.

The genus *Klasterskya* is characterized by long-necked, dark ascomata bearing basally arranged asci. The ascospores are hyaline, two-celled and may have a narrow gelatinous sheath. Ascospore germination appears to occur by the production of short conidiogenous cells directly from the ascospore (50). According to Petrak (58), the type species, *K. acuum*, occurs on needles of fallen branches of *Pinus* and *Abies* spp. in the spring immediately after they are uncovered by melting snow. Minter (50) reports this species to grow on the needles in association with apothecia of *Dasyscyphus acuum*. Valldosera and Guarro (71) added two coprophilous species to *Klasterskya, K. coronata* and *K. crenata*. No information is available on the biology of any of the species of *Klasterskya* but the long-necked ascomata and evanescent asci suggest that arthropods are involved in their dispersal.

Ophiostoma H. Sydow & P. Sydow, Ann. Mycol. 17:43. 1919.

The largest genus of ophiostomatoid fungi, *Ophiostoma* is characterized by dark, usually long-necked ascomata bearing uniformly disposed asci. The ascospores are unicellular and usually provided with a gelatinous sheath. *Ophiostoma* species produce a rich array of anamorphs, often several within one species, but these are never endophialidic as in the *Chalara* anamorphs of *Ceratocystis* species. Most species of *Ophiostoma* are reported to be inhabitants of living or recently dead wood, especially within the tunnels and galleries of wood- and bark-boring beetles (Scolytidae, Platypodidae). The similarities between species of *Ophiostoma* and some of the ambrosia fungi "cultivated" and consumed by ambrosia beetles (Scolytidae, Platypodidae) have not gone unnoticed. Neger (55) even suggested that the ambrosia were "adaptive forms" of *Ophiostoma* species. While some authors (61) have included species of *Ophiostoma, Ceratocystis*, and other ophiostomatoid forms in the same family (Endomycetaceae) as some ambrosia fungi, including *Ascoidea* and *Hansenula*, there is no general agreement on the relationships between *Ophiostoma* species and ambrosia fungi (see Kendrick *et al.*, this volume). On the other hand, some species of *Ophiostoma* appear actually to serve as ambrosia fungi (4,22) and to be selectively maintained in the mycangia of bark- and ambrosia beetles (3). Even those species that are not ambrosia fungi, such as the bluestain organisms, may be beneficial and symbiotic with the beetles that serve as their vectors (13,22,73). Paine and Birch (56) found that spores of *O.*

nigrocarpum required eight to ten days to develop in the mycangium of *Dendroctonus brevicomus* (Scolytidae) and that these beetles delayed invading a new host for this very period. *Ophiostoma* species are frequent associates of ambrosia fungi. For example, Hinds and Davidson (36) found three species of *Ophiostoma* occurring in ambrosia galleries of *Typodendron retusum* (Scolytidae) in *Populus tremuloides*. *Ophiostoma* species are not the only fungal inhabitants of ambrosia galleries. In fact, these galleries are the site of complex microbial and insect interactions. Webber (72) and Crowson (19) both discussed a species of *Phomopsis* that is apparently a strong competitor to *Rhinosimus ruficollis* (Salpingidae), a vector of *O. ulmi*, which thus may affect populations of this fungus. However, there is no evidence that the *Phomopsis* is dispersed in the mycangia of *R. ruficollis* (Webber, personal communication).

Details of life cycle events in *Ophiostoma* species are remarkably few, considering the amount of time and money spent on them. Most studies have concentrated on *O. ulmi* and have been more epidemiological than ecological. Although *O. ulmi* may not be a typical species of *Ophiostoma*, what is known about it may be fairly representative of many others. It occurs in the tunnels of elm bark beetles in the Old World and has been introduced into the New World. It is associated with and dispersed by the bark beetles *Scolytus* spp. and, in North America, *Hylurgopinus rufipes* (all Scolytidae). It produces perithecia and synnemata within the beetle tunnels and depends upon the latter for local dissemination and perhaps fertilization as well (11). In *in vitro* experiments, Brasier (11) found that the mite *Tyrophagus putriscentiae* (Acaridida: Acaridae), isolated from beetle galleries in elm, ate the mycelium but left perithecia of *O. ulmi* undamaged. Microscopic examination of mites from diseased elm bark showed many conidia and some ascospores of the fungus. However, mites disperse not only *O. ulmi*; Doberski (21) discovered that diseases of the bark beetles were also spread by mites. Dispersal between elm trees may be through consumed spores in the beetle's gut or those borne externally, but not by means of mycangia, as elm scolytids apparently do not have mycangia (73). Leach *et al.* (43) had earlier demonstrated that ascospores of *O. ips* could survive passage through the gut of *Ips pini* Say and *I. gradicollis* (Scolytidae).

The role of mites in the life histories of *Ophiostoma* spp. is not restricted to local dispersal. Bridges and Moser (12) investigated the mite dispersal of *O. minus* associated with the southern pine beetle *Dendroctonus frontalis* (Scolytidae). Although this beetle is known to act as a vector of *O. minus*, it was not known how the beetle disseminated the fungus since it does not occur in the mycangium of the beetles. In fact, Moser and Bridges (52) found that *D. frontalis* produces larvae that leave the galleries and pupate in the outer bark. By doing so, the emerging adults do not come in contact with the fungus developing in the galleries. As early as 1949, however, Hetrick (33) suggested that phoretic mites could be instrumental in the transfer of the fungus. Later it was found that the mites *Tarsonemus krantzi* and *T. ips* (Acariformes: Tarsonemidae) are phoretic on the beetles and have sporothecae in which they carry ascospores of the fungus (51). Before the adult beetles leave the tree, they acquire a load of phoretic *Tarsonemus* individuals with fungus-filled sporothecae. The mites attached to the beetles in different locations, *T. ips* only under the thorax and *T. krantzi* under the elytra. Between 85 and 88% of all mites bore spores of the fungus and these carried an average of 18 spores/mite. Moreover, beetles with mites had significantly more fungus than did mite-free beetles. It was concluded that these mites were equally effective as vectors of *O. minus*.

Moser *et al.* (53) removed phoretic mites from adults of *Ips typographus* (Scolytidae) trapped in Sweden and found that 85% of the individuals examined carried ascospores. The most common of these were of *Ophiostoma* spp. Levieux *et al.* (44) carried out similar studies in France and also demonstrated phoretic mites to be major vectors of *Ophiostoma* spp. They found more spore types attached to the mites than to the beetles and that the mites were more uniformly covered with spores.

Insects can also form galleries in tree roots. These galleries may become inhabited by ophiostomatoid fungi at depths to 100 cm below the soil surface. Goheen and Cobb (24) studied *O. wageneri* in roots and found that it was dispersed by beetles of the families Buprestidae and Cerambycidae as well as Scolytidae.

The occurrence of *Ophiostoma* species in insect tunnels is common but the economic significance of this may be such that it has distracted mycological attention from other interesting habitats. *Ophiostoma narcissi* causes head rot of *Narcissus* (45,54) and may be dispersed locally and between plants by bulb flies and mites. *Ophiostoma stenoceras* occurs on dead wood and in insect tunnels (38, Summerbell *et al.*, this volume) but also is commonly reported from human infections. It is probably dispersed by arthropods in the insect tunnel habitat but human infections must have some other route, possibly direct inoculation from infected plant material. *Ophiostoma epigloeum* is related to *Ophiostoma stenoceras* (38) and is apparently confined to basidiomata of *Tremella fuciformis* (27). R.G. Thorn (personal communication) discovered that ascomata of this species can be found commonly on basidiomata of *T. fuciformis* imported from China and sold in grocery stores in Toronto. Ascomata were observed only on basidiomata collected on natural substrate and not on those that appear to have been cultivated. The dispersing agent is unknown, but could be one of several fungivorous insects. Lacy (42), for example, reported collecting *Drosophila chargrinensis* (Diptera: Drosophilidae) from a species of *Tremella* in New York. Indeed, some insects have mouthparts specialized for feeding on the hymenial surfaces of basidiomycetes (1) and undoubtedly come into contact with parasitic fungi. The parasitic association of *Ophiostoma* species with other fungi is rarely discussed. However, Hutchison and Reid (39) reported *O. piceae*, a species related to *O. epigloeum*, to be stimulated to produce ascomata in culture by the presence of an *Aspergillus* species. The nutritional relationship between *Ophiostoma* and other fungi in insect tunnels is still unclear but their co-occurrence is often reported. It is interesting in this regard that *O. piceae* has been found to be an aggressive competitor to *Ceratocystis fagacearum* (23,41,62). Perhaps the semiparasitic relationships with other fungi suspected in some ophiostomatoid fungi extend to species of *Ophiostoma*.

Pyxidiophora Bref. & Tav., Unters. Gesamptgeb. Mykol. 10: 189. 1891.

Possibly a large genus of ophiostomatoid fungi, *Pyxidiophora* remains largely unexplored. The species are characterized by mostly long-necked, partly to wholly hyaline ascomata bearing a basal cluster of asci. The ascospores are initially two-celled and provided with a sheath-like outer membrane and a dark melanized area on the upper cell when mature. Ascospore germination is initially repetitive in some species.

The life cycles of most species of *Pyxidiophora* are unknown but it appears that there is a considerable amount of structural variation among them. Unfortunately, the least variable feature among species appears to be the teleomorph, the form most often described and preserved to the exclusion of all others. Because our knowledge of *Pyxidiophora* is mostly restricted to immature and taxonomically transparent structures, the taxonomy of the genus is in disarray. Currently the species that has been most thoroughly explored biologically (8) cannot be named reliably because its teleomorph resembles those of the holotypes of no fewer than three different species. Without details from the life cycles of these three named species, it is impossible at present to know whether they represent three distinct taxa or are, in fact, synonymous with each other and with the species we have studied.

The *Pyxidiophora* species reported in our study (8) occurs commonly on moose dung in eastern Canada. It is found on dung less than a week old and is generally recognized by the production of clusters of synnemata and later ascomata on parasitized apothecia of *Lasiobolus* spp. (Pezizales) (see Blackwell, *et al.*, this volume). We assume it is mycoparasitic not only because of our observations but also because of several other reports of mycoparasitism in the genus (18,67,74). It is quite likely that all species of *Pyxidiophora* will be discovered to be mycoparasites (7). During the time that the synnemata are producing conidia, nymphal stages of macrochelid and parasitid mites can be observed running rapidly over the dung in search of prey (probably nematodes and other mites). The conidia can be found attached to these mites and are probably spread around the substrate by them. When the mites enter the last stage of development before dispersal, the ascomata mature and contaminate them with ascospores. These ascospores become firmly attached to the mites by means of a melanized region at the spore apex and later perhaps by a haustorium. Concomitantly with this last event, the adult stages of coprophilous beetles (Histeridae, Scarabidae, Staphylinidae and others) and flies (Sciaridae, Mycetophilidae, Tipulidae, etc.) emerge from their pupae and within a few minutes leave the dung pile for a newer one. At this precise moment of ascospore extrusion, mite maturity and insect emergence, the mites move onto the emerging insects and fasten themselves there. They do not leave the insect until arrival at the new substrate.

During the time that the ascospores are attached to the mite, they begin to differentiate into spore-bearing thalli. These thalli may be only few-celled and produce just a few conidia or they may become large and complex and produce many conidia. This size difference may be determined by the success of the ascospore in establishing a productive haustorium. When the mite is finally carried to a new substrate, the fungus has produced multiple conidia and is probably spread over a considerable area. These conidia germinate to produce a simple mononematous anamorph or they may bud and remain yeast-like. At this stage, the developing apothecia of *Lasiobolus* are probably infected and the synnemata can begin to form.

The remarkably complex life cycle of *Pyxidiophora* involves at least five separate spore types and two distinct substrates, the host fungus and the host mite. *P. spinuliformis*, has a teleomorph similar to that of *Pyxidiophora* sp. but with very different anamorphs (8). We examined other species of *Pyxidiophora* on moose and deer dung and found that they are also distinct in their development.

Although our work has concentrated on coprophilous species, it is clear that species of *Pyxidiophora* occur on different substrates as well. Blackwell *et al.* (6,10) have described a life cycle for *Pyxidiophora kimbroughi* occurring in bark beetle (Scolytidae) galleries in Louisiana and later (9) demonstrated that bark beetles worldwide carry a great variety of *Pyxidiophora* ascospores representing a considerable number of species. Moser *et al.* (53) sampled mites phoretic on *Ips typographus* and found *Pyxidiophora* ascospores to be among the most common. *Pyxidiophora* species are reported from a number of different habitats including fleshy fungi (67), stored grain (18) and submerged branches (74).

Rhynchonectria Höhnel, Sitzungsb. K. Akad. Wiss. Wien, math.-nat. Kl., 1. Abt., 111: 1023. 1902.

Eleutheromyces longispora was originally described as a parasite of myxomycetes. Höhnel (37) transferred it as the type of *Rhynchonectria* because *Eleutheromyces* is a genus of coelomycetes. It may be close to *Pyxidiophora* but Malloch and Blackwell (48) rejected the name on the basis of its confusing diagnosis and lack of authentic material. Nothing is known of its biology.

Sphaeronaemella Karsten, Hedwigia 23: 17. 1884.

Species of *Sphaeronaemella* are common mycoparasites occurring in a variety of habitats. They are characterized by hyaline, long-necked perithecia bearing uniformly distributed asci. The ascospores are unicellular and lack gelatinous appendages. In spite of their common occurrence and the attention they have received from mycologists, they are still poorly understood. Although generally recognized as mycoparasites, there is little agreement on the degree of host specificity. The type species, *S. helvellae*, for

example, is most commonly found on *Gyromitra infula* and *G. ambigua* and is found on *Pseudorhizina sphaerospora* (Helvellaceae) (59), but it also has been reported as parasitic on fungi rotting the insides of cornstalks (60,69,70). *Sphaeronaemella fimicola* is generally known as a coprophilous species, parasitic on other coprophilous fungi (14), yet Pease (57) reported it from fruits of the Cucurbitaceae and Hutchison and Reid (39) found it in beetle galleries on pine in New Zealand. It is not known whether these anomalies are due to taxonomic confusion or wide host ranges.

There is still little known about the dispersal of *Sphaeronaemella* species. The anamorphs are invariably assignable to *Gabarnaudia* (63). In *S. fimicola*, we have observed that the anamorph appears on fresh dung within two or three days of deposition and precedes the appearance of the ascomata. The conidia are produced from phialides in long curved chains that may extend 200 micrometers or more above the surface of the substrate. The conidia are easily detached and will adhere to most objects that contact them, including dissecting needles and pieces of glass. It is likely that these conidia are spread over the surface of the substrate by mites: in fact, we have often observed them attached to immature mites along with conidia of *Pyxidiophora* species. The conidia germinate easily and colony growth is relatively rapid, suggesting that this species is capable of occupying large areas of substrate before most of the other coprophilous community has become established. The conidia are also capable of germination by repetition, whereby germinating conidia give rise directly to small secondary phialides producing rod-shaped conidia (63). We have observed relatively large pieces of deer dung entirely covered with conidiophores of *S. fimicola* while still lying in the field. This *in vivo* observation of *S. fimicola* contrasts with largely *in vitro* appearances of *Pyxidiophora* species.

Perithecial production in *S. fimicola* follows the maturation of conidia. We have found that perithecia occur among the masses of conidia and extend their spore-bearing necks several hundred micrometers above the conidia. The ascospores are borne in masses that are not dispersed in water and possibly do not separate until encountering specific chemical conditions of the new substrate surface.

Dispersal events are unknown in other species of *Sphaeronaemella*. Malloch (47) suggested that *S. helvellae* might be dispersed by an insect specific to the *Gyromitra* species it parasitizes but offered no evidence for this. The introduction of *S. helvellae* into rotting cornstalks in the system described by Vakili (69) could occur at the leaf bases as it apparently does with the rot organisms. Introduction of both *S. helvellae* and pathogenic fungi may be mediated by insects, but this possibility remains unsubstantiated.

Spumatoria Massee & Salmon, Ann. Bot. p. 350. 1901.

Spumatoria longicollis, the type species of the monotypic genus, was described from fresh horse dung in England. The perithecia are dark, long-necked and bear a basal paraphysate cluster of cylindrical asci. The ascospores are two-celled and measure 15-19 x 5 μm. The genus may be close to *Klasterskya* or *Kathistes* but the type culture of *S. longicollis* has been lost and the species never again reported (48).

Subbaromyces Hesseltine, Bull. Torrey Bot. Club 80: 511. 1953.

Subbaromyces splendens is the only known species of *Subbaromyces*. It is characterized by dark, long-necked perithecia bearing a basal cluster of asci. The ascospores are two-celled and have a gelatinous sheath. It also produces large holoblastic conidia. The only reports of this species to date describe its occurrence on sewage filters and water. It appears to be aquatic or semiaquatic and can be grown on hemp seed in water (17). Hesseltine (32) reported *S. splendens* to grow and sporulate best in the presence of other fungi or bacteria. Williams (76) found that it was able to grow under nearly anaerobic conditions and confirmed that the presence of bacteria was necessary for maximum growth. Gray (25) reported it to be the most common cause of fouling in sewage filters in the U.K. According to Gray (25), it is most abundant in autumn and early winter in Ireland and not very abundant or absent during the warmer months. Macrograzers (unspecified) did not appear to adversely affect *S. splendens*; in fact, the species was best able to compete with bacteria at times of high macrograzer activity. Nothing is known of the natural habitat of *S. splendens* nor how it is dispersed.

Treleasia Spegazzini, Reg. Fac. Agr. Vet. La Plata 18: 235. 1896.

Two species of *Treleasia* are known: *T. sacchari* and *T. musicola*. They are only known from the type collections on decaying leaves of sugar cane and banana respectively. Apparently, type material is no longer available (46). *Treleasia* species are difficult to separate from those of *Pyxidiophora* or *Kathistes* solely on the basis of earlier studies. Malloch and Blackwell (48) included them in their key to the ophiostomatoid fungi but separated them from *Pyxidiophora* and *Kathistes* on the assumption that they lacked the characteristic features of these two genera; however, Lundqvist (46) suggested that *Treleasia* is congeneric with *Pyxidiophora*.

ADAPTATIONS FOR ARTHROPOD DISPERSAL

Ascomata

The ophiostomatoid fungi differ considerably from one another in the structure of their ascomata. These differences probably reflect details in life histories, particularly those involving dispersal. Although the significance of most differences is unknown, some deserve attention.

Ascomatal color

Many ophiostomatoid fungi occur in covered situations where protection from solar radiation is unnecessary. In spite of this, many produce highly melanized ascomata and conidiophores. By definition, the ophiostomatoid fungi should have long perithecial necks but some clearly related species have very short necks or are even cleistothecial. As noted above, Brasier (11) found that the mite *Tyrophagus putriscentiae* ate the mycelium of *Ophiostoma ulmi* but left perithecia undamaged. Although seldom reported, empty dark ascomata of ophiostomatoid fungi are common in nature and seem to be relatively immune to grazing. Pale or hyaline ascomata seem to be much more evanescent and are rarely found after maturity. Although it is difficult to document, it appears that rapidly-sporulating, early-successional species, such as those of *Pyxidiophora* and *Sphaeronaemella*, tend to lack large amounts of melanin pigments in their perithecia and avoid predation by rapid development rather than chemical defense. It is interesting in this regard that Hinds (35) reported *Ceratocystiopsis alba* to be the earliest ophiostomatoid fungus in the succession on aspen wood as well as the earliest to disappear. Most species of *Ceratocystiopsis* have black ascomata but those of *C. alba* are nearly colorless.

Ascomatal height

Most authors describe the ophiostomatoid fungi as having great variation in perithecial neck length. While this is certainly so, the variation of any particular species hardly encompasses that of the entire group. For example, *Ophiostoma ulmi* is described as having necks 100 to 350 μm long (68). The variation here is indeed great but other species also can have quite different dimensions. *Ophiostoma bicolor* has necks 470 to 1400 μm long while those of *O. minus* are only 55 to 160 μm long. Some species lack necks altogether. Since the significance of height to dispersal is probably best measured by the height of the spore drop above the substrate, neck length alone can be misleading. *Ophiostoma clavigerum* lacks a neck yet has ascomata up to 650 μm in diameter. *Ophiostoma minus* has an entire ascoma, including neck, only up to 270 μm high. The extremes range from a mean height of 95 μm in *Ceratocystiopsis pallidobrunnea* to 3500 μm in *Ceratocystis adiposa* (68). Our observations on coprophilous ophiostomatoid fungi suggest that ascomatal height is important in determining how the spores will be dispersed. In these systems, *Pyxidiophora* species having ascomata 300-500 μm high commonly have their spore masses removed by mites. We found (8) that macrochelid mites on dung often carried more spores of *Pyxidiophora* sp. than parasitid mites and suggested that these differences might be due to slight differences in posture or behavior between these two co-occurring mites. The macrochelids had a slightly higher posture when running over the dung surface and slightly delayed phoretic behavior when compared with parasitid mites. We have observed some ascospores of *Pyxidiophora* spp. only on the tarsi of mites while other species occur most commonly on the palps. *Sphaeronaemella fimicola* produces larger ascomata having the spore mass at a mean height of about 1000 μm. These spores are produced well above the largest mites and are likely to attach mainly to insects or to mites having specific behavior patterns. Thus, even though species of *Pyxidiophora* and *Sphaeronaemella* can fruit at the same time, there is probably little competition for vectors.

The influence of ascomatal height on dispersal has not been studied in detail for other genera (but see chapter by Wingfield, this volume), but is likely to be as great in insect tunnels or plant surfaces as it is on dung.

Ascospores

Ascospores of the ophiostomatoid fungi vary from species to species. Most are colorless and lack germ pores or slits although those of *Pyxidiophora* species have a melanized region at the upper end and can, in addition, be entirely pale brown. Cannon and Hawksworth (15) reported ascospores of *Sphaeronaemella helvellae* to have germ slits; they transferred *S. fimicola* to the genus *Viennotidia* because they believed its ascospores to have germ pores. Hutchison and Reid (39), however, suggested that these observations were probably based on artifacts of specimen preparation. Probably most important in dispersal are the shape of the ascospores and the chemical nature of the adhesives holding them to their vectors.

Ascospore shape

Almost without exception, ascospores of ophiostomatoid fungi have one or more concave surfaces. This is especially interesting in that the conidia of these fungi rarely have concave surfaces. We believe this is probably related to the time the spores must remain attached to the vector or to each other in mass. Spores with a concave surface, regardless of their overall shape, will tend to contact the surface of the vector at a minimum of two points. A multiple or extensive area of contact, combined with an effective adhesive, probably insures that ascospores of the ophiostomatoid fungi are not easily removed. This suggests to us that the ascospores of these fungi might be especially useful during transit between substrates, where wind and irregular movements of the vector might tend to loosen less specialized spores. If this is correct, then we would expect to find ascospores predominating on vectors trapped in transit. In our work with *Pyxidiophora* this seems to be so; phoretic mites removed from trapped scarabeid beetles rarely carry conidia of *Pyxidiophora* species but commonly have ascospores. As discussed below, however, ascospores of *Pyxidiophora* species adhere by more than surface contact alone and may not be the best examples in support of our thesis. We have observed numerous ascospores of *Sphaeronaemella fimicola* on histiostomatid mites phoretic on mooseflies (*Haematobosca alcis*) but only rarely conidia, in spite of the fact that the two spore forms usually co-occur (unpublished data). The occurrence of ascospores of *Ophiostoma* spp. on phoretic mites has been reported several times (12,44,52,53). In *Ceratocystis fagacearum,* the usual mode of transport between trees appears to be by ascospores attached to beetles (23). Juzwik and French (41) reported mainly conidia of *C. fagacearum* on beetles collected in April, but this may have been because the beetles were collected from fungal mats rather than trapped after arrival from a distant source.

Ascospore adhesives

Most ophiostomatoid fungi produce their ascospores in a droplet of liquid at the apex of the ascomatal neck. The liquid is not just water and seems to aid in attaching the spores to the surface of the vector. Bandoni (2) found that many fungi bear their spores in slimy masses but these differ in their behavior towards water. In that study, 24 species of fungi were brought into contact with water on a microscope slide and the reaction of the spores observed. Four categories of behaviour were defined: 1) spores highly surface-active, spreading evenly over the water surface; *Cephaloascus fragrans* Hanawa is the only possible relative to the ophiostomatoid fungi in this group, 2) spores spreading throughout the water, not just on the surface - no ophiostomatoid fungi, 3) spreading weak, inconsistent or none in water - *Ceratocystis fimbriata* and 4) activity in oil or lactophenol - *C. fimbriata*.

Whitney and Blauel (75) reported ascospore masses of several species of *Ceratocystis, Ceratocystiopsis* and *Ophiostoma* to disperse in conifer resin but not in water. These were: *Ceratocystis adiposa* (as *C. major), Ceratocystiopsis minuta, Ceratocystiopsis minuta-bicolor, O. bicolor, O. clavigerum, O. ips, O. minus* and *O. montium.* Exceptions were *C. fimbriata* and *O. piliferum,* which could be dispersed in resin and water, and *O. leucocarpa,* which dispersed in water but not resin. It was suggested that the ascospores adhere closely to their insect vectors and then become dispersed in the resin of the new host. *Ophiostoma montium* dispersed in a variety of non-aqueous liquids including toluene, benzene, xylene, linoleic acid, oleic acid and corn oil but not acetone, ethanol, Tween 20, or detergent.

The adhesion to the substrate by means of a melanized area in *Pyxidiophora* species (8) is probably the most specialized mechanism of ascospore adhesion known and is further strengthened by the production of a suspected haustorium in at least one species (Blackwell and Malloch, unpublished).

Anamorphs

The ophiostomatoid fungi produce a great variety of anamorphs, often even within one species. It is beyond our mandate to discuss this diversity of asexual reproduction, except to emphasize the fact that this is probably not due purely to fungal exuberance. Each spore form probably has an essential part in the life cycle of the fungus and reflects the ecological environment prevailing when it is produced. Tsuneda (65) studied the fungi occurring in beetle galleries in oak and pine, including *Ophiostoma clavigerum,* and reported that all were pleomorphic. They were usually in a yeast stage when the beetles were resident but became mycelial after they left. Tsuneda and Hiratsuka (66) reported that *O. clavigerum* produced six different anamorphs in culture: i) *Graphiocladiella,* ii) *Verticicladiella,* iii) *Hyalorhinocladiella,* iv) *Leptographium,* v) a holoblastic yeast and vi) an annellidic yeast. In axenic culture, there was evidence that the sympodial and annellidic modes of conidiogenesis were interconvertible. Complexity of conidiogenous structures tended to reduce during repeated transfers. The type of conidiogenous structures appeared to be determined in part by environmental conditions in culture: for example the synnematous form appeared at the tops of agar slants and Petri dish lids while the mononematous forms occurred on the center of the slants.

The findings of Blackwell and Malloch (8) with *Pyxidiophora* species, already discussed, suggests that such complex adaptations occur in many species of ophiostomatoid fungi and that each spore form has a specific function. In several of the species we have studied, the conidia appear to be viable for only a short time after they develop. In some cases, conidium germination occurs before conidia are released to the substrate. Early conidium formation and rapid germination on bare substrates are well suited to early spread on the immediate surface by invertebrates. Vectors may differ from spore type to spore type, thus adding another level of complexity.

As discussed in the section on ascospores, most conidia of ophiostomatoid fungi are without concave surfaces and thus adhere to their vector at only one tangential point. This suggests that conidia are removed easily and may function in relatively local dispersal on the substrate.

CONCLUSIONS

The ophiostomatoid fungi form a large group of organisms having complex relationships with arthropod vectors. Most species produce at least two spore types and use these to accomplish fertilization and dispersal. Dispersal must be effected in two environments, i) within the substrate, usually over contiguous or nearly contiguous surfaces and ii) between substrates, often over great distances and to relatively isolated locations. The first requires the utilization of non-flying arthropods and other invertebrates for generalized spreading of inocula while the second needs vectors able to detect specific substrata at considerable distances and fly to them. While overcoming these difficulties and establishing intimate associations with the their vectors, the ophiostomatoid fungi have also often maintained complex host-parasite relationships with the plants and fungi they consume. We have much to learn about these interesting organisms and this can only be accomplished by painstaking observation and experimentation.

ACKNOWLEDGEMENTS

Our work has been supported by the Natural Sciences and Engineering Research Council of Canada (OGP0000145 to D.M.) and the National Science Foundation (BSR-8604656, BSR-8918167 to M.B.).

LITERATURE CITED

1. Ashe, J.S. 1984. Major features of the evolution of relationships between gyrophaenine staphylinid beetles (Coleoptera: Staphylinidae: Aleocharinae) and fresh mushrooms. Pages 227-255 in: Fungus-insect relationships: perspectives in ecology and evolution. Q. Wheeler and M. Blackwell, eds. Columbia University Press, New York. 514 pp.

2. Bandoni, R.J. 1975. Surface-active spore slimes. Can. J. Bot. 53:2543-2546.

3. Barras, S.J. and Perry, T. 1972. Fungal symbionts in the prothoracic mycangium of *Dendroctonus frontalis* (Coleopt.: Scolytidae). Z. Ang. Entomol. 71:95-104.

4. Beaver, R.A. 1989. Insect-fungus relationships in the bark and ambrosia beetles. Pages 121-134 in: Insect-fungus interactions. N. Wilding, N. M. Collins, P. M. Hammond and J. F. Webber. eds. Academic Press, London. 344 pp.

5. Biel, A.K., Brand, J.M., Markovetz, A.J., and Bridges, R. 1977. Dimorphism in *Ceratocystis minor* var. *barrasii*.

Mycopathologia. 62:179-182.

6. Blackwell, M., Bridges, J.R., Moser, J.C. and Perry, T.J. 1986. Hypophoretic dispersal of a *Pyxidiophora* anamorph. Science 232:993-995.

7. Blackwell, M. and Malloch, D. 1989. *Pyxidiophora* (Pyxidiophoraceae): a link between the Laboulbeniales and hyphal ascomycetes. Mem. N.Y. Bot. Gard. 49:23-32.

8. Blackwell, M. and Malloch, D. 1989. *Pyxidiophora*: life histories and arthropod associations of two species. Can. J. Bot. 67:2552-2562.

9. Blackwell, M., Moser, J.C. and Wisniewski, J. 1988. Ascospores of *Pyxidiophora* on mites associated with beetles in trees and wood. Mycol. Res. 3:397-403.

10. Blackwell, M., Perry, T. J., Bridges, J. R. and Moser, J. C. 1986. A new species of *Pyxidiophora* and its *Thaxteriola* anamorph. Mycologia 78:605-612.

11. Brasier, C. M. 1978. Mites and reproduction in *Ceratocystis ulmi* and other fungi. Trans. Br. Mycol. Soc. 70:81-89.

12. Bridges, J. R. and Moser, J. C. 1983. Role of two phoretic mites in transmission of bluestain fungus, *Ceratocystis minor*. Ecol. Entomol. 8:9-12.

13. Bridges, J. R. and Perry, T. J. 1985. Effects of mycangial fungi on gallery construction and distribution of bluestain in southern pine beetle-infested pine bolts. J. Entomol. Sci. 20:271-275.

14. Cain, R.F. and Weresub, L.K. 1957. Studies on coprophilous ascomycetes V. *Sphaeronaemella fimicola*. Can. J. Bot. 35:119-131.

15. Cannon, P.F. and Hawksworth, D.L. 1982. A re-evaluation of *Melanospora* Corda and similar pyrenomycetes, with a revision of the British species. Bot. J. Linn. Soc. 84:115-160.

16. Chang, V.C.S. and Jensen, L. 1974. Transmission of the pineapple disease organism of sugar cane by nitidulid beetles in Hawaii. J. Econ. Entomol. 67:190-192.

17. Cole, G.T., Hardcastle, R.V. and Szaniszlo, P.T. 1974. *Subbaromyces splendens*: development and ultrastructure. Can. J. Bot. 52:2453-2457.

18. Corlett, M. 1986. *Pyxidiophora lundqvistii* n. sp. (Hypomycetales, Ascomycetes). Can. J. Bot. 64:805-807.

19. Crowson, R.A. 1984. The associations of Coleoptera with ascomycetes. Pages 256-285 in: Fungus-insect relationships: perspectives in ecology and evolution. Q. Wheeler and M. Blackwell, eds. Columbia University Press. New York. 514 pp.

20. Davidson, R.W. 1966. New species of *Ceratocystis* from conifers. Mycopath. Mycol. Appl. 28:273-286.

21. Doberski, J. W. 1978. Studies on entomogenous fungi in relation to the control of the Dutch elm disease vector *Scolytus scolytus*. Thesis, Cambridge University, U.K. 288 pp. (only abstract seen)

22. Franke-Grosmann, H. 1967. Ectosymbiosis in wood-inhabiting insects. Pages 141-205 in: Symbiosis. S.M. Henry, ed. Academic Press, New York. 443 pp.

23. Gibbs, J.N. 1980. The role of *Ceratocystis piceae* in preventing infections by *Ceratocystis fagacearum* in Minnesota. Trans. Br. Mycol. Soc. 74:171-174.

24. Goheen, D.J. and Cobb, F.W., JR. 1978. Occurrence of *Verticicladiella wagenerii* and its perfect state, *Ceratocystis wageneri* sp. nov., in insect galleries. Phytopathology 68:1192-1195.

25. Gray, N.F. 1983. Ponding of a random plastic percolating filter medium due to the fungus *Subbaromyces splendens* Hessletine in the treatment of sewage. Water Res.

17:1295-1302.

26. Griffin, H.D. 1968. The genus *Ceratocystis* in Ontario. Can. J. Bot. 46:689-718.

27. Guerrero, R.T. 1971. On the real nature of the "setae" in *Tremella fuciformis*. Mycologia 63:920-924.

28. Hartig, R. 1844. Ambrosia des *Botrichus dispar*. Allg. Forst-Jagdztg. 13:73.

29. Hartig, R. 1878. Die Zersetzungserscheinungen des Holzes, der Nadelbaume und der Eiche. Berlin, Julius Springer. 151 pp.

30. Hepperly, P.R. and Rodriguez-Cancel, R.E. 1987. Fruity aromas from pink mold and their association with insect attraction. J. Agric. Res. Univ. Puerto Rico 71:327-330.

31. Harrington, T.C. and P.J. Zambino. 1990. *Ceratocystiopsis ranaculosus*, not *Ceratocystis minor* var. *barrasii*, is the mycangial fungus of the southern pine beetle. Mycotaxon 38:103-115.

32. Hesseltine, C.W. 1953. Study of trickling filter fungi. Bull. Torrey Bot. Club 80:507-514.

33. Hetrick, L.A. 1949. Some overlooked relationships of southern pine beetle. J. Econ. Entomol. 42:466-469.

34. Hinds, T.E. 1972. *Ceratocystis* canker of aspen. Phytopathology 62:213-220.

35. Hinds, T.E. 1972. Insect transmission of *Ceratocystis* species associated with aspen cankers. Phytopathology 62:221-225.

36. Hinds, T.E. and Davidson, R.W. 1972. *Ceratocystis* species associated with the aspen ambrosia beetle. Mycologia 64:405-409.

37. Höhnel, F. von. 1902. Fragmente zur Mykologie I. Sber. Akad. Wiss. Wien, Math.-Naturw. Cl. 111:987-1056.

38. Hoog, G.S. de. 1974. The genera *Blastobotrys*, *Sporothrix*, *Calcarisporium* and *Calcarisporiella* gen. nov. Stud. Mycol. 7:1-84.

39. Hutchison, L.J. and Reid, J. 1988. Taxonomy of some potential wood-staining fungi from New Zealand 1. Ophiostomataceae. N.Z. J. Bot. 26:63-81.

40. Ingold, C.T. 1971. Fungal spores, their liberation and dispersal. Clarendon Press, Oxford, U.K. 302 pp.

41. Juzwik, J. and French, D.W. 1983. *Ceratocystis fagacearum* and *C. piceae* on the surfaces of free-flying and fungus-mat-inhabiting nitidulids. Phytopathology 73:1164-1168.

42. Lacy, R.C. 1984. Ecological and genetic responses to mycophagy in Drosophilidae. Pages 286-301 in: Fungus-insect relationships: perspectives in ecology and evolution. Q. Wheeler and M. Blackwell, eds. Columbia University Press, New York. 514 pp.

43. Leach, J.G., Orr, L.W. and Christensen, C. 1934. The interrelationships of bark beetles and blue-staining fungi in felled Norway pine timber. J. Agric. Res. 49:315-341.

44. Livieux, J., Lieutier, F., Moser, J.C., and Perry, T.J. 1989. Transportation of phytopathogenic fungi by the bark beetle *Ips sexdentatus* Boerner and associated mites. J. Appl. Entomol. 108:1-11.

45. Limber, D.P. 1950. *Ophiostoma* on *Narcissus* bulbs. Phytopathology 40:493-496.

46. Lundqvist, N. 1980. On the genus *Pyxidiophora* sensu lato (Pyrenomycetes). Bot. Notiser 133:121-144.

47. Malloch, D. 1974. *Sphaeronaemella helvellae*. Fungi Canadenses 53.

48. Malloch, D. and Blackwell, M. 1990. *Kathistes*, a new genus of pleomorphic ascomycetes. Can. J. Bot. 68:1712-1721.

49. Malloch, D. and Blackwell, M. 1992. Dispersal of fungal diaspores. Pages 147-171 in: The Fungal Community: Its organization and Role in the Ecosystem. G. C. Carroll and D. T. Wicklow, eds. 2nd Edition. Marcel Dekker, New York, Basel, Hong Kong. 976 pp.

50. Minter, D.W. 1983. Redisposition of *Klasterskya* in the Ophiostomataceae. Trans. Br. Mycol. Soc. 80: 162-163.

51. Moser, J. C. 1985. Use of sporothecae by phoretic *Tarsonemus* mites to transport ascospores of coniferous bluestain fungi. Trans. Br. Mycol. Soc. 84:750-753.

52. Moser, J.C. and Bridges, J.R. 1986. *Tarsonemus* (Acarina: Tarsonemidae) mites phoretic on the southern pine beetle (Coleoptera: Scolytidae): attachment sites and numbers of bluestain (Ascomycetes: Ophiostomataceae) ascospores carried. Proc. Entomol. Soc. Wash. 88:297-299.

53. Moser, J.C., Perry, T.J. and Solheim, H. 1989. Ascospores hyperphoretic on mites associated with *Ips typographus*. Mycol. Res. 93:513-517.

54. Muller, P.J. and Bergman, B.H.B. 1966. The influence of cultural practices on the occurrence of head rot in *Narcissus*. Neth. J. Plant. Pathol. 72:204-211.

55. Neger, F.W. 1909. Ambrosiapilze II. Ber. Deut. Bot. Ges. 27:372-389.

56. Paine, T.D. and Birch, M.C. 1983. Acquisition and maintenance of mycangial fungi by *Dendroctonus brevicomus* LeConte (Coleoptera: Scolytidae). Environ. Entomol. 12:1384-1386.

57. Pease, D. 1948. *Sphaeronaemella fimicola*: some characteristics in culture. Mycologia 40:114-124.

58. Petrak, F. 1940. Mycologische Notizen. XIII. Ann. Mycol. 28:181-267.

59. Pfister, D.H. 1982. A new host for *Sphaeronaemella helvellae* -- *Pseudorhizina sphaerospora*. Mycotaxon 16:165-166.

60. Pierce, R. 1986. Mold eating mold. Agric. Res. 34:12-13.

61. Redhead, S.A. and Malloch, D. 1977. The Endomycetaceae: new concepts, new taxa. Can. J. Bot. 55:1701-1711.

62. Ruetze, M. and Parameswaran, N. 1984. Observations on the colonization of oak wilt mats (*Ceratocystis fagacearum*) by *Pesotum piceae*. Eur. J. For. Pathol. 14:326-333.

63. Samson, R.A. 1974. *Paecilomyces* and some allied hyphomycetes. Stud. Mycol. 6:1-120.

64. Schmodberger, J. 1836. Naturgeschichte des Apfelborkenkafers *Apate dispar*. Beitr. Obs. Nat. Obst. Schad. Insekt. 4:213-230.

65. Tsuneda, A. 1988. Pleomorphism in beetle-gallery conidial fungi and protoplast reversion. Proc. Japan Acad. 64, Ser. B:135-138.

66. Tsuneda, A. and Hiratsuka, Y. 1984. Sympodial and annellidic conidiation in *Ceratocystis clavigera*. Can. J. Bot. 62:2618-2624.

67. Tulasne, L.R. and Tulasne, C. 1865. *Selecta fungorum carpologia*. III. Typographie Impériale, Paris, France. 201 pp.

68. Upadhyay, H.P. 1981. A monograph of *Ceratocystis* and *Ceratocystiopsis*. University of Georgia Press, Athens, G.A. 176 pp.

69. Vakili, N.G. 1985. Mycoparasitic fungi associated with potential stalk rot pathogens of corn. Phytopathology 75:1201-1207.

70. Vakili, N.G. and Bailey, T.B., Jr. 1989. Yield response of

D. MALLOCH and M. BLACKWELL

corn hybrids an inbred lines to phylloplane treatment with mycopathogenic fungi. Crop Sci. 29:183-190.

71. Valldosera, M. and Guarro, J. 1989. Coprophilous fungi from Spain: *Klasterskya coronata* sp. nov. Mycol. Res. 92:113-116.

72. Webber, J. 1981. A natural biological control of Dutch elm disease. Nature 292:449-451.

73. Webber, J.F. and Gibbs, J.N. 1989. Insect dissemination of fungal pathogens of trees. Pages 161-193 in: Insect-fungus interactions. N. Wilding, N.M. Collins, P.M. Hammond and J.F. Webber, eds. Academic Press, London. 344 pp.

74. Webster, J. and Hawksworth, D.L. 1986. *Pyxidiophora spinulo-rostrata*, a new species with denticulate conidiophores from submerged twigs in south-west England. Trans. Br. Mycol. Soc. 87:77-79.

75. Whitney, H.S. and Blauel, R.A. 1972. Ascospore dispersion in *Ceratocystis* spp. and *Europhium clavigerum* in conifer resin. Mycologia 64:410-414.

76. Williams, I. L. 1981. *Subbaromyces splendens*, a fungus of highly polluted aquatic environments. Bull. Br. Mycol. Soc. 15 (Suppl.): 5-6.

77. Wingfield, M.J., van Wyk, P.S. and Marasas, W.F.O. 1988. *Ceratocystiopsis proteae* sp. nov., with a new anamorph genus. Mycologia 80:23-30.

Chapter 22

TREE RESPONSES TO INFECTION BY SPECIES OF *OPHIOSTOMA* AND *CERATOCYSTIS*

E.B. SMALLEY, K.F. RAFFA, R.H. PROCTOR and K.D. KLEPZIG

INTRODUCTION

Defensive strategies in trees to wound-invading fungi are complex and often highly evolved, with responses differing greatly between Angiosperms and Gymnosperms. The type of host response induced may differ depending upon the location of the infection court. Responses can be further complicated if ophiostomatoid fungi are involved because of the frequent interposition of arthropod vectors. These vector systems range from those in which fungal spores are transported passively on the insect's exterior, to those in which the spores are carried in highly evolved mycangia within the body of the beetle (25,93). They can be casual relationships or associations that are essential for the survival of one or both partners.

Most species of *Ophiostoma* are weak parasites or saprophytes, although a few such as *Ophiostoma ulmi* are important tree pathogens. Various *Leptographium* species with *Ophiostoma* teleomorphs also cause major xylem root diseases in conifers, such as black stain root disease caused by *L. wageneri* and red pine decline caused by *L. terebrantis* (30,36,61,62,63, Harrington, this volume). However, even the less pathogenic species of *Ophiostoma* such as *O. ips, O. minus, O. montia, O. penicillatum* and *O. piceae* cause serious economic losses as incitants of blue stain in harvested timber (Seifert, this volume), especially in association with bark beetle outbreaks (85, Gibbs, Solheim, this volume). Many of the *Ophiostoma* species have bark beetle associations (85,89,90,91). In contrast, species of *Ceratocystis sensu stricto* are virtually all pathogenic and rarely have bark beetle associations.

The fungi involved and the manner of host response to invasion by the pathogenic species of ophiostomatoid fungi can conveniently be divided into two general forms or categories. In the first, the host plant is most susceptible in youth, when growing vigorously or when generally good growing conditions prevail. Under these conditions, the host plant defenses are at their lowest. Under conditions of dormancy or stress, when active shoot elongation ceases in response to day length changes, low or high temperatures, water stress, or lack of available soil nutrients, host defenses are at their highest. Stress induced resistance, however, may be confounded or negated by increases in attractiveness to insect vectors. These fungi are major plant pathogens and cause serious economic loss. Only a few ophiostomatoid fungi with hardwood hosts such as *O. ulmi*, certain races of *Ceratocystis fimbriata* and *Ceratocystis fagacearum* fall into this group. They are often termed the vascular wilt diseases and have much in common with other non-ophiostomatoid pathogens such as the *Fusarum oxysporum, Verticillium albo-atrum* and *V. dahliae* (50). Presently, it is unclear whether the pathogens of conifer roots such as *L. wageneri* and *L. terebrantis* that invade xylem tracheids belong to this class or not.

The second category includes 'stress diseases', in which the host is highly susceptible during stress but resistant or even immune under conditions of adequate soil moisture and favorable growing conditions. Most of the numerous 'blue stainers' (e.g. *O. ips, O. montia, O. minus, C. coerulescens, C. laricicola*) and the various sap stainers such as *Ceratocystis virescens* and certain races of *C. fimbriata*, either fall into this second group or have not been studied sufficiently to be assigned to either category. The bark or phloem invading races of *C. fimbriata* (e.g. almond, cacao, prune) probably also fall into the second group, but details from controlled studies are lacking. Other similar diseases, such as *Cytospora* canker (*Leucostoma kunzei*) of blue spruce (66,67), and *Hypoxylon* canker of aspen caused by *Hypoxylon mammatum*, clearly fall into the latter (stress) group (2).

THE CONIFER SYSTEM

A major feature of coniferous response to bark beetle-fungus attack is the broad array of chemical groups involved in defense. Total monoterpene content within the reaction zone increases; changes in the relative proportions of monoterpenes occur, although the degree of qualitative change that occurs varies between tree species. A number of other chemical conversions take place during induction; resin acids, sesquiterpenes and phenolics all undergo both qualitative and quantitative changes. Chemicals that accumulate during defensive reactions are largely responsible for the failure of bark beetles and fungi to become established. Purified components of reaction tissue affect the invading complex in several ways. Induced monoterpenes are repellent to adult beetles, ovicidal, and fungitoxic at concentrations present in reacting tissue (4,57,58,59,60,69,70). The extent of the induced response is seasonal, genetic, often age-related and reduced by stress such as water deficit, defoliation, disease, mechanical damage and intraspecific competition. The coniferous responses to invasion by species of *Ophiostoma* and accompanying insect associates (primarily Coleoptera:Scolytidae) are the subject of numerous technical papers and reviews (1,42,56), and are also the subject of several other chapters in this volume.

Our discussion will be confined primarily to our own research on red pine decline, especially as it pertains to developing model systems to study conifer/pathogen/bark beetle interactions.

Red Pine Decline

Red pine decline was first observed in the mid-1970's in the North Central U. S. (Wisconsin, Michigan, and Illinois) affecting 20-40 year old plantation-grown *Pinus resinosa* (36). The decline is characterized by the progressive development of large circular openings of dead and dying trees ringed by trees in various stages of decline. Several species of insects develop high populations in association with decline pockets. They included three weevil species, *Hylobius radicis*, *H. pales* and *Pachylobius picivorus*, and two bark beetle species, *Dendroctonus valens* and *Hylastes porculus* (36).

Adult insects associated with red pine decline pockets consistently carry *L. terebrantis* and *L. procerum* either singly or together as fungal symbionts. Additionally, *H. porculus* carries *O. huntii*. Trenching to expose tree roots through decline pockets reveals extensive mortality and black staining within the largely grafted red pine root systems of affected pockets. Isolations from blackened roots near the margin between living and dead roots consistently yield pure cultures of *L. terebrantis* and occasionally *L. procerum* and *O. huntii* as well (36).

In many aspects, red pine decline in Wisconsin resembles a number of other conifer root diseases associated with bark beetles, root weevils and

Leptographium species in various parts of the world (30,32,40,92). As such, we believe it contains most of the necessary ingredients for use as a model system in developing detailed studies on the nature of the conifer response to invasion by beetle vectored members of the ophiostomatoid fungi.

Inoculations

Invasion of red pine, *P. resinosa*, by *Hylobius* root weevils, red turpentine beetles, *D. valens*, and pine engravers, *Ips pini*, was simulated by inoculating mature healthy plantation-grown pines with their respective fungal symbonts, *L. terebrantis*, *O. ips* and *O. nigrocarpum*. Trees responded to inoculation by forming necrotic lesions in advance of the spread of the fungi, which resulted in containment of the infections; systemic lesions never developed (61,62,63). Lesions developing in response to inoculation were relatively small (7-10 cm in length), the largest lesions being produced by *O. ips* and *L. terebrantis*. *Ophiostoma nigrocarpum* lesions differed little from wounded controls. The largest lesions were formed in May and became progressively smaller in response to later season inoculations (61). *Leptographium terebrantis* formed significantly longer lesions in roots than in trunk inoculation sites (e.g. 14.6 cm vs 11.0 cm), while *O. ips* produced significantly longer trunk than root lesions (13.4 cm vs 11.0 cm) (Klepzig *et al.*, unpublished data).

When two year old red pine transplants were inoculated in the greenhouse with similar fungal symbionts from a range of North American sources, as in the field inoculations, no trees died as a result of stem inoculations, although many trees were virtually girdled (Smalley, *et al.*, unpublished data). Xylem discoloration induced by *L. terebrantis* isolates ranged from 9.2 mm (California) to 24.5 mm (Wisconsin) in length (Fig. 1). *Leptographium procerum* strains induced longer xylem stem lesions than did *L. terebrantis* (Fig. 1). *Ophiostoma ips* strains were generally more pathogenic than the *Leptographium* species and developed xylem lesions ranging from 16.8 mm to 34.0 mm in length. Strains of *O. nigrocarpum* and *L. wageneri* mostly were avirulent. In root inoculations, however *L. terebrantis* strains were extremely virulent (Fig. 1). Seven of the test strains were lethal to all inoculated pines, while 14 strains induced severe root xylem discoloration. In contrast to their stem invading characteristics, all but one strain of *L. procerum* were avirulent, and *L. wageneri* strains were avirulent.

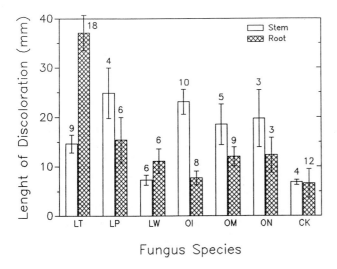

Fig. 1. Xylem discoloration developing from wounds in large red pine seedlings inoculated with fungal symbionts from bark beetles and root weevils. Data represents means of 6 replications/isolate/geographic source. Small numbers above each bar indicate the number of sources/fungus species. Fungi include: *L. terebrantis* (LT); *L. procerum* (LP); *L. wageneri* (LW); *O. ips* (OI); *O. minus* (OM); *O. nigrocarpum* (ON); and wounded controls (CK).

These studies suggested that *L. terebrantis*, a symbiont or associate of the red turpentine beetle (*Dendroctonus valens*) and to a lesser extent of the root collar weevil (*Hylobius radicis*), is the primary root xylem pathogen in red pine, whereas *O. ips*, found principally in association with *Ips* spp., is primarily a stem pathogen. The ability of red pine to limit root invasion of *L. terebrantis* in the field, while failing in greenhouse grown transplants suggests the possible importance of 'stress factors' in limiting the host response.

Monoterpene Changes and Phytoalexin Production in Reaction Zones

Monoterpene concentrations in the reaction zone of healthy red pines became elevated in response to fungal inoculation. More than six-fold increases were detected after three days and 32-fold increases after two weeks. In general, these chemical changes were associated with the extent of lesion development; that is, strong phytochemical changes develop in *P. resinosa* in response to inoculation with live *O. ips* and *L. terebrantis*, moderate responses to

autoclaved mycelium, and only minor changes following *O. nigrocarpum* inoculation or mechanical wounding (Raffa and Smalley, unpublished data). Linear growth of *L. terebrantis* was significantly reduced in media appended with purified methanol extracts from red pine inoculated with *L. terebrantis*. These results suggested that the response of red pine to fungal invasion or wounding involved the production of phytoalexins not present in unwounded tissue (35).

THE HARDWOOD SYSTEM

In comparison to the conifer system, detailed attention to responses in hardwoods to infection by species of *Ophiostoma* and *Ceratocystis* has been confined to a few diseases. Major research on *Ceratocystis s. str.* has been directed primarily to diseases caused by *C. fimbriata*. This ubiquitous pathogen, with it's many forms and races, is the causal agent of numerous rots of herbaceous plants and cankers of trees (e.g. sweet potato, coffee, cacao, taro, sycamore, poplar, *Gmelina*, pimento, rubber and stone fruits) (71). Much of the research on host responses has been directed towards the black rot disease of sweet potato. This work has been the topic of numerous technical reports and reviews (86,95, see also Kojima, this volume).

In contrast, research on host responses in trees to infection by *Ceratocystis* species has received only limited attention. Work on the canker development in almonds, produced following infection by *C. fimbriata*, focused on the dynamics of wound periderm formation and other anatomical barriers (5). These authors suggest that *C. fimbriata* penetrates the defensive barriers of partially closed wounds or weakened wound periderm, but that significant resistance develops within seven days of wounding. The development of this resistance is related to extensive deposition of lignin and suberin in a well developed wound periderm. Similarly, Przybyl (55) found that the spread and development of *C. fimbriata* in a resistant poplar clone was inhibited by condensed tannins and a layer of cork that developed on the border between the necrotic and healthy tissue. Although these responses resemble those of normal suberin deposition in the wound reaction zone in various tree species (3), periderm formation has been associated with induced resistance mechanisms in plants (34,87).

Oak wilt, caused by *C. fagacearum*, resembles Dutch elm disease in its general symptomatology, host response, seasonal susceptibility and transmission via root grafts (71,84,89). But unlike the bark beetle borne *Ophiostoma* species, long distance transmission is accomplished primarily by various sap and fungus feeding beetles (Family: Nitidulidae)(84). Oak species in the red oak group are generally susceptible, while the members of the white oak group are more or less resistant, although detailed studies of species resistance under comparable conditions are limited. Struckmeyer *et al.* (81) described the anatomical symptomatology of vessel plugging, tyloses and gums in wilting oaks. Jacobi and MacDonald (33) observed that pathogen growth was restricted laterally and longitudinally in vessels of resistant white oaks and that darkly stained parenchyma cells developed in all species in response to infection. Sachs *et al.* (64) reported that in the resistant bur oak (white oak group), masses of dark, amorphous, electron-dense material develop in parenchyma cells adjacent to infected vessels. In such oaks, the fungus is often restricted to the initially invaded sapwood tissue and fails to develop further. However, the biochemical nature of the host response materials has apparently not been investigated.

Virtually the only definitive studies on host responses to a pathogenic species of *Ophiostoma* have focused on the *Ophiostoma/Ulmus* system of Dutch elm disease. During pathogenesis, *O. ulmi* develops within the xylem vessels of the elm with associated tylosis and vessel plugging, ultimately resulting in the development of a wilt syndrome. These processes, which involve production by the fungus of cell wall degrading enzymes, toxins and growth substances, have been reviewed by Scheffer (65), Elgersma (22), Pegg (50) and others. Resistance to *O. ulmi* is recognized at the species level (*U. pumila* and *U. parvifolia* being the most resistant) as well as in selected individuals within the more susceptible species (31,76, and others). Anatomical features in elms (e.g. small diameter, scattered and less contiguous vessels) have been correlated with resistance (21,22,43,72,), but Gkinis (28) failed to confirm such correlations. Various investigators have noted that although *O. ulmi* can grow in resistant elms, its spread generally is limited to the inoculation area (22,41). That *O. ulmi* can grow, even in resistant elms, suggests that nutrients are not operating as major limiting mechanisms (22).

To really understand the hardwood system, it is important to consider the gross host responses as well as the various host biochemical responses that follow pathogen attack. Understanding the various factors that influence or condition the host response is the key to development of techniques and procedures to understand the physical and biochemical processes. Emphasis in this section will be given to the *Ophiostoma/Ulmus* system illustrated with examples from our research in Wisconsin.

Ophiostoma/Ulmus

The *Ophiostoma/Ulmus*/bark beetle system has been intensively studied and numerous reviews are available (8,9,10,11,12,15,27,37,80). The system is obviously complex and the response is under control of a variety of environmental and genetic factors. Histologic studies of the host response are numerous and detailed, but can only give a one dimensional, cross-sectional view of a three dimensional system (38,43,46,47,48, and others). Elgersma and Miller (23,45) have achieved the most revealing views of the infection process using scanning electron microscopy (SEM). The problems that beset the investigator in studying the 'micro-environment of the vascular pathogen' are discussed eloquently by Pegg (50).

The Pathogen

Dutch elm disease is incited by several recognized races or subgroups of the pathogen, *O. ulmi*. Two subgroups are present in North America and have been variously called the 'fluffy, aggressive strain', or the North American subgroup (NAN), while the 'waxy, non-aggressive strain', is referred to as the non-aggressive or NA (7). In addition to NAN and NA, the Eurasian aggressive subgroup (EAN) is also recognized in Europe and Asia (7). The subgroups are readily recognized by their colony morphology and more specifically by their distinctly different modes of spore germination. The genetics and population biology of these various forms of *O. ulmi* have been intensively studied by Brasier and co-workers (7,9,10). Recently, Brasier (12) has applied the specific epithet *O. novo-ulmi* to these to describe the aggressive (NAN & EAN) forms of the pathogen.

Transmission

Scolytid bark beetles are the principal agents of the long distance transmission of Dutch elm disease, introducing the pathogen into healthy trees during adult feeding. The site of inoculation is a major determinant of the nature of the host response. If the pathogen invades via vector feeding grooves in twig crotches of small branches, host defenses are primarily against upward spread of the pathogen with the sap stream. Where these primary defenses fail, secondary responses may still prevent the development of systemic disease.

Root graft transmission is the major cause of elm tree death in urban areas in North America and probably elsewhere (74). In root graft transmission via connections from adjacent infected trees, or where the infection court is a bark beetle feeding groove or brood gallery in a large branch or in the main trunk, the host response must be more intensive to prevent systemic disease. Experimentally, lower trunk wound inoculations in large susceptible elms result in much more severe disease than upper branch inoculations in similar trees (77).

The principal bark beetle vectors of *O. ulmi* in North America are the introduced Smaller European Elm bark beetle, *Scolytus multistriatus*, and the indigenous American elm bark beetle, *Hylurgopinus rufipes*. In Europe, the principal vectors are *S. scolytus* and *S. multistriatus*, although other vector species are recognized (39,88). Since the Eurasian land mass constitutes the gene center of palearctic species of *Scolytus* as well as *Ulmus*, the genus *Scolytus* probably originated in Asia in association with *Ulmus* (44). It is possible, therefore, that resistance to *O. ulmi* in Asian elms originates as a result of their co-evolution as hosts of *Scolytus* rather than through development of specific anatomical or physiological features such as small vessel diameters, slow growth or drought resistance as suggested by various authors (11,31,43). The resistant response may have developed more or less non-specifically as an elicited response to spores of any microorganism deposited in feeding niches or brood galleries by the bark beetles.

Resistance

The major sources of genes for resistance to *O. ulmi* in elms are possessed by the Asiatic species, *U. parvifolia*, *U. pumila*, *U. wallichiana*, *U. villosa*, *U. japonica*, *U. laciniata*, and *U. wilsoniana*. The resistance of at least 16 other Asian elm species (26) has yet to be adequately assessed. The European and North American elms are moderately susceptible to *O. ulmi* but their responses vary depending on the individual subgroups of the pathogen.

Most of our knowledge of resistance, pathogen virulence and population genetics in the *Ophiostoma/Ulmus* system is based on the results of field inoculations with one or several elm cultivars (7,8,14,28). Field results, however, can be misleading, and in our experience, always overestimate the

genetic resistance of the host. Under controlled environments in the greenhouse or plant growth chambers, we always find increased susceptibility as contrasted to similar field experiments (17,29).

Aside from major species differences, all elms vary seasonally in their resistance to *C. ulmi* and the actual periods of susceptibility can often be quite short, although environmental factors play an important role (73,77,78,79,82,83). The highly susceptible period is correlated with the spring period of branch elongation but the length of the susceptible period may vary significantly from year to year. In drier years, the susceptible period is shortened (77), resulting in a form of environmentally induced resistance (77). Resistance also increases and the length of the susceptible period decreases as trees age, while the more resistant elms species have the shortest periods of susceptibility (77,79).

Phytoalexins and Barrier Zones

The principal reaction compounds developing in elms following invasion by *O. ulmi* are cadinane sesquiterpenoids called mansonones (24,49). These are considered to be elm phytoalexins because they accumulate in elms infected with *O. ulmi* or other pathogens and are not detectable in healthy sapwood (16,19). They inhibit the growth of fungi *in vitro* (20,24,49,94). Induction of mansonones is generally correlated with specific genetic or seasonal levels of resistance (18,19). However, although mansonone elicitation in elms has been extensively studied, its role as a resistance factor to *O. ulmi* remains poorly understood (51,53). Although some studies indicate that mansonones accumulate more rapidly in resistant than in susceptible elms (18,19), other results suggest that mansonone accumulation does not differ in resistant and susceptible elms, while still others indicate that accumulation can be greater in susceptible elms (18,24,51,54).

Barrier zones containing starch-filled parenchyma and swollen ray parenchyma have also been observed in infected American elms (6,68). These act as a tangential shield between the infected xylem and the healthy regenerating mycelium.

Both pathogen virulence and host response to infection are affected by the temperature. Indeed, the definition of pathogen subgroups are based, in part, on linear growth rates at various temperatures (13,12). Isolates of the aggressive subgroups grow most rapidly on Oxoid Malt Agar at 20-22°C, while in the NA isolates the optimum is 30°C. Linear growth of North American isolates of *O. ulmi* on

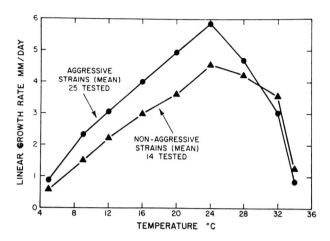

Fig. 2. Linear growth rate of North American isolates of aggressive (NAN) and non-aggressive (NA) isolates of *Ophiostoma ulmi* on potato dextrose agar at controlled temperatures.

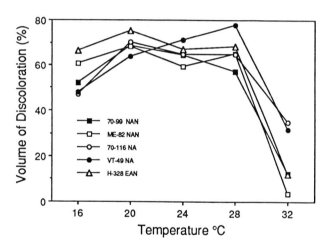

Fig. 3. Dutch elm disease symptoms developing in American elm seedlings incubated at various temperatures in plant growth rooms for 30 days after inoculation with different subgroups of *Ophiostoma ulmi*. Pooled means of inoculated seedlings from two half-sib parents; 10 tree replications/seed source. One-year old plants grown at 24°C under 16 hr. day high-intensity fluorescence illumination for 60 days prior to inoculation and incubation at the appropriate temperatures. NA = Non-aggressive subgroup; NAN = North American subgroup; EAN = Eurasian aggressive subgroup.

potato dextrose agar (PDA) is more rapid and both subgroups peak at 24°C. At higher temperatures, the growth rates of the NAN isolates decline more rapidly than the NA isolates (Fig. 2). Temperature effects on disease induced in American elms inoculated with the different subgroups of *O. ulmi*

paralleled growth on culture media but was most significant at the higher temperatures (29). Most of our inoculation trials under controlled environments show only slight differences in virulence between non-aggressive and aggressive forms in *U. americana*. Expressions of virulence are clearly under temperature control, however, and at temperatures above 24°C, the NA subgroup is significantly more virulent than the NAN subgroup on American elm (Fig. 3).

In the early 1970's, we sought a rapid and less labor intensive method for screening elm breeding progenies for resistance to *O. ulmi* and for studying the details of host/pathogen interactions. Initially, we considered the use of tissue culture methods used successfully in studying certain non-vascular diseases. The principal short-coming in the use of un-differentiated tissue culture systems is the absence of relevance to the principal site of action, ie. the vessel and its surrounding xylem parenchyma.

Eventually, we found that the most effective technique for studying the *Ulmus/Ophiostoma* system consisted of inoculating the freshly exposed cambium of aseptically peeled elm twigs (75). Inoculum applied to the cambium as single droplets containing *O. ulmi* spores produced a browning response within a few hours after inoculation (Fig. 4). Growth retardation of the fungus was often prolonged on intensely browned twigs. The intensity of the response was directly correlated with the resistance of the species or hybrid, intensified with plant age and was correlated with increasing host resistance in inoculated intact elms (Fig. 5). It was also proportional to spore concentration and only limited reactions developed below 10^4 spores/ml with cell-free culture filtrates; pure toxin preparations of cerato-ulmin or peptidorhamnomannan failed to elicit any responses (Smalley, unpublished data). Following cambial inoculation of *U. americana* twigs with *O. ulmi*, mansonones E and F recovered in twig extractives (18). The twig assay offers promise as a model system for studying the production of antifungal compounds by elms in response to inoculation with *O. ulmi*.

Using the cambial assay as a model system for studying phytoalexin elicitation, our initial efforts were directed towards the development of analytical techniques for phytoalexin elicitation, extraction and quantification (18). The cambial assay was modified for the large scale production of the mansonones (e.g. mg to g quantities). Peeled twigs were dipped into *O. ulmi* conidial suspensions and incubated under moist, aseptic conditions for 36 to 48 hours prior to

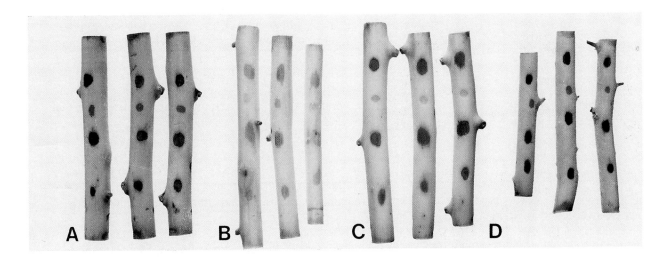

Fig. 4. Axenic cambial responses of resistant and susceptible elm clones 5 days after inoculation with conidia of NAN strain 70-99 of *Ophiostoma ulmi*. Droplets 1, 3, 4 (top to bottom) applied to cambium 24 hr after bark removal; droplet 2 applied 72 hr after bark removal. Sets of reacting twigs A and B are *Ulmus americana* (W411-3) (A - resistant state; B - susceptible state). Set C represents *U. pumila* x *U. rubra* (W7-4) - resistant state and set D *U. pumila* (W198) - resistant state.

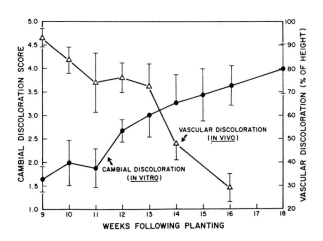

Fig. 5. Comparison the 5 day axenic (*in vitro*) cambial responses of twigs from greenhouse grown *Ulmus americana* seedlings inoculated with conidia of NAN strain 70-99 of *Ophiostoma ulmi*. The *in vivo* response was measured as the length of internal xylem vascular discoloration developing 30 days after inoculation. Note that as intact seedling 'seasonal' susceptibility declines over time, the cambial discoloration score increases. Cambial discoloration score defined as: 1= no discoloration; 5= intense cambial browning.

extraction, purification and quantification of the phytoalexins. In field grown *U. americana*, mansonone elicitation as measured by the cambial assay was least in mid-June, peaked in mid-July, then declined in response to heavy rains, and then increased again by the end of August. In greenhouse studies, elicitation of mansonone E and F by *O. ulmi* in the *in vitro* cambial assay generally correlated with the *in vitro* whole plant measurement of resistance (Table 1). In contrast, however, in whole plant measurements susceptible cultivars often produced high concentrations of mansonones (18). By sampling only infected tissue in very early stages of infection, mansonone concentrations tended to correlate with results obtained in the *in vitro* cambial assay (51,52,54). Mansonone elicitation in the cambial assay provided a near-absolute measure of the host's potential to produce antifungal mansonones in response the presence of the pathogen.

Mansonone tolerance and virulence

We examined the virulence of mansonone sensitive mutants of *O. ulmi* to determine if tolerance to mansonones is necessary for virulence on elm (52, 53). To generate mutants, yeast-like cells of *O. ulmi* were treated with nitrosoguanidine and then screened for increased sensitivity to 1,2-naphthoquinone,

TABLE 1. Mansonone elicitation in the *in-vitro* cambial assay in greenhouse grown elms varying in resistance *Ophiostoma ulmi*[a].

Clone	Species or cultivar[b]	Mansonone E (μg/g)[c]	Mansonone F (μg/g)[c]	Xylem discoloration (% height)[d]
228-4	'Regal'	33.0+19.8h	226.8+104.7h	11.9+8.7d
196-8	(p x p)	18.2+7.0efg	124.9+37.3fg	3.2+0.6d
44-11	'Sapporo'	13.5+7.9a-f	13.9+4.2ab	0.6+1.0d
44-27	(p x j)	12.2+5.4a-f	10.8+7.1ab	5.6+3.2d
7-4	(p x r)	10.7+2.6a-e	9.7+6.8ab	3.0+1.8d
Amer	U. amer	4.5+3.4a-d	7.5+5.3ab	64.6+11.9a
M-8	U. amer	2.2+3.1ab	5.4+5.0ab	43.3+8.8a

[a]Plants from root cuttings or 1 year old seedlings were grown in the greenhouse for more than 2 months prior to use. Column means followed by different letters differ at $P < .05$ (18).
[b]p=*U. pumila*; j=*U. japonica*; r=*U. rubra*; U. amer=*U. americana*.
[c]*In vitro* mansonone concentrations are expressed as μg mansonone/g dry wt of twigs 5 days after inoculation (N=3-5).
[d]Xylem discoloration measured 30-45 days after inoculation (N=10-12).

a mansonone analogue. Strains that exhibited increased sensitivity to 1,2-naphthoquinone were also highly sensitive to mansonones E and F. In culture media amended with 0.4 mM mansonone E, mycelial growth of the mutants was inhibited up to 95%, while that of the wild type was inhibited 43%. Three mutants were less virulent on elm than the wild type

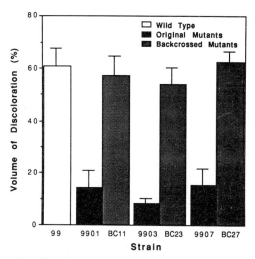

Fig. 6. Results of greenhouse study contrasting the virulence of the mansonone E insensitive NAN strain 70-99 of *Ophiostoma ulmi* with selected nitrosoguanidine induced sensitive mutants (9901, 9903, 9907) and backcross mutants (BC11, BC23, BC27). Data is expressed as lesion volume developing 30 days after inoculation. Note that the virulence of the mansonone E sensitive mutants was restored in backcrosses to insensitive wild strains, while retaining mansonone E sensitivity. Data is adapted from Proctor (52).

strain from which they were derived, however, two mutants were just as virulent as the wild type. Mansonone sensitive progeny from back-crosses of weakly virulent, mansonone sensitive mutants and tolerant wild type strains exhibited levels of virulence equal to that of the wild type (Fig. 6). These data indicate that levels of mansonone tolerance as exhibited by wild type strains of *O. ulmi* may not be necessary for virulence on elm.

The problems encountered in interpretation of phytoalexin elicitation results point out the need for precisely defining the environment and the state of susceptibility of the host. The lack of association between mansonone tolerance and virulence in *O. ulmi* suggests that mansonones alone do not play a major role in the resistance of elms to Dutch elm disease. These studies also bring into serious question the real importance of phytoalexins as major host determinants of plant resistance. It seems probable that virulent plant pathogens such as *O. ulmi*, which require wounds for host entry, have developed mechanisms that resist or avoid the effects of phytoalexins elicited as a part of the wound response.

ACKNOWLEDGMENTS

We thank Steve Vicen for preparation of the photographs and figures used in the manuscript and Dr. S. H. Mai, Ms. N. S. Ehlke, and Jim Adams for their technical assistance. This work was supported by the College of Agricultural and Life Sciences, UW-Madison.

LITERATURE CITED

1. Anderson, J.M., Rayner, A.D.M. and Walton, D.W.H., (eds.). 1984. Invertebrate-Microbial Interactions. Cambridge University Press, Cambridge. 349 pp.

2. Bagga, D.K. and Smalley, E.B. 1974. The development of *Hypoxylon* canker of *Populus tremuloides*: role of interacting environmental factors. Phytopathology 64:658-662.

3. Biggs, A.R. 1987. Occurrence and location of suberin in wound reaction zones in xylem of 17 tree species. Phytopathology 77:718-725.

4. Bordasch, R.P., and Berryman, A.A. 1977. Host resistance to the fir engraver beetle, *Scolytus ventralis* (Coleoptera: Scolytidae). 2. Repellency of *Abies grandis* resins and some monoterpenes. Can. Entomol. 109:95-100.

5. Bostock, R.M. and Middleton, G.E. 1987. Relationship of wound periderm formation to resistance to *Ceratocystis fimbriata*. Phytopathology 77:1174-1180.

6. Bonsen, K.J.M., Scheffer, R.J. and Elgersma, D.M. 1985. Barrier zone formation as a resistance mechanism of elms to Dutch elm disease. IAWA Bulletin 6:71-77.

7. Brasier, C.M. 1982. Occurrence of three sub-groups within *Ceratocystis ulmi*. Pages 298-321 in: Proc. Dutch elm disease symposium and workshop. E.S. Kondo, Y. Hiratsuka, and W.B.G. Denyer, eds. Manitoba, Canada, Manitoba Department of Natural Resources. 517 pp.

8. Brasier, C.M. 1986. The population biology of Dutch elm disease: its principal features and some implications for other host-pathogen systems. Pages 53-118 in: Advances in Plant Pathology, Vol. 5. D.S. Ingram and P.E. Williams, eds. Blackwell Scientific Publications, Oxford. 270 pp.

9. Brasier, C.M. 1987. Some genetical aspects of necrotrophy with special reference to *Ophiostoma ulmi*. Pages 297-310 in: Genetics and Plant Pathogenesis. P.R. Day and G.J. Jellis, eds. Blackwell Scientific Publications, Boston. 352 pp.

10. Brasier, C.M. 1988. *Ophiostoma ulmi*, cause of Dutch elm disease. Adv. Pl. Pathol. 6:207-23.

11. Brasier, C.M. 1990. China and the origins of Dutch elm disease: an appraisal. Plant Pathol. 39:5-16.

12. Brasier, C.M. 1991. *Ophiostoma novo-ulmi* sp. nov., causative agent of the current Dutch elm disease pandemics. Mycopathologia 115:151-161.

13. Brasier, C.M., Lea, J., and Rawlings, M.K. 1981. The aggressive and non-aggressive strains of *Ceratocystis ulmi* have different temperature optima for growth. Trans. Br. Mycol. Soc. 76:213-218.

14. Brasier, C.M. and Webber, J.F. 1987. Positive correlations between *in-vitro* growth rate and pathogenesis in *Ophiostoma ulmi*. Plant Pathol. 36:462-466.

15. Burdekin, D.A., (ed.). 1983. Research on Dutch elm disease in Europe. Forestry Commission Bull. 60. HMSO, London. 113 pp.

16. Burden, R.S. and Kemp, M.S. 1984. Sesquiterpene phytoalexins from *Ulmus glabra*. Phytochemistry 23:383-385.

17. Chen, M.M., Smalley, E.B. and Guries, R.P. 1988. Comparative resistance of Chinese sources of *Ulmus pumila* to North American and Eurasian strains of *Ceratocystis* (=*Ophiostoma*) *ulmi*. Proc. Beijing Int. Symp. Plant Pathol., Beijing, China, Sept. 1-5, 1985. 3:1-2.

18. Clark, E.F. 1984. Biochemical aspects of resistance to Dutch elm disease: The role of mansonones. M.S. Thesis, University of Wisconsin, Madison. 109 pp.

19. Duchesne, L.C., Hubbes, M. and Jeng, R.S. 1986. Mansonone E and F accumulation in *Ulmus pumila* resistant to Dutch elm disease. Can. J. For. Res. 16:410-412.

20. Dumas, M.T., Strunz, G.M., Hubbes, M., and Jeng, R.S. 1986. Inhibition of *Ceratocystis ulmi* by mansonones A, C, D, E, F & G isolated from *Ulmus americana*. Eur. J. For. Pathol. 16:217-222.

21. Elgersma, D.M. 1970. Length and diameter of xylem vessels as factors in resistance of elms to *C. ulmi*. Neth. J. Plant Path. 76:179-182.

22. Elgersma, D.M. 1983. Host-parasite interactions in Dutch elm disease. Pages 78-81 in: Research on Dutch elm disease in Europe. D. A. Burdekin, ed. Forestry Commission Bull. 60. HMSO, London. 114 pp.

23. Elgersma, D.M. and Miller, H.J. 1977. Tylose formation in elms after inoculation with an aggressive or a non-aggressive strain of *Ophiostoma ulmi* or with a non-pathogen to elms. Neth. J. Plant Path. 83:241-243.

24. Elgersma, D.M. and Overeem, J.C. 1971. The relation of mansonones to resistance against Dutch elm Disease and their accumulation, as induced by several agents. Neth. J. Plant Pathol. 77:168-174.

25. Francke-Grosmann, H. 1959. Beitrage zur Kenntnis der Übertragungdweise von Pflanzenkrankheiten durch Käfer. Proc. Int. Congr. Bot. 4(1):805-809.

26. Fu, L.K. 1980. Notulae de *Ulmus sinensibus*. J. N. E. For. Inst. 3:1-40. (In Chinese).

27. Gibbs, J.N. 1978. Intercontinental epidemiology of Dutch elm disease. Ann. Rev. Phytopathol. 16:287-307.

28. Gkinis, A. 1977. Factors affecting resistance of elms to Dutch elm disease. Ph.D. Thesis, University of Wisconsin, Madison. 195 pp.

29. Green, C.E., Guries, R.P. and Smalley, E.B. 1985. Early screening of elms for resistance to Dutch elm disease. Plant Dis. 69:60-63.

30. Harrington, T.C. and Cobb, F.W., Jr. 1983. Pathogenicity of *Leptographium* and *Verticicladiella* spp. isolated from roots of Western North American conifers. Phytopathology 73:596-599.

31. Heybroek, H.M. 1983. Resistant elms for Europe. Pages 108-111 in: Research on Dutch elm disease in Europe. D.A. Burdekin, ed. HMSO, London. 113 pp.

32. Higley, L. and Tattar, T.A. 1985. *Leptographium terebrantis* and black turpentine beetles associated with blue stain and mortality of black and scots pine on Cape Cod, Massachusetts. Plant Dis. 69:528-530.

33. Jacobi, W.R. and MacDonald, W.L. 1980. Colonization of resistant and susceptible oak by *Ceratocystis fagacearum*. Phytopathology 60:1399-1404.

34. Kahl, G. 1982. Molecular biology of wound healing: The conditioning phenomenon. Pages 211-267 in: Molecular Biology of Plant Tumors. G. Kahl and J.S. Schell, eds. Academic Press, New York. 615 pp.

35. Klepzig, K.D., Smalley, E.B. and Raffa, K.F. 1990. Fungistatic activity of extracts from red pine towards *Leptographium terebrantis*. Mycol. Soc. Am. Newsl. 41:22.

36. Klepzig, K., Raffa, K.F. and Smalley, E.B. 1991. Association of an insect-fungal complex with red pine decline in Wisconsin. For. Sci. 37:1119-1139.

37. Kondo, E.S., Hiratsuka, Y. and Denyer, W.B.C., (eds.). 1982.

Proceedings of the Dutch elm disease symposium and workshop. 5-9 October, 1981, Winnipeg, Manitoba, Canada. 517 pp.

38. Krause, C.R. and Wilson, C.L. 1972. Fine structure of *Ceratocystis ulmi* in elm wood. Phytopathology 62:1253-1256.

39. Lanier, G.N. 1978. Vectors. Pages 13-17 in: Dutch elm disease: Perspectives after 60 years. W. A. Sinclair and R. J. Campana, eds. Cornell Univ. Agric. Exp. Stn. Search (Agric) 8:1-52.

40. Lewis, K.J. and Alexander, S.A, 1986. Insects associated with the transmission of *Verticicladiella procera*. Can. J. For. Res. 16:1330-1333.

41. MacHardy, W.E. 1978. Mechanisms of resistance. Pages 25-26 in: Dutch elm disease: Perspectives after 60 years. W.A. Sinclair and R.J. Campana, eds. Cornell Univ. Agric. Exp. Stn. Search (Agric) 8:1-52.

42. Mattson, W.J., Levieux, J., and Bernard-Dagan, C. (eds.). 1988. Mechanisms of Woody Plant Defenses Against Insects: Search for pattern. Springer-Verlag, N.Y. 416 pp.

43. McNabb, H.S., Heybroek, H.M., and MacDonald, W.L. 1970. Anatomical factors in resistance to Dutch elm disease. Neth. J. Plant Path. 76:196-204.

44. Michalski, J. 1973. Revision of the palearctic species of the genus *Scolytus* Geoffroy (Coleoptera: Scolytidae). Polska Akad. Nauk Zak. Zool. Syst. I. Doswiadczalnej. Warszawa. 214 pp + 49 plates.

45. Miller, H.J. and Elgersma, D.M. 1976. The growth of aggressive and non-aggressive strains of *Ophiostoma ulmi* in susceptible and resistant elms, a scanning microscope study. Neth. J. Plant Path. 82:51-65.

46. Ouellette, G.B. 1978a. Fine structural observations on substances attributable to *Ceratocystis ulmi* in American elm and aspects of host cell disturbances. Can. J. Bot. 56:2550-2566.

47. Ouellette, G.B. 1978b. Ultrastructural observations on pit membrane alterations and associated effects in elm xylem tissues infected by *Ceratocystis ulmi*. Can. J. Bot. 56:2567-2588.

48. Ouellette, G.B. 1978c. Light and electron microscope studies on cell wall breakdown in American elm xylem tissues infected with Dutch elm disease. Can. J. Bot. 56:2666-2693.

49. Overeem, J.C. and Elgersma, D.M. 1970. Accumulation of mansonones E and F in *Ulmus hollandica* infected with *Ceratocystis ulmi*. Phytochemistry 9:1949-1952.

50. Pegg, G.F. 1985. Presidential address: Life in a black hole - The microenvironment of the vascular pathogen. Trans. Br. Mycol. Soc. 85:1-20.

51. Proctor, R.H. 1988. Identification, accumulation, and inhibitory effects of the elm phytoalexins mansonones E and F. M.S. Thesis. University of Wisconsin, Madison. 82 pp.

52. Proctor, R.H. 1990. Phytoalexins and Dutch elm disease resistance. Ph.D. Thesis. University of Wisconsin, Madison. 132 pp.

53. Proctor, R.H. and Smalley, E.B. 1990. Effects of mansonone E on the growth of *Ophiostoma ulmi* and other fungi. Mycol. Soc. Am. Newsl. 41:33

54. Proctor, R.H. and Smalley, E.B. 1990. Lack of association between mansonone tolerance and virulence in *Ophiostoma ulmi*. Phytopathology 80:968.

55. Przybyl, K. 1984. Pathological changes and defense responses in poplar tissues caused by *Ceratocystis fimbriata*. Eur. J. For. Pathol. 14:183-191.

56. Raffa, K.F. 1991. Induced defenses in conifer-bark beetle systems. Pages 245-276 in: Phytochemical Induction by Herbivores. D.W. Tallamy and M. Raupp, eds. Academic Press, New York.

57. Raffa, K.F., and Berryman, A.A. 1982. Gustatory cues in the orientation of *Dendroctonus ponderosae* (Coleoptera: Scolytidae) to host trees. Can. Entomol. 114:97-104.

58. Raffa, K.F., and Berryman, A.A. 1983. The role of host plant resistance in the colonization behavior and ecology of bark beetles. (Coleoptera: Scolytidae). Ecol. Monogr. 53:27-49.

59. Raffa, K.F., and Berryman, A.A. 1983. Physiological aspects of lodgepole pine wound response to a fungal symbiont of the mountain pine beetle. Can. Entomol. 115:723-734.

60. Raffa, K.F., Berryman, A.A., Simasko, J., Teal, W., and Wong, B.L. 1985. Effects of grand fir monoterpenes on the fir engraver beetle (Coleoptera: Scolytidae) and its symbiont fungi. Environ. Entomol. 4:552-556.

61. Raffa, K.F. and Smalley, E.B. 1988a. Seasonal and longterm responses of host trees to microbial associates of the pine engraver, *Ips pini*. Can. J. For. Res. 18:1624-1634.

62. Raffa, K.F. and Smalley, E.B. 1988b. Response of red and jack pines to inoculation with microbial associates of the pine engraver, *Ips pini*. Can. J. For. Res. 18:581-586.

63. Raffa, K.F. and Smalley, E.B. 1988c. Host resistance to invasion by lower stem root infesting insects of pine: Response to controlled inoculations with the fungal associate *Leptographium terebrantis*. Can J. For. Res. 18:675-681.

64. Sachs, I.B., Nair, V.M.G. & Kuntz, J.E. 1970. Penetration and degradation of cell walls in oak infected with *Ceratocystis fagacearum*. Phytopathology 60:1399-1404.

65. Scheffer, R.J. 1983. Toxins in Dutch elm disease. Pages 82-85 in: Research on Dutch elm disease in Europe. D.A. Burdekin, ed. Forestry Commission Bull. 60. HMSO, London. 114 pp.

66. Schoeneweiss, D.F. 1981. The role of environmental stress in diseases of woody plants. Plant Dis. 65:308-314.

67. Schoeneweiss, D.F. 1983. Drought predisposition to *Cytospora* canker in blue spruce. Plant Dis. 67:383-385.

68. Shigo, A.L. and Tippet, J.T. 1981. Compartmentalization of American elm tissues infected with *Ceratocystis ulmi*. Plant Dis. 65:715-718.

69. Shrimpton, D.M. 1973. Extractives associated with the wound response of lodgepole pine attacked by the mountain pine beetle and associated microorganisms. Can. J. Bot. 51:527-534.

70. Sinclair, W.A. and Campana, R.J. (eds.). 1978. Dutch elm Disease: Perspectives after 60 years, Cornell University Agricutural Experiment Station. Search (Agriculture) 8:1-52.

71. Sinclair, W.A., Lyon, H.H. and Johnson, W.T. 1987. Diseases of Trees and Shrubs. Cornell University Press, Ithaca, NY. 574 pp.

72. Sinclair, W.A., Zahand, J.P. and Melching, J.B. 1975. Anatomical marker for resistance of *Ulmus americana* to *Ceratocystis ulmi*. Phytopathology 65:349-352.

73. Smalley, E.B. 1963. Seasonal fluctuations in susceptibility of young elm seedlings to Dutch elm disease.

Phytopathology 53:846-853.

74. Smalley, E.B. 1967. Present status of Dutch elm disease research in Plant Pathology at Wisconsin. Pages 16-20 in: Proc. USDA Regional Conference on the Control of Dutch Elm Disease. Delaware, Ohio, June 29-30.

75. Smalley, E.B., Ehlke, N.S., Clark, E.F. and Mai, S.H. 1982. Cambial reactions in *Ulmus* following inoculation with *Ceratocystis ulmi*. Phytopathology 72:981.

76. Smalley, E.B. and Guries, R.P. 1986. Dutch elm disease: resistant cultivars. Grass Roots 13:42-43.

77. Smalley, E.B. and Kais, A.G. 1966. Seasonal variations in the resistance of various elm species to Dutch elm disease. Pages 279-292 in: Breeding Pest-Resistant Trees. H.D. Gerhold, E.J. Schreiner, R.E. McDermott and J.A. Winieski, eds. Permagamon Press, NY. 505 pp.

78. Smalley, E.B. and Lester, D.T. 1973. 'Sapporo Autumn Gold' elm. Hort. Sci. 8:514-515.

79. Smalley, E.B. and Lester, D.T. 1983. 'Regal' elm. Hort. Sci. 18:960-961.

80. Stipes, R.J. and Campana, R.J. 1981. Compendium of elm diseases. American Phytopathological Society Press, St. Paul. MN. 96 pp.

81. Struckmeyer, B.E., Beckman, C.H., Kuntz, J.E. and Riker, A.J. 1954. Plugging of vessels by tyloses and gums in wilting oaks. Phytopathology 44:148-153.

82. Takai, S. and Kondo, E.S. 1979. Seasonal development of Dutch elm disease on white elms in central Ontario, Canada. I. Following wound inoculation. Can J. Bot. 7:341-352.

83. Takai, S., Kondo, E.S. and Thomas, J.B. 1979. Seasonal development of Dutch elm disease on white elms in central Ontario, Canada. II. Following feeding by the North American native elm bark beetle. Can. J. Bot. 57:353-359.

84. True, R.P., Barnett, H.L., Dorsey, C.K. and Leach, J.G. 1960. Oak wilt in West Virginia. West Va. Univ. Agric. Exp. Sta. Bull. 448T. 119 pp.

85. Upadhyay, H.P. 1981. A monograph of *Ceratocystis* and *Ceratocystiopsis*. University of Athens Press, Athens, GA. 176 pp.

86. Uritani, I. 1978. Biochemistry of host response to infection chiefly by *Ceratocystis fimbriata*. Prog. Phytochem. 5:29-63.

87. Vance, C.P., Kirk, T.K. and Sherwood, R.T. 1980. Lignification as a mechanism of disease resistance. Ann. Rev. Phytopathol. 18:259-288.

88. Webber, J.F. and Brasier, C.M. 1984. The transmission of Dutch elm disease: study of the processes involved. Pages 271-306 in: Invertebrate-Microbial Interactions, J. M. Anderson, A.D.M. Rayner, and D.W.H. Walton, eds. Cambridge University Press, Cambridge. 349 pp.

89. Webber, J.F. and Gibbs, J.N. 1989. Insect dissemination of fungal pathogens of trees. Pages 161-194 in: Insect-Fungus Interactions, N. Wilding, N.M. Collins, P.M. Hammond, and J.F. Webber, eds. Proc. 14th Symposium Royal Ent. Soc. London. Academic Press, London. 349 pp.

90. Wheeler, Q. and Blackwell, M. 1984. Fungus-insect relationships: Perspectives in Ecology and Evolution. Columbia University Press, New York. 514 pp.

91. Wilding, N., Collins, N.M., Hammond, P.M. and Webber, J. F. (eds) 1989. Insect-Fungus Interactions, Academic Press, London. 344 pp.

92. Wingfield, M.J., Capretti, P., and MacKenzie, M. 1988. *Leptographium* root diseases of conifers. An international perspective. pages 113-128 in: *Leptographium* root diseases of conifers. T.C. Harrington, and F.W. Cobb, Jr., eds. American Phytopathological Society Press, St. Paul, MN. 144 pp.

93. Wood, S.L. 1982. The Bark and Ambrosia Beetles of North and Central America, (Coleoptera:Scolytidae), a Taxonomic Monograph. Great Basin Naturalist Memoirs No. 6. Brigham Young University, Provo, Utah. 1359 pp.

94. Wu, W.D., Jeng, R.S. and Hubbes, M. 1989. Toxic effects of elm phytoalexin mansonones on *Ophiostoma ulmi*, the causal agent of Dutch elm disease. Eur. J. For. Pathol. 19:343-357.

95. Yasuda, K. and Kojima, M. 1986. The role of stress metabolites in establishing host-parasite specificity between sweet potato and *Ceratocystis fimbriata*, black rot fungus. Agric. Biol. Chem. 50:1839-1846.

Chapter 23

HOST DEFENSE REACTIONS IN RESPONSE TO INOCULATION WITH *OPHIOSTOMA* SPECIES

T.D. PAINE, F.M. STEPHEN and R.G. CATES

INTRODUCTION

Species of bark beetles in the family Scolytidae have well known associations with many species of fungi. Whitney (59) has compiled an extensive list from North America of microorganisms isolated either from the beetles or from the habitat colonized by these insects. However, not all of the isolations necessarily represent a close biological association. Although contact may be accidental or a contamination of the external surface of the insect, there are associations that are either symbiotic or mutualistic between the beetles and specific fungal species. Examples of these associations with linked life histories include *Dendroctonus ponderosae* with *Ophiostoma clavigerum*, *D. brevicomis* with *O. nigrocarpum* and an unidentified basidiomycete, *D. frontalis* with *Ceratocystiopsis ranaculosis* and a basidiomycete (SJB 122), and *Scolytus ventralis* with *Trichosporium symbioticum* (16).

Many of the beetle species have evolved specialized structures (mycangia) to hold and culture these fungi. In the genus *Dendroctonus*, there are two principal types of mycangia. *Dendroctonus ponderosae* and *D. jeffreyi* are examples of species possessing maxillary mycangia (60, Paine unpublished data). The fungus bearing structures are within the cardines of each maxilla with the openings at the base. In contrast, four species (*D. adjunctus, D. approximatus, D. brevicomis,* and *D. frontalis*) have thoracic mycangia (16). These structures consist of invaginations of cuticle along the anterior margin of the pronotum. They open to the exterior near the attachment of the cervical membrane behind the head and extend around the entire prothorax above the base of the coxae. Unlike the species with maxillary mycangia, species with thoracic mycangia show strong sexual dimorphism. Females have large well-developed mycangia, while these are reduced to pseudo-mycangia in males (4,5).

How the fungal spores enter the mycangia is unclear but in all species, the fungi are acquired in the structures after the individuals molt from the pupal stage to adults (35). One of the intriguing questions that has been raised but not answered is how the beetles or the fungi create an environment within the mycangium that is suitable for the growth of specific fungi but apparently inhibitory to potentially contaminating species. It has been suggested that cells beneath the cuticle lining these structures secrete fluids that may nourish the specific fungal associates (5).

Where specific associations have been studied in some detail, the beetles appear to benefit from the presence of the fungi in several ways. For example, the development time and reproductive success of *D. frontalis* was reduced when the mycangial fungi were absent (2). In addition, there was a reduction in beetle success if they were forced to breed in tissue previously colonized by the blue-staining *O. minus,* which is normally found on the exterior body surface but is not a mycangial associate (1,20). Bridges (9) has demonstrated that female *D. frontalis* carrying mycangial fungi were significantly heavier than females that had neither fungus. Goldhammer, Stephen and Paine (19) suggested that oviposition rates were higher and gallery lengths were longer for beetles that were associated with the mycangial fungi than when those fungi were absent. Clearly, these fungi may modify the nutritional environment of the host (22,3) to favor beetle reproductive success. Indeed, Barras and Perry (5) suggested that the spore type of at least one of the mycangial fungi of *D. frontalis* appeared similar to the ambrosia fungi of other wood-boring beetles; Goldhammer, Stephen and Paine (18) demonstrated that chlamydospore production of both mycangial fungi of the beetle was enhanced if beetle frass was added to culture media.

An additional benefit provided to the beetle by the mycangial fungi may be through physically conditioning the host tissue. Graham (21) suggested that beetle success (successful larval development) may be enhanced by fungal colonization which reduced inner bark water content and increased tissue aeration. Nelson (31) and Reid (50) showed that water content of the beetle-colonized areas was reduced. *Dendroctonus frontalis* larval development time and mortality increased with increased phloem moisture content (57,58).

The third potential benefit for the beetles derived from the fungal associates could be in overcoming the resistance of the host tree. The beetles inoculate both mycangial and non-mycangial fungal associates into the trees during the colonization process. *Leptographium terebrantis* is associated with *D. valens* and has been found to block water penetration through *Pinus ponderosa* stems (32,44). Paine (33) demonstrated a similar reduction in water flow through seedling *P. ponderosa* by fungi associated with *D. brevicomis*. Three phytotoxic polyphenolic compounds have been isolated from cultures of *O. minus* isolated from *D. frontalis*, and it has been hypothesized that the mycangial associates of this beetle may also produce similar toxic compounds (23).

Host Reactions to Inoculated Fungi

Reid, Whitney and Watson (52) described the induced response of lodgepole pine, *Pinus contorta* var. *latifolia*, to invasion by *D. ponderosae* and its associated fungi. The reaction included a decrease in sapwood and inner bark moisture, starch hydrolysis, bark adhesion, resinosis and subsequent necrosis of inner bark and sapwood cells, callus formation, formation of traumatic resin ducts and production of new cambium and periderm. This reaction was the same both following beetle attack or inoculation with *Ophiostoma* spp. They noted that resistant trees produced this reaction, but trees killed by beetle attack failed to react. Subsequently, Berryman (7) described a similar reaction, including secondary resinosis of phloem parenchyma, cell necrosis, formation of traumatic resin cavities, and production of wound callus in *Abies grandis* in response to attack by *S. ventralis* and its associated fungus, *T. symbioticum*. Susceptible trees produced only a limited reaction to invasion (7). The reaction is induced by fungal invasion and appears to precede the hyphal strands (61). It has been demonstrated recently that fungal cell wall components (chitosan) and a proteinase inhibitor inducing factor (chemical signals associated with tissue damage) are also able to elicit this induced reaction in the absence of any fungi (30). However, Lieutier and Berryman (24) found that resinosis of the inner phloem, earlywood and sapwood in response to chitosan and *O. clavigerum* were more extensive than the reaction to the proteinase inhibitor inducing factor.

Two elements associated with the induced reaction of conifers to infection are lesion size and chemical composition of the resinous tissue. The size of the reaction can be influenced by several factors, including height and growing conditions. In *P. contorta*, the reactions to *O. clavigerum* were largest to inoculations at ca. 6.5m up the stem. In contrast, the size of the response to *O. minus* by *Pinus taeda* was the same at all sample heights (38). There were high degrees of within-tree and among-tree variation in lesion size in *P. taeda* that were not related to differences in inoculum dose or to site conditions (Paine, Stephen, and Cates, unpublished). However, there was a significant positive correlation between the extent of lesion length and growth of inoculated *O. minus* (Paine, Stephen, and Cates, unpublished).

The second quantitative element of the response of conifers to inoculated fungi is the accumulation of monoterpenes, resin acids, or phenolics and a decrease in carbohydrate levels in induced tissues. Raffa and Berryman reported similar patterns for both *P. contorta* (45) and *A. grandis* (46) inoculated with different fungi; resistant trees formed greater quantities of resins in reaction zones than did susceptible trees. The resins in *A. grandis* reactions were quantitatively and qualitatively from pre-formed cortical blister resins (53). In subsequent studies with *P. contorta*, the accumulation of monoterpenes was accompanied by a decrease in carbohydrate levels, but the authors suggested that there was both synthesis and translocation of terpenes into the reaction zones (29). Similar chemical changes were reported by Cook and Hain (13) for inoculated *P. taeda*. However, unlike the *P. contorta* system, not only are there quantitative changes in monoterpene composition of the *P. taeda* reaction lesions, but the resin in the induced zones may vary qualitatively as well (36,17).

Reaction resins can be an effective defense against infection and invasion. Secondary resins or monoterpene constituents of *A. grandis* induced reactions to *T. symbioticum* were either repellent (8) or toxic (49) to *S. ventralis* and the monoterpenes were inhibitory to growth of the fungus (49). *Ophiostoma* species associated with *D. brevicomis* were not inhibited by extracts of *P. ponderosa* reaction lesions (34) but extracts or constituents of the resin within the response tissues were inhibitory in the *P. contorta* (54,55) and *P. taeda* (10) systems. The phenolic composition of the reaction tissue of *P. taeda* completely inhibited growth of *O. minus* but only partially reduced growth of *C. ranaculosis*, and there were differences in the growth responses of these fungi to the different enantiomers of α-pinene and limonene (Cates, Khan, and Paine, unpublished data).

Response of trees to inoculation with fungi from bark beetles has been used as an indication of resistance to insect invasion. Raffa and Berryman (47) demonstrated that resistant *P. contorta* had greater amounts of the secondary chemicals in lesions than did susceptible trees, while Paine and Stephen (39) found that suppressed *P. taeda* produced smaller lesions than dominant trees growing in the same stand. However, there may be a limit to the ability of a tree to respond to fungi associated with bark beetles. Several independent investigations have suggested that the resources of the tree to respond are finite and in dose response tests show an initial increase in response followed by a decline once the threshold number of inoculations within a specific area is surpassed (11,12,25,47). However, Paine and Stephen (40) inoculated *P. taeda* with different size doses in single treatment sites and found that trees responded similarly despite an eight-fold increased dose of *O. minus*.

Thus, the resistance of trees to colonization by bark beetles and their associated fungi may be a function of both intensity of the response (size and resin content) and rate of lesion formation. Rapid colonization by large numbers of beetles may kill the tree before the induced reaction can form, even though it may be highly effective in preventing successful attack by fewer individuals. *Pinus taeda* shows no significant visible response until ca. 60 hours after inoculation with *O. minus*, followed by a period of very rapid resinosis (43). Similarly, *A. grandis* has a slow appearance of visible lesion formation during the initial three days after inoculation with *T. symbioticum*, and then very rapid changes through the next four days (61,46). In contrast, the response of *P. contorta* to inoculation with *O. clavigerum* appears to be rapid and immediate (24,47).

Formation of the induced response is not temporally constant and varies with conifer species. *Pinus contorta* responses to inoculation with *O. clavigerum* increase during May and June, are at a maximum during July, and decline during the period between August and September (51). In contrast, responses of *P. ponderosa* to *O. minus* associated with *D. brevicomis* were longer and produced faster in October (mid-fall) than in August (mid-summer), and were smallest and slowest to form in late May - early June (late-spring) (34). There were no differences in the size of the response of *P. taeda* to inoculations of *O. minus* made between February and October, but they were significantly smaller for the remaining months (56). Similar results for lesion size were

obtained by Cook, Hain and Nappen (15) with both *P. taeda* and *P. echinata* inoculated with the same fungus. However, the rate of response was significantly slower during the period from February-May compared to the period June-September (56). It has been hypothesized that there is a shift in allocation of resources, primarily photosynthate, in the southern pines from favoring growth during the spring months when temperatures are warm and water is readily available to the tree, to favoring differentiation of tissues and defenses when moisture becomes relatively limited (26). There is a basis of support for the hypothesis from the studies of growth rates of the induced response (56) and the flow of preformed resin throughout the year (27).

There are still uncertainties as to whether the induced reaction is generalized or specific. That is, do trees respond to infection by all fungi in the same way or do different fungi elicit different patterns of response. *Pinus ponderosa* responded in similar ways to the blue-stain fungus *O. minus*, the two mycangial fungi of *D. brevicomis* (*O. nigrocarpum* and an unnamed Basidiomycete), and to a *Penicillium* sp. (34). Results from studies by Cook and Hain (13), following inoculations of *O. minus* and *C. ranaculosis* into *P. taeda*, seem to support the hypothesis of a generalized response. However, other studies have indicated that *P. taeda* responds to *O. minus*, but the responses to the mycangial fungi of *D. frontalis* (*C. ranaculosis* and an unnamed basidiomycete) are not significantly different from the response to sterile wounds (41,43). Similarly, *P. resinosa* and *P. sylvestris* responded significantly to inoculations of *L. terebrantis* but not to *O. ips* (6). Although *P. rigida* responded to a significantly greater degree to inoculations of *O. ips* than to sterile wounds, these responses were significantly smaller than the responses to *L. terebrantis* (6). It is apparent that responses to inoculation are characteristic for each conifer species (6,13,14,25) and generalizations for different species should be made with caution.

CONCLUSIONS

The preformed and induced responses of conifers are generally effective against colonization by pathogens and insects. The physical and chemical barriers can be either toxic or inhibitory to the invading organisms. Even when beetle colonization is successful, if the induced response has formed in localized areas, those regions are avoided by the bark beetles. Furthermore, beetle reproduction is significantly reduced if the insects are forced to colonize the resinous and necrotic zones (42). Conifer species may be colonized by different bark beetle and/or fungal pathogens. Several hypotheses have been proposed to explain the interactions among these organisms (23,28,37,48). It is, however, obvious that the interactions are adapted to the ecological constraints of each system (e.g. temperature, host range and host availability of beetles and fungi, colonization behavior, flight period, larval feeding behavior). It is also obvious that generalizations are currently restricted to our limited understanding of the dynamic nature of these systems. New techniques, new collaborations, and new information are improving our ability to understand these complex biological interactions.

LITERATURE CITED

1. Barras, S.J. 1970. Antagonism between *Dendroctonus frontalis* and the fungus *Ceratocystis minor*. Ann. Entomol. Soc. Am. 63:1187-1190.
2. Barras, S.J. 1973. Reduction of progeny and development in the southern pine beetle following removal of symbiotic fungi. Can. Entomol. 105:1295-1299.
3. Barras, S.J. and Hodges, J.D. 1969. Carbohydrates of inner bark of *Pinus taeda* as affected by *Dendroctonus frontalis* and associated microorganisms. Can. Entomol. 101:489-493.
4. Barras, S.J. and Perry, T. 1971. Gland cells and fungi associated with prothoracic mycangium of *Dendroctonus adjunctus* (Coleoptera: Scolytidae). Ann. Entomol. Soc. Am. 64:123-126.
5. Barras, S.J. and Perry, T. 1972. Fungal symbionts in the prothoracic mycangium of *Dendroctonus frontalis* (Coleopt: Scolytidae). Z. Ang. Entomol. 71:95-104.
6. Bennet, E.M. and Tattar, T.A. 1988. Bluestain fungi and insect vector interaction in Japanese black pine and scots pine mortality. Abor. J. 12:237-247.
7. Berryman, A.A. 1969. Responses of *Abies grandis* to attack by *Scolytus ventralis* (Coleoptera: Scolytidae). Can. Entomol. 101:1033-1041.
8. Bordasch, R.P. and Berryman, A.A. 1977. Host resistance to the fir engraver beetle, *Scolytus ventralis* (Coleoptera: Scolytidae). 2. Repellency of *Abies grandis* resins and some monoterpenes. Can. Entomol. 109:95-100.
9. Bridges, J.R. 1983. Mycangial fungi of *Dendroctonus frontalis* (Coleoptera: Scolytidae) and their relationship to beetle population trends. Environ. Entomol. 12:858-861.
10. Bridges, J.R. 1987. Effects of terpenoid compounds on growth of symbiotic fungi associated with the southern pine beetle. Phytopathology 77:83-85.
11. Christiansen, E. 1985. *Ips/Ceratocystis*-infection of Norway spruce: what is a deadly dosage. Z. Ang. Entomol. 99:6-11.
12. Christiansen, E. and Horntvedt, R. 1983. Combined *Ips/Ceratocystis* attack on Norway spruce, and defensive mechanisms of the trees. Z. Ang. Entomol.
96:110-118.
13. Cook, S.P. and Hain, F.P. 1985. Qualitative examination of the hypersensitive response of loblolly pine, *Pinus taeda* L., inoculated with two fungal associates of the southern pine beetle, *Dendroctonus frontalis* Zimmermann (Coleoptera: Scolytidae). Environ. Entomol. 14:396-400.
14. Cook, S.P. and Hain, F.P. 1986. Defensive mechanisms of loblolly and shortleaf pine against attack by southern pine beetle, *Dendroctonus frontalis* Zimmermann, and its fungal associate, *Ceratocystis minor* (Hedgecock) Hunt. J. Chem. Ecol. 12:1397-1406.
15. Cook, S.P., Hain, F.P. and Nappen, P.B. 1986. Seasonality of the hypersensitive response by loblolly and shortleaf pine to inoculation with a fungal associate of the southern pine beetle (Coleoptera: Scolytidae). J. Entomol. Sci. 21:283-285.
16. Francke-Grosmann, H. 1967. Ectosymbiosis in wood-inhabiting insects. Pages 141-205 in: Symbiosis. Vol. 2. S.M. Henry, ed. Academic Press, New York. 443 pp.
17. Gambliel, H.A., Cates, R.G., Caffey-Moquin, M.K. and Paine, T.D. 1985. Variation in the chemistry of loblolly pine in relation to infection by the bluestain fungus. Pages 177-184 in: Integrated Pest Management Research Symposium: the Proceedings. S. J. Branham and R.C. Thatcher, eds. USDA For. Serv., South. For. Exp. Stn., Gen. Tech. Rep. SO-56.
18. Goldhammer, D.S., Stephen, F.M. and Paine, T.D. 1989. Average radial growth rate and chlamydospore production of *Ceratocystis minor*, *Ceratocystis minor* var. *barrasii*, and SJB 122 in culture. Can. J. Bot. 67:3498-3505.
19. Goldhammer, D.S., Stephen, F.M. and Paine, T.D. 1990. The effect of the fungi *Ceratocystis minor* (Hedgecock) Hunt, *Ceratocystis minor* (Hedgecock) Hunt var. *barrasii* Taylor, and SJB 122 on the reproduction of the southern pine beetle, *Dendroctonus frontalis* Zimmermann (Coleoptera: Scolytidae). Can. Entomol. 122:407-418.
20. Goldman, S.E. and Franklin, R.T. 1977. Development and feeding habits of southern pine beetle larvae. Ann. Entomol. Soc. Am. 70:54-56.
21. Graham, K. 1967. Fungal-insect mutualism in trees and timber. Ann. Rev. Entomol. 20:75-95.
22. Hodges, J.D., Barras, S.J. and Mauldin, J.K. 1968. Amino acids in inner bark of loblolly pine, as affected by the southern pine beetle and associated microorganisms. Can. J. Bot. 46:1467-1472.
23. Hodges, J.D., Nebeker, T.E., DeAngelis, J.D., Karr, B.L. and Blanche, C.A. 1985. Host resistance and mortality: a hypothesis based on the southern pine beetle-microorganism-host interactions. Bull. Entomol. Soc. Am. 31:31-34.
24. Lieutier, F. and Berryman, A.A. 1988. Preliminary histological investigations of the defense reactions of three pines to *Ceratocystis clavigera* and two chemical elicitors. Can. J. For. Res. 18:1243-1247.
25. Lieutier, F., Cheniclet, C. and Garcia, J. 1989. Comparison of the defense reactions of *Pinus pinaster* and *Pinus sylvestris* to attacks by two bark beetles (Coleoptera: Scolytidae) and their associated fungi. Environ. Entomol. 18:228-234.

26. Lorio, P.L., Jr. 1986. Growth-differentiation balance: a basis for understanding southern pine beetle-tree interactions. For. Ecol. Man. 14:259-273.

27. Lorio, P.L., Jr. and Sommers, R.A. 1986. Evidence of competition for photosynthates between growth processes and oleoresin synthesis in *Pinus taeda* L. Tree Physiol. 2:301-306.

28. Mattson, P.A. and Hain, F.P. 1985. Host conifer defense strategies: a hypothesis. Pages 33-39 in: The Role of the Host in the Population Dynamics of Forest Insects. L. Safranyik, ed. Can. For. Serv. and USDA For. Serv., Victoria, British Columbia, Canada.

29. Miller, R.H. and Berryman, A.A. 1985. Energetics of conifer defense against bark beetles and associated fungi. Pages 13-23 in: The Role of the Host in the Population Dynamics of Forest Insects. L. Safranyik, ed. Can. For. Serv. and USDA For. Serv., Victoria, British Columbia, Canada.

30. Miller, R.H., Berryman, A.A., and Ryan, C.A. 1986. Biotic elicitors of defense reactions in lodgepole pine. Phytochemistry 25:611-612.

31. Nelson, R.M. 1934. Effect of blue stain fungi on southern pines attacked by bark beetles. Phytopathol. Z. 7:325-353.

32. Owen, D.R., Lindahl, K.Q., Jr., Wood, D.L. and Parmeter, J.R., Jr. 1987. Pathogenicity of fungi isolated from *Dendroctonus valens, Dendroctonus brevicomis, Dendroctonus ponderosae* to ponderosa pine seedlings. Phytopathology 77:631-636.

33. Paine, T.D. 1984a. Influence of the mycangial fungi of the western pine beetle on water conduction through ponderosa pine seedlings. Can. J. Bot. 62:556-558.

34. Paine, T.D. 1984b. Seasonal response of ponderosa pine to inoculation of the mycangial fungi from the western pine beetle. Can. J. Bot. 62:551-555.

35. Paine, T.D. and Birch, M.C. 1983. Acquisition and maintenance of mycangial fungi by *Dendroctonus brevicomis* LeConte (Coleoptera: Scolytidae). Environ. Entomol. 12:1384-1386.

36. Paine, T.D., Blanche, C.A., Nebeker, T.E. and Stephen, F.M. 1987. Composition of loblolly pine resin defenses: comparison of monoterpenes from induced lesion and sapwood resin. Can. J. For. Res. 17:1202-1206.

37. Paine, T.D., Stephen, F.M. and Taha, H.A. 1984. Conceptual model of infestation probability based on bark beetle abundance and host tree susceptibility. Environ. Entomol. 13:619-624.

38. Paine, T.D. and Stephen, F.M. 1987a. The relationship of tree height and crown class to the induced plant defenses of loblolly pine. Can. J. Bot. 65:2090-2092.

39. Paine, T.D. and Stephen, F.M. 1987b. Influence of tree stress and site quality on the induced defense system of loblolly pine. Can. J. For. Res. 17:569-571.

40. Paine, T.D. and Stephen, F.M. 1987c. Response of loblolly pine to different inoculum doses of *Ceratocystis minor*, a blue-stain fungus associated with *Dendroctonus frontalis*. Can. J. Bot. 65: 2093-2095.

41. Paine, T.D. and Stephen, F.M. 1987d. Fungi associated with the southern pine beetle: avoidance of induced defense response in loblolly pine. Oecologia (Berlin) 74:377-379.

42. Paine, T.D. and Stephen, F.M. 1988. Induced defenses of loblolly pine, *Pinus taeda*: potential impact on *Dendroctonus frontalis* within-tree mortality. Entomol. Exp. Appl. 46:39-46.

43. Paine, T.D., Stephen, F.M. and Cates, R.G. 1988. Phenology of an induced response in loblolly pine following inoculation of fungi associated with the southern pine beetle. Can. J. For. Res. 18:1556-1562.

44. Parmeter, J.R., Jr., Slaughter, G.W., Chen, M.-M., Wood, D.L. and Stubbs, H.A. 1989. Single and mixed inoculations of ponderosa pine with fungal associates of *Dendroctonus* spp. Phytopathology 79:768-772.

45. Raffa, K.F. and Berryman, A.A. 1982a. Physiological differences between lodgepole pines resistant and susceptible to the mountain pine beetle and associated microorganisms. Environ. Entomol. 11:486-492.

46. Raffa, K.F. and Berryman, A.A. 1982b. Accumulation of monoterpenes and associated volatiles following inoculation of grand fir with a fungus transmitted by the fir engraver, *Scolytus ventralis* (Coleoptera: Scolytidae). Can. Entomol. 114:797-810.

47. Raffa, K.F. and Berryman, A.A. 1983. Physiological aspects of lodgepole wound responses to a fungal symbiont of the mountain pine beetle, *Dendroctonus ponderosae* (Coleoptera: Scolytidae). Can. Entomol. 115:723-734.

48. Raffa, K.F. and Berryman, A.A. 1987. Interacting selective pressures in conifer-bark beetle systems: a basis for reciprocal adaptations? Am. Nat. 129:234-262.

49. Raffa, K.F., Berryman, A.A., Simasko, J., Teal, W. and Wong, B.L. 1985. Effects of grand fir monoterpenes on the fir engraver, *Scolytus ventralis* (Coleoptera: Scolytidae), and its symbiotic fungus. Environ. Entomol. 14:552-556.

50. Reid, R.W. 1961. Moisture changes in lodgepole pine before and after attack by mountain pine beetle. For. Chron. 37:368-375.

51. Reid, R.W. and Shrimpton, D.M. 1971. Resistant response of lodgepole pine to inoculation with *Europhium clavigerum* in different months and at different heights on stem. Can. J. Bot. 49:349-351.

52. Reid, R.W., Whitney, H.S. and Watson, J.A. 1967. Reactions of lodgepole pine to attack by *Dendroctonus ponderosae* Hopkins and blue stain fungi. Can. J. Bot. 45:1115-1126.

53. Russell, C.E. and Berryman, A.A. 1976. Host resistance to the fir engraver beetle. 1. Monoterpene composition of *Abies grandis* pitch blisters and fungus-infected wounds. Can. J. Bot. 54:14-18.

54. Shrimpton, D.M. 1973. Extractives associated with wound response of lodgepole pine attacked by the mountain pine beetle and associated microorganisms. Can. J. Bot. 51:527-534.

55. Shrimpton, D.M. and Whitney, H.S. 1968. Inhibition of growth of blue stain fungi by wood extractives. Can. J. Bot. 46:757-761.

56. Stephen, F.M. and Paine, T.D. 1985. Seasonal patterns of host tree resistance to fungal associates of the southern pine beetle. Z. Ang. Entomol. 99:113-122.

57. Wagner, T.L., Gagne, J.A., Doraiswamy, P.C., Coulson, R.N. and Brown, K. W. 1979. Development time and mortality of *Dendroctonus frontalis* in relation to changes in tree moisture and xylem water potential. Environ. Entomol. 8:1129-1138.

58. Webb, J.W. and Franklin, R.T. 1978. Influence of

phloem moisture on brood development of the southern pine beetle (Coleoptera: Scolytidae). Environ. Entomol. 7:405-410.

59. Whitney, H.S. 1982. Relationships between bark beetles and symbiotic organisms. Pages 183-211 in: Bark Beetles in North American Conifers. J.B. Mitton and K.B. Sturgeon, eds. University of Texas Press, Austin. 539 pp.

60. Whitney, H.S. and Ferris, S.H. 1970. Maxillary mycangium in the mountain pine beetle. Science 167:54-55.

61. Wong B.L. and Berryman, A.A. 1977. Host resistance to the fir engraver beetle. 3. Lesion development and containment of infection by resistant *Abies grandis* inoculated with *Trichosporium symbioticum*. Can. J. Bot. 55:2358-2365.

Chapter 24

INDUCED DEFENCE REACTION OF CONIFERS TO BARK BEETLES AND THEIR ASSOCIATED *OPHIOSTOMA* SPECIES

F. LIEUTIER

INTRODUCTION

Conifers have two defence systems to respond to attacks by bark beetles and their associated fungi (2). The initial response involves preformed resin that is located throughout the tree in a network of longitudinal and radial resin ducts. As the beetle bores its gallery into the phloem, the cambium and sometimes the superficial part of the sapwood, it severs the network allowing the resin to flow out. This primary response of the tree, immediate, passive and involving preformed resin, may, in some situations, be responsible for the complete failure of the beetle attacks (15,17).

In contrast, the secondary response is only visible some hours after beetle attack. It is localized around the point of infestation and is characterized by a vertical and elliptical resin impregnated zone visible in the phloem and sapwood. It involves a neosynthesis of resin by the tree in response to the attack and has been termed the 'induced' or 'hypersensitive response' (2). Unlike the preformed resin, which is localized in resin ducts, the neosynthesized resin impregnates the sieve cells of the phloem and the tracheids of the sapwood, causing death of the conducting tissues (1,8,20). This process is dynamic and localized and generally halts the activity of the beetles and their associated fungi. It is usually considered to be induced by the fungi (mainly *Ophiostoma* species), which are introduced by the beetles as they excavate their galleries but it can also be induced by the mechanical stress caused by insect boring (2,3,4,13,19,20).

In this paper, I present a brief review of the research at my institute, which has concentrated on four species of European bark beetles, with or without associated fungi. They include *Ips sexdentatus, Tomicus piniperda* and *Ips acuminatus* in *Pinus sylvestris* and *Pinus pinaster* and *Dendroctonus micans* in *Picea abies*. This review focuses mainly on the working mechanisms of the induced response.

ORIGIN OF THE INDUCED RESPONSE

Ips sexdentatus attacks Scots pine (*Pinus sylvestris*) and is associated with the fungi *Ophiostoma brunneo-ciliatum* and *Ophiostoma ips* (12,16,22). To distinguish the role of the fungi from that of mechanical stress in inducing the secondary response, inoculations of *O. brunneo-ciliatum* and introductions of *I. sexdentatus* have been compared in *P. sylvestris* and *P. pinaster* (10 and Fig. 1a)

In such experiments, the induced response to the beetle, expressed as the total terpene quantity in the reaction zone, can sometimes equal that caused by the fungus alone, or sometimes be less. Where the induced response is reduced, it is also usually impossible to isolate any fungi from the beetle galleries. To examine this in more detail, beetle mass attacks were induced on healthy Scots pine using pheromone baits (13). After eight weeks, all the attacks failed but the length of the reaction zone extending beyond the edge of the gallery system varied considerably. The reactions were much greater when an *Ophiostoma* species was present in the gallery, compared with those occasions when no fungus was isolated; they were also unrelated to the length of the gallery. With *Ips sexdentatus* attacks, therefore, it seems reasonable to conclude that the secondary reaction is induced largely by the *Ophiostoma* species introduced by the beetles and does not result from the mechanical damage produced by the insect alone. *Ips sexdentatus* is thus comparable to many other bark beetle species (2,3,4,19,20,21).

In contrast, three different species of fungi are more or less closely associated with *T. piniperda* on Scots pine. They are *Leptographium wingfieldii, Ophiostoma minus* and *Hormonema dematioides*. Comparisons between *L. wingfieldii* inoculations and beetle introductions in *P. sylvestris* and in *P. pinaster* indicate that the tree response to beetle introductions is always much less than the response to fungus inoculations (10 and Fig. 1b). However, failed mass attacks on living Scots pine do not show any relation between the length of the reaction zone and the presence of a fungus in the gallery. Instead, the length of the reaction lesion extending beyond the

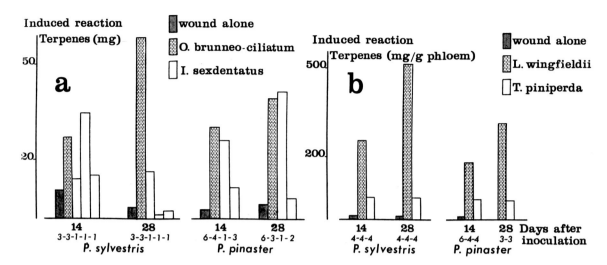

Fig. 1. Induced response of *Pinus sylvestris* and *Pinus pinaster* to bark beetle introductions and fungus inoculations. 1a - *Ips sexdentatus* and its fungal associate *Ophiostoma brunneo-ciliatum*. 1b - *Tomicus piniperda* and its fungal associate *Leptographium wingfieldii* (Results from pooled samples; data in italics indicate the number of samples in each case; modified from 1, used with permission of the Entomological Society of America).

gallery is positively correlated with the gallery length (13 and Fig. 2). With *T. piniperda,* therefore, the secondary response may be induced by the mechanical stress caused by the insect boring into the host tissue (13). These results appear to contradict the fact that the fungi associated with *T. piniperda* induce strong defence reactions in the absence of the beetle (10,12). This apparent anomaly may occur when too few spores of *L. wingfieldii* are introduced during beetle attack to induce a significant response from the tree (10).

In the example of *D. micans*, no association with any *Ophiostoma* species, or indeed any fungi, has been demonstrated. Experiments using numerous synchronous artificial introductions on *P. abies* show that, as for *T. piniperda* on Scots pine, the longitudinal extension of the tree response is linearly correlated with the length of the gallery (Fig. 3), despite the fact that the galleries of *D. micans* are transverse. This again suggests that mechanical stress is responsible for the induction of the tree's secondary response.

All these examples indicate the induced response can have a number of different origins (fungal or mechanical stress). These different triggers seem to depend on the beetle species involved, even within the same tree species (i.e., Scots pine for *T. piniperda* and *I. sexdentatus*). However, in the case of *I. sexdentatus*, this beetle also may provoke some mechanical stress. Indeed, some mechanical stress

must accompany any beetle attack but the tree response to that stress may be hidden by the strong reaction caused by the presence of the fungus. I propose that in any bark beetle attack, whether it is associated with an *Ophiostoma* species or not, the secondary reaction is always induced by the repeated wounding caused by insects boring into the tissues of the tree. The role of the fungus is to considerably amplify the tree's response, possibly by causing new wounds, or by further stimulating tree cell activity already initiated by the wound.

ROLE OF A DIFFUSIBLE PRODUCT (ELICITOR) WITHIN THE TREE

In all our experiments using inoculations of fungi or beetle attacks in living trees, when the attacks failed, the induced reaction extended longitudinally far ahead of where the attacking agents (aggressors) could be found (11,12). Thus, resin impregnation of the phloem was clearly visible in zones where no fungus or beetle gallery was present. These results coincide with those of Coutts and Dolezal (5) working with *Pinus radiata* and those of Wong and Berryman (24) with *Abies grandis.* Clearly, this response must involve the translocation of a message from the damaged tissue to the surounding responding cells, in the form of a diffusible chemical, originating from the tree or from the aggressors (fungus or beetle). Such a substance

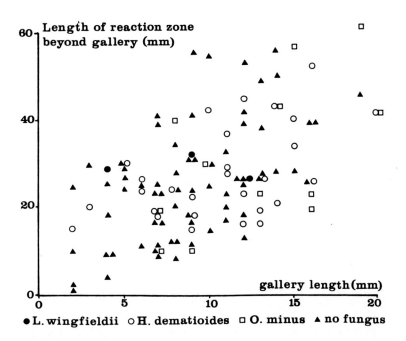

Fig. 2. Longitudinal extension of the secondary resinosis beyond the galleries of *T. piniperda* eight weeks after a natural mass attack in which all attacks eventually failed. Fungi isolated from the galleries included *L. wingfieldii, H. dematioides* and *O. minus* (from 13, used with permission of Springer-Verlag).

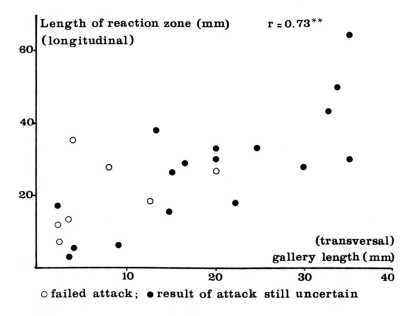

Fig. 3. Longitudinal extension of the induced response in the phloem of Norway spruce one month after artificial introductions of *Dendroctonus micans*. r = correlation coefficient significantly different from zero at the 99% level.

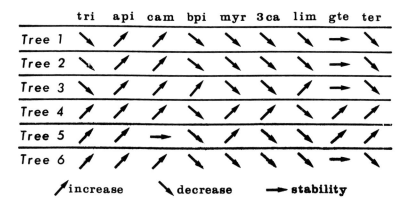

Fig. 4. Changes of the proportions of various monoterpenes, including preformed and induced resins, in six different Scots pine trees. tri = tricyclene; api = alpha-pinene; cam = camphene; bpi = beta-pinene; myr = myrcene; 3ca = delta-3carene; lim = limonene; gte = gamma-terpinene; ter = terpinolene.

is termed an elicitor of the defence reaction.

SPECIFICITY OF THE TREE RESPONSE

Specificity of host response has been investigated through analyses of monoterpenes and phenolics. To do this, the compositions of phloem reaction zones induced by various aggressors have been compared with each other and with that of the constitutive phloem.

Monoterpenes

In Scots pine, inoculations of *L. wingfieldii*, *O. ips* and *O. brunneo-ciliatum* were performed on the same trees. The monoterpenes were then analyzed in both the unwounded phloem and in the reactive phloem using gas chromatography. The concentration of each monoterpene increased considerably in the defence reaction and modifications were observed in the relative composition of the reacting phloem compared with the control phloem. The response also differed slightly from tree to tree (Fig. 4), although for any given tree the modifications in the phloem composition were consistant whatever the treatment (6, and Fig. 5).

In a further experiment, single trees of *Pinus ponderosa*, *Pinus contorta* and *Pinus monticola* were each inoculated with *O. clavigerum*, a fungus associated in nature with *D. ponderosae*. The trees also received inoculations of a solution of chitosan in sterile phosphate buffer, a solution of "Proteinase Inhibitor Inducing Factor" (PIIF) in sterile phosphate buffer, and sterile phosphate buffer alone. Chitosan and PIIF were chosen because they had both been suggested as possible elicitors of resistant responses

in plants subject to natural pest attacks (7,23). Again, aside from a general increase in concentration, the reactive phloem always had a monoterpene composition that differed from the constitutive phloem. Furthermore, although all these pines regularly acted as hosts to this bark beetle-fungus complex, the responses differed widely depending on the tree. For a given tree, nevertheless, the monoterpene qualitative response was the same whatever the treatment, fungus, chemical or buffer inoculation (9). This confirms the findings of Cook and Hain (4) who also found that the qualitative monoterpene composition of the response of *Pinus taeda*, following inoculation with *Ophiostoma minus*, did not depend on the strain that had been inoculated.

Phenolics

Artificial inoculations with *O. brunneo-ciliatum* and *L. wingfieldii* and artificial introductions of *T. piniperda* were performed on the same Scots pine. The phenolics in the unwounded phloem were then analyzed and compared with the components in the reactive phloem, using thin layer two dimensional chromatography (14). A total of 64 chromatographic spots were identified in the constitutive or the reactive phloem, but seven of them exhibited strong differences between the two kinds of phloem. Regardless of the nature of the agressor, the abundance of three of the spots increased in the reactive phloem relative to the constitutive phloem, one of these being amplified by a 20 to 100-fold magnitude; the remaining four chromatographic spots decreased in relative abundance. In addition, two chromatographic spots appeared frequently that

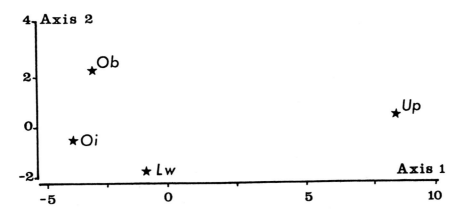

Fig. 5. Comparison using Principal Component Analysis (PCA) of the monoterpene composition of the unwounded phloem with that of reactive phloem following inoculation with various fungi into a single Scots pine tree. Up = unwounded phloem; Ob = phloem reaction induced by *Ophiostoma brunneo-ciliatum*; Oi = phloem reaction induced by *Ophiostoma ips*; Lw = phloem reaction induced by *Leptographium wingfieldii*.

rarely had been present previously (14).

Thus, for terpenes as well as for phenolics, the composition of the reactive phloem clearly differs from that of the constitutive one. This qualitative response differs among trees but is always consistant within any tree and independent of the nature of the aggressor.

Such non-specificity of the induced response to an aggressor has also been demonstrated histologically by Mullick (18) who suggested that the host response to injury is not a defence mechanism but part of tissue restoration. Our data are insufficient to make the same conclusion but the idea of no one specific response fits well with the hypothesis that mechanical stress (wounding) induces the host response. It also suggests that the elicitor may originate from the tree itself. Between-tree differences also indicate that where a rapid response is essential, each tree responds individually with an 'emergency' biosynthesis and not with a general defined scheme. Consequently, the tree induced response is not adapted to a particular aggressor.

KINETICS OF THE INDUCED RESPONSE

The kinetics of the induced response in trees involves a number of variables, including the rate of fungal growth, the fungal species involved and seasonal variations. The extent of the induced response can also be evaluated by measuring the length of the reaction zone, the concentration of resin in a defined area of the zone, the total quantity of resin in the reaction zone or the percentage of sieve cells filled with resin (11).

Relationship between elicitation and resin quantity

Kinetic comparisons of host response with growth of various fungi (such as *H. dematioides, L. wingfieldii, O. minus, O. brunneo-ciliatum* and *O. ips*) have revealed a relationship between the length of the reaction zone and the growth of the fungus. This is not surprising, because, as already discussed, fungi are probably responsible, at least in part, for strongly amplifying the induced reaction. Nevertheless, the relationship is not a perfect one; for example in the autumn, fungal growth is less than in the summer but the reaction zone is not correspondingly shorter. A better correlation exists between host response and fungal growth, however, if the host response is considered in terms of the total quantity of induced resin (11).

The production of an elicitor is also linked to the presence of the fungus, either directly if it is produced by the fungus itself, or indirectly if it is produced by the tree following the stimulus caused by wounding. Thus, the quantity of neosynthesized resin should depend on the quantity of elicitor released,

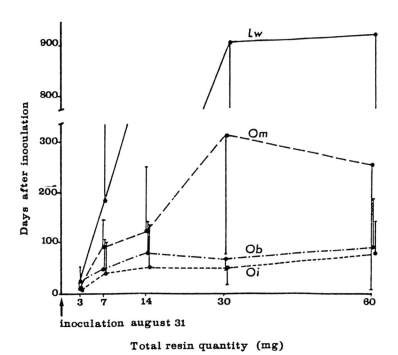

Fig. 6. Variation in the total resin quantity recorded in the phloem reactions of Scots pine following inoculation with various fugi. Om = *O. minus*; Ob = *O. brunneo-ciliatum*; Oi = *O. ips*; Lw = *L. wingfieldii*. Vertical bars are the confidence intervals at the 95% level (modified from 11, used by permission of Elsevier).

while the length of the reaction zone is more likely to reflect the diffusibility of the elicitor. Generally, we have found the kinetic curve for the quantity of neosynthesized resin tends to plateau after an initial phase of rapid increase (11, and Fig. 6). If the quantity of resin produced is dependent on the quantity of elicitor released, this plateau should correspond to the consumption of the elicitor. In fact, we have observed that for each individual fungus species and for each season, the plateau in resin production occurs simultaneously or very soon after fungal growth ceases. When no plateau is observed there is also no cessation in fungal growth. Nonetheless, there are other possible explanations for the arrest in resin accumulation; firstly, that the host tissues become resin saturated or secondly, that a depletion of the trees defensive ability occurs. If these alternatives do play a role, however, the level of resin concentration should be independent of fungus species and season. Instead, total resin concentration throughout the induced reaction zone and close to the inoculation point varies considerably according to fungus species and season (11).

Resin concentration gradient within defence reaction

Several studies suggest that resin concentration gradients exist within a defence reaction. I will consider only one example given by the kinetics of phloem sieve cells filled with resin in a transverse section of the reaction zone (mid-way between the inoculation point and one distal end of the reaction zone). Of course, the distance between the inoculation point to the zone edge increases as the reaction extends. Consequently, when the percentage of cells filled with resin decreases at this mid-way point, it indicates that the reaction zone is growing faster than the resin can accumulate. A stabilization in the proportion of resin-filled sieve cells corresponds to a point when the extension of reaction zone is balanced by the speed of resin accumulation. Later on, an increase in the percentage of resin filled cells indicates a recovery in resin accumulation. This type of pattern, a decrease followed by an increase, was observed frequently with various fungi and at different seasons (11, and see for example Fig. 7). It is characteristic of the irregular distribution of resin inside the defence reaction and, most probably, characteristic of a gradient of resin concentration, with the highest concentration located near the point of inoculation and the lowest at the distal ends of the reaction zone.

The existence of a resin concentration gradient may be explained by the rapid diffusion of the elicitor within the host tissues. This elicitor could stimulate the tree tissues at many different points simul-

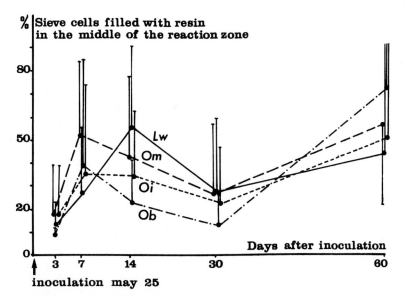

Fig. 7. Variation in the percentage of resin filled sieve cells in transversal sections of the reactive phloem of Scots pine samples in the middle of the reaction zone (mid-way between the inoculation point and the distal end of the reaction). Om = *O. minus*; Ob = *O. brunneo-ciliatum*; Oi = *O. ips*; Lw = *L. wingfieldii*. Vertical bars are the confidence intervals at the 95% level (modified from 11, used with permission of Elsevier).

taneously or successively, inducing a varying response in space and time and causing a resin concentration gradient within the growing reaction zone. When the growth of the reaction zone slows or stops, equilibration would occur, either by continued resin synthesis if the elicitor had accumulated locally, or by resin diffusion from zones of high concentration to zones of low concentration.

Role of the induced resin and of the wound periderm

There are two main physical components in the defence reaction. These include the resin itself, which impregnates the phloem inside the reaction zone, and the wound periderm, composed of several layers of cells that separate the reaction zone from the non-reactive phloem.

The resinous reaction may be responsible for stopping, or at least considerably slowing, fungal growth through quantitative or qualitative action. This can be illustrated by comparing the effect of inoculating fungi into freshly cut logs as opposed to inoculations into living trees (11). Freshly cut logs have only a very slight defence reaction, allowing extensive fungal growth to occur. In contrast, in living trees, fungal growth is generally very limited and the

reaction zone produced is always much longer than in the logs. In these conditions, the defence reaction may be largely responsible for the differences in fungal growth observed.

Apart from the reaction zone, another observable response following attacks by biotic agents is the formation of a wound periderm. Currently, however, there is little evidence to suggest that wound periderm formation actually is able to arrest fungal growth. In our observations, we compared the dates at which fungal growth stopped, when the reaction zone ceased extending and when wound periderm formation were first observed in histological sections (11). We found in all seasons and for each fungus species, the formation of the wound periderm was always initiated after fungal growth had stopped or, at least, had strongly slowed. In addition, the fungus was always distant from the border of the reaction when it stopped. Thus, wound periderm does not seem responsible for arresting fungal growth. It is conceivable that much reduced fungal growth, followed by a slow rate of the reaction zone extension, allows time for wound periderm to build up and eventually completely isolate the aggressors by compartmentalization (18,24).

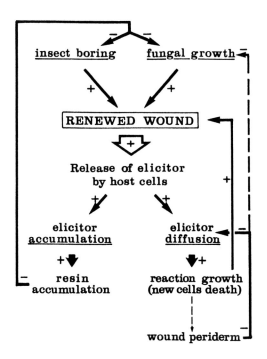

Fig. 8. Hypothetical mechanisms of the induced reaction of conifers responding to bark beetle and fungus invasion. + indicates stimulatory action; — indicates inhibitory action.

CONCLUSIONS: HYPOTHETICAL MECHANISMS OF THE INDUCED REACTION

Based entirely on the role of endogenous elicitors, this hypothesis tries to consider the results already discussed (Fig. 8). Insect attack and fungal invasion would cause a continously renewed wound, produced either mechanically or enzymatically. Within the wounded tissue, elicitors are released by the dying host cells. The local accumulation of elicitors triggers local resin accumulation, while the diffusion of elicitors would produce an extending reaction zone and thereby causes new cell death and a further release of elicitors. Eventually, resin accumulation has a negative effect on insect boring and fungal growth and one of two situations might then occur.

If the effect of induced resin on the fungus and attacking insect is sufficiently strong, the aggressors are prevented from extending the wound; the release of elicitor is then limited to lysed cells within the reaction zone. In this condition, the quantity of elicitor is low and its diffusion slow; extension of the reaction zone slows considerably, which would allow formation of wound periderm to begin. This wound

periderm limits the diffusion of the elicitor and confines the extension of the reaction zone.

Typically, this situation corresponds to a failed beetle attack, occuring after an often long period of struggle between the tree and its aggressors. This explains the variable reaction zones enclosing the failed attacks.

Alternatively, if the resin accumulates too slowly for a variety of reasons, perhaps because the tree lacks vigor, there is no slowing of the aggressors, which in turn allows them to develop faster than the reaction zone. The attack succeeds and the beetle with associated fungi becomes established.

LITERATURE CITED

1. Berryman, A.A. 1969. Response of *Abies grandis* to attack by *Scolytus ventralis* (Coleoptera : Scolytidae). Can. Entomol. 101:1033-1041.
2. Berryman, A.A. 1972. Resistance of conifers to invasion by bark beetle-fungus associations. Bioscience 22:599-601.
3. Christiansen, E. and Horntvedt, R. 1983. Combined *Ips/Ceratocystis* attack on Norway spruce, and defensive mechanisms of the trees. Z. Ang. Entomol. 96:110-118.
4. Cook, S.P. and Hain, F.P. 1985. Qualitative examination of the hypersensitive response of loblolly pine *Pinus taeda* L. inoculated with two fungal associates of the southern pine beetle, *Dendroctonus frontalis* Zimmermann (Col. Scol.). Environ. Entomol. 14:396-400.
5. Coutts, M.P. and Dolezal, J.E. 1966. Polyphenols and resin in the resistance mechanism of *Pinus radiata* attacked by the wood wasp, *Sirex noctilio*, and its associated fungus. Commonw. Austr. For. Tim. Bur., Leaflet no. 101, 19 pp.
6. Delorme, L. and Lieutier, F. 1990. Monoterpene composition of the preformed and induced resins of scots pine, and their effect on bark beetles and associated fungi. Eur. J. For. Pathol. 20:304-316.
7. Hadwiger, L.A., Beckman, J.M. and Adams, M.J. 1981. Localization of fungal components in the pea-*Fusarium* interaction detected immunochemically with antichitosan and antifungal cell wall antisera. Plant Physiol. 67:170-175.
8. Lieutier, F. and Berryman, A.A. 1988. Preliminary histological investigations on the defense reactions of three pines to *Ceratocystis clavigera* and two chemical elicitors. Can. J. For. Res. 18:1243-1247.
9. Lieutier, F., Berryman, A.A. and Millstein, J.A. 1991. Monoterpene response of three pines to *Ophiostoma clavigerum* (Ascomycete : Ophiostomatales) and two chemical elicitors. Ann. Sci. For. 48:377-388.
10. Lieutier, F., Cheniclet, C., and Garcia, J. 1989. Comparison of the defense reaction of *Pinus pinaster* and *Pinus sylvestris* to attacks by two bark beetles (Coleoptera : scolytidae) and their associated fungi. Environ. Entomol. 18:228-234.
11. Lieutier, F., Yart, A., Garcia, J. and Ham, M.C. 1990. Cinétique de croissance des champignons associés à *Ips sexdentatus* Boern. et à *Tomicus piniperda* L. (Coleoptera : Scolytidae) et des réactions de défense des pins sylvestres (*Pinus sylvestris*) inoculés. Agronomie 10:243-256.

12. Lieutier, F., Yart, A., Garcia, J., Ham, M.C., Morelet, M. and Levieux, J. 1989. Champignons phytopathogènes associés à *Ips sexdentatus* Boern. et *Tomicus piniperda* L. (Coleoptera : Scolytidae) et étude préliminaire de leur agressivité pour le pin sylvestre. Ann. Sci. For. 46:201-216.

13. Lieutier, F., Yart, A., Garcia, J., Poupinel, B. and Levieux, J. 1988. Do fungi influence the establishment of bark beetles in scots pine? Pages 317-330 in: Mechanisms of woody plant defenses against insects, search for pattern. W.J. Mattson, J. Lévieux and C. Bernard-Dagan, eds. Springer-Verlag, New York. 416 pp.

14. Lieutier, F., Yart, A., Jay-Allemand, C. and Delorme, L. 1991. Preliminary investigations on phenolics as a response of scots pine phloem to the attacks by bark beetles and associated fungi. Eur. J. For. Pathol. 21:354-364.

15. Lorio, P.L. Jr. 1986. Growth-Differentiation balance : a basis for understanding southern pine-beetle-tree interactions. For. Ecol. Man. 14:259-273.

16. Mathiesen, A. 1950. Über einige mit Borhenkäfer assoziierte Bläuepilze in Schweden. Oikos 2:275-308.

17. Matson, P.A. and Hain, F.P. 1985. Host conifer defense strategies : a hypothesis. Proc. IUFRO Conference, Banff, Alberta, Canada, pp. 33-42.

18. Mullick, D.B. 1977. The non-specific nature of defence in bark and wood during wounding insect and pathogen attack. Recent Adv. Phytochem., Vol 2, Plenum Press, New York.

19. Raffa, R.F. and Berryman, A.A. 1983. The role of host resistance in the colonization behavior and ecology of bark beetles (Coleoptera : Scolytidae). Ecol. Monogr. 53:27-49.

20. Reid, R.W., Whitney, H.S., and Watson, J.A. 1967. Reactions of lodgepole pine to attack by *Dendroctonus ponderosae* Hopkins and blue stain fungi. Can. J. Bot. 45:1115-1126.

21. Safranyk, L., Shrimpton, D.M. and Whitney, H.S. 1975. An interpretation of the interaction between lodgepole pine, the mountain pine beetle, and its associated blue stain fungi in western Canada. Pages 406-428 in: Management of Lodgepole Pine ecosystems. D.M. Baumgartner, ed., Washington State University Cooperative Extension Service, Pullman.

22. Upadhyay, H.P. 1981. A monograph of *Ceratocystis* and *Ceratocystiopsis*. The University of Georgia Press, Athens. GA. 176 pp.

23. Walker-Simmons, M., Jin, D., West, C.A. Hadwiger, L.A. and Ryan, C.A. 1984. Comparison of proteinase inhibitor inducing activities and phytoalexin elicitor activities of pure fungal endopolygalacturonase, pectic fragments and chitosans. Plant Physiol. 76:833-836.

24. Wong, B.L. and Berryman, A.A. 1977. Host resistance to the fir engraver beetle. 3 - Lesion development and containment of infection by resistant *Abies grandis* inoculated with *Trichosporium symbioticum*. Can. J. Bot. 55:2358-2365.

Chapter 25

ECOLOGICAL ASPECTS OF FUNGI ASSOCIATED WITH THE SPRUCE BARK BEETLE *IPS TYPOGRAPHUS* IN NORWAY

H. SOLHEIM

INTRODUCTION

The spruce bark beetle *Ips typographus* attacks mostly weakened or dead trees and timber of Norway spruce (*Picea abies*). Occasionally, however, it can attack healthy trees and may cause severe damage in forest stands, as seen in Norway during the 1970's. This catastrophe started after widespread storm damage and accelerated during three consecutive drought summers (12). As part of its life-cycle, *I. typographus* generally overwinters as adult beetles in the forest litter and these adults emerge and fly in spring when the maximum air temperature rises to about 20°C (1,2). The flight period consists of two phases, dispersal and searching. When searching for a suitable host as breeding material, the beetles communicate and coordinate their activities with aggregation as well as anti-aggregation pheromones (12). The aggregation pheromones are important because they ensure synchronized mass attacks by the beetles, which can overwhelm the resistance of living trees.

A successful mass attack of living conifers by certain bark beetles also results in the introduction of blue-stain fungi vectored by these beetles and, as the fungi become established, there is rapid desiccation of bark and wood. *Ophiostoma penicillatum* was the first fungal species regarded as an associate of *I. typographus* (23,24) and has since been considered the most important associate, while others, such as *Ceratocystiopsis minuta*, *Graphium pycnocephalum*, *Ophiostoma piceae* and *O. polonicum* have been reported only occasionally (30,33,34,44,48). During the last *I. typographus* epidemic in Norway, questions were raised about the importance of the fungi associated with this beetle in overcoming host resistance. A number of different studies were then initiated to explore the association and a brief review of this work is presented here.

TRANSMISSION OF FUNGI

Many bark beetles have specialized organs, mycangia, for transmission of fungal associates. However, *I. typographus* has no mycangium and scanning electron microscope studies have shown that spores are carried externally in pits on the pronota and elytra (22). Spores may also be transferred internally within the digestive tract of the insects (22,48). The beetles carry spores of several fungal species but in southeastern Norway, four species are commonly associated with *I. typographus*. They are *Ophiostoma bicolor*, *O. penicillatum*, *O. polonicum* and a presently unidentified *Graphium* species (22).

Thousands of ascospores and conidia may be transferred with each beetle but there is a great variation between individuals. Scanning electron microscopy revealed ascospores of *Ophiostoma bicolor* and yeasts to be much more common than spores of other associated fungi but all the *Ophiostoma* species were isolated at about the same frequency when logs were inoculated with beetles or parts of beetles (22). Studies by Moser *et al.* (37) have shown that mites associated with *I. typographus* also carry different fungal spores and again *O. bicolor* spores are particularly common. These observations have parallels with some other bark beetle systems, such as *Dendroctonus frontalis* and the associated fungus *Ophiostoma minus*, in which phoretic mites add significantly to the overall transmission of *O. minus* compared with bark beetle spread alone (9,36). However, we have not tried to quantify the importance of mite-transmitted spores in *I. typographus* attack on Norway spruce.

FUNGAL INVASION OF SAPWOOD

When a new substrate is available, the invading microorganisms often appear in a temporal succession. This also occurs during the invasion of Norway spruce infested by *I. typographus*, as described by Solheim (52,53). Despite the fact that *I. typographus* apparently introduces several *Graphium* and *Ophiostoma* species simultaneously into the fresh substrate, *O. polonicum* is the only species that can be isolated in the sapwood one week after attack. Over the next few weeks, secondary invaders enter the sapwood and these are subsequently followed by other closely related species (Fig. 1).

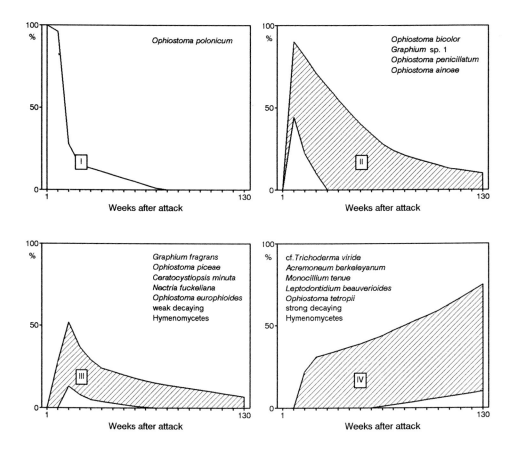

Fig. 1. Frequency of primary (I), secondary (II), tertiary (III) and quaternary (IV) invaders of sapwood of Norway spruce attacked by the bark beetle *Ips typographus* (53).

Isolations within the sapwood have revealed that *O. polonicum* is at the leading edge of fungal penetration until heartwood is reached, while *O. bicolor* trails an average of 5 mm behind the front of fungal penetration (52). Other species trail more than 10 mm behind the front (Fig. 2). The earliest invaders of sapwood correspond to the same species Furniss *et al.* (22) found to be frequently transferred by beetles in the same area.

The first Hymenomycetes, which are rather weak wood-decaying white-rotters, appear among the tertiary invaders. The first three groups of invaders reach their peak during the first summer after beetle attack and subsequently decrease, while the next group of invaders, which includes strong wood-decaying Hymenomycetes, is still increasing after 130 weeks (Fig. 1).

The appearance of the quaternary invaders appears to be influenced by the moisture content of the wood. Hymenomycetes are mostly isolated near the base of the trees where the moisture content remains favorable for longest, whereas cf. *Tricho-*

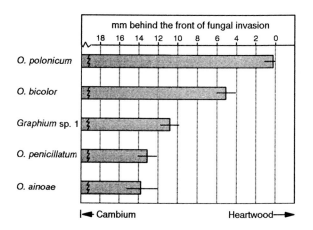

Fig. 2. The invasion of five fungal species in the sapwood of Norway spruce attacked by the spruce bark beetle *Ips typographus* in relation to the leading edge of the fungal penetration (52).

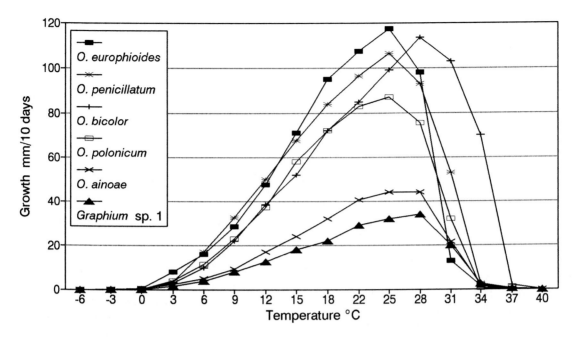

Fig. 3. Mean radial growth rates of blue-stain fungi associated with the spruce bark beetle *Ips typographus* on malt agar at different temperatures (50).

derma viride dominates at higher levels, where the moisture content was found to reach fiber saturation point within two and a half years.

Käärik (29) found a similar succession in Norway spruce trees attacked by *I. typographus* in Sweden, except that *O. penicillatum* and *O. piceae* were the primary invaders and a wave of secondary blueing fungi, including *O. bicolor* and *O. polonicum*, invaded during late summer.

GROWTH RESPONSE TO TEMPERATURE

The temperature that *I. typographus* needs for flying (20°C or more) is mostly reached intermittently during late spring and summer in areas showing heavy attack in southeastern Norway. Fungal colonization must also be influenced by the great variation in the temperature conditions, as some trees are exposed to sunshine while others are in dense stands. Trees in warm sites are infested first when *I. typographus* starts swarming (2).

The growth rate at different temperatures has been tested for many of the fungal species associated with *I. typographus* (49,51). The optimum has been found to be mostly around 25-28°C. Some species grow faster than others, and *O. bicolor, O. europhioides* and *O. penicillatum* grow faster than *O.*

polonicum at most temperatures (Fig. 3).

HOST DEFENSE

Conifers generally have two different defence systems. The constitutive host defence includes the release of resin from ducts holding preformed or primary resin (oleoresin). This has long been regarded as an important defence of Norway spruce against *I. typographus* attack (12). There is, however, great variation in resin exudation, both between trees and within a single tree (14,46), and exudation decreases with an increasing number of wounds (46).

In contrast, the induced host defense involves a dynamic hypersensitive tissue response around the infection point with production of lesion resin, which is a secondary resinosis (4,43). This defense appears to be primarily a response against infection by microorganisms associated with the bark beetles; a necrotic area is formed around the infection point, which deprives the invader of nutrients (57).

The *Ophiostoma* species associated with *I. typographus* produce typical reaction zones in Norway spruce, with an inner dark zone where fungal growth has been arrested and an outer, lighter area which contains no detectable fungal mycelium (Fig. 4). The lesions produced by *O. bicolor* and *O. penicillatum* are

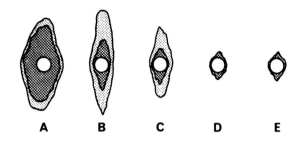

Fig. 4. Typical wound reaction in the phloem of Norway spruce 10 weeks after mass inoculation with some blue-stain fungi associated with the spruce bark beetle *Ips typographus*, A) *Ophiostoma polonicum,* B) *O. penicillatum,* C) *O. bicolor,* D) *Graphium* sp. E) control (50).

similar, with a small dark zone enclosing the fungus, but the lesions of the latter are usually longest. Because *O. penicillatum* has a more rapid growth rate than *O. bicolor* at most temperatures (Fig. 3), the larger reaction zone around the *O. penicillatum* lesion probably reflects the faster growth rate. The very slow-growing *Graphium* sp. produces the same reaction zones as the control. Thus, growth rate may be of importance in overcoming resistance mechanisms but it is certainly not the only factor influencing the sequence of fungal invasion that occurs following *I. typographus* attack on Norway spruce.

The reaction zone produced by the primary invader *O. polonicum* differs from the others. It shows greater radial expansion and the area containing the fungus fills up most of the reaction zone (Fig. 4). *Ophiostoma polonicum* is a more aggresive pathogen than the other species and is capable of killing healthy Norway spruce trees when mass inoculated in the absence of beetle vectors (28,50). *Ophiostoma polonicum* has therefore been used in many inoculation experiments to study various aspects of tree resistance (10,11,13,14,15,27).

The necrotic area surrounding the infection point becomes impregnated with resinous and phenolic compounds that prevent fungal proliferation (4,43) and inhibit the growth of various blue-stain fungi (8,17,20,21,42,47). Generally, the infecting fungi are enclosed within this reaction zone but under certain conditions may break out and a new periderm is formed (16). With an increasing number of infection points, the resin concentration of each reaction zone decreases with the effect that the fungi gradually succeed in invading the tree (10,41). Clearly,

tree vigor is important in determining the number of infection points necessary to overcome the tree's resistance (38,55,56). Berryman (5,6) has formulated a model for the relationship between the tree resistance and the threshold of successful attack of bark beetles with associated fungi. With increasing beetle population or lower tree resistance, the situation in the forest will change from endemic to epidemic. The most conspicuous feature of successfully attacked trees is the lack of secondary resinosis (4,43), which is also observed on Norway spruce mass attacked by *I. typographus* (53).

RESPONSE TO RESIN

The particular form of reaction zones observed with *O. polonicum* after artificial inoculations suggests that this species is able to tolerate the resin impregnation better than the other species introduced by *I. typographus*. To explore the effect of spruce resin, some *I. typographus*-associated fungi were exposed to both preformed resin or induced lesion resin *in vitro*. The preformed resin was obtained by inserting plastic collecting tubes into holes cut into the cambium of healthy Norway spruce, while induced lesion resin was sampled from the reaction zones of resin-soaked phloem produced after inoculation with *O. polonicum* (51).

Under these conditions, lesion resin, in contrast to preformed resin, inhibited all tested species and, in particular, the primary invader *O. polonicum* (Table 1). This was perhaps surprising, but as the lesion resin used in these tests originated from an *O. polonicum* lesion, it cannot be ruled out that trees produce specific substances in response to infection by particular fungi. Reaction to fungal infection is, however, thought to be non-specific and parenchyma cells apparently act in a similar way to various stimuli, including fungal invasion and chemical elicitors (7). In this context, neither Cook and Hain (18) nor Delorme and Lieutier (21) could find differences in the monoterpene content of lesions after inoculation with different species of fungi, even though the lesion size differed with the various fungi. Nonetheless, substances other than monoterpenes are also produced in response to inoculation. In the study by Solheim (51), mainly non-volatile components were responsible for the inhibition of fungal growth. In addition, it may be that the colonizing success of *O. polonicum* in living Norway spruce trees reflects the speed with which this fungus is able to penetrate tissues before secondary resinosis is induced, rather than its ability to tolerate lesion resin. Whatever the

TABLE 1. Radial growth and percent inhibition after four days of blue-stain fungi associated with the spruce bark beetle *Ips typographus* on malt agar-covered (1.25% malt, 1.5% agar) filter papers with resin, taken from Solheim (51).

Treatment	*O. polonicum* growth mm	inhib. %	*O. bicolor* growth mm	inhib. %	*O. penicillatum* growth mm	inhib. %	*Graphium* sp. growth mm	inhib. %
Control	21.7 a[1]		23.7 a		32.8 a		9.1 a	
Preformed resin	19.8 a	8.8	22.5 a	5.1	30.4 a	7.3	7.4 b	18.7
Lesion resin	1.7 b	92.2	11.9 b	49.8	18.8 b	42.7	6.2 c	31.9

[1] Values within columns followed by the same letter are not significantly different (P=0.005) by Duncan's multiple range test.

circumstances, it is clear that further studies are needed to clarify the importance of different components to the inhibition of blue-stain fungi during colonization.

TOLERANCE OF OXYGEN DEFICIENCY

Because of its high moisture content, fresh unwounded sapwood is likely to be deficient in oxygen and the primary invaders of such tissue must be able to grow under such oxygen-deficient conditions. The ability to withstand such conditions was tested simply by growing the blue-stain fungi on malt agar in tubes filled with nitrogen and sealed with rubber stoppers. The atmosphere within the tubes consisted largely of nitrogen, with just a small quantity of contaminant oxygen (51).

At 21°C, the linear growth of *O. ainoae*, *O. bicolor*, *O. penicillatum* and *Graphium* sp. was completely arrested after 7-11 days in this almost oxygen free environment, whereas *O. polonicum* remained growing throughout the test period. *Ophiostoma europhioides* showed an intermediate response, with slowed growth after 11 days and arrested growth after 18-21 days (Fig. 5). At 15°C, a similar pattern was evident, although growth in the airtight tubes was slower and continued for a longer time. Once again, *O. europhioides* and *O. polonicum* were the least affected, while the other species ceased growing completely before the ends of the tubes were reached.

The potential of *O. polonicum* to act as a primary invader appears to be linked to its ability to grow actively for prolonged periods under oxygen-deficient conditions. These are the very conditions that are likely to prevail during the invasion of fresh sapwood, which is characterized by high moisture content and

low oxygen tensions. The variation in ability to respond to oxygen-deficient conditions may be an indicator of ecological niche in other species within the Ophiostomataceae. *Ophiostoma minus*, for example, is an effective primary invader of several European and North American pine species (3,32,35,39,40, 54) and can tolerate much lower oxygen pressures than *O. piliferum* (45), which is generally considered to be a secondary blueing fungus of pine timber.

It is surprising, perhaps, that *O. europhioides*, a fungus found to be a tertiary invader in Norway spruce (53), grew almost as well as *O. polonicum* under poor oxygen conditions. This fungus has been found associated with the beetle *Hylurgops palliatus* (19,26, Solheim unpublished), which apparently prefers colonizing bark with high moisture content (31) and may intermingle with *I. typographus* on spruce logs. As it is able to tolerate low oxygen pressure, *O. europhioides* is potentially a pathogen when carried by more aggresive beetles than *H. palliatus*. Indeed, it may act as a primary invader in Norway spruce plantations in Denmark, where *O. europhioides* is more commonly associated with *I. typographus* than *O. polonicum* (25).

CONCLUSIONS

Research in Norway concerning blue-stain fungi associated with *I. typographus* has revealed that the beetles carry a variety of fungal spores externally and internally. Of these, *Ophiostoma polonicum* is most important in overcoming the host resistance of healthy Norway spruce trees infested by the beetles. *Ophiostoma polonicum* invades the trees first and is in the leading edge of fungal penetration into sapwood until heartwood is reached, while other

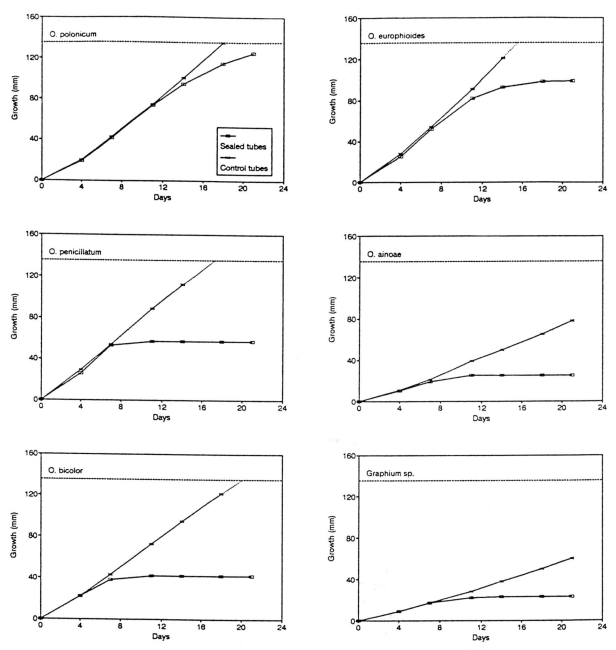

Fig. 5. Mean linear growth of blue-stain fungi associated with the spruce bark beetle *Ips typographus* incubated at 21 °C on malt agar in tubes under oxygen-deficient conditions (51).

species followed successively. The ability of *O. polonicum* to tolerate low oxygen pressure together with its rapid growth rate seem to be important attributes for the successful invasion of living trees.

The conflicting results from different studies concerning the significance of the fungi associated with *I. typographus* may have several explanations. The methodology adopted by different researchers may influence results, while different species may dominate in phloem or sapwood of healthy trees,

dying trees or timber attacked by the beetles. For example, *O. penicillatum* seems to play a more important role in colonizing phloem than sapwood (25,52). Since *I. typographus* carries spores of several fungal species, the inoculum composition may vary between individual beetles and between beetle populations with associated species adapted to different substrate conditions. The pathogenic species, *O. polonicum*, may thus be replaced by other associated species during endemic periods when the

240

beetles utilize dead trees and timber. However, during epidemics, the frequency of *O. polonicum* may increase as more and more living trees are attacked. It should also be remembered that the studies in Norway have been performed in connection with an epidemic situation, while other studies have been performed in endemic periods. More studies are needed, however, to examine various aspects of the interaction between *I. typographus* and associated fungi, including the importance of various resin components to the inhibition of fungal growth, the dynamics of the fungal composition under varying conditions and the ecological significance of the various species carried by the beetles.

LITERATURE CITED

1. Annila, E. 1969. Influence of temperature upon the development and voltinism of *Ips typographus* L. (Coleoptera, Scolytidae). Ann. Zool. Fenn. 6:161-207.

2. Bakke, A., Austarå, Ø. and Pettersen, H. 1977. Seasonal flight activity and attack pattern of *Ips typographus* in Norway under epidemic conditions. Medd. Nor. Inst. Skogforsk. 33:253-268.

3. Basham, H.G. 1970. Wilt of loblolly pine inoculated with blue-stain fungi of the genus *Ceratocystis*. Phytopathology 60:750-754.

4. Berryman, A.A. 1969. Responses of *Abies grandis* to attack by *Scolytus ventralis* (Coleoptera: Scolytidae). Can. Entomol. 101:1033-1041.

5. Berryman, A.A. 1978. A synoptic model of the lodgepole pine/mountain pine beetle interaction and its potential application in forest management. Pages 98-105 in: Theory and practice of mountain pine beetle management in lodgepole pine forests. D.L. Kibbee, A.A. Berryman, G.D. Amman, & R.W. Stark, eds. Forest, Wildlife and Range Experiment Station, University of Idaho, Moscow.

6. Berryman, A.A. 1982. Biological control, thresholds, and pest outbreaks. Environ. Entomol. 11:544-549.

7. Berryman, A.A. 1988. Towards a unified theory of plant defense. Pages 39-56 in: Mechanisms of woody plant defenses against insects. Search for pattern. W.J. Mattson, J. Levieux & C. Bernard-Dagan, eds. Springer Verlag, New York. 416 pp.

8. Bridges, J.R. 1987. Effects of terpenoid compounds on growth of symbiotic fungi associated with the southern pine beetle. Phytopathology 77:83-85.

9. Bridges, J.R. and Moser, J.C. 1983. Role of two phoretic mites in transmission of bluestain fungus, *Ceratocystis minor*. Ecol. Entomol. 8:9-12.

10. Christiansen, E. 1985. *Ceratocystis polonica* inoculated in Norway spruce: Blue-staining in relation to inoculum density, resinosis and tree growth. Eur. J. For. Pathol. 15:160-167.

11. Christiansen, E. 1985. *Ips/Ceratocystis*-infection of Norway spruce: what is a deadly dosage? Z. Ang. Entomol. 99:6-11.

12. Christiansen, E. and Bakke, A. 1988. The spruce bark beetle of Eurasia. Pages 479-503 in: Dynamics of forest

13. Christiansen, E. and Ericsson, A. 1986. Starch reserves in *Picea abies* in relation to defence reaction against a bark beetle transmitted blue-stain fungus, *Ceratocystis polonica*. Can. J. For. Res. 16:78-83.

14. Christiansen, E. and Horntvedt, R. 1983. Combined *Ips/Ceratocystis* attack on Norway spruce, and defensive mechanisms of the trees. Z. Ang. Entomol. 96:110-118.

15. Christiansen, E. and Solheim, H. 1990. The bark beetle-associated blue-stain fungus *Ophiostoma polonicum* can kill various spruces and Douglas fir. Eur. J. For. Pathol. 20:436-446.

16. Christiansen, E., Waring, R.H. and Berryman, A.A. 1987. Resistance of conifers to bark beetle attack: searching for general relationships. For. Ecol. Man. 22:89-106.

17. Cobb, F.W. Jr., Krstic, M., Zavarin, E. and Barber, H.W. Jr. 1968. Inhibitory effects of volatile oleoresin components on *Fomes annosus* and four *Ceratocystis* species. Phytopathology 58:1327-1335.

18. Cook, S.P. and Hain, F.P. 1985. Qualitative examination of the hypersensitive response of loblolly pine, *Pinus taeda* L., inoculated with two fungal associates of the southern pine beetle, *Dendroctonus frontalis* Zimmermann (Coleoptera: Scolytidae). Environ. Entomol. 14:396-400.

19. Davidson, R.W., Francke-Grosmann, H. and Käärik, A. 1967. A restudy of *Ceratocystis penicillata* and report of two American species of this genus from Europe. Mycologia 59:928-932.

20. De Groot, R.C. 1972. Growth of wood-inhabiting fungi in saturated atmospheres of monoterpenoids. Mycologia 64:863-870.

21. Delorme, L. and Lieutier, F. 1990. Monoterpene of the preformed and induced resins of Scots pine, and their effect on bark beetles and associated fungi. Eur. J. For. Pathol. 20:304-316.

22. Furniss, M.M., Solheim, H. and Christiansen, E. 1990. Transmission of blue-stain fungi by *Ips typographus* (Coleoptera: Scolytidae) in Norway spruce. Ann. Entomol. Soc. Am. 83:712-716.

23. Grosmann, H. 1931. Beiträge zur Kenntnis der Lebensgemeinschaft zwischen Borkenkäfern und Pilzen. Z. Parasitkde. 3:56-102.

24. Grosmann, H. 1932. Über die systematischen Beziehungen der Gattung *Leptographium* Lagerberg et Melin zur Gattung *Ceratostomella* Sacc. nebst einigen Bemerkungen über *Scopularia venusta* Preuss und *Hantzschia phycomyces* Awd. Hedwigia 72:183-194.

25. Harding, S. 1989. Blue stain fungi associated with *Ips typographus* L. (Coleoptera: Scolytidae) in host trees of different vitality and at different beetle population levels. Pages II 1-30 in: The influence of mutualistic blue stain fungi on bark beetle population dynamics. Ph.D. thesis, Department of Zoology, Royal Veterinary and Agricultural University, Copenhagen.

26. Harding, S. 1989. Blue stain fungi associated with *Hylurgops palliatus* Gyll. (Coleoptera:Scolytidae) in Norway spruce. Pages V 1-11 in: The influence of mutualistic blue stain fungi on bark beetle population dynamics. Ph.D. thesis, Department of Zoology, Royal Veterinary and Agricultural University, Copenhagen.

27. Horntvedt, R. 1988. Resistance of *Picea abies* to *Ips typographus*: Tree response to monthly inoculations with

insect population. Patterns, causes, implications. A.A. Berryman, ed. Plenum Press, New York and London. 603 pp.

Ophiostoma polonicum, a beetle transmitted blue-stain fungus. Scand. J. For. Res. 3:107- 114.

28. Horntvedt, R., Christiansen, E., Solheim, H. and Wang, S. 1983. Artificial inoculation with *Ips typographus*- associated blue-stain fungi can kill healthy Norway spruce trees. Medd. Nor. Inst. Skogforsk. 38(4):1-20.

29. Käärik, A. 1975. Succession of microorganisms during wood decay. Pages 39-51 in: Biological transformation of wood by microorganisms. W. Liese, ed. Springer Verlag, Berlin, Heidelberg, New York. 203 pp.

30. Kotynková-Sychrová, E. 1966. Mykoflóra chodeb kurovcu v Ceskoslovensku. Ceská Mykol. 20:45-53.

31. Lekander, B., Bejer-Petersen, B., Kangas, E. and Bakke, A. 1977. The distribution of bark beetles in the Nordic countries. Acta Entomol. Fenn. 32:1-36.

32. Lieutier, F., Yart, A., Garcia, J., Ham, M.C., Morelet, M. and Levieux, J. 1989. Champignons phytopathogènes associés à deux coléoptères scolytidae du pin sylvestre (*Pinus sylvestris* L.) et étude préliminaire de leur agressivité envers l'hôte. Ann. Sci. For. 46:201-216.

33. Mathiesen, A. 1950. Über einige mit Borkenkäfern assoziierte Bläuepilze in Schweden. Oikos 2:275-308.

34. Mathiesen-Käärik, A. 1953. Eine Übersicht über die gewöhnlichsten mit Borkenkäfern assoziierten Bläuepilze in Schweden und einige für Schweden neue Bläuepilze. Meddn. St. Skogsforsk. Inst. 43(4):1-74.

35. Mathre D.E. 1964. Pathogenicity of *Ceratocystis ips* and *Ceratocystis minor* to *Pinus ponderosa*. Contr. Boyce Thompson Inst. Plant Res. 22:363-388.

36. Moser, J.C. and Bridges, J.R. 1986. *Tarsonemus* (Acarina: Tarsonemidae) mites phoretic on the southern pine beetle (Coleoptera: Scolytidae): attachment sites and numbers of bluestain (Ascomycetes: Ophiostomataceae) ascospores carried. Proc. Entomol. Soc. Wash. 88:297-299.

37. Moser, J.C., Perry, T.J. and Solheim, H. 1989. Ascospores hyperphoretic on mites associated with *Ips typographus*. Mycol. Res. 93:513-517.

38. Mulock, P. and Christiansen, E. 1986. The threshold of successful attack by *Ips typographus* on *Picea abies*: a field experiment. For. Ecol. Man. 14:125-132.

39. Nelson, R.M. 1934. Effect of bluestain fungi on southern pines attacked by bark beetles. Phytopathol. Z 7:327-353.

40. Owen, D.R., Lindahl, K.Q. Jr., Wood, D.L. and Parmeter, J.R. Jr. 1987. Pathogenicity of fungi isolated from *Dendroctonus valens*, *D. brevicomis* and *D. ponderosae* to ponderosa pine seedlings. Phytopathology 77:631-636.

41. Raffa, K.F. and Berryman, A.A. 1983. Physiological aspects of lodgepole pine wound responses to a fungal symbiont of the mountain pine beetle, *Dendroctonus ponderosae* (Coleoptera: Scolytidae). Can. Entomol. 115: 723-734.

42. Raffa, K.F., Berryman, A.A., Simasko, J., Teal, W. and Wong, B.L. 1985. Effects of grand fir monoterpenes on the fir engraver, *Scolytus ventralis* (Coleoptera: Scolytidae), and its symbiotic fungus. Environ. Entomol. 14:552-556.

43. Reid, R.W., Whitney, H.S. and Watson, J.A. 1967. Reactions of lodgepole pine to attack by *Dendroctonus ponderosae* Hopkins and bluestain fungi. Can. J. Bot. 45:1115-1126.

44. Rennerfelt, E. 1950. Über den Zusammenhang zwischen dem Verblauen des Holzes und den Insekten. Oikos 2:120-137.

45. Scheffer, T.C. 1986. O_2 requirements for growth and survival of wood-decaying and sapwood-staining fungi. Can. J. Bot. 64:1957-1963.

46. Schwerdtfeger, F. 1955. Pathogenese der Borkenkäfer-Epidemie 1946-1950. Nordwestdeutschland. Schr. Reihe Forstl. Fak. Univ. Göttingen. 13/14:1-135.

47. Shrimpton, D.M. and Whitney, H.S. 1968. Inhibition of growth of blue stain fungi by wood extractives. Can. J. Bot. 46:757-761.

48. Siemaszko, W. 1939. Zespoly grzybów towarzyszacych kornikom polskim. Planta Pol. 7:1-54 + plates.

49. Solheim, H. 1986. Species of Ophiostomataceae isolated from *Picea abies* infested by the bark beetle *Ips typographus*. Nord. J. Bot. 6:199-207.

50. Solheim, H. 1988. Pathogenicity of some *Ips typographus*-associated bluestain fungi to Norway spruce. Medd. Nor. Inst. Skogforsk. 40:1-11.

51. Solheim, H. 1991. Oxygen deficiency and spruce resin inhibition of growth of fungi associated with *Ips typographus*. Mycol. Res. 95:1387-1392.

52. Solheim, H. 1992. The early stages of fungal invasion in Norway spruce infested by the bark beetle *Ips typographus*. Can. J. Bot. 70:1-5.

53. Solheim, H. 1992. Fungal succession in sapwood of Norway spruce infested by the beetle *Ips typographus*. Eur. J. For. Pathol. 22:136-148.

54. Solheim, H. and Långström, B. 1991. Blue-stain fungi associated with *Tomicus piniperda* in Sweden and preliminary observations on their pathogenicity. Ann. Sci. For. 48:149-156.

55. Waring, R.H. and Pitman, G.B. 1980. A simple model of host resistance to bark beetles. Oregon State Univ. For. Res. Lab. Res. Note 65:1-2.

56. Waring, R.H. and Pitman, G.B. 1983. Physiological stress in lodgepole pine as a precursor for mountain pine beetle attack. Z. Ang. Entomol. 96:265-270.

57. Wong, B.L. and Berryman, A.A. 1977. Host resistance to the fir engraver beetle. 3. Lesion development and containment of infection by resistant *Abies grandis* inoculated with *Trichosporium symbioticum*. Can. J. Bot. 55:2358-2365.

Chapter 26

PHYTOALEXINS AND OTHER BIOCHEMICAL FACTORS ASSOCIATED WITH INFECTION BY *CERATOCYSTIS FIMBRIATA*

M. KOJIMA

INTRODUCTION

When plants are infected by parasitic fungi, they defend themselves against the invaders using various strategies either singly or in combination (18). These defenses of host plants range from pre-formed antifungal compounds or physical barriers to defensive systems induced in response to fungal attack (see Lieutier, Paine *et al.*, Smalley *et al.* this volume). The induced defense reactions include hypersensitive necrosis, the production of phytoalexins and the induction of hydrolytic enzymes such as chitinase. Conversely, the fungi counteract the host reactions by employing various strategies, again often in combination, such as secretion of toxins or hydrolytic enzymes. These interactions determine the specificity of the host-fungus interaction. However, since the interactions between host plants and fungi can be complex and diverse as mentioned above, it has often been found difficult to identify the factors that are responsible in a particular host-fungus interaction.

There are a considerable number of phytopathogenic fungi that belong to the genus *Ceratocystis sensu lato* including *C. fimbriata*, *C. ulmi*, *C. paradoxa* and *C. fagacearum*. Host-parasite interactions have been studied intensively only in the first two species. This paper deals mainly with *C. fimbriata*.

C. fimbriata is distributed throughout the tropical and temperate regions and causes black rot disease on various plants such sweet potato, coffee, prune, cacao, oak, taro and almond. In Japan, the species has been isolated from lesions on sweet potato and taro. Black rot disease of sweet potato caused by this fungus was very serious in Japan until about forty years ago.

Strains of *C. fimbriata* isolated from different host plants show different host specificity. In our laboratory, we have studied the factors involved in host specificity of *C. fimbriata*, using mainly sweet potato roots and taro tubers as the hosts and the seven strains isolated from black rot lesions on sweet potato, coffee, prune, cacao, oak, taro and almond. On sweet potato, only the sweet potato strain is pathogenic, while only the taro strain is pathogenic on taro. These studies have demonstrated that phytoalexins, Ca^{2+} ions, spore-agglutinating factors in the host plants and spore-agglutination inhibitory proteins on germinated spores may all be involved in determining host-pathogen specificity.

The Action of Phytoalexins

Sweet potato roots infected by *C. fimbriata* accumulate furanoterpenoids containing ipomeamarone as a main component. Ipomeamarone has been isolated (4) and its structure has been determined (14). Uritani and co-workers (5,11) studied its roles in the host-parasite interaction and elucidated its nature as a phytoalexin. Since then, many other furanoterpenoids have been isolated from infected sweet potato and their structures and biosynthetic routes have also been elucidated (19). Their structures were rather diverse (Fig. 1).

By incubating the spores of *C. fimbriata* in the extract from infected sweet potato roots, differential effects on the growth of various strains of *C. fimbriata* can be observed (10). With the sweet potato strain, mycelial growth and spore germination were only slightly inhibited in the infected tissue extract, whereas the mycelial growth and spore germination of incompatible strains from coffee, prune, cacao, oak, taro and almond are usually severely inhibited (Fig. 2). Furanoterpenoid phytoalexins such as ipomeamarone and ipomeamaronol are the main cause of this differential inhibitory activity of the infected tissue extract. However, the insensitivity of the sweet potato strain to the terpenoids is apparently not a result of its ability to degrade these compounds because no metabolites of the terpenoids have ever been detected during growth in the medium containing the terpenoids (20). Interestingly, the terpenoids in sweet potato tissues infected by the taro strain begin to show an increase after only 12 hours, while tissues infected by the sweet potato strain have an increased terpenoid content after 18 hours (22).

There are also differences in the depth of cell

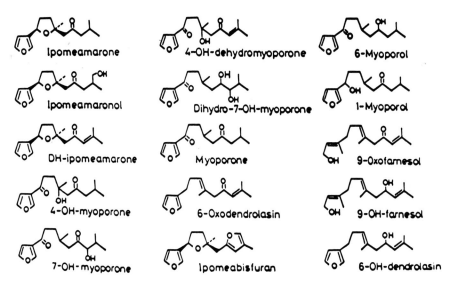

Fig. 1. The structures of main furanoterpenoid phytoalexins isolated from sweet potato roots infected by *C. fimbriata* (Courtesy I. Uritani).

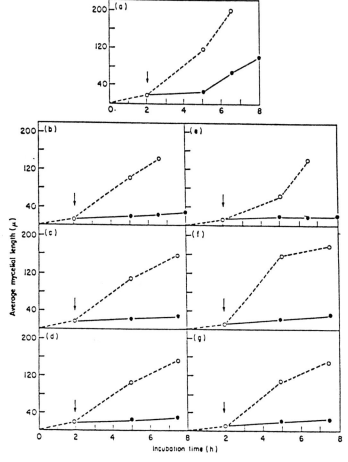

Fig. 2. Mycelial growth of seven strains of *C. fimbriata* in extract of uninfected sweet potato root tissue (--o--) and in extracts of sweet potato root tissue previously infected with sweet potato strain of *C. fimbriata* (—•—). a. Sweet potato strain; b. coffee strain; c. prune strain; d. cacao strain; e. oak strain; f. taro strain; g. almond strain. The arrow indicates the time of transfer of spores from uninfected tissue extract to the infected tissue extract. (reproduced with permission from 10).

layers found to contain the accumulated furanoterpenoids and in their concentration throughout the tissues infected by various strains of the fungus. Tissue infected by the sweet potato strain accumulates furanoterpenoids to a much greater depth and concentration than tissues infected by all other non-pathogenic strains. Nonetheless, all concentrations of furanoterpenoids in the tissues infected by the seven strains appear to be high enough to inhibit growth of the fungi.

Sweet potato roots infected by *C. fimbriata* also accumulate umbelliferone, which exerts an antifungal activity in an earlier stage of infection than the furanoterpenoids (17,22). When the antifungal activity of umbelliferone is tested at concentrations between 0 and 150 μg/ml *in vitro*, it inhibits only germ tube growth of the taro strain but not the sweet potato strain (22). Umbelliferone in the infected sweet potato, however, is not classified as a phytoalexin because some of this chemical can be detected in wounded sweet potato roots in the absence of *C. fimbriata*.

Antifungal compounds are also produced in taro tubers infected by *C. fimbriata* (15). One of these antifungal compounds has been isolated and identified as 9,12,13-trihydroxy-(E)-10-octadecenoic acid (Fig. 3). The structure of this compound suggests that it could be produced from linolenic acid and/or linoleic acid by a peroxidative reaction *in vivo*. Indeed, antifungal activity was detected in assay mixtures containing lipoxygenase and linolenic acid with three double bonds or linoleic acid with two double bonds. However, antifungal activity was not detected in the assay mixture containing lipoxygenase and oleic acid, which has only one double bond, or in a mixture containing palmitic acid, a saturated fatty acid.

Lipid peroxidation takes place at similar magnitude and with a similar time-course pattern in taro tubers infected either by the taro strain or sweet potato strain (16) (Fig. 4). Furthermore, the activities of phospholipase A$_2$ and lipoxygenase change in a manner that accounts for the production of lipid peroxides observed in taro tubers following inoculation with sweet potato or taro strains of *C. fimbriata*.

The Effect of Ca^{2+} ions

Spores of *C. fimbriata* do not germinate well in a synthetic medium that contains glucose, casein hydrolyzate and various vitamins, although they germinate readily in a water extract of sweet potato

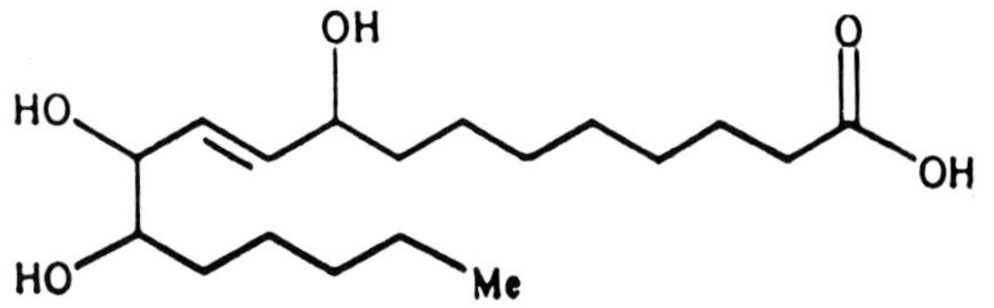

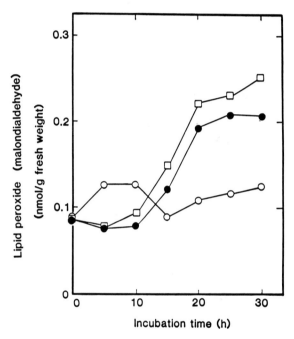

Fig. 3. Structure of the antifungal compound, 9,12,13-trihydroxy-(E)-10-octadecenoic acid, isolated from taro tubers infected by *C. fimbriata*.

Fig. 4. Lipid peroxidation in taro tuber disks wounded (incubated without inoculation), (-○-), inoculated by taro (-■-) and sweet potato strains (-●-) of *C. fimbriata*. Amount of lipid peroxides were determined by thiobarbituric acid reaction. The amount of peroxides was denoted by the amount of malondialdehyde produced (reproduced with permission from 16).

roots. This suggests that sweet potato root extract contains some germination-inductive factor(s). Therefore, we tried to isolate the germination inductive factor(s) in sweet potato roots using an oak strain that is the most sensitive indicator of such the germination-inductive factors (12).

To do this, the host extract was applied to an anionic exchange resin column to separate the anionic substance from the nonanionic fraction. Good germination (100%) was observed in the nonanionic fraction of the extract, indicating that the germination-inductive factor(s) was not anionic. Next,

TABLE 1. Spore germination of the oak strain of *C. fimbriata* in various fractions obtained from sweet potato root water extract[a].

Fraction	Germination (%)
Tissue extract	100
Unabsorbed fraction[b]	0
Absorbed fraction[b]	0
Mixture of unabsorbed and absorbed fraction[c]	100

[a]   Reprinted from Kojima and Uritani (12).
[b]   The fraction was prepared by applying tissue extract to a cation exchange resin column.
[c]   One volume of the unabsorbed fraction was mixed with two volumes of the absorbed fraction.

spore germination was examined in the unabsorbed and absorbed fraction prepared by applying the extract to a cation exchange resin column (Table 1); spore germination did not occur in either fraction. However, spores germinated well in a mixture of both fractions, indicating that the oak strain required both cationic factor(s) in the absorbed fraction and noncationic factor(s) in the unabsorbed fraction for germination.

The germination-inductive factors in the absorbed fraction have been identified as metallic ions such as Ca^{2+} and Mg^{2+}; atomic absorption analysis indicated that the absorbed fraction also contained Fe^{2+} and K^+. When the germination- inductive activities of these cations were examined in the presence of the unabsorbed fraction, Ca^{2+} at a concentration of 1.0×10^{-3} M showed the highest activity (Fig. 5), although Mg^{2+}, Mn^+ and Zn^{2+} also induced germination. Other cations such as Fe^{2+} and Co^{2+} did not induce germination.

The germination-inductive factor(s) in the unabsorbed fraction, however, has not yet been identified. The unabsorbed fraction could not be replaced by nutrients such as di-and monosaccharides, amino acids, organic acids, vitamins, nucleotides, plant hormones or yeast extract.

Further studies on the effect of Ca^{2+} indicated that spores of the sweet potato, coffee and cacao strains of *C. fimbriata* germinate well in the unabsorbed fraction, while germination of the prune, oak, taro and almond strains tends to be poor but can be enhanced by addition of Ca^{2+}. Thus, the strains of *C. fimbriata* divided into two groups in terms of Ca^{2+} requirement for germination; one group including the sweet potato, coffee and cacao strains does not require exogenous Ca^{2+} for germination, while the other group, which includes the prune, oak, taro and

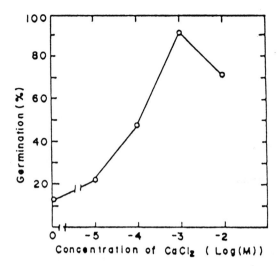

Fig. 5. Effect of concentration of $CaCl_2$ on the germination of the oak strain of *C. fimbriata*. Germination was assayed in the unabsorbed fraction containing various concentrations of $CaCl_2$ (reproduced with permission from 12).

almond strains, does.

In comparisons of the Ca^{2+} and Mg^{2+} content of spores using the sweet potato and oak strains as representatives of the two groups, spores of the oak strain have been found to contain more Ca^{2+} and Mg^{2+} than those of the sweet potato strain. This suggests that the Ca^{2+} content of spores is not related to exogenous Ca^{2+} requirement for germination. Moreover, if Ca^{2+} is administered to spores of the oak strain preincubated in the unabsorbed fraction for various time periods, germ tubes emerge 1.5 h after Ca^{2+} administration regardless of the period of preincubation. These results suggest that Ca^{2+} ions are functioning as triggers of germination, but not as a nutrient, in some strains of *C. fimbriata*.

The Spore-Agglutinating Factor

When spores of various strains of *C. fimbriata* are incubated in a heat-treated extract of host plants such as sweet potato, potato, taro, cucumber and kidney bean, spores of all strains germinate and the germinated spores show differential agglutination. We examined the relation between spore agglutination *in vitro* and host-parasite compatibility in 35 combinations and found close correlations between compatibility and spore agglutination. In the incompatible combinations, the germinated spores agglutinate in the host extract; however, agglutination usually does not take place in the compatible combinations, although there can be some exceptions

TABLE 2. Agglutination of the germinated spores of various strains of *C. fimbriata* treated with the spore-agglutinating factor of sweet potato[a].

Concentration of spore-agglutinating factor (μg/ml)[d]	Relative agglutination[b]						
	Sweet potato[c] strain	Coffee strain	Prune strain	Cacao strain	Oak strain	Taro strain	Almond[c] strain
0	0	0	0	0	0	0	0
0.5	0	0	0	0	0	-	-
1.0	0	1	0	1	0	1	0
1.5	0	2	0	1	1	1	0
2.0	0	3	0	2	2	2	0
2.5	0	4	1	2	3	3	0
3.0	0	5	2	2	3	4	0

[a] Reproduced with permission from 13.
[b] The degree of agglutination is presented as a relative agglutination value on an arbitrary scale where 1 represents the lowest amount of agglutination detectable by the unaided eye. Zero denotes no agglutination.
[c] Agglutination was observed in an assay mixture containing a high level (10 μg galacturonic acid/ml) of the spore-agglutinating factor.
[d] Concentration in galacturonic acid equivalents.

(11).

The spore-agglutinating factor has been isolated from sweet potato (13) and requires Ca^{2+} for its activity. It is mainly composed of galacturonic acid (53% of dry weight), with minor amounts of arabinose, fucose and an unidentified component. From this sugar composition, it can be assumed that the factor is a component of the cell wall. The factor can also agglutinate A-, B-, AB- and 0 types of human erythrocytes to almost the same degree, providing Ca^{2+} is available. The differential agglutinating activity of the factor toward the germinated spores depends on the pH of the assay medium; it agglutinates similarly the germinated spores of various strains at pH 7.5 and 5.5, whereas it displays a differential agglutinating activity at pH 6.5 (Table 2). However, the ungerminated spores of all strains are agglutinated by the factor similarly with only small differences between the strains at any pH.

Spore-agglutinating factor can also be isolated from taro tubers (6). The factor has similar properties to that of factor from sweet potato roots. However, the agglutinating activity toward various strains of *C. fimbriata* differs between the two factors; the germinated spores of the almond strain are insensitive to the factor from sweet potato roots but sensitive to that from taro tubers.

Spore Agglutination-Inhibitory Proteins on Germinated Spores

As described in the preceding section, ungerminated spores of various strains of *C. fimbriata* can be highly sensitive to the spore-agglutinating factor derived from sweet potato. However, spores of the sweet potato strain become less sensitive to the factor after germination, although other incompatible strains remain sensitive both before and after germination. This suggests that some agglutination-inhibitory substance(s) become activated on the spores of the sweet potato strain following germination.

Evidence for a inhibitory substance was obtained by the experiment detailed in Table 3 (7). When germinated spores of the sweet potato strain are sonicated, they become sensitive to the agglutinating factor and are agglutinated by lowest concentration of the factor. The sonicated spores, however, return to the insensitive state when they are re-incubated with the surface substances released by sonication. It seems likely that the acquisition of insensitivity is caused by rebinding of the surface substances to the sonicated spores. The substances appear to rebind most efficiently to the surface of the sonicated spores at pH 6.5 in the presence of Ca^{2+} (10mM). From the inactivation by heat and trypsin treatments, the spore-

247

TABLE 3. Effects of sonication and pre-treatment with sonication-released substances on agglutination of germinated spores of *C. fimbriata*, sweet potato strain[a].

Concentration of spore-agglutinating factor (μ/ml)[d]	Relative agglutination[b]		
	Germinated spores pre-incubated with water	Sonicated spores[c] pre-incubated with water	Sonicated spores[c] pre-incubated with sonication-released substances
0	0	0	0
25	0	1	0
50	0	1	0
75	0	2	0
100	0	2	0
125	0	3	0

[a] Reproduced with permission from 7.
[b] The degree of agglutination is presented as in Table 2.
[c] The germinated spores of the sweet potato were sonicated. The sonicated spores were pre-incubated by 20 °C for 30 min in assay medium on a shaker at 100 strokes/min. Then varied amount of spore-agglutinating factor and $CaCl_2$ (10 mM) were added to the mixture, which was incubated for another 30 min to assay for agglutination.
[d] Concentration in galacturonic acid equivalents.

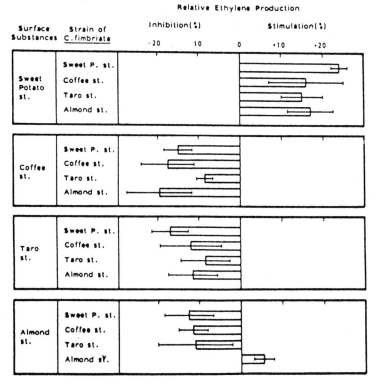

Fig. 6. Effects of the surface substances from germinated spores of various strains of *C. fimbriata* on ethylene production in sweet potato root tissues infected by various strains of *C. fimbriata* (reproduced with permission from 8).

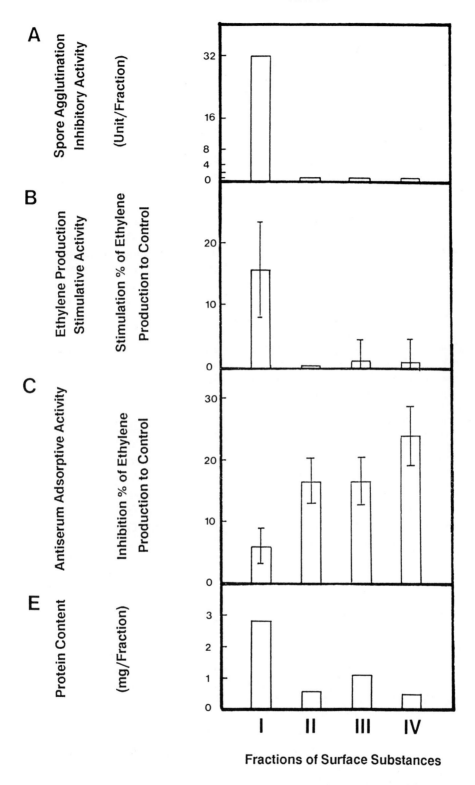

Fig. 7. A. Distribution of spore agglutination inhibitory activity; B. ethylene production stimulative activity; C. antiserum adsorptive activity; and D. protein contents; in various fractions of the surface substances from germinated spores of sweet potato strain. Fractions I,II,III and IV are fractions of the surface substances precipitated by 0-20%, 20-40% and 40-60% saturation of ammonium sulfate and the final supernatant, respectively (reproduced with permission from 9).

agglutination inhibitory factor in the surface substance fraction can be assumed to be protein. It is also capable of diminishing sensitivity to spore agglutinating factor(s) of germinated spores of the seven strains of *C. fimbriata*.

The surface substances from the incompatible strains such as coffee, taro and almond strains only weakly inhibit spore agglutination compared with the substances from the sweet potato strain (8). The surface substances from the sweet potato strain also increase ethylene production from sweet potato roots infected by several strains including the sweet potato, coffee, taro and almond strains, which is possibly an index of pathogenicity. Conversely, the similar substances from incompatible strains suppress ethylene production from the tissue infected by all four strains except the substances from the almond strain (Fig. 6). These effects on ethylene production in the infected sweet potato roots are extinguished by heat and trypsin treatments in the same way that the spore-agglutination inhibitory activity is removed with the same treatments.

Antiserum raised against the surface substances from germinated spores of the sweet potato strain agglutinated the germinated spores of this strain and also decreased ethylene production in sweet potato roots infected by this strain (9). In contrast, the antiserum had little effect on ethylene production in roots infected by the coffee strain. When surface substances from germinated spores of the sweet potato strain were separated into four fractions with ammonium sulfate (consisting of 0-20%, 20-40% and 40-60% saturated ammonium sulfate and the final supernatant) and the fractions assayed for spore agglutination inhibitory activity, ethylene production stimulative activity and antiserum absorptive activity, all three activities were localized in the 0-20% fraction (Fig. 7).

The Host-Pathogen Interaction

Ceratocystis fimbriata can infect a host plant only through open wounds. Spores lodge in wounds of host plants, then germinate and initiate a complex and diverse interaction with the host. During the initial stages of infection, some strains of *C. fimbriata* require Ca^{2+} ions to trigger germination. Water extracts of all plants tested appear to contain Ca^{2+} as well as other unidentified factor(s) that can induce spore germination of *C. fimbriata*. However, it is likely that there are different availabilities of Ca^{2+} and the unidentified spore-germination inductive factor(s) at the sites of infection by various strains

and they influence growth of the pathogen. Thus Ca^{2+} and the unidentified factor(s) might constitute one of the first steps in the host-specificity determination of *C. fimbriata*.

We also know that Ca^{2+} is required for the activity of spore-agglutinating factors that are present in sweet potato roots and taro tubers. From their sugar compositions, it can be assumed that the factors are components of cell walls and this may be a widespread phenomenon throughout plant kingdom.

It is now well established that carbohydrate moieties on the plasma membrane of animal cells function as determinants of specificity in various cellular recognition systems (3, 21). However, in contrast to animal cells, the plasma membranes of plant cells are not exposed but are covered with cell walls composed of complex carbohydrates. Moreover, it is the cell wall that interacts first with invading parasites. Thus, it seems most plausible that the walls of plant cells participate in cellular recognition on host-parasite interactions. In this connection, it should be noted that the pectic fragments from plant cell walls are capable of inducing phytoalexins (1) and proteinase inhibitors (2).

When spores of *C. fimbriata* germinate, alterations of the surface structure occur in the spores. For example, a spore-agglutination inhibitory protein appears on the germinated spores of the sweet potato strain. This inhibitory protein stimulates the pathogenicity of the sweet potato strain and some incompatible strains as well. On the other hand, the corresponding proteins from the germinated spores of incompatible strains suppress the pathogenicity of various strains to sweet potato.

In response to infection by *C. fimbriata*, sweet potato roots first accumulate umbelliferone and later also furanoterpenoid phytoalexins. There are differences in accumulation times of furanoterpenoid phytoalexins in the tissues infected by different strains. Accumulation of furanoterpenoid phytoalexins is delayed in tissue infected by the sweet potato strain (a compatible strain) compared with tissue infected by the taro strain (an incompatible strain). In addition, the sweet potato strain is less sensitive to both umbelliferone and furanoterpenoid phytoalexins.

CONCLUSIONS

From the results and discussions described above, I present the following mechanism of differential pathogenicity of various strains of *C. fimbriata* on sweet potato roots. Upon germination, spores of the sweet potato strain produce the spore-agglutination inhibitory protein on their surface to weaken the interaction between the spore-agglutinating factor in the cell walls of host plant (sweet potato) and the receptors on the spores. This weakened interaction results in the production of less stimuli and inefficient recognition by the host. The inefficient recognition then results in delayed phytoalexin production by the host plant. Moreover, the sweet potato strain is rather insensitive to phytoalexins, allowing successful invasion into the inner tissue of sweet potato roots. On the other hand, strains incompatible with a sweet potato host, such as taro and coffee strains, produce upon germination spore surface proteins that differ from those of the sweet potato strain. The proteins produced by taro and coffee strains cannot weaken the interactions between the spore-agglutinating factors and the receptors on the spores. The strong interaction results in production of more stimuli and efficient recognition by the sweet potato host. Efficient recognition results in earlier phytoalexin production by the host, and in addition, the incompatible taro and coffee strains are more sensitive to phytoalexins. Thus, the incompatible strains cannot invade into inner tissue of sweet potato.

ACKNOWLEDGEMENTS

I am grateful to Dr. I. Uritani as well as other co-workers and express my thanks to Dr. P. McCourt for his help in the preparation of the manuscript.

LITERATURE CITED

1. Ayres, A., Valent, B., Ebed, J. and Albersheim, P. 1976. Host pathogen interactions. VI. Composition and structure of wall-released elicitor fractions. Plant Physiol. 57:766-774.

2. Bishop, P., Makus, D.J., Pearce, G. and Ryan, C.A. 1981. Proteinase inhibitor inducing factor activity in tomato leaves resides in oligosaccharides enzymatically released from cell walls. Proc. Nat. Acad. Sci. USA. 78:3536-3640.

3. Hausman, R.E. and Moscona, A.A. 1979. Immunologic detection of retina cognin on the surface of embryonic cells. Exp. Cell Res. 119:191-204.

4. Hiura, M. 1943. Studies on storage and rot of sweet potato (2). Rep. Gifu Agric. Coll. 50:1-5

5. Hyodo, H., Uritani, I. and Akai, S. 1969. Production of furanoterpenoids and other compounds in sweet potato root tissue in response to infection by various isolates of Ceratocystis fimbriata. Phytopathol. Z. 65:332-340.

6. Kawakita, K. and Kojima, M. 1983. The isolation and properties of a factor in taro tuber that agglutinates spores

7. Kawakita, K. and Kojima, M. 1984. Studies on agglutination-inhibitory substances on germinated spores of Ceratocystis fimbriata, black rot fungus. Agric. Biol. Chem. 48:3063-3069.

8. Kawakita, K. and Kojima, M. 1985. Role of surface substances on germinated spores of Ceratocystis fimbriata, black rot fungus, in host-parasite interation. Agric. Biol. Chem. 49:2119-2123.

9. Kawakita, K. and Kojima, M. 1986. Possible involvement of surface substances on germinated spores of Ceratocystis fimbriata, black rot fungus, in determination of host-parasite specificity. Agric. Biol. Chem. 50:431-436.

10. Kojima, M. and Uritani, I. 1976. Possible involvement of furanoterpenoid phytoalexins in establishing host-parasite specificity between sweet potato and various strains of Ceratocystis fimbriata. Physiol. Plant Pathol. 8:97-111.

11. Kojima, M. and Uritani, I. 1974. The possible involvement of a spore agglutinating factor(s) in various plants in establishing host specificity by various strains of black rot fungus, Ceratocystis fimbriata. Plant Cell Physiol. 15:733-737.

12. Kojima, M. and Uritani, I. 1978. Studies on factors in sweet potato root which induce spore germination of Ceratocystis fimbriata. Plant Cell Physiol. 19:91-97.

13. Kojima, M., Kawakita, K. and Uritani, I. 1982. Studies on a factor in sweet potato root which agglutinates spores of Ceratocystis fimbriata, black rot fungus. Plant Physiol. 69:474-478.

14. Kubota, N. and Matsuura, T. 1953. Chemical studies on black rot disease of sweet potato (6). Structure of ipomeamarone. J. Chem. Soc. Japan. 74:248-251.

15. Masui, H., Kondo, T. and Kojima, M. 1989. Antifungal compound, 9,12,13-trihydroxy-(E)-10-octadecenoic acid, from Colocasia antiquorum inoculated with Ceratocystis fimbriata. Phytochemistry 28:2613-2615.

16. Masui, H. and Kojima, M. 1990. Lipid peroxidation and its role in taro tubers infected by Ceratocystis fimbriata. Agric. Biol. Chem. 54:1689-1695.

17. Minamikawa, T., Akazawa, T. and Uritani, I. 1963. Analytical study of umbelliferone and scopoletin synthesis in sweet potato roots infected by Ceratocystis fimbriata. Plant Physiol. 38:493-497.

18. Ryan, C.A. 1988. Oligosaccharide signalling for proteinase inhibitor genes in plant leaves. Pages 163-180 in: Recent Avances in Phytochemistry, XXII. E.E. Conn, ed. Plenum, New York. 201 pp.

19. Schneider, J.A., Lee, J., Naya, Y., Nakanishi, K., Oba, K. and Uritani, I. 1984. The fate of the phytoalexin ipomeamarone; furanoterpenes and butenolides from Ceratocystis fimbriata-infected sweet potatoes. Phytochemistry 23:759-764.

20. Takeuchi, A., Oguni, I., Oba, K., Kojima, M. and Uritani, I. 1978. Interactions between diseased sweet potato terpenoids and Ceratocystis fimbriata. Agric. Biol. Chem. 42:935-939.

21. Watkins, W.M. 1966. Blood-group substances. Science 152:172-181.

22. Yasuda, K. and Kojima, M. 1986. The role of stress metabolites in establishing host-parasite specificity between sweet potato and Ceratocystis fimbriata, black rot fungus. Agric. Biol. Chem. 50:1839-1846.

of Ceratocystis fimbriata, black rot fungus. Plant Cell Physiol. 24:41-49.

PART V

RESEARCH AIDS AND FUTURE CONSIDERATIONS

Chapter 27

METHODS FOR STUDYING SPECIES OF *OPHIOSTOMA* AND *CERATOCYSTIS*

K.A. SEIFERT, J.F. WEBBER and M.J. WINGFIELD

This paper provides a brief introduction to methods used to collect, isolate, grow, preserve and study species of *Ophiostoma* and *Ceratocystis* and their associated anamorphs. Techniques for basic genetic studies are also outlined. More detailed methods pertaining to specific species or genera have been published by Brasier (2) for *O. ulmi* and Harrington (7) for *Leptographium* spp. General reviews on collection, isolation and preservation of fungi have been published by Tuite (16), Booth (1), Smith and Onions (13), Stevens (15) and Seifert (12).

COLLECTION

Most species of *Ophiostoma* and *Ceratocystis* are lignicolous or corticolous and are found on freshly exposed sapwood, between the bark and the sapwood, in bark beetle tunnels or on roots of diseased trees. With practice, colonized specimens are recognizable in the field with a hand lens; minute slimy spore masses at the tips of black stalks can often be observed. Colonies can sometimes be detected by examining the specimen in profile against diffuse light.

Lumber that has seasoned outdoors and has not been chemically treated or kiln dried often has profuse development of perithecia or conidiophores.

Trees or logs attacked by bark beetles usually have many small holes 1-2 mm diam penetrating through the bark. The tunnels can be exposed by pulling or cutting away the bark. Perithecia or conidiophores are often produced in the tunnels.

Specimens intended for isolation should be processed as soon as possible after collection because of the tendency of aggressive, secondary fungi to colonize fresh specimens.

Specimens where species of *Ophiostoma* or *Ceratocystis* are suspected of growing but are not yet sporulating can be placed in a damp chamber. The material is incubated in a petri dish or similar vessel lined with damp filter paper, usually at room temperature, under incident lighting conditions, and examined periodically using a dissecting microscope. Surface sterilization will retard growth of unwanted saprophytic fungi.

ISOLATION

Isolations are made directly from masses of spores detected under a dissecting microscope or indirectly from mycelium growing in soil or plant parts.

Direct isolations should be made onto media such as 1-2% malt extract agar or oatmeal agar, incorporating antibacterial antibiotics (see below). Under a dissecting microscope, masses of ascospores from perithecia or conidia from conidiophores are transferred from the specimen directly to an agar medium using a sterilized needle. Fine needles are made from narrow gauge wire, such as 00 insect pins, mounted in a handle. Very fine but fragile needles can be made by softening the middle of 15 cm long pieces of 3 mm diam glass rod over a bunsen burner and pulling the two ends apart.

Several species of *Ophiostoma* and/or *Ceratocystis* may occur on a single specimen and a useful habit is to make an isolation from the spore mass of an individual fruiting body, then immediately make a slide preparation of that fruiting body. In this way, cultural morphology can be correlated with that of the original specimen, even if typical perithecia or conidiophores do not occur *in vitro*. After isolations are made, the specimen should be dried to allow comparison with the living culture. If the resulting cultures are used in published studies, the voucher specimen and slide preparations should be deposited in a recognized herbarium and the culture in a recognized culture collection, and the accession details included in the paper. This will ensure that the published information can always be linked to a morphological or genetic entity, even if taxonomic concepts or nomenclature change.

Indirect isolations are made from sterile specimens suspected of harboring the mycelium of ophiostomatoid fungi. These substrates include sapstained wood, wood or bark adjacent to scolytid

---

[1]This paper has been compiled by the editors and incorporates suggestions made in the discussions at the Ophiostomatales workshop, observations from the literature and our own experiences from working with ophiostomatoid fungi on three different continents.

beetle galleries, captured scolytid beetles or phoretic mites, and soil near infected roots. With wood or bark, small particles (around 1 mm in size) are aseptically removed with sterile scalpel and forceps to the isolation medium. Insects may be squashed and spread onto the isolation medium, or dissected and the individual body parts plated separately. *Ophiostoma* species can be isolated using selective media incorporating the antibiotic cycloheximide. Concentrations from 100-1000 mg/ℓ are used, in conjunction with antibacterial antibiotics, usually in malt agar (11,8,7). *Ceratocystis* species are sensitive to this antibiotic and will not grow on these media; no selective media have yet been devised for these species.

Ophiostoma species or related anamorphs can be isolated from soil close to infected roots using cycloheximide emended media, although it should be stressed that many other cycloheximide tolerant fungi, particularly *Penicillium* spp., may also be isolated. Hicks *et al.* (8) used PDA containing 800 mg/ℓ cycloheximide, 200 mg/ℓ streptomycin sulfate and 100 mg/ℓ $MnCl_2$ for isolating *Ophiostoma wageneri* from soil dilution plates. The manganese stimulated growth of *O. wageneri*.

Isolation plates can generally be incubated at room temperature (20-25°C), but Harrington (7) has noted that *Leptographium wageneri* grows best at 15°C, with little or no growth at 25°C.

Because of the tendency for several ophiostomatoid fungi to grow in close proximity, Harrington (7) has recommended that single hyphal tips or single spore isolations be made of fresh isolates to ensure homogeneity.

CULTIVATION FOR IDENTIFICATION

No single medium is appropriate for all *Ceratocystis* and *Ophiostoma* species. For the identification of unknowns, experimentation with different media is generally required.

Dalpé and Neumann (4,5) have demonstrated that the presence of fatty acids stimulates production of perithecia and conidiophores in some species. Small disks of filter paper are dipped in 0.10-0.20 g/ℓ solutions of linoleic acid in methanol and placed on the margin of a growing colony.

Production of perithecia *in vitro*

Perithecia will sometimes develop in isolation plates that have been derived from mass transfer of ascospores or conidia. Perithecial production should

occur readily in homothallic species on appropriate media. For heterothallic species, single ascospore isolates representing individual mating types must be crossed, as outlined below.

Water or malt agar with twigs or wood of the original substrate is a logical way to begin in an attempt to obtain perithecia. Oatmeal agar, cellulose agar, or malt agar are suitable for some species. Cycloheximide may enhance perithecial production in some species. Prolonged incubation of cultures at low temperatures (5-10°C) seems to stimulate perithecial production in some strains.

Hutchison and Reid (9) describe a stepwise regime for inducing perithecial production in fresh isolates. These included growing cultures 1) on 2% MEA in complete darkness, 2) on 2% MEA in alternating light and dark, with the light including fluorescent and black light, 3) on wood disks in complete darkness, 4) on 2% MEA supplemented with 100 μg/ℓ thiamine, 100 μg/ℓ pyridoxine and 50 μg/ℓ biotin and 5) in paired culture with the mycoparasite *Gliocladium roseum*.

Production of anamorphs *in vitro*

Anamorphs occur much more readily in culture than do perithecia. Many species produce more than one type of anamorph, and the relative abundance of the synanamorphs varies according to the medium composition and the number of times the culture has been transferred. Mycelial anamorphs that lack differentiated, darkly pigmented conidiophores (*Sporothrix*, *Hyalorhinocladiella* and *Chalara* anamorphs) occur readily on most media and may completely dominate the colony in degenerated cultures. The more complicated *Leptographium* and *Graphium* anamorphs tend to be fastidious, requiring media with complex carbohydrates. As with perithecia, the use of a relatively weak medium with twigs of the original substrate is probably a good medium to start with. For development of synnemata, oatmeal agar is usually good. Complex conidiophores often disappear with subculturing. In order to maintain production of these conidiophores, it is important to transfer the conidia they produce, rather than transferring conidia from aerial mycelium or agar plugs.

MAINTENANCE OF CULTURES

Cultures of some *Ophiostoma* species degenerate quite rapidly. Degeneration may occur if the medium is too rich or if carbon dioxide accumulates in the culture. Degenerated cultures may not produce perithecia, may produce morphologically abnormal anamorphs (or no anamorphs at all) and do not perform reliably in vegetative compatability tests. Cultures that have felty or cottony white aerial mycelium, or sectors of such mycelium, are no longer representative of the wild type and should be discarded or at least used with discretion. Some cultures are inherently unstable and require constant vigilance. The wild type can sometimes be recovered by re-isolating spores from 'normal' sectors of degenerated colonies.

For most studies, it is preferable to use freshly isolated cultures. Many *Ophiostoma* and *Ceratocystis* cultures available from culture collections are no longer representative of the original isolate. However, fresh isolates can be maintained in optimal conditions for many years if they are maintained with care.

Serial transfer, maintenance of cultures on rich media, and storage of cultures under mineral oil should be avoided. Sporulating cultures can be maintained by lyophilization, using standard methods described by, for example, Smith and Onions (13). Lyophilized cultures should remain viable for 20-40 years if stored in a cool, dark place. Cultures freshly revived from the lyophilized state often sporulate profusely.

A less laborious alternative is to freeze cultures in plastic or glass vials with tightly fitted lids, preferably with some sort of rubber gasket. The lids are left slightly loose until the culture just covers the agar surface. Then the lids are tightened and the vials are placed immediately into a -20°C freezer. The culture is transferred by chipping a piece of frozen agar onto a fresh medium without allowing the vial to thaw. If the vial thaws, it should not be refrozen. The culture must be retransferred into a new vial and the new culture stored in its place.

Storage of cultures in the vapor phase of liquid nitrogen is the method of choice if the facilities are available. Smith and Onions (13) discuss the methodology involved. An alternative to using plastic vials is to use short pieces of drinking straws, as described by Stalpers *et al.* (14).

GENETIC ANALYSIS

Isolating Single Ascospores

Webber *et al.* (17) developed a method for isolating single ascospores of *Ophiostoma ulmi* that is applicable to most *Ophiostoma* and *Ceratocystis* species. Select a single perithecium from the substrate that has ascospores oozing from the neck. Roll the perithecium gently around a water agar plate to remove surface mycelium or contaminating conidia. Surface sterilize the perithecium by dipping it in a drop of 50% ethanol for 20 seconds, then 2-3% household bleach (2 g/ℓ chlorine) for 20 seconds on a microscope slide. Cut the neck off the perithecium using a sterilized scalpel, then place the base in a drop of sterile water on a sterile microscope slide. Ascospores will ooze out into the drop. Remove loops of spores to agar plates, and spread over the plates using sterile glass rods. Alternatively, put the perithicium onto an agar plate for 3-5 seconds, allowing the ascospores to ooze out, then transfer to a second plate and so on. Add 0.1 mℓ sterile water to each plate and spread. Single germinating ascospores can be located on the plates using a dissecting microscope with substage illumination after about 24 hours, and removed using a fine needle to fresh media.

Homothallic species

Perithecia will sometimes develop in isolation plates that have been derived from mass transfer of ascospores or conidia. This may indicate homothallism, but it may also indicate that the original inoculum had both mating types present. The only way to confirm homothallism is to demonstrate perithecial production by single ascospore isolates.

Heterothallic species

In order for heterothallic species to produce perithecia, both mating types must be present. If compatable mating types are inoculated onto an appropriate agar medium about 2 cm apart, perithecia should form where the two colonies meet. Placing a piece of sterilized wood or twig where the two colonies meet may increase success. A second strategy is to make a spread plate of one mating type on an agar plate, incubate until a uniform growth covers the medium, then make point inoculations of the opposite mating type (using a drop of spore suspension). Perithecia should develop on those spots where opposite mating types are present. For twigs, dip twig in spore suspension of one mating type, incubate for three days, then spot inoculate with the opposite mating type.

Vegetative Compatibility

Using wild-type single ascospore cultures, pair isolates on agar media as described above for perithecial development. Choice of media for vegetative compatibility studies is critical, and varies among species. Researchers should be prepared to experiment with several media before beginning large scale studies. To determine the appearance of a compatible reaction, pair a single ascospore isolate against itself and observe the appearance of the interaction zone.

Using *nit*-mutants: A more unequivocal method of studying vegetative compatibility is the use of nitrate non-utilizing, or *nit*, mutants. Zambino and Harrington (18) employed nitrate *nit*-mutants to study vegetative compatibility in *Leptographium wageneri*. This method exploits the tendency of nitrate utilizing species to reduce the nitrate analog sodium chlorate to the toxic sodium chlorite. Spontaneous *nit*-mutants on chlorate media are able to grow rapidly because chlorite is not produced. Pairing of complementary *nit*-mutants on a minimal medium results in profuse development of aerial mycelium at the interaction zone. A detailed explanation of the method involved is presented by Zambino and Harrington (18) and is outlined below. The method is not suitable for species of *Ophiostoma* that do not utilize nitrate, such as *O. canum*, *O. ips*, *O. piceae*, *O. tetropii* and *O. ulmi* (10).

Spontaneously arising *nit*-mutants were isolated by inoculating wild-type cultures onto Malt Yeast Extract Agar (MYEA) or Complete Medium (CM) containing 1.5% KClO₃. Fast growing sectors were isolated and transferred to fresh MYEA-chlorate plates. Complementation tests were done using inoculum from 2 wk old cultures on CM. Mycelial plugs from the two strains were placed side by side on nitrate minimal medium with Triton X-100 (MMT). The cultures were examined at 6, 9 and 12 weeks for the presence of the dense band of aerial mycelia between the two colonies, which indicates complementation.

MEDIA REFERRED TO IN TEXT

Fungi grow best in carbohydrate rich media that have a slightly acidic pH. Antibacterial antibiotics or chemicals should be added to most isolation media to reduce contamination.

Unless otherwise noted, the formulae should be mixed with 1000 ml distilled water, 1.5-2.0% agar, and sterilized for 15-20 min at 121°C and 15 psi pressure.

General Media

Malt Extract Agar (MA): The malt extract concentration employed is usually 2% (=2% MA), but may range from 1-5%.

Oatmeal Agar (OA): In a wide-mouthed vessel such as a beaker, boil 30 g of oat flakes in 100 ml distilled water for 2 hr, taking care to ensure the liquid does not boil dry. Filter through cheese cloth, make volume up to 1000 ml, add agar, and sterilize (6).

Potato Dextrose Agar (PDA): A widely used medium with many variations. Peeled potatoes (200 - 500 g) are sliced or cubed and boiled for 1 hr. The resulting solution is filtered through cheesecloth or homogenized and the volume adjusted to 1000 ml. Twenty grams of glucose are added prior to autoclaving. Commercially available powdered versions of this medium are generally a poor substitute.

Bacterial inhibitors: Three categories of antibiotics are commonly employed in isolation media to retard bacteria. Streptomycin, neomycin and kanamycin are effective against many gram-negative and gram-positive bacteria and should be used at a concentration of 100-200 mg/ℓ. Tetracycline, aureomycin, and chloramphenicol are broad spectrum antibiotics that disturb bacterial protein synthesis. Tetracycline and aureomycin are used at concentrations of 25-100 mg/ℓ and chloramphenicol is used at around 200 mg/ℓ. Penicillins are effective against most gram-positive bacteria and gram-negative cocci and are used at concentrations of 12-1500 mg/ℓ. Except for chloramphenicol, which is heat stable, all of these antibiotics are heat labile and should be added to the medium after autoclaving. Penicillins should not be used in highly acidic media. For preparing a small number of plates, it is practical to keep stock solutions in a refrigerator, to be added to petri dishes with a syringe or pipette prior to pouring the agar (12).

Media used for genetic analysis

Elm Sapwood Agar (ESA): Collect young elm twigs less than 0.5 cm in diameter, peel, and dry overnight. Mill to 1-2 mm sawdust. Autoclave 50 g elm sapwood with 15 g agar and 500 ml distilled water for 15 minutes. Agitate constantly during pouring to ensure even distribution of the sawdust particles (2).

Media used for generation and testing of *nit*-mutants (18)

Basal medium (BM): Glucose 20 g, KH$_2$PO$_4$ 1.0 g, MgSO$_4$·7H$_2$O 0.5 g, KCl 0.5 g, CaCl$_2$ 0.1 g, 0.2 ml trace element solution, 10 ml vitamin solution.

Trace element solution: Citric acid 5.0 g, ZnSO$_4$ 5.0 g, Fe(NH$_4$)$_2$(SO)$_4$·6H$_2$O 1.0 g, CuSO$_4$·5H$_2$O 0.25 g, MnSO$_4$·H$_2$O 50 mg, H$_3$BO$_4$ 50 mg, NaMoO$_4$·2H$_2$O 50 mg, distilled water 95 ml (3).

Vitamin solution: Thiamine HCl 0.1 mg, pyridoxine HCl 0.075 mg, biotin 0.005 mg per 1.0 ml 50% ethanol.

Complete medium (CM): Basal medium with 1.0 g L-asparagine added.

Nitrate minimal medium with Triton X-100 (MMT): Basal medium with 1.0 g NaNO$_3$ and 2 ml Triton X-100 added.

ACKNOWLEDGEMENTS:

We are grateful to Tom Harrington for providing a prepublication copy of his paper on methods for studying *Leptographium* species, and to the many participants of the Ophiostomatales workshop for suggestions made during discussions.

LITERATURE CITED

1. Booth, C. (ed.). 1971. Methods in Microbiology, vol. 4. Academic Press, London and New York. 795 pp.
2. Brasier, C.M. 1981. Laboratory investigation of *Ceratocystis ulmi*. Pages 76-79 in: Compendium of Elm Diseases. R.J. Stipes and R.J. Campana, eds. American Phytopathological Society Press, St. Paul, MN. 96 pp.
3. Correll, J.C., Klittich, C.J.R. and Leslie, J.F. 1987. Nitrate nonutilizing mutants of *Fusarium oxysporum* and their use in vegetative compatibility tests. Phytopathology 77:1640-1646.
4. Dalpé, Y. and Neumann, P. 1976. L'effet d'acides gras sur la stimulation des périthèces de *Ceratocystis ips, C. minor* et *C. capillifera*. Eur. J. For. Pathol. 6:335-342.
5. Dalpé, Y. and Neumann, P. 1977. L'induction chez *Ceratocystis* de fructifications de types *Graphium* et *Leptographium* par des acides gras insaturés. Can. J. Bot. 55:2159-2167.
6. Gams, W., van der Aa, H.A., van der Plaats-Niterink, A.J., Samson, R.A. and Stalpers, J.A. 1987. CBS Course of Mycology, Third ed. Centraalbureau voor Schimmelcultures, Baarn. 136 pp.
7. Harrington, T.C. 1992. *Leptographium*. Pages 129-133 in: Methods for Research on Soilborne Phytopathogenic Fungi. L.L. Singleton, J.D. Mihail and C. Rush, eds. American Phytopathological Society Press, St. Paul, MN. 265 pp.
8. Hicks, B.R., Cobb, F.W. Jr. and Gersper, P.L. 1980. Isolation of *Ceratocystis wageneri* from forest soil with a selective medium. Phytopathology 70:880-883.
9. Hutchison, L.J. and Reid, J. 1988. Taxonomy of some potential wood-staining fungi from New Zealand 1. Ophiostomataceae. N.Z. J. Bot. 26:63-81.
10. Käärik, A. 1960. Growth and sporulation of *Ophiostoma* and some other blueing fungi on synthetic media. Symb. Bot. Upsal. 16:1-168.
11. Schneider, I.R. 1956. A selective medium for the routine isolation of *Graphium ulmi* Schwartz. Plant. Dis. Rep. 40:816-820.
12. Seifert, K.A. 1990. Isolation of filamentous fungi. Pages 21-51 in: Isolation of Biotechnological Organisms from Nature. D.P. Labeda, ed. McGraw-Hill Publishing Co., New York. 322 pp.
13. Smith, D. and Onions, A.H.S. 1983. The preservation and maintenance of living fungi. Commonwealth Mycological Institute, Kew, England. 52 pp.
14. Stalpers, J.A., de Hoog, A. and Vlug, I.J. 1987. Improvement of the straw technique for the preservation of fungi in liquid nitrogen. Mycologia 79:82-89.
15. Stevens, R.B. (ed.). 1974. Mycology Guidebook. University of Washington Press, Seattle and London (reprinted 1981). 703 pp.
16. Tuite, J. 1969. Plant Pathological Methods, Fungi and Bacteria. Burgess, Minneapolis. 239 pp.
17. Webber, J., Mitchell, A.G. and Smith, F. 1986. Linkage of the genes determining mating type and fungicide tolerance in *Ophiostoma ulmi*. Plant Pathol. 35:512-516.
18. Zambino, P. and Harrington, T.C. 1990. Heterokaryosis and vegetative compatibility in *Leptographium wageneri*. Phytopathology 80:1460-1469.

Chapter 28

A SYNOPTIC KEY TO SPECIES OF *OPHIOSTOMA, CERATOCYSTIS* AND *CERATOCYSTIOPSIS*

B.T. GRYLLS and K.A. SEIFERT

INTRODUCTION

Upadhyay (19) included ninety species in his monograph of *Ceratocystis* and *Ceratocystiopsis*, and provided dichotomous keys to sections and species. Since the publication of that monograph, the genus *Ophiostoma* has become widely accepted (Samuels, this volume) and a number of new species have been described while some species have been declared synonyms. This paper provides a synoptic key to 110 species that we presently accept in these three genera.

For the most part, we have followed the species concepts of Upadhyay (19), with the understanding that some of his synonymies are not accepted by other workers (for example, see Hausner *et al.*, this volume). We have not included the species of *Sphaeronaemella* in this key, although Upadhyay included these species in *Ceratocystis*. We accept *Ophiostoma* as distinct from *Ceratocystis* and use the appropriate names in *Ophiostoma* where these are available. Morphological data has been extracted from Upadhyay (19), Olchowecki and Reid (15), Griffin (7), Hunt (8) and from the original descriptions of the recently described species. In several cases, descriptions were incomplete and certain characters had to be interpreted from illustrations, or inferred in other ways. We hope that this has not introduced errors.

Synoptic keys were introduced to mycology by Korf (11), where a detailed explanation of this kind of key can be found. Synoptic keys offer two main advantages over traditional dichotomous keys. First, they allow users to select conspicuous characters that are easily observed. This is particularly valuable when all the characteristics needed to navigate through a dichotomous key (for example, the anamorph) cannot be determined. The second advantage, particularly germane for groups where generic concepts are controversial, is that identification is made directly to species, without the need to decide beforehand what genus a collection belongs to.

To use this key, scan the list of characters and choose one that fits the specimen in hand. Copy the list of numbers accompanying the character, then select a second character. Delete any number that does not appear in both lists. Then choose a third character and delete numbers from the modified list that do not appear in this character list. Repeat this process until a single number, or a small group of numbers, remains. The numbers correspond to taxa in the list at the end of the key. The specimen can then be compared with descriptions of these taxa for final identification.

Selection of characters is important. The following notes should be helpful in selecting useful characters.

CHARACTER SELECTION

The character states are divided into nine groups, four pertaining to the teleomorph, four to the anamorph, and one to the host or substrate. For quantitative characters, we recommend that average values rather than extreme values, be used.

Characters of the teleomorph are of primary importance and should be considered first. The characters of the perithecia are self explanatory. For the ascospores, we have used three general spore shapes in combination with three general sheath categories. For ascospores with sheaths or secondary walls, the measurements given include the sheath.

Species of *Ophiostoma* are sometimes distinguished based on minute differences in ascospore morphology. Such pairs of species will be difficult (or impossible) to separate using this key. If several unsuccessful attempts are made to further shorten a list of three species, a critical comparison of ascospore descriptions is probably in order.

Because of disagreements over anamorph generic concepts, we have chosen anamorph characters that can be interpreted without assignment of the anamorph to a genus. For species with both a

---

A computerized version of this key for IBM or MS-DOS microcomputers is available from the junior author. Send one 5 1/4 inch 360 K or 1.2 M floppy, or one 3 1/2 inch 720 K floppy, preformatted.

synnematous and mononematous anamorph, only the characters of the synnematous anamorph are included in the key. In general, the presence of both a mononematous and a synnematous anamorph is indicated only for species where these synanamorphs are clearly different (for example, a *Sporothrix* with a *Graphium*). That is, mononematous anamorphs that are probably only reduced conidiomata are not considered different and only the synnematous anamorph is recorded.

In our opinion, the anamorphs of these fungi are very difficult to interpret (see many chapters in this book). There are many contradictions in the literature, some of which may not have been eliminated from this key. A further complicating factor is the tendency of several species of *Ophiostoma* to grow in close proximity, introducing the possible confusion of their anamorphs. Therefore, we would like to stress that anamorph characters should be used with caution and some scepticism.

The final category, host or substrate, should also be used with caution. Our collections of these fungi are heavily skewed towards coniferous wood, and the absence of records on other substrates is probably a reflection of a lack of surveys.

PERITHECIAL BASE

base dark brown to black
1-6, 8-14, 16-27, 29-47, 49-52, 54-59, 61-67, 69-84, 86-110

base light brown or olivaceous
15, 25, 28, 31, 32, 37, 43, 52, 60, 68-72, 85, 87, 93

base white or hyaline
7, 15, 48, 53

base with conical spines
14, 33, 40, 57, 61, 71, 72, 81, 84, 95, 105

base surrounded with collar-like structure
24

base acorn shaped
86

centrum filled with yellow contents
49

base up to 50 μm diam.
5, 9, 21, 26, 29, 30, 40, 57, 60, 64, 71, 86, 95, 97, 99

base 50-100 μm diam.
1, 3, 5-11, 13, 14, 18, 21, 24-27, 29-35, 39, 40, 54, 57-61, 64, 65, 68, 70, 71, 75, 77, 78, 80, 82, 84, 86, 87, 92, 95-99, 102, 105, 109

base 100-150 μm diam.
1, 3, 5-8, 10, 11, 13, 14, 16, 18-21, 23, 25, 27, 28, 29, 31, 33, 35, 37, 41-43, 46, 49, 50, 52-54, 58, 61-65, 67, 70, 73, 75, 77, 78, 80, 83-87, 90-94, 96, 98, 99, 101, 102, 105, 106, 108-110

base 150-200 μm diam.
1, 2, 8, 10, 15-17, 19-21, 23, 25, 27, 28, 36, 37, 41-43, 46, 49, 50, 52, 53, 55, 61-63, 65, 67, 69, 70, 72, 73, 75-78, 81, 83, 85, 88-91, 94, 96, 98-101, 103, 106-110

base 200-300 μm diam.
2, 4, 8, 12, 15, 17, 19, 22, 25, 28, 36, 38, 41, 47-51, 55, 61, 62, 65, 72-74, 76-79, 81, 83, 85, 88, 89, 91, 100, 101, 103, 104, 107, 109

base 300-500 μm diam.
4, 12, 15, 19, 22, 38, 47, 48, 50, 55, 56, 66, 88, 89, 100

base more than 500 μm diam.
4, 22, 44, 45, 55, 66

PERITHECIAL NECK

neck present
1-11, 13-21, 23-103, 105-110

neck absent
12, 22, 88, 104

neck dark brown to black
1-6, 8-11, 13-47, 49-52, 54-67, 69-87, 89-103, 105-110

neck white or hyaline
7, 37, 48, 53, 68

neck with terminal gelatinous pad
3, 8, 25, 55, 99

neck with annellations
13, 33, 34, 62, 66-68, 78, 81, 82, 98, 99

neck less than 50 μm long
2, 24, 26, 27, 29, 39, 40, 54, 57, 59, 71, 86, 95

neck 50-100 μm long
2, 3, 7, 26, 27, 29, 33, 40, 48, 54, 58-60, 65, 68, 71, 79, 80, 82, 84, 86, 87, 95, 97, 105

neck 100-200 μm long
2, 3, 5, 7, 9, 18, 30, 32-34, 36, 37, 43, 48, 52, 58-60, 63-65, 68, 70, 73, 79, 80, 82, 83, 84, 87, 90, 92-94, 97, 99, 105

neck 200-300 μm long
2, 3, 5, 7, 9, 10, 14, 16, 18, 19, 31, 32, 34, 36-38, 41, 43, 47, 48, 50, 60, 63, 65, 69, 70, 73, 79, 83, 90, 92, 94, 98, 99, 106, 107

neck 300-500 μm long
1-3, 5, 6, 8-11, 13, 14, 16, 18, 19, 25, 31, 32, 35-38, 41, 43, 46-50, 63, 65, 69, 70, 73, 77, 79, 83, 85, 90-92, 96, 98, 99, 101, 102, 106, 109,110

neck 500-750 μm long
1, 2, 5, 6, 8, 11, 13, 15, 17, 19-21, 23, 25, 28, 31, 35-37, 41, 42, 46, 47, 49-51, 53, 55, 61, 62, 66, 67, 69, 72, 73, 75-79, 81, 85, 89-91, 96, 98-102, 108-110

neck 750-1000 μm long
2, 8, 11, 15, 17, 19-21, 23, 25, 41, 42, 46, 50, 51, 53, 55, 56, 61, 62, 66, 67, 72, 73, 75-79, 81, 85, 89, 96, 98, 100, 101, 103, 108, 109

neck 1000-1500 μm long
2, 4, 8, 15, 17, 20, 25, 50, 51, 55, 56, 62, 66, 67, 72, 74, 75, 77-79, 81, 89, 96, 98, 100, 101, 103

neck 1500-5000 μm long
4, 25, 44, 55, 62, 66, 67, 74, 77-79, 101

neck more than 5000 μm long
45, 62, 66, 67

neck less than 10 μm wide at tip
1-3, 5, 7, 9, 13, 21, 24, 26, 27, 30, 33, 34, 39, 40, 51, 54, 58, 60, 62, 65, 71, 75, 77, 78, 80, 82, 84, 86, 89, 95, 98, 99

neck 10-20 μm wide at tip
1-8, 10, 11, 13-18, 20, 21, 23, 25-35, 37, 41, 42, 44, 46-52, 54-65, 67-71, 73-79, 81-84, 86, 87, 89, 90, 92, 94, 96-103, 105-110

neck 20-30 μm wide at tip
2, 4, 6, 8, 14-19, 28, 43, 44, 46-50, 52, 55, 57, 59, 65, 70, 72, 73, 75, 76, 79, 81, 83, 85, 87, 89-92, 94, 100-103

neck 30-45 μm wide at tip
2, 8, 15, 19, 36, 44, 47-49, 67, 70, 72, 73, 76, 81, 85, 87, 89, 91

neck more than 45 μm wide at tip
2, 19, 36, 38, 44, 45, 48, 53, 66, 89, 93

OSTIOLAR HYPHAE

ostiolar hyphae present
1, 4-8, 11, 13, 14, 16-18, 20, 23, 24, 26-35, 38, 40-44, 46, 51-54, 56-62, 64, 65, 67-72, 75, 77, 78, 80-85, 87, 90, 92, 93, 95, 96, 98-103, 106, 107

ostiolar hyphae absent
2, 3, 8-10, 12, 15, 19-22, 25, 36, 37, 39, 45, 47-50, 55, 58, 63, 66, 73-75, 76, 79, 86, 88, 89, 91, 94, 97, 104, 105, 109

ostiolar hyphae brown to black
4, 6, 17, 18, 27, 31, 32, 34, 38, 42-44, 46, 52, 57, 70, 71, 72, 83, 90, 92, 93, 103

ostiolar hyphae hyaline
1, 4, 5, 7, 8, 11, 13, 14, 16-18, 20, 23, 24, 26, 28-31, 33-35, 38, 40-43, 46, 51-54, 56-62, 64, 65, 67-72, 75, 77, 78, 80-85, 87, 90, 95, 96, 98-103, 106, 107, 108, 110

ostiolar hyphae up to 50 μm long
1, 5-8, 11, 13, 14, 16-18, 20, 23, 24, 26-35, 38, 40-44, 46, 51-54, 56-62, 64, 65, 67-71, 75, 77, 78, 80-85, 87, 90, 92, 93, 95, 96, 98-100, 102, 103, 106, 107, 108, 110

ostiolar hyphae 50-100 μm long
4, 13, 16, 17, 28, 31, 32, 38, 41, 43, 44, 46, 52, 56, 70, 77, 78, 81, 85, 87, 92, 93, 96, 101, 103

ostiolar hyphae more than 100 μm long
4, 32, 38, 70, 72, 87, 101

divergent
1, 4-6, 11, 13, 14, 17, 18, 20, 23, 28-31, 33, 34, 38, 41, 42, 44, 46, 51-53, 56, 58, 61, 62, 64, 65, 67-69, 72, 75, 77, 78, 80-85, 87, 90, 96, 98-101, 103, 106, 107, 108, 110

parallel
5, 7, 8, 16, 29, 30, 32-35, 38, 40, 41, 43, 44, 52, 56, 59, 65, 68-72, 77, 80, 92, 93, 102

convergent
7, 16, 24, 26, 27, 40, 44, 54, 57, 59, 60, 69, 71, 93, 95

ASCOSPORES

ascospores oblong-ellipsoidal
6, 11, 13-15, 17, 18, 25, 33, 38, 41, 42, 48, 50, 51, 62, 63, 65, 73, 85, 86, 93, 94, 105, 107

ascospores curved allantoid reniform or orange section shaped
1-5, 8-10, 12, 16, 19-23, 28, 31, 32, 34-38, 41, 43-47, 49, 51-53, 55, 56, 58, 59, 61, 62, 64, 66-70, 72-82, 84, 88-92, 96-104, 106, 108-110

ascospores fusiform x falcate
5, 7, 24, 26, 27, 29, 30, 39, 40, 54, 57, 59, 60, 68, 71, 83, 86, 87, 95, 97

ascospores tadpole shaped
86

ascospore appearing sheathed
3-7, 11-13, 15-19, 22-27, 29-33, 36, 38-43, 46-48, 50-52, 54, 55, 57, 59-61, 65, 68-74, 76, 80, 83, 85-88, 91-95, 97, 101, 103-105, 108

ascospore not appearing sheathed
1, 2, 8-10, 14, 20, 21, 28, 34, 35, 37, 44, 45, 49, 53, 56, 58, 62-64, 66, 67, 75, 77-79, 81, 82, 84, 89, 90, 96, 98-100, 102, 106-110

ascospore secondary wall hat shaped
3, 12, 19, 22, 31, 41, 47, 61, 69, 70, 73, 76, 88, 92, 103, 104

ascospore secondary wall ossiform or pillow shaped
13, 15, 17, 18, 25, 33, 42, 48, 50, 52, 65, 93, 94, 105

ascospore secondary wall same shape as spore
4-7, 11, 16, 23, 24, 26, 27, 29, 30, 32, 36, 38-40, 43, 46, 51, 54, 55, 57, 59, 60, 68, 71, 72, 74, 80, 83, 85, 87, 91, 95, 97, 101, 103, 105, 108

ascospores < 3 μm long
3, 5, 8, 9, 11, 20, 25, 35, 37, 49, 53, 55, 56, 58, 62, 63, 65, 74, 75, 84, 91, 96, 99-101

ascospores 3-5 μm long
1-3, 5, 6, 8-13, 15, 17-22, 25, 28, 32-35, 37, 41-51, 53, 55, 56, 58, 61-67, 69, 70, 74-82, 84, 88-94, 96-107,110

ascospores 5-7 μm long
4, 7, 8, 12, 14-16, 18, 19, 21-23, 28, 30-33, 35, 36, 38, 41, 43, 48, 50, 52, 58, 59, 61, 65, 69, 70, 72, 73, 76-78, 85, 88, 90, 92-94, 97, 99, 102, 104, 106, 107, 108, 110

ascospores 7-10 μm long
4, 7, 14, 16, 23, 24, 26, 27, 29, 30, 38, 40, 41, 48, 52, 54, 59, 72, 83, 85, 86, 92, 95, 97, 108-110

ascospores 10-20 μm long
14, 24, 26, 27, 29, 38, 40, 54, 57, 59, 60, 68, 71, 83, 85-87, 95

ascospores more than 20 μm long
39, 60

ascospores 1-2 μm wide
2, 3, 5-11, 13, 14, 17-21, 24-28, 30, 32-37, 39, 40, 42, 44-47, 49, 50, 53-60, 62-65, 67, 69, 71, 74, 75, 77-82, 84, 86, 87, 89-91, 94-102, 105-107, 110

ascospores 2-3 μm wide
1, 3, 8, 11-13, 15-19, 21-23, 25, 31, 32, 34, 36, 38, 41, 43, 47, 48, 50-52, 61, 65, 66, 68-70, 72, 73, 76, 80, 81, 83, 85, 86, 88, 90, 92-94, 98, 102-104, 108, 109

ascospores 3-4 μm wide
4, 12, 15, 16, 19, 22, 29, 31, 32, 36, 38, 41, 48, 52, 68, 70, 72, 73, 76, 83, 85, 88, 92, 104

ANAMORPHS

no anamorph known
3, 48, 68, 97

synnematous anamorph produced
6, 10, 11, 17, 19, 21, 22, 25, 31, 32, 49, 50, 67, 69, 70, 72, 75, 92, 94, 101, 106, 110

mononematous anamorph produced
1, 2, 4, 5, 7-10, 12-18, 20-24, 26-30, 33-47, 50-67, 71-91, 93, 95, 96, 98-100, 102-110

both synnematous and mononematous anamorphs produced
10, 17, 21, 22, 32, 50, 67, 72, 75, 106, 110

anamorph dematiaceous
2, 4, 6, 12, 13, 16, 17, 19, 21-23, 25, 29, 31, 32, 36, 38, 41, 43, 46, 47, 50-52, 55, 61, 67, 69, 70, 72, 73, 75, 76, 83, 85, 88, 91, 92, 101, 104, 106-110

anamorph hyaline
1, 5, 7-11, 14, 15, 18, 20, 23, 24, 26-28, 30, 33-35, 37-40, 42, 44, 45, 49, 53, 54, 56-66, 71, 74, 77-82, 84-87, 89, 90, 93-96, 98-100, 102, 103, 105, 108

CONIDIOPHORES

conidiophores penicillately branched
2, 6, 10-12, 16, 17, 19, 22, 25, 29, 31, 32, 36, 43, 46, 47, 49, 50, 52, 55, 67, 69, 70, 73, 75, 76, 83, 88, 91, 92, 94, 101, 104, 106-110

conidiophores unbranched or sparingly branched
1, 4, 5, 7-9, 13-15, 18, 20, 21, 23, 24, 26-28, 30, 33-35, 37-42, 44, 45, 50, 51, 53, 54, 56-66, 71, 72, 74, 77-82, 84-87, 89, 90, 93, 95, 96, 98-100, 102, 103, 105,108

CONIDIOGENESIS

phialides
2, 4, 13, 19, 23, 25, 31, 32, 38, 39, 41, 43, 50, 51, 61, 69, 70, 72, 76, 83, 85, 92, 104, 108

annellides
16, 21, 22, 25, 47, 50, 52, 55, 69, 76, 87, 94, 104

apparently sympodial
1, 5-15, 17-20, 22, 24, 26-30, 33-37, 40, 42, 44-46, 49, 53-60, 62-67, 71, 73-82, 84, 86, 88-91, 93, 95, 96, 98-110

denticulate
1, 9, 20, 24, 26, 28, 33, 34, 37, 42, 44, 53, 56, 62-64, 66, 71, 74, 77-82, 86, 89, 90, 95, 96, 98-100

CONIDIA

conidia aseptate
1, 2, 4-47, 49-67, 69-96, 98-110

conidia sometimes septate
22, 89

conidia globose
4, 13, 21, 24, 28, 43, 87, 95

conidia ellipsoidal or ovate
2, 4-10, 12-15, 17, 18, 20, 21, 23, 24, 27, 28, 30-37, 40, 42-47, 50, 52, 55-67, 69, 70, 72-77, 81-84, 87-93, 95, 96, 98-110

conidia oblong-ellipsoidal
1, 2, 4, 6-9, 11, 13-17, 19, 20, 23, 25, 27, 29-32, 35, 38-41, 43, 45, 49-55, 57, 59-62, 67, 69-73, 75-83, 85, 86, 89, 92-94, 100, 103, 105, 106, 108, 110

conidia clavate
1, 5-12, 14-16, 19, 22, 25-27, 30, 33, 36, 37, 40, 42, 46,
49, 50, 53-58, 63-65, 73, 74, 79, 80, 84, 86, 87, 90, 92, 93, 96, 98, 99, 101, 102, 105, 106, 110

conidia Y or T shaped
26, 33, 42, 54, 95

conidia fusiform
7, 9, 20, 34, 53, 62, 77, 78, 81, 89

conidia 2-5 μm long
5, 6, 8-11, 13-21, 23-33, 35, 37-40, 42-47, 49, 50, 52-54, 56-60, 62-67, 69-71, 73-78, 80-84, 87, 88, 90-96, 98-101, 103-110

conidia 5-7 μm long
1, 2, 5-9, 11-17, 19-21, 23, 25, 27-35, 37-40, 42, 44, 47, 50, 52-54, 56-65, 69-74, 76-79, 81-93, 95, 96, 98-100, 102-105, 108, 109

conidia 7-10 μm long
1, 2, 4, 6-8, 11, 12, 15, 16, 19-21, 23, 28, 29, 31, 32, 34-36, 38-42, 47, 50-52, 54-56, 61-63, 65, 69, 70, 72, 74, 76-79, 81, 85-90, 92, 99, 102-104, 108

conidia 10-20 μm long
2, 4, 11, 12, 20-22, 23, 29, 36, 38, 41, 51, 54, 61, 62, 72, 77-79, 81, 85, 89, 108

conidia more than 20 μm long
22, 23, 38, 41, 51, 72, 85, 108

conidia 1-2 μm wide
1, 2, 5, 6, 8-20, 24-27, 29-33, 35, 37, 39, 40, 42, 44-47, 49, 50, 52-54, 56-67, 69-71, 73-75, 77, 78, 80-82, 84, 86, 87, 89-91, 93-96, 98-106, 109, 110

conidia 2-3 μm wide
2, 5-8, 11-16, 18-21, 23, 25, 27, 30-38, 41-44, 47, 50, 52-54, 56, 58, 61-65, 69, 70, 72, 75-79, 81-85, 88, 90, 91, 93, 95, 96, 98, 99, 102-104, 107, 108

conidia 3-4 μm wide
4, 6-8, 11, 12, 15, 20-23, 28, 31, 34, 36, 38, 41-43, 47, 51, 54, 55, 58, 62, 63, 70, 72, 76, 77, 81, 83-85, 88, 92, 98, 103, 104, 108

conidia > 4 μm wide
4, 15, 21, 23, 28, 34, 36, 38, 41, 43, 47, 51, 72, 85, 88, 92, 103, 108

conidia in slimy masses
2, 5-12, 14-22, 24-37, 40, 42, 43, 45-47, 49-60, 64, 65, 67, 69-71, 73-76, 79-84, 86, 88-96, 98, 99-110

conidia dry
1, 4, 13, 23, 33, 38, 39, 41, 44, 51, 58, 61-63, 66, 72, 77-79, 81, 85, 87, 93, 103, 108

conidia catenate
4, 13, 20, 21, 23, 24, 26, 28, 33, 34, 37-39, 41, 42, 44, 51, 53, 61, 62, 64, 72, 74, 77, 78, 81, 85, 89, 98, 103, 108

conidia solitary
1, 2, 5-19, 21, 22, 25-27, 29-32, 34-37, 40, 42, 43, 45-47, 49, 50, 52-60, 63-67, 69-71, 73-76, 79-84, 86-88, 90-96, 98-109

HOSTS AND SUBSTRATES

conifer wood or bark
1, 2, 4-9, 11-13, 15, 17-36, 39, 40, 42, 47, 48, 50, 51, 53-55, 57-60, 62, 64, 65, 67-70, 73, 75-78, 84, 86, 88, 91-94, 96, 98-100, 104, 105, 109

angiosperm wood or bark
3, 4, 7, 14, 16, 29, 35, 38, 41, 43, 45, 46, 49, 52, 56, 61, 66, 70, 71, 74, 75, 77, 78, 80-82, 87, 90, 91, 95-97, 99, 101, 102, 106, 107, 108, 110

other fungi
7, 37, 44, 79, 89

fruits vegetables or other crops
4, 41, 61, 72, 85

Narcissus bulbs
63

Protea
41, 83

palm
85

Araucaria
10, 103

humans or animals
75, 96

LIST OF TAXA (page numbers refer to Upadhyay (19), except as noted).

ACKNOWLEDGEMENT

This key was compiled using the computer program SYNOPKEY, written by David Malloch of the University of Toronto.

LITERATURE CITED

1. Brasier, C.M. 1991. *Ophiostoma novo-ulmi* sp. nov., causative agent of current Dutch elm disease pandemics. Mycopathologia 115:151-161.

2. Bridges, J.B. and Perry, T.J. 1987. *Ceratocystiopsis ranaculosus* sp. nov. associated with the southern pine beetle. Mycologia 79:630-633.

3. Butin, H. and Aquilar, A.M. 1984. Bluestain fungi on *Nothofagus* from Chile- Including two new species of *Ceratocystis* Ellis & Halst. Phytopathol. Z. 109:80-89.

4. Constantinescu, O. and Ryman, S. 1989. A new *Ophiostoma* on polypores. Mycotaxon 34:637-642.

5. Davidson, R.W. 1979. A *Ceratocystis* associated with an ambrosia beetle in *Dendroctonus*-killed pines. Mycologia 71:1085-1089.

6. Goheen, D.J. and Cobb, F.W. Jr. 1978. Occurrence of *Verticicladiella wagnerii* and its perfect state, *Ceratocystis wageneri* sp. nov., in insect galleries. Phytopathology 68:1192-1195.

7. Griffin, H.D. 1968. The genus *Ceratocystis* in Ontario. Can. J. Bot. 46:689-718.

8. Hunt, J. 1956. Taxonomy of the genus *Ceratocystis*. Lloydia 19:1-58.

9. Hutchison, L.J. and Reid, J. 1988. Taxonomy of some potential wood-staining fungi from New Zealand 1. Ophiostomataceae. N.Z. J. Bot. 26:63-81.

10. Kile, G.A. and Walker, J. 1987 *Chalara australis* sp. nov. Hyphomycetes, a vascular pathogen of *Nothofagus cunninghamii* (Fagaceae) in Australia and its relationship to other *Chalara* species. Austr. J. Bot. 35:1-32

11. Korf, R.P. 1972. Synoptic key to the genera of the Pezizales. Mycologia 64:937-994.

12. Kowalski, T. and Butin, H. 1989. Taxonomie bekannter und neuer *Ceratocystis*-Arten an Eiche (*Quercus robur* L.). J. Phytopathol. 124:236-248.

13. Livingston, W.H. and Davidson, R.W. *Ophiostoma subannulatum*, a new fungal species pathogenic to Grand Fir roots. Mycologia 79:144-147.

14. Marmalejo, J.G. and Butin, H. 1990. New conifer inhabiting species of *Ophiostoma* and *Ceratocystiopsis* (Ascomycetes, Microascales) from Mexico. Sydowia 42:193-199.

15. Olchowecki, A. and Reid, J. 1974. Taxonomy of the genus *Ceratocystis* in Manitoba. Can. J. Bot. 52:1675-1711.

16. Redfern, D.B., Stoakley, J.T., Steele, H. and Minter, D.W. 1987. Dieback and death of larch caused by *Ceratocystis* sp. nov. following attack by *Ips cembrae*. Plant Pathol. 36:467-480.

17. Samuels, G.J. and Müller, E. 1979. Life-history studies of Brazilian Ascomycetes 5. Two new species of

Ophiostoma and their *Sporothrix* anamorphs. Sydowia 31:169-179.

18. Solheim, H. 1986. Species of Ophiostomataceae isolated from *Picea abies* infested by the bark beetle *Ips typographus*. Nord. J. Bot. 6:199-207.

19. Upadhyay, H.P. 1981. A monograph of *Ceratocystis* and *Ceratocystiopsis*. University of Georgia Press, Athens, GA. 176 pp.

20. Wingfield, M.J., Van Wyk, P.S. and Marasas, W.F.O. 1988. *Ceratocystiopsis proteae* sp. nov., with a new anamorph genus. Mycologia 80:23-30.

Chapter 29

A NOMENCLATOR FOR DESCRIBED SPECIES OF *CERATOCYSTIS, OPHIOSTOMA, CERATOCYSTIOPSIS, CERATOSTOMELLA* AND *SPHAERONAEMELLA*

K.A. SEIFERT, M.J. WINGFIELD and W.B. KENDRICK

INTRODUCTION

In the early chapters of this book, the debate over generic concepts in the ophiostomatalean fungi is presented at length. The conflicts over the application of the names *Ceratocystis* and *Ophiostoma* continue (10) but it is our impression that a consensus is close at hand. We can appreciate the frustration of the non-taxonomist trying to decide which name to use. The monograph by Upadhyay (27) presents a unified system but his generic concepts and broad species concepts have been the subject of frequent criticism.

The lists that comprise the bulk of this chapter represent our attempt to present an alternative classification to that of Upadhyay (27). The accepted species of *Ceratocystis, Ceratocystiopsis, Ophiostoma* and *Sphaeronaemella* are listed, with complete synonymies, notes on the generic identity of the anamorphs and references to illustrations or descriptions in the literature. Most of these species are included in the synoptic key by Grylls and Seifert (this volume). Some species that we accept in *Ophiostoma* have yet to be transferred to that genus. This is noted with the hope that scientists working with those species will do the necessary background work to substantiate the transfers. Similarly, several species of *Ceratocystis* are listed with no known anamorph. The correct generic placement of these species will have to be re-evaluated when additional material is studied.

In the lists, the specific synonymies conform with, for the most part, Upadhyay (27), but we have noted specific cases where those synonymies have been questioned. In some cases, we have accepted species that were considered synonyms by Upadhyay (27) and in other cases, we have accepted as synonyms species that he considered distinct. In a few of these cases, we have been unable to make a decision and the species is listed both as the synonym proposed by Upadhyay (27) and as an accepted species.

We have also adopted the broadened anamorph generic concepts proposed in the early chapters of this book. Mycelial anamorphs are referred to either *Sporothrix* (anamorphs with denticulate conidiogenous cells, including species with both solitary and catenate conidia) or *Hyalorhinocladiella* (anamorphs with conidiogenous cells that lack denticles and appear to proliferate sympodially or percurrently). Macronematous anamorphs are referred to *Phialocephala* (complexly branched conidiophores with phialidic conidiogenous cells), *Leptographium* (complexly branched conidiophores with percurrent or apparently sympodial conidiogenous cells) or *Graphium* (synnematous conidiophores irrespective of type of conidiogenous cells). Anamorphs of *Sphaeronaemella* are included in *Gabarnaudia*.

Key references are provided in the "Literature Cited" section and, as is consistent with the rest of the book, these are arranged numerically. For the purpose of simplicity and ease of handling, we have however chosen to provide complete references and in some cases also page numbers in these lists.

ACCEPTED SPECIES OF *CERATOCYSTIS*

Ceratocystis acericola Griffin, Can. J. Bot. 46:694. 1968.
    Anamorphs unknown.
    See Griffin (1968, p. 694), Upadhyay (1981, p. 35 figs. 24-25).
    Note: The absence of a known anamorph leaves the correct systematic position of this species open to question.

Ceratocystis adiposa (Butler) Moreau, Rev. Mycol. (Paris) Suppl. Col. 17:22. 1952. =*Ceratostomella adiposa* (Butler) Sartoris, J. Agric. Res. 35:585. 1927. =*Endoconidiophora adiposa* (Butler) Davidson, J. Agric. Res. 50:802. 1935. =*Sphaeronema adiposum* Butler, India Dept. Agric. Mem. Bot. Ser. 1(3):40. 1906. =*Ophiostoma adiposum* (Butler) Nannf., Svenska Skogsfor. Tidskr. 32:408. 1934.
> Anamorph: *Chalara.*
> See Hunt (1956, p. 10), Upadhyay (1981, p. 35 figs. 26-30), Davidson (1935), Moreau (1952), Nag Raj and Kendrick (1975).

=*Ceratostomella major* van Beyma, Zbl. Bakt. ParasitKde. 2, 91:348. 1935. =*Ophiostoma majus* (van Beyma) Goid., Boll. Staz. Patol. Veg. Roma, n.s. 15:158. 1935. =*Ceratocystis major* (van Beyma) Moreau, Rev. Mycol. (Paris) Suppl. Col. 17:22. 1952.

Ceratocystis autographa Bakshi, Ann. Bot. n.s. 15:55. 1951.
> Anamorphs: *Chalara, Sporothrix.*
> See Hunt (1956, p. 23), Olchowecki and Reid (1974, p. 1695), Upadhyay (1981, p. 73 figs. 223-231).
> Note: The generic placement of this species requires careful consideration in light of its two synanamorphs, one of which would suggest a placement in *Ceratocystis,* the other of which would suggest *Ophiostoma.*

Ceratocystis coerulescens (Münch) Bakshi, Trans. Br. Mycol. Soc. 33:114. 1950. =*Endoconidiophora coerulescens* Münch, Naturw. Z. Land. Forstw. 5:564. 1907. =*Ophiostoma coerulescens* (Münch) Nannf., Svenska Skogsfor. Tidskr. 32:408. 1934.
> Anamorph: *Chalara ungeri* Sacc., Syll. Fung. 4:336. 1886.
> See Hunt (1956, p. 21), Griffin (1968, p. 700), Olchowecki and Reid (1974, p. 1705), Upadhyay (1981, p. 65 figs. 191-196), Bakshi (1951), Nag Raj and Kendrick (1975).
> Note: Upadhyay (1981) included *Ceratocystis virescens* in his list of synonyms for *C. coerulescens.* This has been challenged by several authors (Gibbs this volume, Kile this volume) and we consider the two species distinct here.

Ceratocystis fagacearum (Bretz) Hunt, Lloydia 19:21. 1956. =*Endoconidiophora fagacearum* Bretz, Phytopathology 42:437. 1952.
> Anamorph: *Chalara quercina* Henry, Phytopathology 34:631. 1944.
> See Hunt (1956, p. 21), Upadhyay (1981, p. 66), Nag Raj and Kendrick (1975).

Ceratocystis fimbriata Ellis and Halstead, Bull. N.J. Agric. Sta. 76:14. 1890. =*Sphaeronaema fimbriatum* (Ellis and Halstead) Sacc., Syll. Fung. 10:125. 1892. =*Ceratostomella fimbriata* (Ellis and Halstead) Elliot, Phytopathology 13:56. 1923. =*Ophiostoma fimbriatum* (Ellis and Halstead) Nannf., Svenska Skogsfor. Tidskr. 32:408. 1934. =*Endoconidiophora fimbriata* (Ellis and Halstead) Davidson, J. Agric. Res. 50:800. 1935).
> Anamorph: *Chalara.*
> See Hunt (1956, p. 14), Griffin (1968, p. 703), Olchowecki and Reid (1974, p. 1699), Upadhyay (1981, p. 44 figs. 69-72), Nag Raj and Kendrick (1975), Viégas (1960).

=*Rostrella coffeae* Zimmermann, Medded. s'Lands Plantentuin 37:24. 1900.

=*Endoconidiophora variospora* Davidson, Mycologia 36:303. 1944. =*Ceratocystis variospora* (Davidson) Moreau, Rev. Mycol. (Paris) Suppl. Col. 17.22 1952. =*Ophiostoma variosporum* (Davidson) von Arx, Antonie van Leeuwenhoek 18:212. 1952.

Ceratocystis hyalothecium Davidson, Mem. N.Y. Bot. Gard. 28:47. 1976.
> Anamorphs unknown.
> See Upadhyay (1981, p. 78 figs. 257-261).
> Note: The absence of a known anamorph and the hyaline to lightly pigmented perithecia leave the correct systematic position of this species open to question.

Ceratocystis laricicola Redfern and Minter, Plant Pathol. 36:468. 1987.
> Anamorph: *Chalara.*

Ceratocystis magnifica Griffin, Can. J. Bot. 46:704. 1968.

Anamorphs unknown.

See Griffin (1968, p. 704); Upadhyay (1981, p. 49 figs. 101-103).

Note: The absence of a known anamorph leaves the generic placement of this species in question.

Ceratocystis moniliformis (Hedgcock) Moreau, Rev. Mycol. (Paris) Suppl. Col. 17:22 1952. =*Ceratostomella moniliformis* Hedgcock, Mo. Bot. Gard. Ann. Rept 17:78. 1906. =*Ophiostoma moniliforme* (Hedgcock) H. and P. Sydow, Ann. Myc. 17:43. 1919. =*Endoconidiophora moniliformis* (Hedgcock) Davidson, J. Agric. Res. 50:800. 1936.

Anamorph: *Chalara.*

See Hunt (1956, p. 18), Upadhyay (1981, p. 51 figs. 109-115), Davidson (1935), Luc (1952), Kowalski and Butin (1989), Nag Raj and Kendrick (1975).

=*Endoconidiophora bunae* Kitajima, Bull. Imp. For. Exp. Sta., Meguro, Tokyo 35:126. 1936. =:*Ceratocystis bunae* (Kitajima) Moreau, Rev. Mycol. (Paris) Suppl. Col. 17:22. 1952.

=*Ceratocystis wilsonii* Bakshi, Mycol. Pap. 35:4. 1951.

=*Ceratocystis filiformis* Roldan, Philip. J. Sci. 91:418. 1962.

Ceratocystis paradoxa (Dade) Moreau, Rev. Mycol. (Paris) Suppl. Col. 17:22. 1952. =*Ceratostomella paradoxa* Dade, Trans. Br. Mycol. Soc. 13:191. 1928. =*Ophiostoma paradoxum* (Dade) Nannf., Svenska Skogsfor. Tidskr. 32:408. 1934. =*Endoconidiophora paradoxa* (Dade) Davidson, J. Agric. Res. 50:802. 1935.

Anamorph: *Chalara paradoxa* (de Seynes) Sacc., Syll. Fung. 10: 595. 1892. = *Sporoschisma paradoxum* de Seynes, Rech. Serv. d'Hist. Nat. Veg. Inf. 3:30. 1886. = *Thielaviopsis paradoxa* (de Seynes) Höhnel, Hedwigia 43:295. 1904. Other synonyms are given by Nag Raj and Kendrick (1975).

See Hunt (1956, p. 19), Upadhyay (1981, p. 67 figs. 197-204).

=*Ceratocystis musarum* Reidl, Sydowia 15:248. 1961.

Ceratocystis radicicola (Bliss) Moreau, Rev. Mycol. (Paris) Suppl. Col. 17:22/1952. =*Ceratostomella radicicola* Bliss, Mycologia 33:468. 1941. =*Ophiostoma radicicola* (Bliss) von Arx, Antonie van Leeuwenhoek 18:211. 1952.

Anamorph: *Chalara.*

See Hunt (1956, p. 20), Upadhyay (1981, p. 69 figs. 205-213).

Ceratocystis stenospora Griffin, Can. J. Bot. 46:714. 1968.

Anamorphs unknown.

See Griffin (1968, p. 714), Olchowecki and Reid (1974, p. 1688), Upadhyay (1981, p. 70 figs. 214-216).

Note: The absence of a known anamorph leaves the generic position of this species open to question.

Ceratocystis virescens (Davidson) Moreau, Rev. Mycol. (Paris) Suppl. Col. 17:22. 1952. =*Endoconidiophora virescens* Davidson, Mycologia 36:301. 1944.

Anamorph: *Chalara.*

Note: This species was considered a synonym of *C. coerulescens* by Upadhyay (1981) but several other authors, including Nag Raj and Kendrick (1975), Gibbs (this volume) and Kile (this volume), consider the two species distinct.

ACCEPTED SPECIES OF *CERATOCYSTIOPSIS*

Ceratocystiopsis alba (DeVay, Davidson and Moller) Upadhyay, Monograph of *Ceratocystis* p. 120. 1981. =*Ceratocystis alba* DeVay, Davidson and Moller, Mycologia 60:636. 1968.

Anamorph: *Hyalorhinocladiella.*

See Olchowecki and Reid (1974, p. 1679), Upadhyay (1981, p. 120 figs. 428-431).

Ceratocystiopsis collifera Marmolejo and Butin, Sydowia 42:197. 1990.
    Anamorph: *Sporothrix.*

Ceratocystiopsis concentrica (Olchow. and Reid) Upadhyay, Monograph of *Ceratocystis* p. 121. 1981.
=*Ceratocystis concentrica* Olchow. and Reid, Can. J. Bot. 52:1679. 1974.
    Anamorph: *Sporothrix.*
    See Olchowecki and Reid (1974, p. 1679), Upadhyay (1981, p. 121 figs. 432-435).

Ceratocystiopsis conicollis (Olchow. and Reid) Upadhyay, Monograph of *Ceratocystis* p. 122. 1981.
=*Ceratocystis conicollis* Olchow. and Reid, Can. J. Bot. 52:1680. 1974.
    Anamorph: *Hyalorhinocladiella.*
    See Olchowecki and Reid (1974, p. 1680), Upadhyay (1981, p. 122 figs. 436-439).

Ceratocystiopsis crenulata (Olchow. and Reid) Upadhyay, Monograph of *Ceratocystis* p. 124. 1981.
=*Ceratocystis crenulata* Olchow. and Reid, Can. J. Bot. 52:1681. 1974.
    Anamorph: *Hyalorhinocladiella.*
    See Olchowecki and Reid (1974, p. 1681), Upadhyay (1981, p. 124 figs. 445-448).

Ceratocystiopsis falcata (Wright and Cain) Upadhyay, Monograph of *Ceratocystis* p. 125. 1981. =*Ceratocystis falcata* Wright and Cain, Can. J. Bot. 39:1226. 1961.
    Anamorph: *Chalara.*
    See Olchowecki and Reid (1974, p. 1688), Upadhyay (1981, p. 125 figs. 449-453), Hutchison and Reid (1988).

Ceratocystiopsis fasciata (Olchow. and Reid) Upadhyay, Monograph of *Ceratocystis* p. 126. 1981. =*Ceratocystis fasciata* Olchow. and Reid, Can. J. Bot. 52:1682. 1974.
    Anamorph: *Hyalorhinocladiella.*
    See Olchowecki and Reid (1974, p. 1682), Upadhyay (1981, p. 126 figs. 454-465).
=*Ceratocystis spinifera* Olchow. and Reid, Can. J. Bot. 52:1686. 1974.

Ceratocystiopsis longispora (Olchow. and Reid) Upadhyay, Monograph of *Ceratocystis* p. 128. 1981.
=*Ceratocystis longispora* Olchow. and Reid, Can. J. Bot. 52:1683. 1974.
    Anamorph: *Sporothrix.*
    See Olchowecki and Reid (1974, p. 1683), Upadhyay (1981, p. 128 figs. 466-471).

Ceratocystiopsis minima (Olchow. and Reid) Upadhyay, Monograph of *Ceratocystis* p. 129. 1981. =*Ceratocystis minima* Olchow. and Reid, Can. J. Bot. 52:1684. 1974.
    Anamorph: *Hyalorhinocladiella.*
    See Olchowecki and Reid (1974, p. 1684), Upadhyay (1981, p. 129 figs. 472-482).
=*Ceratocystis parva* Olchow. and Reid, Can. J. Bot. 52:1686. 1974.

Ceratocystiopsis minuta (Siemaszko) Upadhyay and Kendrick. Mycologia 67:800. 1975. =*Ophiostoma minutum* Siemaszko, Planta Pol. 7(3):23. 1939. =*Ceratocystis minuta* (Siemaszko) Hunt, Lloydia 19: 49. 1956.
    Anamorph: *Hyalorhinocladiella.*
    See Hunt (1956, p. 49), Griffin (1968, p. 705), Olchowecki and Reid (1974, p. 1685), Upadhyay (1981, p. 130 figs. 483-494), Davidson (1942), Mathiesen (1951), Solheim (1986).
=*Ceratocystis dolominuta* Griffin, Can. J. Bot. 46:702. 1968.

Ceratocystiopsis minuta-bicolor (Davidson) Upadhyay and Kendrick, Mycologia 67:800. 1975. =*Ceratocystis minuta-bicolor* Davidson, Mycopath. Mycol. Appl. 28:280. 1966.
    Anamorph: *Hyalorhinocladiella minuta-bicolor* Upadhyay and Kendrick, loc. cit.
    See Olchowecki and Reid (1974, p. 1688), Upadhyay (1981, p. 131 figs. 495-498).

=*Ceratocystis pallida* Griffin, Can. J. Bot. 46:708. 1968.

Ceratocystiopsis ochracea (Griffin) Upadhyay, Monograph of *Ceratocystis* p. 132. 1981. =*Ceratocystis ochracea* Griffin, Can. J. Bot. 46:706. 1968.
> Anamorphs unknown.
> See Griffin (1968, p. 706), Olchowecki and Reid (1974, p. 1688), Upadhyay (1981, p. 132 figs. 499-501). Note: The lack of a known anamorph leaves the correct generic position of this species an open question.

Ceratocystiopsis pallidobrunnea (Olchow. and Reid) Upadhyay, Monograph of *Ceratocystis* p. 133. 1981. =*Ceratocystis pallidobrunnea* Olchow. and Reid, Can. J. Bot. 52:1685. 1974.
> Anamorph: *Sporothrix.*
> See Olchowecki and Reid (1974, p. 1685), Upadhyay (1981, p. 133 figs. 502-505).

Ceratocystiopsis proteae Wingfield, van Wyk and Marasas, Mycologia 80:24. 1988.
> Anamorph: *Knoxdaviesia proteae* Wingfield, van Wyk and Marasas, (loc. cit.).

Ceratocystiopsis ranaculosus Perry and Bridges, Mycologia 79:630. 1987.
> Anamorph: *Sporothrix.*

Ceratocystiopsis retusi (Davidson and Hinds) Upadhyay, Monograph of *Ceratocystis* p. 135. 1981. =*Ceratocystis retusi* Davidson and Hinds, Mycologia 64:407. 1972.
> Anamorphs: see notes
> See Upadhyay (1981, p. 135 figs. 506-509).
> Note: Upadhyay (1981) referred the anamorph of this species to *Allescheriella*. This is clearly an error, as this generic name is used for aleuriosporic anamorphs of basidiomycetes (Hughes 1951). The anamorph illustration in the protologue, and those by Upadhyay (1981, figs. 506-507) appears similar to *Sporothrix* in most respects.

Ceratocystiopsis spinulosa (Griffin) Upadhyay, Monograph of *Ceratocystis* p. 136. 1981. =*Ceratocystis spinulosa* Griffin, Can. J. Bot. 46:713. 1968.
> Anamorph: *Sporothrix.*
> See Griffin (1968, p. 713), Olchowecki and Reid (1974, p. 1687), Upadhyay (1981, p. 136 figs. 510-513).

ACCEPTED SPECIES OF *OPHIOSTOMA*

Ophiostoma abietinum Marmolejo and Butin, Sydowia 42:194. 1990.
> Anamorph: *Sporothrix.*

Ophiostoma abiocarpum (Davidson) Harrington, Mycotaxon 28:41. 1987. =*Ceratocystis abiocarpa* Davidson, Mycopath. Mycol. appl. 28:273. 1966.
> Anamorph: *Leptographium* complex fide Upadhyay p. 87 and Harrington 1988.
> See Olchowecki and Reid (1974, p. 1709), Upadhyay (1981, p. 87 figs. 295-302).

Ophiostoma adjuncti (Davidson) Harrington, Mycotaxon 28:41. 1987. =*Ceratocystis adjuncti* Davidson, Mycologia 70:35. 1978.
> Anamorph: *Leptographium* complex.
> See Upadhyay (1981, p. 79).
> Note: Considered a synonym of *O. ips* by Upadhyay (1981); considered distinct by Harrington (1987).

Ceratocystis aequivaginata Olchow. and Reid, Can. J. Bot. 52:1696. 1974.
> Anamorph: *Hyalorhinocladiella.*
> See Olchowecki and Reid (1974, p. 1696), Upadhyay (1981, p. 36).

Note: Should be transferred to *Ophiostoma*. The figures cited by Upadhyay (1981) are those in Olchowecki and Reid (1974), not those in his book.

Ophiostoma ainoae Solheim, Nord. J. Bot. 6:201. 1986.
    Anamorph: *Graphium (Pesotum* fide Solheim).

Ceratocystis allantospora Griffin, Can. J. Bot. 46:694. 1968.
    Anamorph: *Hyalorhinocladiella.*
    See Griffin (1968, p. 694), Upadhyay (1981, p. 88).
    Note: Should be transferred to *Ophiostoma*. The figures referred to in the description of *C. allantospora* by Upadhyay (1981) are not those in his monograph, but those in Griffin (1968).

Ceratocystis angusticollis Wright and Griffin, Can. J. Bot. 46:697. 1968.
    Anamorph: *Sporothrix.*
    See Griffin (1968, p. 697), Upadhyay (1981, p. 89 figs. 303-307).
    Note: Should be transferred to *Ophiostoma*.

Ophiostoma araucariae (Butin) de Hoog and Scheffer, Mycologia 76:297. 1984. =*Ceratocystis araucariae* Butin. Can. J. Bot. 46:61. 1968.
    Anamorphs: *Graphium (Hyalopesotum) Hyalorhinocladiella.*
    See Olchowecki and Reid (1974, p. 1709), Upadhyay (1981, p. 90 figs. 308-313).

Ceratocystis arborea Olchow. and Reid, Can. J. Bot. 52:1688. 1974.
    Anamorph: *Graphium (Hyalopesotum).*
    See Olchowecki and Reid (1974, p. 1688), Upadhyay (1981, p. 72 figs. 217-222).
    Note: Should be transferred to *Ophiostoma*. See Seifert and Okada (this volume) for an illustration of this anamorph.

Ophiostoma aureum (Robinson-Jeffrey and Davidson) Harrington, Mycotaxon 28:41. 1987. =*Europhium aureum* Robinson-Jeffrey and Davidson, Can. J. Bot. 46:1225. 1968. =*Ceratocystis aurea* (Robinson-Jeffrey and David.) Upadhyay, Monograph of *Ceratocystis* p. 37. 1981.
    Anamorph: *Leptographium aureum* Wingfield, Trans. Br. Mycol. Soc. 85:92. 1985.
    See Upadhyay (1981, p. 37 figs. 31-36.).

Ophiostoma bacillosporum (Butin and Zimmermann) de Hoog and Scheffer, Mycologia 76:297. 1984. =*Ceratocystis bacillospora* Butin and Zimmermann, Phytopathol. Z. 74:281. 1972.
    Anamorph: *Hyalorhinocladiella.*
    See Upadhyay (1981, p. 91 figs. 314-317).

Ophiostoma bicolor Davidson and Wells, Mycologia 47:63. 1955. =*Ceratocystis bicolor* (Davidson and Wells) Davidson, Mycologia 50:665. 1958.
    Anamorph: *Hyalorhinocladiella.*
    See Griffin (1968, p. 697), Olchowecki and Reid (1974, p. 1695), Upadhyay (1981, p. 73 figs. 232-235), Solheim (1986).

Ophiostoma brevicolla (Davidson) de Hoog and Scheffer, Mycologia 76:297. 1984. =*Ceratocystis brevicollis* Davidson, Mycologia 50:667. 1958.
    Anamorph: *Leptographium.*
    See Upadhyay (1981, p. 38 figs. 37-42).

Ophiostoma brunneo-ciliatum Mathiesen-Käärik, Meddn. St. Skogsfor. sk. Inst. 43:21. 1953. =*Ceratocystis brunneo-ciliata* (Mathiesen-Käärik) Hunt, Lloydia 19: 32. 1956.
    Anamorph: *Graphium (Pesotum).*

See Hunt (1956, p. 32), Upadhyay (1981, p. 74 figs. 236-241).

Ceratocystis brunneocrinita Wright and Cain, Can. J. Bot. 39:1218. 1961.
 Anamorph: *Hyalorhinocladiella.*
 See Griffin (1968, p. 699), Olchowecki and Reid (1974, p. 1689), Upadhyay (1981, p. 75 figs. 242-246).
 Note: Should be transferred to *Ophiostoma.*

Ophiostoma cainii (Olchow. and Reid) Harrington, Mycotaxon 28:41. 1987. =*Ceratocystis cainii* Olchow. and Reid, Can. J. Bot. 52:1697. 1974.
 Anamorph: *Graphium.*
 See Olchowecki and Reid (1974, p. 1697), Upadhyay (1981, p. 39 figs. 43-47).

Ceratocystis californica Devay, Davidson and Moller, Mycologia 60:639. 1968.
 Anamorph: *Sporothrix.*
 See Upadhyay (1981, p. 92 figs. 318-324).
 Note: Should be transferred to *Ophiostoma.*

Ophiostoma canum (Münch) H. and P. Sydow, Ann. Myc. 17:43. 1919. =*Ceratostomella cana* Münch, Naturw. Z. Forst. Landw. 5:558. 1907. =*Ceratocystis cana* (Münch) Moreau, Rev. Mycol. (Paris) Suppl. Col. 17:22. 1952.
 Anamorph: *Graphium (Pachnodium canum* Upadhyay and Kendrick, Mycologia 67: 802. 1975.)
 See Hunt (1956, p. 35), Olchowecki and Reid (1974, p. 1709), Upadhyay (1981, p. 93).
 Note: Seifert and Okada (this volume) place this anamorph in *Graphium.*

Ophiostoma clavigerum (Robinson-Jeffrey and Davids.) Harrington, Mycotaxon 28:41. 1987. =*Europhium clavigerum* Robinson-Jeffrey and Davidson, Can. J. Bot. 46:1523. 1968. =*Ceratocystis clavigera* (Robinson-Jeffrey and Davidson) Upadhyay, Monograph of *Ceratocystis* p. 40. 1981.
 Anamorph: *Graphium (Graphiocladiella clavigerum* Upadhyay, Monograph of *Ceratocystis* p. 138. 1981.)
 See Upadhyay (1981, p. 138 figs. 48-57), Upadhyay (1981, p. 138 figs. 48-57), Tsuneda and Hiratsuka (1984).

Ceratocystis columnaris Olchow. and Reid, Can. J. Bot. 52:1689. 1974. =*Ceratocystis ossiformis* Olchow. and Reid, Can. J. Bot. 52:1692. 1974.
 Anamorph: *Graphium.*
 See Olchowecki and Reid (1974, p. 1689), Upadhyay (1981, p. 76 figs. 247-252).
 Note: Should be transferred to *Ophiostoma.*

Ophiostoma conicolum Marmolejo and Butin, Sydowia 42: 195. 1990.
 Anamorph: *Sporothrix.*

Ceratocystis coronata Olchow. and Reid, Can. J. Bot. 52:1705. 1974.
 Note: Should be transferred to *Ophiostoma.* Upadhyay (1981) reduced this species to synonymy with *C. tenella*, but this synonymy was rejected by Hutchison and Reid (1988) because of differences in the shape of ascospores.

Ophiostoma crassivaginatum (Griffin) Harrington, Mycotaxon 28:41. 1987. =*Ceratocystis crassivaginata* Griffin, Can. J. Bot. 46:701. 1968. =*Ceratocystiopsis crassivaginata* (Griffin) Upadhyay, Monograph of *Ceratocystis* p. 123. 1981.
 Anamorph: *Leptographium crassivaginatum* Wingfield, Trans. Br. Mycol. Soc. 85:92. 1985
 See Griffin (1968, p. 701), Olchowecki and Reid (1974, p. 1679), Upadhyay (1981, p. 123 figs. 440-444).

Ophiostoma cucullatum Solheim, Nord. J. Bot. 6:202. 1986.
    Anamorph: *Graphium (Phialographium)*.
    See Wingfield *et al.* (1989).

Ophiostoma davidsonii (Olchow. and Reid) Solheim, Nord. J. Bot. 6:203. 1986. =*Ceratocystis davidsonii* Olchow. and Reid, Can. J. Bot. 52:1698. 1974.
    Anamorph: *Graphium (Phialographium)*.
    See Olchowecki and Reid (1974, p. 1698), Upadhyay (1981, p. 42 figs. 58-62).

Ceratocystis deltoideospora Olchow. and Reid, Can. J. Bot. 52:1691. 1974.
    Anamorph: *Sporothrix*.
    See Olchowecki and Reid (1974, p. 1691), Upadhyay (1981, p. 77 figs. 253-256).
    Note: Should be transferred to *Ophiostoma*.

Ceratocystis denticulata Davidson, Mycologia 71:1088. 1979.
    Anamorph: *Sporothrix*.
    Notes: Should be transferred to *Ophiostoma*.

Ophiostoma distortum (Davidson) de Hoog and Scheffer, Mycologia 76:297. 1984. =*Ceratocystis distorta* Davidson, Mycologia 63:10. 1971.
    Anamorph: *Sporothrix* or *Hyalorhinocladiella*.
    See Olchowecki and Reid (1974, p. 1709), Upadhyay (1981, p. 94 figs. 334-338).
    Notes: Upadhyay (1981) considered the anamorph of this species to be "yeast-like", but the original description by Davidson (which mentions 'sterigmata') and Upadhyay's illustration suggest the anamorph might be assignable to *Sporothrix*.
=*Ceratocystis torulosa* Butin and Zimmermann, Phytopathol. Z. 74:284. 1972.

Ophiostoma dryocoetidis (Kendrick and Molnar) de Hoog and Scheffer, Mycologia 76:297. 1984. =*Ceratocystis dryocoetidis* Kendrick and Molnar, Can. J. Bot. 43:39. 1965.
    Anamorph: *Leptographium dryocoetidis* (Kendrick and Molnar) Wingfield, Trans. Br. Mycol. Soc. 85: 92. 1985 = *Verticicladiella dryocoetidis* Kendrick and Molnar, Can. J. Bot. 43: 39. 1965).
    See Upadhyay (1981, p. 43 figs. 63-38).

Ophiostoma epigloeum (Guerrero) de Hoog, Stud. Mycol. 7:45. 1974. =*Ceratocystis epigloeum* Guerrero. Mycologia 63:921. 1971.
    Anamorph: *Sporothrix*.
    See Upadhyay (1981, p. 95 figs. 339-343).

Ophiostoma europhioides (Wright and Cain) Solheim, Nord. J. Bot. 6:203. 1986. =*Ceratocystis europhioides* Wright and Cain, Can. J. Bot. 39:1222. 1961. =*Ceratocystis pseudoeurophioides* Olchow. and Reid, Can. J. Bot. 52:1700. 1974.
    Anamorph: *Leptographium*.
    See Upadhyay (1981, p. figs. 138-146).
    Note: This species was considered a synonym of *O. piceaperdum* by Upadhyay (1981) but Solheim (1986) and Harrington (1988) considered the two species distinct.

Ophiostoma flexuosum Solheim, Nord. J. Bot. 6:203. 1986.
    Anamorph: *Sporothrix*.

Ophiostoma francke-grosmanniae (Davidson) de Hoog and Scheffer, Mycologia 76:297. 1984. =*Ceratocystis francke-grosmanniae* Davidson, Mycologia 63:6. 1971.
    Anamorph: *Phialocephala*.
    See Upadhyay (1981, p. 45 figs. 73-78).

Note: Harrington (1988) considered the anamorph of this species to be a *Leptographium*, but Upadhyay's (1981) illustrations appear to represent typical phialides.

Ophiostoma grande Samuels and Müller, Sydowia 31:176. 1979.
Anamorph: *Sporothrix.*

Ophiostoma grandicarpum (Kowalski and Butin) Rulamort, Bull. Soc. Bot. Centre-Ouest, n.s. 21:511. 1990.
=*Ceratocystis grandicarpa* Kowalski and Butin, J. Phytopathol. 124: 243. 1989.
Anamorph: *Sporothrix.*
Notes: Although Kowalski and Butin (loc. cit.) reported the presence of two synanamorphs in their cultures of this species, these appear to represent the noncatenate and catenate forms of a *Sporothrix* anamorph.

Ophiostoma grandifoliae (Davidson) Harrington, Mycotaxon 28:41. 1987. =*Ceratocystis grandifoliae* Davidson, Mem. N.Y. Bot. Gard. 28:45. 1976.
Anamorph: *Leptographium grandifoliae* Wingfield, Trans. Br. Mycol. Soc. 85:92. 1985.
See Upadhyay (1981, p. 46 figs. 79-84).

Ophiostoma huntii (Robinson-Jeffrey) de Hoog and Scheffer, Mycologia 76:297. 1984. =*Ceratocystis huntii* Robinson-Jeffrey, Can. J. Bot. 42:528. 1964.
Anamorph: *Leptographium huntii* Wingfield, Trans. Br. Mycol. Soc. 85:92. 1985.
See Griffin (1968, p. 710), Olchowecki and Reid (1974, p. 1699), Upadhyay (1981, p. 47 figs. 85-90).

Ceratocystis introcitrina Olchow. and Reid, Can. J. Bot. 52:1706. 1974.
Anamorph: *Graphium (Hyalopesotum introcitrinum* Upadhyay and Kendrick, Mycologia 67: 802. 1975).
See Olchowecki and Reid (1974, p. 1706), Upadhyay (1981, p. 98 figs. 353-358).
Note: Should be transferred to *Ophiostoma*. Seifert and Okada (this volume) include the anamorph in *Graphium*.

Ophiostoma ips (Rumbold) Nannf., Svenska Skogsfor. Tidskr. 32:408. 1934. =*Ceratostomella ips* Rumbold, J. Agric. Res. 43:864. 1931. =*Grossmania ips* (Rumbold) Goid., Boll. Staz. Patol. Veg. Roma n.s. 16:51. 1936. =*Ceratocystis ips* (Rumbold) Moreau, Rev. Mycol. (Paris) Suppl. Col. 17:22. 1952.
Anamorphs: *Hyalorhinocladiella* and *Graphilbum* fide Upadhyay (1981), *Leptographium* and *Graphium* fide Harrington (1988), or *Graphilbum, Hyalorhinocladiella* and *Acremonium* fide Hutchison and Reid (1988). One binomial has been published referring to this anamorph: *Scopularia rumboldii* Goid., Boll. Stz. Patol. Veg. Roma n.s. 16:51. 1936.
See Hunt (1956, p. 30), Griffin (1968, p. 703), Olchowecki and Reid (1974, p. 1692), Upadhyay (1981, p. 79), Hutchison and Reid (1988), Wingfield and Marasas (1980), Rumbold (1936), Leach *et al.* (1934).
Notes: Upadhyay (1981) adopted a broad concept for *O. ips* that has been challenged. *Ophiostoma adjuncti* and *Ceratocystis montia*, both considered synonyms of *O. ips* by Upadhyay (1981), were considered distinct species by Harrington (1987) and Hausner *et al.* (this volume) respectively.
=*Ceratostomella montia* Rumbold, J. Agric. Res. 62:597. 1941. =*Ophiostoma montium* (Rumbold) von Arx, Antonie van Leeuwenhoek 18: 211. 1952. =*Ceratocystis montia* (Rumbold) Hunt, Lloydia 19:45. 1956.

Ophiostoma leptographioides (Davidson) von Arx, Antonie van Leeuwenhoek 18:211. 1952. =*Ceratostomella leptographioides* Davidson, Mycologia 34:647. 1942. =*Ceratocystis leptographioides* (Davidson) Hunt, Lloydia 19:28. 1956.
Anamorph: *Leptographium.*
See Hunt (1956, p. 28), Upadhyay (1981, p. 48 figs. 91-100).

Ceratocystis leucocarpa Davidson, Mycopath. Mycol. Appl. 28:278. 1966.
Anamorph: *Sporothrix.*
See Olchowecki and Reid (1974, p. 1707), Upadhyay (1981, p. 99 figs. 359-362).

Note: Should be transferred to *Ophiostoma*

Ophiostoma megalobrunneum (Davidson and Toole) de Hoog and Scheffer, Mycologia 76:297. 1984. =*Ceratocystis megalobrunnea* Davidson and Toole, Mycologia 56:796. 1964.

    Anamorph: *Sporothrix* and yeast-like.

    See Olchowecki and Reid (1974, p. 1709), Upadhyay (1981, p. 100 figs. 363-365).

    Note: The anamorph of this species was not illustrated in the original publication or by Upadhyay (1981). It should be re-examined.

Ophiostoma minus (Hedgcock) H. and P. Sydow, Ann. Myc. 17:43. 1906. =*Ceratostomella minor* Hedgcock, Mo. Bot. Gard. Ann. Rep. 17:74. 1906. =*Ceratocystis minor* (Hedgcock) Hunt, Lloydia 19:47. 1956.

    Anamorph: *Hyalorhinocladiella.*

    See Hunt (1956, p. 47), Griffin (1968, p. 704), Olchowecki and Reid (1974, p. 1707), Upadhyay (1981, p. 100).

=*Ceratostomella exigua* Hedgcock, Mo. Bot. Gard. Ann. Rep. 17:76. 1906.

=*Ceratostomella pini* Münch, Naturw. Forst. Landw. 5:541. 1907. =*Ceratocystis pini* (Münch) Moreau, Rev. Mycol. (Paris) Suppl. Col. 17:22. 1952.

=*Ceratostomella pseudotsugae* Rumbold, J. Agric. Res. 52:431. 1936. =*Ceratocystis pseudotsugae* (Rumbold) Moreau, Rev. Mycol. (Paris) Suppl. Col. 17:22. 1952.

Ophiostoma multiannulatum (Hedgcock and Davidson) N. Fries, Symb. Bot. Upsal. 7:21. 1943. =*Ceratostomella multiannulata* Hedgcock and Davidson, J. Agric. Res. 50:797. 1935. =*Ophiostoma multiannulatum* (Hedgcock and Davidson) von Arx, Antonie van Leeuwenhoek 18:211. 1952. =*Ceratocystis multiannulata* (Hedgcock and Davidson) Hunt, Lloydia 19:40. 1956.

    Anamorph: *Sporothrix.*

    See Hunt (1956, p. 40), Upadhyay (1981, p. 102 figs. 371-377).

Ophiostoma narcissi Limber, Phytopathology 40:493. 1950. =*Ceratocystis narcissi* (Limber) Hunt, Lloydia 19:50. 1956.

    Anamorph: *Sporothrix.*

    See Hunt (1956, p. 50), Olchowecki and Reid (1974, p. 1707), Upadhyay (1981, p. 103).

Ophiostoma nigrocarpum (Davidson) de Hoog, Stud. Mycol. 7:62. 1974. =*Ceratocystis nigrocarpa* Davidson, Mycopath. Mycol. Appl. 28:276. 1966.

    Anamorph: *Sporothrix.*

    See Olchowecki and Reid (1974, p. 1709), Upadhyay (1981, p. 104 figs. 378-381).

Ophiostoma nigrum (Davidson) de Hoog and Scheffer, Mycologia 76:297. 1984. =*Ceratocystis nigra* Davidson, Mycologia 50:662. 1958.

    Anamorph: *Hyalorhinocladiella, Acremonium.*

    See Griffin (1968, p. 705), Olchowecki and Reid (1974, p. 1695), Upadhyay (1981, p. 81 figs. 277-285).

=*Ceratocystis curvicollis* Olchow. and Reid, Can. J. Bot. 52:1690. 1974.

=*Ceratocystis pseudonigra* Olchow. and Reid, Can. J. Bot. 52:1693. 1974.

Ophiostoma nothofagi (Butin) Rulamort, Bull. Soc. Bot. Centre-Ouest, n.s. 17:192. 1986. =*Ceratocystis nothofagi* Butin, Phytopathol. Z. 109:84. 1984.

    Anamorph: *Sporothrix.*

Ophiostoma novo-ulmi Brasier, Mycopathologia 115: 155. 1991

    Anamorphs: *Graphium* and *Sporothrix.*

Ophiostoma novae-zelandiae (Hutchison & Reid) Rulamort, Bull. Soc. Bot. Centre-Ouest, n.s. 21:512. 1990 =*Ceratocystis novae-zelandiae* Hutchison and Reid, N.Z. J. Bot. 26:70. 1988.

Anamorphs: *Graphium, Sporothrix.*

Ophiostoma obscura (Davidson) von Arx, Antonie von Leeuwenhoek 18:211. 1952. =*Ceratostomella obscura* Davidson, J. Agric. Res. 50:798. 1935. =*Ceratocystis obscura* (Davidson) Hunt, Lloydia 19:30. 1956.
Anamorph: *Leptographium, Graphium.*
Notes: Hunt (1956) accepted and described this species but Upadhyay (1981) did not find the teleomorph on the type specimen and considered it a *nomen dubium.* Hunt (1956) states that perithecia were formed in the ex-type culture, now accessioned as CBS 125.39.

Ceratocystis olivaceapinii Davidson, Mycologia 63:7. 1971.
Anamorph: *Graphium.*
See Upadhyay (1981, p. 54 figs. 122-129).
Note: Should be transferred to *Ophiostoma*

Ophiostoma olivaceum Mathiesen, Svensk. Bot. Tidskr. 45:212. 1951. =*Ceratocystis olivacea* (Mathiesen) Hunt, Lloydia 19:29. 1956.
Anamorph: *Graphium (Phialographium).*
See Hunt (1956, p. 29), Griffin (1968, p. 707), Olchowecki and Reid (1974, p. 1699), Upadhyay (1981, p. 52 figs. 116-121).
=*Ceratocystis vesca* Davidson, Mycologia 50:666. 1958.

Ophiostoma penicillatum (Grosm.) Siemaszko, Planta Pol. 7(3):24. 1939. =*Ceratostomella penicillata* Grosmann, Hedwigia 72:190. 1932. =*Grosmannia penicillata* (Grosm.) Goid., Boll. Staz. Patol. Veg., Roma, n.s. 15:156. 1935. =*Ceratocystis penicillata* (Grosmann) Moreau, Rev. Mycol. (Paris) Suppl. Col. 17:22. 1952.
Anamorph: *Leptographium penicillatum* Grosmann, Z. ParasitKde. 3:94. 1931 = *Scopularia penicillata* (Grosmann) Goid., Boll. Staz. Patol. Veg. Roma, n.s. 15:156. 1935 = *Verticicladiella penicillata* (Grosmann) Kendrick, Can. J. Bot. 40: 776. 1962
See Hunt (1956, p. 24), Griffin (1968, p. 709), Upadhyay (1981, p. 55 figs. 130-137), Solheim (1986).
=*Ceratostomella imperfecta* Miller and Tcherntzoff, St. For. Tech. Publ. Off. Moscow, 1934.
=*Ceratocystis imperfecta* (Miller and Tcherntzoff) Moreau, Rev. Mycol. (Paris) Suppl. Col. 17:22. 1952.
Note: Hunt (1956) did not see original material of this species but speculated at the synonymy with *O. penicillatum* based on the protologue.
=*Ophiostoma polonicum* Siemaszko, Planta Pol. 7(3):32. 1939. =*Ceratocystis polonica* (Siemaszko) Moreau, Rev. Mycol. (Paris) Suppl. Col. 17:22. 1952.
Note: This species was considered a synonym of *O. penicillatum* by Upadhyay (1981) but Solheim (1986) and Harrington (1988) accepted *O. polonicum* as a separate species.
=*Ceratocystis pseudoeurophioides* Olchow. and Reid, Can. J. Bot. 52:1700. 1974.
Note: This species was considered a synonym of *O. penicillatum* by Upadhyay (1981) and of *O. europhioides* by Harrington (1988).
=*Ophiostoma truncicola* Davidson, Mycologia 47:63. 1955. =*Ceratocystis truncicola* (Davidson) Griffin, Can. J. Bot. 46:711 1968.

Ceratocystis perparvispora Hunt, Lloydia 19:46. 1956.
Anamorph: *Sporothrix.*
See Hunt (1956, p. 46), Griffin (1968, p. 710), Olchowecki and Reid (1974, p. 1709), Upadhyay (1981, p. 50 figs. 104-108).
Note: Should be transferred to *Ophiostoma*
=*Ceratostomella microspora* Davidson, Mycologia 34:650. 1942. =*Ophiostoma microsporum* (Davidson) von Arx, Antonie van Leeuwenhoek 18:211. 1952. =*Ceratocystis microspora* (Davidson) Davidson, J. Col.-Wyom. Acad. Sci. 6:16. 1969.
Note: A later homonym of *C. microspora* Ellis and Everhart, 1893 (see species of uncertain status). See Weresub (1979).

Ophiostoma piceae (Münch) H. and P. Sydow, Ann. Mycol. 17:43. 1919. =*Ceratostomella piceae* Münch, Naturw. Land. Forstw. 5:547. 1907. =*Ceratocystis piceae* (Münch) Bakshi, Trans. Br. Mycol. Soc. 33:113. 1950. Anamorph: *Graphium pirinum* Goid., Boll. Staz. Patol. Veg. Roma, n.s. 15:132. 1935 = *Pesotum piceae* Crane and Schoknecht, Am. J. Bot. 60:348. 1973. An epithet is also available for the *Sporothrix* synanamorph as *Hyalodendron pirinum* Goid., Boll. Staz. Patol. Veg. Roma, n.s. 15:136. 1935.

See Hunt (1956, p. 34), Griffin (1968, p. 711), Upadhyay (1981, p. 106), Solheim (1986) Hutchison and Reid (1988) Kowalski and Butin (1989), Nisikado and Yamauti (1935).

Note: Brasier (this volume) has concluded that the conifer populations represent *O. piceae* and that hardwood populations represent a different species. The epithets listed here as synonyms that originated from hardwoods would then be considered as possible names or synonyms of the latter species.

=*Ceratostomella querci* Georgew., C.R. Acad. Sci. Paris 183:759. 1926. =*Ceratocystis querci* (Georgew.) Moreau, Rev. Mycol. (Paris) Suppl. Col. 17:22. 1952.

=*Ceratostomella fagi* Loos, Arch. Mikrobiol. 3:376. 1932. =*Ophiostoma fagi* (Loos) Melin and Nannf., Svenska Skogsfor. Tidskr. 32:408. 1934. =*Ceratocystis fagi* (Loos) Moreau, Rev. Myc. (Paris) Suppl. Col. 17:22. 1952. =*Ceratostomella catonianum* Goid., Atti Accad. Naz. Linc. Rc. Ser. 6, 21:199. 1935. =*Ophiostoma catonianum* (Goid.) Goid., Boll Staz. Patol. Veg. Roma, n.s. 15:125. 1935. =*Ceratocystis catonianum* (Goid.) Moreau, Rev. Myc. (Paris) Suppl. Co. 17:22. 1952.

Note: A *nomen dubium fide* Hunt (1956), but de Hoog (1974), Upadyay (1981) and Przybyl and de Hoog (1989) treat it as a synonym of *Ophiostoma piceae*. Hunt (1956) was unable to identify the degenerated ex-type culture, CBS 263.35, but de Hoog (1974) identified the fungus from the *Sporothrix* synanamorph.

=*Ophiostoma roboris* Georgescu and Teodoru, Anal. Inst. Cerc. Exp. For., Ser 1, 11:207. 1948. =*Ceratocystis roboris* (Georgescu and Teodoru) Potlajchuk, Nov. Sist. Niz. Rast. 22:154. 1985.

Note: A fungus with this identity has been associated by many authors with oak decline in Eastern and Central Europe. According to Przybyl and de Hoog (1989), *O. roboris* is a possible synonym of *O. piceae*, but they were unable to locate authentic material. *Ophiostoma roboris* may in fact represent the 'hardwood *O. piceae*' (Brasier, this volume).

=*Ophiostoma valachicum* Georgescu and Teodoru, Anal. Inst. Cerc. Exp. For., Ser. 1, 11:198. 1948. =*Ceratocystis valachicum* (Georgescu and Teodoru) Potlajchuk, Nov. Sist. Niz. Rast. 22:155. 1985.

Note: Upadhyay (1981) considered this species a *nomen dubium*, but Przybyl and de Hoog (1989) considered it a possible synonym of *O. piceae*. They did not examine authentic material.

=*Ophiostoma floccosum* Mathiesen, Svensk. Bot. Tidskr. 45:219. 1951. =*Ceratocystis floccosa* (Mathiesen) Hunt, Lloydia 19:36. 1956.

=*Ceratocystis perfecta* Davidson, Mycologia 50:665. 1958. =*Ophiostoma perfectum* (Davidson) de Hoog, Stud. Mycol. 7:54. 1974.

See Olchowecki and Reid (1974, p. 1707), Upadhyay (1981, p. 105).

Note: This species was accepted as distinct by de Hoog (1974), Olchowecki and Reid (1974) and Upadhyay (1981). Przybyl and de Hoog (1989) subsequently declared it a synonym of *O. piceae*.

Ophiostoma piceaperdum (Rumbold) von Arx, Antonie van Leeuwenhoek 18:211. 1952. =*Ceratostomella piceaperda* Rumbold, J. Agric. Res. 52:432. 1936. =*Grosmannia piceaperda* (Rumbold) Goid., Boll. Staz. Patol. Veg. Roma, n.s. 16:255. 1936. =*Ceratocystis piceaperda* (Rumbold) Moreau, Rev. Mycol. (Paris) Suppl. Col. 17:22. 1952. Anamorph: *Leptographium*.

See Hunt (1956, p. 25), Upadhyay (1981, p. 55 figs. 138-152), Hutchison and Reid (1988), Solheim (1986).

Note: Upadhyay (1981) considered *O. europhioides* a synonym of *O. piceaperdum*, a conclusion endorsed by Hutchison and Reid (1988). Harrington (1988) considered the two species distinct.

=*Ceratocystis europhioides* Wright and Cain, Can. J. Bot. 39:1222. 1961. =*Ophiostoma europhioides* (Wright and Cain) Solheim, Nord. J. Bot. 6: 203. 1986.

Ophiostoma piliferum (Fries) H. and P. Sydow, Ann. Myc. 17:43. 1919. =*Sphaeria pilifera* Fries, Syst. Mycol. 2:472. 1822. =*Ceratostomella piliferum* (Fries) Fuckel, Symb. Mycol. p. 128. 1869. =*Ceratostomella pilifera*

(Fries) Winter, Rabenh. Kryptogamen-Flora 1:252. 1887. =*Linostoma piliferum* (Fries) von Höhnel, Ann. Myc. 16:91. 1918. =*Ceratocystis pilifera* (Fries) Moreau, Rev. Mycol. (Paris) Suppl. Col. 17:22. 1952.

> Anamorph: *Sporothrix.*
> See Hunt (1956, p. 41), Griffin (1968, p. 711), Olchowecki and Reid (1974, p. 1707), Upadhyay (1981, p. 107 figs. 382-386), Hutchison and Reid (1988), Butin and Aquilar (1984).

=*Ceratostomella capillifera* Hedgcock, Mo. Bot. Gard. Ann. Rep. 17:71. 1906. =*Ophiostoma capilliferum* (Hedgcock) H. and P. Sydow, Ann. Myc. 17:43. 1919. =*Ceratocystis capillifera* (Hedgcock) Moreau, Rev. Mycol. (Paris) Suppl. Col. 17:22. 1952.

=*Ceratostomella schrenkiana* Hedgcock, Mo. Bot. Gard. Ann. Rep. 17:67. 1906. =*Ophiostoma schrenkianum* (Hedgcock) H. and P. Sydow, Ann. Myc. 17:43. 1919. =*Ceratocystis schrenkiana* (Hedgcock) Moreau, Rev. Mycol. (Paris) Suppl. Col. 17:22. 1952.

=*Ceratostomella coerulea* Münch, Naturw. Land. Forstw. 5:561. 1907. =*Ceratocystis coerulea* (Münch) Moreau, Rev. Mycol. (Paris) Suppl. Col. 17:22. 1952.

=*Ceratostomella echinella* Ellis and Everhart, North American Pyrenomycetes p. 195. 1892.

> Note: Species concept emended by Hedgcock, Mo. Bot. Gard. Ann. Rep. 17:71. 1906.
> =*Ceratocystis ambrosia* Bakshi, Trans. Br. Mycol. Soc. 33:116. 1950.
> =*Ceratocystis longirostrata* Bakshi, Mycol. Pap. 35:8. 1951. =*Ophiostoma longirostratum* (Bakshi) von Arx and Müller, Beitr. Kryptogamenflora Schweiz II:395. 1954.

Ophiostoma pluriannulata (Hedgcock) H. and P. Sydow, Ann. Myc. 17:43. 1919. =*Ceratostomella pluriannulata* Hedgcock, Mo. Bot. Gard. Ann. Rep. 17:72. 1906. =*Ceratocystis pluriannulata* (Hedgcock) Moreau, Rev. Mycol. (Paris) Suppl. Col. 17:22. 1952.

> Anamorph: *Sporothrix.*
> See Hunt (1956, p. 39), Upadhyay (1981, p. 109 figs. 387-392).

Ophiostoma polonicum Siemaszko, Planta Pol. 7(3):32. 1939. =*Ceratocystis polonica* (Siemaszko) Moreau, Rev. Mycol. (Paris) Suppl. Col. 17:22. 1952.

> Note: This species was considered a synonym of *O. penicillatum* by Upadhyay (1981), but Solheim (1986) and Harrington (1988) accepted *O. polonicum* as a separate species.

Ophiostoma polyporicola Constantinescu and Ryman, Mycotaxon 34:637. 1989.

> Anamorph: *Sporothrix.*

Ceratocystis populicola Olchow. and Reid, Can. J. Bot. 52:1700. 1974.

> Anamorph: *Sporothrix.*
> See Olchowecki and Reid (1974, p. 1700), Upadhyay (1981, p. 57 figs. 153-157).
> Note: Should be transferred to *Ophiostoma*

Ophiostoma populinum (Hinds and Davidson) de Hoog and Scheffer, Mycologia 76:297. 1984. =*Ceratocystis populina* Hinds and Davidson, Mycologia 59:1102. 1967.

> Anamorph: *Sporothrix.*
> See Upadhyay (1981, p. 110 figs. 393-398).

=*Ceratocystis ponderosae* Hinds and Davidson, Mycologia 67:715. 1975.

Ophiostoma proliferum (Kowalski and Butin) Rulamort, Bull. Soc. Bot. Centre-Ouest, n.s. 21:511. 1990. =*Ceratocystis prolifera* Kowalski and Butin, J. Phytopathol. 124:245. 1989.

> Anamorph: *Sporothrix.*

Ceratocystis pseudominor Olchow. and Reid, Can. J. Bot. 52:1708. 1974.

> Anamorph: *Hyalorhinocladiella.*
> See Olchowecki and Reid (1974, p. 1708), Upadhyay (1981, p. 111 figs. 399-402).
> Note: Should be transferred to *Ophiostoma*

Ophiostoma robustum (Robinson-Jeffrey and Davidson) Harrington, Mycotaxon 28:41. 1987. =*Europhium robustum* Robinson-Jeffrey and Davidson, Can. J. Bot. 46:1525. 1968. =*Ceratocystis robusta* (Robinson-Jeffrey and Davidson) Upadhyay, Monograph of *Ceratocystis* p. 58. 1981.

    Anamorph: *Leptographium robustum* Wingfield, Trans. Br. Mycol. Soc. 85:92. 1985.

    See Upadhyay (1981, p. 58 figs. 158-162).

Ophiostoma roraimense Samuels and Müller, Sydowia 31:173. 1979. 1978.

    Anamorph: *Sporothrix*.

Ophiostoma rostrocoronatum (Davidson and Eslyn) de Hoog and Scheffer, Mycologia 76:297. 1984. =*Ceratocystis rostrocoronata* Davidson and Eslyn, Mem. N.Y. Bot. Gard. 28:50. 1976.

    Anamorph: *Sporothrix*.

    See Upadhyay (1981, p. 112), Hutchison and Reid (1988).

    Note: Upadhyay (1981) lists figs. 399-402 as representing both *O. rostrocoronatum* and *Ceratocystis pseudominor*. As the plate itself is labelled with the latter name, we conclude that the former species is not illustrated.

Ophiostoma rostrocylindricum (Davidson) von Arx, Antonie van Leeuwenhoek 18:212. 1952. =*Ceratostomella rostrocylindrica* Davidson, Mycologia 34:658. 1942. =*Ceratocystis rostrocylindrica* (Davidson) Hunt, Lloydia 19:26. 1956.

    Anamorph: *Leptographium*.

    See Hunt (1956, p. 26), Upadhyay (1981, p. 59 figs. 163-166).

Ophiostoma sagmatospora (Wright and Cain) Solheim, Nord. J. Bot. 6:203. 1986. =*Ceratocystis sagmatospora* Wright and Cain, Can. J. Bot. 39:1226. 1961.

    Anamorph: *Phialographium sagmatosporae* Upadhyay and Kendrick, Mycologia 66:183. 1974. = *Graphium sagmatosporae* Wingfield and Kendrick, Mycol. Res. 95:1332.1991.

    See Griffin (1968, p. 712), Olchowecki and Reid (1974, p. 1701), Upadhyay (1981, p. 60 figs. 167-171).

    Note: The anamorph is considered a species of *Graphium* by Seifert and Okada (this volume).

Ophiostoma serpens (Goid.) von Arx, Antonie von Leeuwenhoek 18:211. 1952. =*Grosmannia serpens* Goid., Boll. Staz. Patol. Veg. Roma n.s. 16:42. 1936. =*Ceratocystis serpens* (Goid.) Moreau, Rev. Myc. (Paris) Suppl. Col. 17:22. 1952.

    Anamorph: *Leptographium serpens* (Goid.) Siemaszko, Planta Pol. 17:22. 1952. = *Scopularia serpens* Goid., Boll. Staz. Pat. Veg. Roma 16:42. 1936. = *Verticicladiella serpens* (Goid.) Kendrick, Can. J. Bot. 40:781. 1962. = *Verticicladiella alacris* Wingfield and Marasas, Trans. Br. Mycol. Soc. 75:22. 1980.

    Note: Upadhyay (1981) considered this species a *nomen dubium*, but the presumed anamorph is a well-established species. The holomorph name should be reconsidered if the teleomorph of *L. serpens* is ever rediscovered.

Ophiostoma seticolle (Davidson) de Hoog and Scheffer, Mycologia 76:297. 1984. =*Ceratocystis seticollis* Davidson, Mycopath. Mycol. Appl. 28:282. 1966.

    Anamorph: *Hyalorhinocladiella*.

    See Olchowecki and Reid (1974, p. 1695), Upadhyay (1981, p. 83 figs. 286-289).

Ophiostoma sparsum (Davidson) de Hoog and Scheffer, Mycologia 76:297. 1984. =*Ceratocystis sparsa* Davidson, Mycologia 63:14. 1971.

    Anamorph: *Graphium* (*Graphilbum sparsum* Upadhyay and Kendrick, Mycologia 67:800. 1975).

    See Olchowecki and Reid (1974, p. 1695), Upadhyay (1981, p. 83 figs. 290-294).

    Note: Seifert and Okada (this volume) refer this anamorph to *Graphium*.

Ophiostoma stenoceras (Robak) Melin and Nannf., Svenska Skogsfor. Tidskr. 32:408. 1934. =*Ceratostomella stenoceras* Robak, Nyt. Mag. Naturvid. Oslo 71:214. 1932. =*Ceratocystis stenoceras* (Robak) Moreau, Rev.

Mycol. (Paris) Suppl. Col. 17:22. 1952.
>Anamorph: *Sporothrix.*
>See Olchowecki and Reid (1974, p. 1709), Upadhyay (1981, p. 113 figs. 403-407), Davidson (1942), Kowalski and Butin (1989).
>Note: The anamorph of this species has often been referred to as *Sporothrix schenckii*, but this is an error (see Summerbell *et al.*, this volume).

=*Ophiostoma albidum* Mathiesen-Käärik, Meddn. St. sk. Inst. 43:50. 1953. =*Ceratocystis albida* (Mathiesen-Käärik) Hunt, Lloydia 19:48. 1956.

=*Ceratocystis gossypina* Davidson, Mycologia 63:12. 1971. =*Ophiostoma gossypinum* (Davidson) J. Taylor, Mycopath. Mycol. Appl. 38:112. 1976.

=*Ceratocystis gossypina var. robusta* Davidson, Mycologia 63:13. 1971.

=*Ceratocystis eucastaneae* Davidson, Mycologia 70:856. 1978.

Ophiostoma subannulatum Livingston and Davidson, Mycologia 79:145. 1987.
>Anamorph: *Sporothrix subannulata* Livingston and Davidson, (loc. cit.).

Ceratocystis tenella Davidson, Mycologia 50:666. 1958.
>Anamorph: *Sporothrix.*
>See Griffin (1968, p. 715), Olchowecki and Reid (1974, p. 1708), Upadhyay (1981, p. 114 figs. 408-412), Hutchison and Reid (1988).
>Note: Should be transferred to *Ophiostoma.*

=*Ceratocystis capitata* Griffin, Can. J. Bot. 46:699. 1968.

=*Ceratocystis coronata* Olchow. and Reid, Can. J. Bot. 52:1705. 1974.
>Note: Hutchison and Reid (1988) rejected the synonymy of *C. coronata* with *C. tenella* because of differences in shapes of the ascospores.

Ophiostoma tetropii Mathiesen, Svensk. Bot. Tidskr. 45:223. 1951. =*Ceratocystis tetropii* (Mathiesen) Hunt, Lloydia 19:45. 1956.
>Anamorph: *Sporothrix.*
>See Hunt (1956, p. 45), Griffin (1968, p. 715), Olchowecki and Reid (1974, p. 1709), Upadhyay (1981, p. 115 figs. 413-417), Solheim (1986).

Ceratocystis torticiliata Olchow. and Reid, Can. J. Bot. 52: 1701. 1974.
>Anamorph: *Graphium (Pesotum).*
>See Olchowecki and Reid (1974, p. 1701), Upadhyay (1981, p. 61 figs. 172-177).
>Note: Should be transferred to *Ophiostoma.* The anamorph is illustrated by Seifert and Okada (this volume).

Ophiostoma tremulo-aureum (Davidson and Hinds) de Hoog and Scheffer, Mycologia 76:298. 1984. =*Ceratocystis tremulo-aurea* Davidson and Hinds. Mycologia 56:794. 1964.
>Anamorph: *Hyalorhinocladiella.*
>See Olchowecki and Reid (1974, p. 1709), Upadhyay (1981, p. 115 figs. 418-421).

Ophiostoma triangulosporum Butin, Phytopathol. Z. 91:230. 1978. =*Ceratocystis triangulospora* (Butin) Upadhyay, Monograph of *Ceratocystis* p. 62. 1981.
>Anamorph: *Hyalorhinocladiella.*
>See Upadhyay (1981, p. 62 figs. 178-184).

Ophiostoma trinacriforme (Parker) Harrington, Mycotaxon 28:41. 1987. =*Europhium trinacriforme* Parker, Can. J. Bot. 35:175. 1957. =*Ceratocystis trinacriforme* (Parker) Upadhyay, Monograph of *Ceratocystis* p. 63. 1981.
>Anamorph: *Leptographium.*
>See Upadhyay (1981, p. 63 figs. 185-190).

Ceratocystis tubicollis Olchow. and Reid, Can. J. Bot. 52:1694. 1974.

    Anamorph: *Hyalorhinocladiella.*

    See Olchowecki and Reid (1974, p. 1694), Upadhyay (1981, p. 84).

    Notes: Should be transferred to *Ophiostoma.* The figures referred to by Upadhay (1981) are those from the original description.

Ophiostoma ulmi (Buisman) Nannf., Svenska Skogsfor. Tidskr. 32:408. 1934. =*Ceratostomella ulmi* Buisman, Tijdskr. Plantenziekt. 38:1. 1932. =*Ceratocystis ulmi* (Buisman) Moreau, Rev. Mycol. (Paris) Suppl. Col. 17:22. 1952.

    Anamorphs: *Sporothrix, Graphium ulmi* Schwarz, Meded. Phytopathol. Lab "Willie Commelin Scholten" 5:13. 1922. = *Pesotum ulmi* (Schwarz) Crane and Schoknecht, Am. J. Bot. 60:348. 1973.

    See Hunt (1956, p. 38), Griffin (1968, p. 715), Olchowecki and Reid (1974, p. 1709), Upadhyay (1981, p. 117 figs. 422-427), Wingfield *et al.* (1992).

    Note: Brasier (1991) has recently segregated the new species *O. novo-ulmi* for strains formerly placed in the aggressive groups of *O. ulmi.*

Ophiostoma valdivianum (Butin) Rulamort, Bull. Soc. Bot. Centre-Ouest, n.s. 17:192. 1986. =*Ceratocystis valdiviana* Butin, Phytopathol. Z. 109:86. 1984. =*Ophiostoma valdivianum* (Butin) Harrington, Mycotaxon 28:42. 1987. (superfluous combination).

    Anamorph: *Leptographium.*

Ophiostoma wageneri (Goheen and Cobb) Harrington, Mycotaxon 28:42. 1987. =*Ceratocystis wageneri* Goheen and Cobb, Phytopathology 68:1193. 1978.

    Anamorph: *Leptographium wagenerii* (Kendrick) Wingfield var. *ponderosum* (Harrington and Cobb) Harrington and Cobb, Mycotaxon 30:505. 1987. = *Verticicladiella wageneri* Kendrick var. *ponderosa* Harrington and Cobb, Mycologia 78:568. 1986.

ACCEPTED SPECIES OF *SPHAERONAEMELLA*

Sphaeronaemella fimicola (Marchal) Marchal, Bull. Soc. Roy. Bot. Belg. 33:12. 1894. =*Sphaeria fimicola* Marchal, Bull. Soc. Roy. Bot. Belg. 30:143. 1891. =*Ceratocystis fimicola* (Marchal) Upadhyay, Monograph of *Ceratocystis* p. 95. 1981. =*Viennotidia fimicola* (Marchal) Cannon and Hawksworth, Bot. J. Linn. Soc. 84:157. 1982.

    Anamorph: *Gabarnaudia fimicola* Samson and W. Gams., Stud. Mycol. 6:92. 1974.

    See Upadhyay (1981, p. 95 figs. 344-347), Hutchison and Reid (1988).

    Note: Upadhyay (1981) included this species in *Ceratocystis* but we concur with Hutchison and Reid's rejection of this disposition.

Sphaeronaemella helvellae (Karsten) Karsten, Hedwigia 23:17. 1884. =*Sphaeria helvellae* Karsten, Fungi Fenn. exs. no. 674. 1867. =*Sphaeronaema helvellae* (Karsten) Jacz., Nouv. Mem. Soc. Imp. Nat. Moscow 15:302. 1898. =*Melanospora karstenii* von Arx and Müller, Beitr. Kryptogamenflora Schweiz 11:146. 1954.=*Ceratocystis helvellae* (Karsten) Upadhyay, Monograph of *Ceratocystis* p. 97. 1981.

    Anamorph: *Gabarnaudia.*

    See Upadhyay (1981, p. 97 figs. 348-352), Malloch (1974).

    Note: Upadhyay (1981) included this species in *Ceratocystis* but we prefer to recognize the genus *Sphaeronaemella.*

Sphaeronaemella humicola Samson and W. Gams, Stud. Mycol. 6:94. 1974. =*Viennotidia humicola* (Samson and Gams) Cannon and Hawksworth, Bot. J. Linn. Soc. 84: 158. 1982.

    Anamorph: *Gabarnaudia humicola* Samson and W. Gams, loc. cit.

    Note: Upadhyay (1981) considered this a *nomen dubium* because he did not find the teleomorph on the type specimen, but the existence of an ex-type culture (CBS 115.72) should make this species readily recognizable from the protologue.

Sphaeronaemella raphani Malloch, Fungi Canadenses 53. 1974.
=*Viennotidia raphani* (Malloch) Cannon and Hawksworth, Bot. J. Linn. Soc. 84:157. 1982.
   Notes: Upadhyay (1981) considered this a *nomen dubium*. Cannon and Hawksworth (1982) reported that there was no type material but transferred the species to *Viennotidia* because they believed the fungus could be recognized from the protologue. *Viennotidia raphani* Negru and Verona, Mycopath. Mycol. appl. 30:307. 1966 is the same fungus, but the original description is illegitimate because the genus was not validly published. The species name is correctly attributed to Malloch

Sphaeronaemella spermosphaerici Malloch, Fungi Canadenses no. 53. 1974.
   =*Viennotidia spermosphaerica* (Malloch) Cannon and Hawksworth, Bot. J. Linn. Soc. 84:159. 1982.
   Notes: Cannon and Hawksworth (1982) reported that there was no type material but transferred the species to *Viennotidia* because they believed the fungus could be recognized from the protologue. *Viennotidia spermosphaerica* Negru and Verona, Mycopath. Mycol. appl. 30:306. 1966 is the same species but was invalidly published. The species name is validly attributed to Malloch

SPECIES OF UNCERTAIN STATUS

Ceratostomella acoma Miller and Tcherntzoff, State For. Tech. Publ. Office Moscow p. 123. 1934.
=*Ceratocystis acoma* (Miller and Tcherntzoff) Moreau, Rev. Mycol. (Paris) Suppl. Col. 17:21. 1952.

Ceratocystis antennaroidospora Roldan, Philipp. J. Sci. 91:415-423. 1962.
   Note: This species was described in a teleomorph genus but no teleomorph was known for the fungus. Therefore, it is an illegitimate name according to Article 59 (Nag Raj and Kendrick 1975).

Ceratocystis asteroides Roldan, Philipp. J. Sci. 91:415-23. 1962.
   Note: See explanation under *C. antennaroidospora* above.

Ceratocystis brunnea Davidson, Mycologia 50:663. 1959.
   See Olchowecki and Reid (1974, p. 1709).
   Note: This species was considered a *nomen dubium* by Upadhyay (1981) because he found no teleomorph on the specimen. Olchowecki and Reid (1974) examined the same material and noted that the species was a member of the *Ophiostoma piliferum* group, a conclusion supported by Davidson's protologue.

Ceratostomella buxi Borissof, USSR Central For. Res. Inst. Bul. 2:21. 1934. =*Ceratocystis buxi* (Borissof) Moreau, Rev. Mycol. (Paris) Suppl. Col. 17:22. 1952.

Ceratostomella castaneae Vanin and Solov, Plant Protection Bull., Leningrad 5:122. 1932. =*Ceratocystis castaneae* (Vanin and Solov) Moreau, Rev. Mycol. (Paris) Suppl. Col. 17:22. 1952.
   Note: Hunt (1956) considered this species imperfectly known because he was unable to obtain material. He did note, however, that the protologue described a species that did not match any that he was aware of. The species is not mentioned by Upadhyay (1981).

Ceratostomella comata Miller and Tcherntzoff, St. For. Tech. Publ. Office, Moscow. 1934. =*Ceratocystis comata* (Miller and Tcherntzoff) Moreau, Rev. Mycol. (Paris) Suppl. Col. 17:120. 1952.

Ceratocystis fraxinopennsylvanica Hinds, Mycologia 67:719. 1975.
   Note: Upadhyay (1981) did not accept this as a species of *Ceratocystis*. He transferred the species to *Calosphaeria* but this combination is illegitimate according to Article 33 of the ICBN.

Ceratocystis haranszkyi Tóth, Ann. Hist.-Nat. Mus. Hung. 55:182. 1963.

Ceratostomella lignorum Wollenweber and Stapp,. Biol. Reichs. Land Forstw. Arb., Berlin 16:310. 1928.
  Anamorph: *Graphium.*
  See Hunt (1956, p. 53).

Ceratostomella merolinense Georgew., Mitt. Inst. Forstw. Forsch., Belgrade 16:25. 1930. =*Ceratocystis merolinense* (Georgew.) Moreau, Rev. Mycol. (Paris) Suppl. Col. 17:22. 1952.
  Anamorph: *Graphium.*
  Note: This species was considered a *nomen dubium* by Hunt (1956) and was not considered by Upadhyay (1981).

Ceratostomella microcarpa Karsten, Hedwigia 17:86. 1884. =*Ceratocystis microcarpa* (Karsten) Moreau, Rev. Mycol. (Paris) Suppl. Col. 17:22. 1952.
  Anamorphs unknown.
  See Hunt (1956, p. 54).

Ceratostomella microspora Ellis and Everhart, Proc. Acad. Nat. Sci. Phil. 45:444. 1893.
  Note: Hunt (1956) examined type material and excluded the species from *Ceratocystis* because it has persistent asci.

Ophiostoma clavatum Mathiesen, Svensk. Bot. Tidskr. 45:222. 1951. =*Ceratocystis clavata* (Mathissen) Hunt, Lloydia 19:37. 1956.
  Anamorph: *Graphium.*
  See Upadhyay (1981, p. 136).
  Note: Upadhyay (1981) considered this a *nomen dubium* because there was no teleomorph on the type specimen. The protologue includes a good illustration-- this name should probably be neotypified or resurrected.

Ophiostoma galeiformis (Bakshi) Mathiesen-Käärik, Meddn. St. Skogsfor. sk. Inst. 43:47. 1953. =*Ceratocystis galeiformis* Bakshi, Mycol. Pap. 35:13. 1951.
  Anamorphs: *Leptographium, Graphium.*
  Note: Upadhyay (1981) declared this species a *nomen dubium* because no teleomorph could be found on the type specimen. Bakshi's original illustration and diagnosis should be sufficient to recognize this species.

Ophiostoma kubanicum Shcherbin-Parfenko,Rak. Sos. Bol. List. Porod (Moscow) p. 49. 1953. =*Ceratocystis kubanica* (Shcherbin-Parfenko) Potlajchuk, Nov. Sist. Niz. Rast. 22:153. 1985.
  Note: Invalidly published name, Article 36.1. Przybyl and de Hoog (1989) considered this a possible synonym of *O. piceae* but did not examine authentic material.

Ceratostomella obscura Davidson, J. Agric. Res. 50:798. 1935. =*Ophiostoma obscura* (Davidson) von Arx, Antonie von Leeuwenhoek 18:211. 1952. =*Ceratocystis obscura* (Davidson) Hunt, Lloydia 19:30. 1956.
  Anamorphs: *Leptographium, Graphium*
  Note: Hunt (1956) accepted and described this species but Upadhyay (1981) did not find the teleomorph on the type specimen and considered it a *nomen dubium*. Hunt (1956) states that perithecia were formed in the ex-type culture, now accessioned as CBS 125.39.

Ophiostoma persicinum Govi and Di Caro, Ann. Speriment. Agraria, n.s. 7:1644. 1953.
  Anamorph: *Sporothrix.*

LITERATURE CITED

1. Bakshi, B.K. 1951. Studies on four species of *Ceratocystis*, with a discussion of fungi causing sapstain in Britain. Mycol. Pap. 35:1-16.

2. Butin, H. and Aquilar, A.M. 1984. Bluestain fungi on *Nothofagus* from Chile - Including two new species of *Ceratocystis* Ellis and Halst. Phytopathol. Z. 109:80-89.

3. Brasier, C.M. 1991. *Ophiostoma novo-ulmi* sp. nov., causative agent of current Dutch elm disease pandemics. Mycopathologia 115:151-161.

4. Cannon, P.F. and Hawksworth, D.L. 1982. A re-evaluation of *Melanospora* Corda and similar Pyrenomyctes with a revision of the British species. Bot. J. Linn. Soc. 84:115-160.

5. Davidson, R.W. 1935. Fungi causing stain in logs and lumber in the southern states, including five new species. J. Agric. Res. 50:789-807.

6. Griffin, H.D. 1968. The genus *Ceratocystis* in Ontario. Can. J. Bot. 46:689-718.

7. Harrington, T.C. 1987. New combinations in *Ophiostoma* of *Ceratocystis* species with *Leptographium* anamorphs. Mycotaxon 28:39-43.

8. Harrington, T.C. 1988. *Leptographium* species, their distributions, hosts and insect vectors. Pages 1-39 in: *Leptographium* Root Diseases on Conifers. T.C. Harrington and F.W. Cobb Jr., eds. American Phytopathological Society Press, St. Paul, MN. 144 pp.

9. Hoog, G.S. de 1974. The genera *Blastobotrys, Sporothrix, Calcarisporium,* and *Calcarisporiella* gen. nov. Stud. Mycol. 7:1-84.

10. Hoog, G. S. de and Scheffer, R.J. 1984. *Ceratocystis* versus *Ophiostoma*: a reappraisal. Mycologia 76:292-299.

11. Hughes, S.J. 1951. Studies on micro-fungi. VII. *Allescheriella crocea, Oidium simplex,* and *Pellicularia pruinata*. Mycol. Pap. 45: 1-36.

12. Hunt, J. 1956. Taxonomy of the genus *Ceratocystis*. Lloydia 19:1-58.

13. Hutchison, L.J. and Reid, J. 1988. Taxonomy of some potential wood-staining fungi from New Zealand 1. Ophiostomataceae. N.Z. J. Bot. 26:63-81.

14. Kowalski, T. and Butin, H. 1989. Taxonomie bekannter und neuer *Ceratocystis*-Arten an Eiche (*Quercus robur* L.). Phytopathol. Z. 124:236-248.

15. Leach, J.G, Orr, L.W. and Christensen, C. 1934. The interrelationships of bark beetles and blue-staining fungi in felled Norway pine timber. J. Agric. Res. 49:315-342.

16. Livingston, W.H. and Davidson, R.W. 1987. *Ophiostoma subannulatum*, a new fungal species pathogenic to Grand Fir roots. Mycologia 79:144-147.

17. Luc, M. 1952. *Ophiostoma moniliforme* (Hedgc.) H. et P. Syd. et ses diverses formes. Rev. Mycol. (Paris), Suppl. Col. 17:10-16.

18. Malloch, D. 1974. *Sphaeronaemella helvellae*. Fungi Canadenses No. 53.

19. Mathiesen, A. 1951. Einige neue *Ophiostoma*-Arten in Schweden. Svensk Bot. Tidskr. 45:203-232.

20. Moreau, C. 1952. Coexistence des formes *Thielavioposis* et *Graphium* chez une souche de *Ceratocystis major* (van Beyma) comb. nov. Rev. Mycol. (Paris), Suppl. Col. 17:17-25.

21. Nag Raj, T.R. and Kendrick, B. 1975. A monograph of *Chalara* and allied genera. Waterloo, Wilfrid Laurier University Press. 200 pp.

22. Nisikado, Y. and Yamauti, K. 1935. Contributions to the knowledge of the sap stains of wood in Japan. III. Studies on *Ceratostomella piceae* Münch, the cause of a bluestain of pine trees. Ber. Ohara Inst. Landw. Forsch. (Kurashiki, Japan) 6:539-560.

23. Olchowecki, A. and Reid, J. 1974. Taxonomy of the genus *Ceratocystis* in Manitoba. Can. J. Bot. 52:1675-1711.

24. Przybyl, K. and Hoog, G.S. de. 1989. On the variability of *Ophiostoma piceae*. Antonie van Leeuwenhoek 55:177-188.

25. Rumbold, C.T. 1936. Three blue-staining fungi, including two new species, associated with bark beetles. J. Agric. Res. 52:419-437.

26. Solheim, H. 1986. Species of Ophiostomataceae isolated from *Picea abies* infested by the bark beetle *Ips typographus*. Nord. J. Bot. 6:199-207.

27. Tsuneda, A. and Hiratsuka, Y. 1984. Sympodial and annellidic conidiation in *Ceratocystis clavigera*. Can. J. Bot. 62:2618-2624.

28. Upadhyay, H.P. 1981. A monograph of *Ceratocystis* and *Ceratocystiopsis*. University of Georgia Press, Athens, GA. 176 pp.

29. Viégas, A.P. 1960. Seca da mangueira. Bragantia 19: 163-182.

30. Weresub, L.K. 1979. Nomenclature of *Ceratocystis microspora*. Mycologia 71:834-835.

31. Wingfield, M.J. and Marasas, W.F.O. 1980. *Ceratocystis ips* associated with *Orthomicus erosus* (Coleoptera: Scoltydiae) on *Pinus* spp. in the Cape Province of South Africa. Phytophylactica 12:65-69.

32. Wingfield, M.J., Kendrick, W.B. and van Wyk, P.S. 1992. Analysis of conidium ontogeny in anamorphs of *Ophiostoma*: *Pesotum* and *Phialographium* are synonyms of *Graphium*. Mycol. Res. 95:1328-1333.

33. Wingfield, M.J., van Wyk, P.S. and van Wyk, P.W.J. 1989. Conidial development in the anamorph of *Ophistoma cucullatum*. Mycol. Res. 93:91-95.

Chapter 30

PROBLEMS AND PROSPECTS FOR FUTURE RESEARCH ON OPHIOSTOMATOID FUNGI

W.B. KENDRICK

The assemblage of fungi considered in this book is a truly fascinating, baffling and eternally surprising group: one which, in addition to the usual bag of fungal tricks, has a wide range of intimate relationships with members of two other kingdoms (Animalia and Plantae). In some ways, the ophiostomatoid fungi really are unique. But those of us who know the fungi well are aware that all other fungi are equally interesting. And this is one message I would like to get across to students of biology who are not mycologists: the fungi are a great group to work with. They are perhaps the least known of all the kingdoms but certainly not the least deserving of attention. Almost everything I say about the ophiostomatoid fungi can be applied to the rest of the fungi as well. In this concluding chapter, l will try to point out the new lines of enquiry that have been opened up by these proceedings, and the gaps that remain in our knowledge of these fungi and their activities.

It is now clear that the fungi we are considering - the ophiostomatoid fungi, as we may now choose to call them - are not a closely related, evolutionarily homogeneous group at the ordinal level (Samuels, this volume). As many of us have suspected for some time, the similarities that led to their being considered together as members of the same order, the Ophiostomatales, and in many cases even of the same genus, were imposed on them during evolution by the exigencies of their rather specialized habitats and their specific vectors. They now appear to constitute several perhaps rather distantly related groups and the elucidation of the membership, and the hierarchies, of those groups, will occupy many of us for some time to come. The time has come to lay what we now realize to be the misleading concept underlying the order Ophiostomatales to rest, although we are not yet sure what will replace it.

We no longer need to rely entirely on traditional character sets supplemented by intuition or speculation: molecular techniques are giving us new kinds of taxonomic information (Blackwell *et al.*, Hausner *et al.*, this volume). While molecular biologists are still trying to decide which are the best areas of the genome to sequence in order to derive the maximum amount of useful information about the taxonomy and phylogeny of each particular group of organisms, it seems clear that sequence data must ultimately provide us with irrefutable evidence about taxonomic affinities (or their absence). Yet, we will continue to need morphological and developmental studies as new taxa are discovered, and taxonomists will still be called upon to make the final interpretations of the database, because only they have the requisite experience derived from working with and observing the whole organisms. We must never forget that a good classification incorporates and reflects everything we know about the organisms.

In fact, everyone will still be needed. There is so much to learn about the morphology, ultrastructure, development, physiology, biochemistry, ecology, epidemiology, and biogeography of these organisms. Areas such as the nature of the chemical attractants that help vectors find the fungus (Hanssen, this volume), the defence mechanisms that help hosts to repel the insects or the fungus (Paine *et al.*, Smalley *et al.*, Solheim, this volume), and possible agents of biological control, are of particular interest and need to be actively explored.

We need better communication among those who work with ophiostomatoid fungi. Perhaps in certain areas of investigation, standardization of media, of techniques for culture storage, or of protocols for experimental and descriptive procedures, might be a good idea, allowing easier and more accurate comparisons of data. I'm not, of course, suggesting that any form of original thought or action be inhibited, merely that co-operation is often more productive in the long run than competition.

Several chapters of this book discuss recently discovered diseases or taxa. This was to be expected, since mycology is in the age of discovery: I have suggested elsewhere that we know only 20% or less of the extant fungi. Not only do we need to look at new hosts (and not just those of economic importance) but we need to examine new substrates and to look in many new niches, to obtain a better understanding of geographic distribution and host-range.

Mycologists should spend more time "fungus-watching" because this may help them to a better understanding of the behavior and thus the special features of each organism. It will also help in the elucidation of vector relationships which must, of course, also be studied experimentally (Malloch and Blackwell, this volume).

We need to look more deeply into the genetic systems of our fungi, and at their potential for variation or rapid evolution (Brasier, this volume); even, as we have seen in the case of *Ophiostoma ulmi*, for almost instant speciation. And it should always be established whether a new species is homothallic or heterothallic. This kind of information will help in the long-term maintenance of viable, fruiting cultures that essentially constitute a gene bank. Existing culture collections need to be critically re-examined to see if all isolates are what they are supposed to be and whether they have degenerated in culture (something that happens all-too-frequently, and with alarming speed, in many ophiostomatoid fungi). This is vitally important because so many researchers rely absolutely and implicitly on culture collections to provide properly named cultures for use as experimental organisms. If the name is wrong, the work will be misleading and possibly even worthless. All taxa also need to be properly typified: the absence of type material leads to endless confusion and even conflict.

I note that even when the order Ophiostomatales was considered as a tightly-knit group, whenever researchers examined specific systems or components, they tended to sample only within the group. Had the group actually been homogeneous, this would have been an unfortunate choice. But now we have a hint of the true diversity which is present among the ophiostomatoid fungi, that may not be a problem, since one will be dealing with members of outgroups as a matter of course. Nevertheless, when working on specific metabolites, or even on DNA, it is advisable to ensure that members of outgroups are included among the organisms examined. This helps to place any study in perspective and is something that biologists have often neglected. Some broadly-based systematists have large experientially generated internal databases and use a very wide spectrum of organisms as points of reference for placing any unknown taxon. This would be wise practice in most other areas of science as well.

In closing this brief survey, I offer a "shopping list" of topics. If we are to gain real understanding of our chosen organisms, we must get busy and acquire information in every one of these areas. The order of the list conforms to the subtitles of this book (and a few additional headings) and does not imply any ranking in terms of importance: each of you will have your own set of priorities. I simply hope that there are enough of us to cover all the angles.

TAXONOMY

(1) **Life cycle: Anamorph-teleomorph relationships.** Knowledge of the life cycle of a fungus, and of the morphological range expressed by its genome, are extremely valuable kinds of information. They can tell us a lot about the biology of the species and its strategies for survival and reproduction. In the case of pathogenic species, knowledge of the life cycle may sometimes allow it to be interrupted at a point where treatment is inexpensive and even environmentally friendly, as when a cultural practice can replace a pesticide.

(2) **Centrum development in the ascoma.** We have now seen some pictures of the pattern of formation of the asci, and their subsequent behavior in a few ophiostomatoid fungi (Van Wyk *et al.*, this volume). These demonstrate a certain diversity of centrum development. We can regard this as an evolutionary clue; as a sign of longstanding divergence, or of much more recent secondary reduction. It is one more piece of the jigsaw puzzle: not much use on its own, but helpful when read in conjunction with other developmental characters, such as the two that follow.

(3) **Ultrastructure of ascospore development and mature morphology.** Here again we have seen an exciting range of phenomena, which tells us that there is more to this group than meets the eye. This information is useful when combined with such features as centrum development and conidiogenesis.

(4) **Ultrastructure of septa.** This is a controversial area, because when we examine septa we may be seeing one of four things: (i) the divergent evolution of different kinds of septa; (ii) the secondary reduction or simplification of one or more of these; (iii) the convergent or parallel evolution of similar septa in different groups; (iv) the re-evolution of the septum in fungi that had originally been mycelial, had become single-celled for a part of their evolutionary history, and are now reinventing the septate hypha. It has also been pointed out that some dolipore septa may be artifacts of fixation. Although this matter of technique should be cleared up, the presence of the

same artifact in different fungi may still indicate close relationship.

(5) **Wall chemistry and ultrastructure.** This area can provide useful information but does not appear as cut and dried as it did ten years ago. People used to say cellulose here, chitin there, xylose here and not there. I now believe that when wall chemistry has been fully worked out, it will show a range of compositions and of layered structures. There may again be evidence for several evolutionary lines.

(6) **Conidiogenesis.** Despite a generation of work on this, we are still discovering new aspects, and reassessing concepts. Dr. Mike Wingfield, Dr. Schalk van Wyk and I are working on some new ideas and approaches that are only now being written up. We may expect further contributions from other developmentally oriented mycologists. The lack of agreement between classifications adopted for anamorph and teleomorph is a constant reminder that we have not yet achieved an acceptable synthesis. But we must consider both morphs in our search for an understanding of the holomorph (the whole fungus).

(7) **Taxonomy of Anamorphs.** Despite the differences in generic concepts, the systematic works published during this century have provided a reasonable teleomorph taxonomy of the ophiostomatalean fungi at the species level. The work with the anamorphs, however, is still less than half done. *Chalara* and *Sporothrix*, two of the major anamorph genera associated with these fungi, have been the subject of careful, modern revisions (Nag Raj and Kendrick, de Hoog, this volume). *Graphium* and *Leptographium*, however, await similar treatment, although preliminary data are now available (Seifert and Okada, Wingfield, this volume). The taxonomy of *Hyalorhinocladiella* anamorphs remains completely unexplored.

(8) **Biogeography.** Records of most fungi reflect the distribution of mycologists or pathologists, rather than those of the fungi themselves. An enormous task lies ahead if we are to understand the distribution of any members of the group other than the most important pathogens.

(9) **The search for new taxa.** Fungi are a large part of the biodiversity present in any habitat; we estimate that we have, as yet, seen perhaps only one-fifth of the world's mycota. Although there are already over a hundred taxa among the ophiostomatoid fungi, new species are still being described. The discovery of new members of the group in the infructescences of certain members of the Proteaceae in South Africa (Wingfield, this volume) makes it likely that many others are awaiting discovery on other hosts and in other places. Each such discovery inevitably gives us a better understanding of the nature, diversity and evolution of the group as a whole.

(10) **Construction of large computer databases.** I recently devised a very simple way of using a database program, not just to store all kinds of information about an organism, but also to retrieve elements of it in a multiple synoptic, and therefore highly specific, manner. Now we have computers that can cope with this flood of information and software which will give us very rapid access to that data in any form we want, many doors are opened. We can go ahead and build databases of previously unimaginable size and complexity, yet gain access to unique combinations of data almost instantaneously. All we have to do now is begin to build those databases. This should be a collaborative effort; it is one that will pay off handsomely.

We have also used image-processing techniques to automatically extract extremely simplified but information-rich "line drawings" from television images of fungal structures. Soon, computers will be able to compare those images and make probabilistic identifications, again virtually without human intervention. The simplified images can be incorporated in our database and displayed alongside the other taxonomic data. All of this will make identification easier, allow better use of taxonomists' time, and reduce taxonomic and nomenclatural confusion.

ECOLOGY

(11) **Specific vectors or other dispersal mechanisms.** This calls for collaboration between mycologists and invertebrate zoologists. Not enough is known about vectors of fungi. Among the ophiostomatoid fungi there are a few examples in which the relationship has been well worked out, and the contrast between the effectiveness of the vectors of *Ophiostoma ulmi* and of *Ceratocystis fagacearum* has been beautifully delineated (Smalley *et al.*, this volume). Yet there are species for which vectors, if such exist, are unknown (Malloch and Blackwell, this volume). And we are still unaware of the ways in which many fungi are dispersed.

(12) **Recognition processes: volatile attractants and other components.** This is another area for the biochemists and for those who specialize in detecting and characterizing extremely small amounts of unusual substances. This area may verge upon the field of pheromones (Hanssen, this volume).

(13) **Relationships with organisms other than host or vector.** I know that there are interactions between our fungi and others inhabiting the same substrate. Such interactions, if better understood, could perhaps provide information leading to biological control of some pathogens. It is also certain that there are interactions between the vectors of ophiostomatoid fungi and other arthropods inhabiting the same ecosystems (Malloch and Blackwell, this volume). These influences lead to a complex web of interactions ranging from competition to interdependence. This web will be very difficult to sort out, and explains why ecology is such a complex subject.

(14) **Chemistry of the slimes in which spores are released.** In the present context, this question was raised by Dr. van der Walt, who was concerned about the possible relationships between the yeasts and the ophiostomatoid fungi. I am not sure whether knowledge of this would clarify relationships but I still think it would be useful to know much more about these slimes. Certainly they are not of uniform composition (Malloch and Blackwell, this volume). Ascospore slimes differ from conidial slimes. Some slimes swell but remain relatively cohesive, or disperse very slowly, when placed in water. Others, when wetted, act like detergents, surface-active agents, that dissolve almost instantly on contact with water, and rapidly disperse the spores they contain across the water surface, or throughout the droplet. We can guess at some of the biological implications of these behaviors, but we still don't know the chemistry behind them.

(15) **Habitats.** Looking in habitats and on hosts previously unexplored for ophiostomatoid fungi is a logical step in our quest for knowledge of the group.

PATHOGENICITY

(16) **Pathogenicity and hypovirulence: host reactions and resistance.** These are areas of great interest for the pathologist, but the information gathered by these researchers has taxonomic and ecological relevance as well. Although qualitative information is now available (Kojima, Lieutier, Paine et al., Smalley et al., Solheim, this volume), there is much to learn about the defence compounds produced by host plants in response to infection and how their production is influenced by stress and genetic variability.

(17) **Host range.** Do we know the host range of all of our fungi? Has anyone tried to inoculate the known pathogens into a wide range of other hosts? We know that some have a wide host range because they attack a number of economically important crops; but what about those which attack only a single economically important plant -- are other hosts out there that we don't know about? When introduced to new areas, can some of these fungi make the jump to new hosts? We have much to learn in these areas.

GENETICS

(18) **DNA or RNA sequences from appropriate parts of the genome.** There are obviously several levels at which this can be attacked. You can start with the entire genomic DNA, cut it with a 4-cutter enzyme, and obtain a gel which is some kind of fungal fingerprint (Hausner et al., this volume). At the other end of the spectrum, you can restrict your attention to very small areas of highly conserved genetic material, such as subunits of ribosomal DNA, and sequence appropriate lengths of these (Blackwell et al., this volume). Each approach has its advantages and disadvantages. The amount of variability within the ribosomal DNA varies so widely from one group to another that we cannot yet guarantee the taxonomic usefulness of any particular base sequence.

For these and other reasons, DNA work is not quite the straightforward panacea we were expecting (and the molecular biologists were predicting) a few years ago. To look at base sequences in isolation is not necessarily to solve our problems. Even if we had the sequence for the whole genome laid out, this would not mean that we knew the organism. There is a world of difference between a line of letters and a living organism and this is the gulf that still yawns between the molecular biologist and the holistic or organismic biologist. We hope that the years ahead will see stable bridges built across that divide.

(19) **Whether cultures are homothallic or heterothallic.** The importance of this determination, often neglected in the past, must be reemphasized. Whether a species is homothallic or heterothallic is fundamental knowledge and should be determined

for new taxa if possible. The possibility of demonstrating heterothallism and the presence of two mating types has existed since the 1930's, when Christina Buisman demonstrated it for two different species of *Ophiostoma*. For heterothallic species, both mating types should be deposited in culture collections.

METHODOLOGY

(20) **Improved culture media**. Persuading many taxa to produce the teleomorph in culture is a real obstacle at present. Until we can do this, work on these fungi at other levels - for example, EM studies of centrum development and ascospore formation - is completely frustrated. Another serious problem with many ophiostomatoid fungi is the rapid decline that begins almost as soon as they are brought into culture; this applies particularly to the anamorph. Tall, complex conidiophores degenerate and lose most of their taxonomic value after only one or two transfers. Sometimes, growing cultures on the natural substrate can reduce this problem, but reliable procedures for maintaining or inducing fecundity would be invaluable.

(21) **Storage techniques**. Method of storage is as important as medium. One of the best ways of avoiding genetic change and loss of viability in many groups is freeze-drying. Another useful, though expensive, technique is storage of cultures under liquid nitrogen. A number of other options also exist (Seifert *et al.*, this volume). These have not all been explored for the full range of organisms represented among the ophiostomatoid fungi.

(22) **Deposit of research cultures in recognized collections**. Despite the volume of information published on the ophiostomatoid fungi during this century, the species are remarkably poorly represented in the worlds' major culture collections. Deposition of cultures is essential for taxonomic purposes but is no less important for other kinds of studies. All physiological, biochemical, genetic and ecological data is tied to names. If the names are incorrect, or need to be reinterpreted, the information becomes orphaned if a culture or voucher specimen is unavailable.

CONCLUSION

The processes of exploration and discovery must continue, and be accelerated, because of the way in which our species is destroying habitats all round the world. The cataloguing of biodiversity is one of the most urgent quests of the late twentieth century. I and many other scientists are extremely worried about the fate of natural ecosystems (my preferred habitat) and ultimately of the entire biosphere, which is in the hands of the human race. In discovering and describing rare and potentially important taxa, we give power to those who wish to preserve biodiversity and endangered natural habitats. In western North America, some of the last remaining tracts of old-growth forest are being protected, albeit somewhat uncertainly at present, because they are the nesting sites of an endangered species of bird - the spotted owl. It may be a little more difficult to persuade the powers that be to save an endangered forest because of the presence of a rare *Ophiostoma* or other fungus, but that only reflects the ignorance of the general public concerning the importance of fungi. How many people know that penicillin, cyclosporine, and aflatoxin, not to speak of beer, wine and bread, are derived from fungi? This ignorance is something we all wish to dispel. We are all crusaders and teachers and we must all do the best we possibly can for our chosen group of organisms - the fungi.